Manual for Disaster Relief Work

Manual for Disaster Relief Work

Muriel Skeet

Chief Nursing Officer, British Red Cross Society; Chief Nursing Officer, Joint Committee (Order of St John of Jerusalem and British Red Cross); Chairman, Advisory Committee, League of Red Cross Societies; President and Chairman, Commonwealth Nurses' Federation; Operational Research Consultant, World Health Organisation and International Hospital Federation

Foreword by John H. Knowles, MD
President, The Rockefeller Foundation

CHURCHILL LIVINGSTONE
Edinburgh London and New York 1977

CHURCHILL LIVINGSTONE
Medical Division of Longman Group Limited

Distributed in the United States of America by
Longman Inc., 19 West 44th Street, New York,
N.Y. 10036 and by associated companies,
branches and representatives throughout
the world.

ISBN 0 443 01493 0

Library of Congress Cataloging in Publication Data

Skeet, Muriel H
Manual for disaster relief work.

Bibliography: p.
Includes index.
1. Disaster relief—Handbooks, manuals, etc.
2. Emergency medical services—Handbooks, manuals, etc.
I. Title.
HV553.S53 361.5 76-54866

Printed in Great Britain
at The Pitman Press, Bath

Foreword

Unfortunately, our increasingly crowded and interdependent planet must prepare itself for expanding numbers of man-made and natural disasters. War, pestilence, famine and death stalk the world. If we are to joust successfully with the four horsemen (here I would like to use the modern word—horsepersons!) of the apocalypse, we must be prepared rationally to deal with the complexities of disaster relief. It seems particularly appropriate that Muriel Skeet of the nursing profession would take the lead in preparing a practical manual for disaster relief work. Over one hundred years ago, another Englishwoman, Florence Nightingale, returned from the Crimean War where her findings that good nursing could reduce morbidity and mortality revolutionized the care of the sick and injured. It is to be hoped that this volume will have similar results.

The Rockefeller Foundation, 1977 John H. Knowles

Preface

The Oxford English Dictionary defined 'disaster' as 'sudden or great misfortune or calamity' and the word 'emergency' as 'a sudden juncture demanding immediate action'.

There are emergencies, known as natural disasters, which are caused by the disruption of the forces of nature: fire, floods, earthquakes, cyclones, etc. There are those due to the outbreak of communicable diseases, and others—increasing in number every year—originating in conflict between peoples or in inadequate social and economic conditions.

Basically, it is the responsibility of the public authorities in each country to assist the victim of calamities occurring on their territory. But in practice, it is unrealistic to expect the authorities alone to provide immediately all the help required. Also, society as a whole has an obligation to protect and ensure the health of its members; this obligation rests with individual members of the society.

A few basic concepts underlie our attitude in regard to disasters.

First, it is generally accepted that it is essential to be prepared for giving service and that the more sudden and urgent the need for assistance, the better prepared one needs to be.

Another basic concept is that emergencies can often be avoided or rendered less disastrous through preventive measures. Preparation of qualified persons can render the effects of wars less inhuman and preventive health measures can help to check disease.

A third important concept, and one upon which the philosophy of this manual is based, is that for an effective response to disasters, the planned joint effort of many people is essential.

The word 'team' is used to mean 'a set of persons working together' and it is suggested that such a group is able to achieve more effective and more satisfying results than would be achieved by individual persons assigned to fragmented tasks. Early involvement and training is basic to such teamwork.

General acceptance of these concepts is demonstrated today by some recent decisions taken at top international level; United Nations General Assemblies, International Conferences of Red Cross, World Health Assemblies and World Food Congresses.

Under the United Nations' Development Programme, intense technical assistance had been provided which covers a variety of fields including Health. Moreover, in an attempt to promote the economic and social advancement of all people, the programme deals with many problems of an emergency nature.

Today's need is great: we are witnessing more man-made conflicts every year of our lives and today's response to meet those needs is also great. National endeavours illustrate the fact that public authorities, private organisations, non-governmental organisations, and individuals everywhere are banded together as never before, in a humanitarian effort to establish and implement both short and long-term relief plans. Whilst this is encouraging, we know that there is room for much improvement. People involved, who pool their skills, experience and personal strengths and weaknesses in the common aim of a true teamwork approach, need to acquire knife-edge competence and comprehensive knowledge.

Generally speaking, a relief operation is comprised of three phases: the first is saving lives; the second is attending to the needs of all victims; and the third is that of rehabilitation.

The process of life-saving is an everyday occurence in the lives of many doctors and nurses who live an everyday kind of professional life. The privilege of saving hundreds of lives can be an everyday occurrence in the lives of a disaster-relief team. Preparation for such an event is of paramount importance: preparation of personnel, preparation of equipment, transport, logistic planning and effective means of communication—whatever form the disaster may take.

Leadership of a team consisting of health, nutritional, sanitarian, engineering, social, laboratory and store personnel—to mention only a few—disciplines is not easy, but it can be made less difficult if the leader knows a little of the work of each team member.

Team members may also have to 'stand in' for each other from time to time and whilst it is essential that each is a 'master' in his own field, it is equally necessary for him to be a 'Jack' of many trades.

The second phase of disaster relief work, that of tending all victims can include programmes of shelter, feeding, clothing distribution, mass inoculation and sanitation, are activities requiring teamwork, leadership and a knowledge of local culture, customs, climate and creeds.

Whilst the third phase of rehabilitation has been left to other pens—development programmes often dovetail with disaster relief work but are a subject to themselves requiring another publication—it is recognised that disasters, either man-made or natural, are not isolated incidents. It has been assessed that in the ten years prior to 1974 the world suffered more than 400 major natural disasters resulting in 3.5 million deaths and over 400 million people were affected. Since 1951 there have been 120 major civil and international conflict situations which have produced over 20 million refugees.

As the response to a disaster situation depends largely on local facilities available at the time of the disaster, and the organisation of these resources at all levels, development programmes should include disaster preparedness, for no country is immune to disasters: wherever there are people there can be a disaster. In every country the history of past disasters should be catalogued and studied as to cause, frequency and effects. Known disaster hazards should be identified and areas likely to be affected, defined. Such factual information, analysis and further study will help us to realise the mistakes we have made in the past; to see why we made those mistakes and how we can prevent them in the future.

It is only by the study of disaster situations and the tabulation and analysis of information gained in these circumstances, that progress can be made in the planning and organisation of services to the many millions who each year are affected by a 'disaster'.

London, 1977 M.S.

Acknowledgements

I am greatly indebted to the many people who made this book possible. Especially would I like to thank the late Colonel T. R. Archer; Brigadier A. P. Dignan, MBE, Brigadier W. S. Millar, Colonel J. C. Crook, Lt. Col. C. Moffat, OBE, Lt. Col. R. H. MacKeith all of the Royal Army Medical Corps; Mr. Peter London, MBE, Miss Margaret Harrison and Miss Mollie Heslip of the Birmingham Accident Hospital.

I also acknowledge with thanks the permission given by the World Health Organisation and the British Medical Association to reproduce from their publications.

For valuable assistance in the selection of photographs I am grateful to the International Committee of the Red Cross, the League of Red Cross Societies and the World Health Organisation.

I am also deeply grateful to Mrs. Wendy Robinson for undertaking the marathon task of editing and to Miss Mary Emmerson who maintained her faith and confidence when the author was most in danger of losing both.

Contents

Introduction

Disaster relief work involves many professions, disciplines and trades. Nursing, by its very nature, covers many aspects of any relief programme.

The activities of which basic nursing is composed have their origin in fundamental and universal human needs. Whether the person concerned is ill or well, the nurse must always bear in mind the inescapable human need for food, shelter and clothing; the need for love, approval and for knowing one is useful. Each culture expresses these needs in a different way; each individual in his own way. This must be borne in mind constantly when undertaking relief work. There is often strong resistance to changes in social customs, eating habits, building techniques and this, coupled with religious fatalism, creates a strong barrier to the instigation and adoption of any preventive measures.

Relief agencies are able to operate only according to government wishes, which are not always in the best interests of all sections of the community. Relief operations can be extremely difficult, for instance when the disaster is a direct result of civil war.

Also, owing to inadequate or inexpert assessment of needs, the type of relief requested by governments may be unsuitable. Bureaucracy and corruption are serious impediments frequently met with and they can produce many problems in the logistics of relief operations.

Most natural disasters—cyclones, droughts, earthquakes, etc.—occur in developing countries which are often politically unstable and subject to civil disturbances. The influence of, and exploitation by, wealthier countries may have caused economic and social changes in these countries. A transition from rural to urban areas often causes certain deteriorations, a breakdown of the traditional social system, and a high incidence of those diseases which result from overcrowding and lack of sanitation.

The trend towards economic dependency on a single cash crop increases the country's vulnerability to pests, vagaries of weather and fluctuations of world food prices. Use of more sophisticated agricultural and industrial equipment increases susceptibility to power failure and shortages of fuel and water; all these factors exacerbate the destructive potential of a disaster, not only the immediate aftermath but also the long term effects. A single natural disaster in such a country may give rise to secondary disasters which would be avoidable in wealthier countries.

In many poor countries there is a delicate balance between population and food supplies. Even a small change in the latter can have serious effects on the former. Governments are seldom able to afford to stockpile food or equipment for times of emergency and national disaster plans are non-existent in many countries. Warning systems and methods of minimising hazards, such as earthquake-proof building techniques and flood control methods, are expensive, whilst medical services often consist of a few hospitals in the cities and an inadequate number of rural dispensaries, poorly staffed and ill equipped.

It goes without saying that, wherever possible, local labour and skills should be used in relief work and that when expatriates are deployed they should be well-briefed and, preferably, have had previous field experience in the country where the disaster occurs. Even so, once on the job they will meet with contingencies for which they are not prepared, and conditions and diseases they have never seen before.

Whilst it is impossible to collate all relevant information on the many aspects of relief work in one volume, this book is a humble attempt to provide a pocket reference library for those many field workers who, like the author, find themselves continually learning the hard way.

1. The ecology of disasters

During the past decade there has been increased public awareness of disaster situations together with a call for better management procedures to be evolved in order to make more effective use of available resources. There are many people involved in the activities associated with a disaster—administrators, medical and nursing staff, lawyers, physicists, meteorologists, engineers, sociologists, volunteers—which means that an organised multi-disciplinary approach to the problems is required.

The purpose of this chapter is to introduce the reader to the complexities of disaster situations. It includes a definition of a disaster and studies the principal causes, effects and frequencies of such events.

1. Definitions and terminology

A disaster could be defined as follows:

An occurrence of such magnitude as to create a situation in which the normal patterns of life within a community are suddenly disrupted and people are plunged into helplessness and suffering, and, as a result, may urgently need food, shelter, clothing, medical attention, protection and other life-sustaining requirements.

For the purposes of this manual, 'disaster' is understood to be a natural catastrophe such as a flood or hurricane or a major accident such as a train crash, which might well have been prevented. It could also be the circumstances resulting from some of man's more destructive activities like warfare. In such a disaster situation the local or even national public health and rescue services may be inadequate and emergency local, national or international resources might be requested to provide the necessary assistance. The term 'disaster relief' will be used to describe this organised emergency assistance given voluntarily to the victims of disasters by government, humanitarian and religious bodies.

2. Types of disasters

Disasters can be divided conveniently into two distinct categories according to their causes:

a. Disasters caused by natural phenomena
b. Man-made disasters

Further classification can be made in respect of the origins of a particular disaster:

a. Natural disasters

i. Meteorological disasters: storms (cyclones, hailstorms, hurricanes, tornadoes, typhoons and snowstorms), cold spells, heatwaves and droughts (possibly causing famine).

ii. Topological disasters: avalanches, landslides and floods.

iii. Telluric and tectonic disasters: earthquakes, tsnuamis and volcanic eruptions.

iv. Biological disasters: insect swarms (e.g. locusts) and epidemics of communicable diseases.

b. Man-made disasters

i. Civil disturbances: riots and demonstrations.

ii. Warfare: conventional warfare (bombardment, blockade and siege), non-conventional warfare (nuclear, biological and chemical), guerilla warfare (including terrorism).

iii. Refugees: forced movements of large numbers of people usually across frontiers.

iv. Accidents: transportation calamities (land, sea and air), collapse of buildings, dams and other structures, mine disasters and technological failures (e.g. a mishap at a nuclear power station, a leak at a chemical plant causing pollution of the atmosphere or the breakdown of a public sanitation system).

The preceding classification, which is by no means fully comprehensive, merely indicates the numerous causes or potential causes of some of the more serious disasters. The division between natural and man-made is to some extent an over-simplification, as many disasters can be caused by either. For example, flooding could be caused by a heavy rain storm, the bombing of a dike or the collapse of a dam. Some of the aforementioned natural occurrences only become disasters when they directly affect man's habitat. An avalanche in an isolated mountain range would probably pass unnoticed but one of equal force in another location might well demolish a village, thus becoming a serious disaster.

Furthermore, the summary does not show how some of the worst calamities are often caused by the cumulative effects of several of the above mentioned factors, both natural and man-made, as occurred in East Pakistan (now Bangladesh) in 1970.

In November 1970 a cyclone followed by one of the worst tidal waves in history struck the coastal region of East Pakistan in the Bay of Bengal. Initial damage especially to buildings was caused by the enormously strong winds; further and more serious destruction was caused by the impact of the tidal wave and other resultant floods which followed the sudden upsurge of water in the complicated interconnecting river systems of the area.

It is estimated that almost 500 000 people perished, most of the livestock drowned, all the crops were destroyed and the soil and water supplies were polluted by silt and salt water. The immense human needs prompted the international agencies to start an immediate relief operation and soon afterwards the United Nations established an office in Dacca to coordinate the work of its numerous operational bodies, e.g. UNICEF, WFP and WHO (see details of UN agencies, Appendix 3).

The suffering caused by the cyclone occurred at a time when there was widespread discontent in the country due to the political, economic and administrative control exerted on the territory by West Pakistan. The civil disturbances which followed the declaration of the New State of Bangladesh in March 1971 forced some ten million people to flee into India, principally around Calcutta, where they were fed and housed in camps run by the Red Cross and other voluntary organisations. Due to overcrowding and inadequate sanitary arrangements, cholera broke out in some of the camps causing yet another problem for the relief workers.

The civil strife in Bangladesh grew steadily worse with the following effects: the authority of the administration ceased, the economy almost collapsed, communications became difficult which together with poor monsoon rains caused famine to spread throughout the country.

The relief operations initiated to bring succour to the cyclone victims were temporarily suspended in December 1971, when the Indian Government sent its army into Bangladesh in support of the local freedom fighters. The war was bloody and immensely destructive producing the usual high number of surgical casualties and the annihilation of strategic roads, bridges and railways. The war also left another serious problem in that approximately 750 000 non-Bengalis, mainly Biharis, who had sided with the previous West Pakistan administration were now in urgent need of food, shelter, clothing and physical protection as they had congregated into what can only be described as ghettos. The refugees also started to make their way back to Bangladesh after the cessation of hostilities only to find their homes destroyed and their lands ravaged.

The successive conditions of disaster and war from November 1970 to January 1972 had affected the entire population of Bangladesh, some 75 million people, and by February 1972, despite all the logistical problems, one of the biggest relief operations since the Second World War was well underway involving governments, UN agencies, the Red Cross and other international organisations.

This sequence of catastrophic interrelated events is summarised diagrammatically in Table 1.1.

3. Phases of a disaster

The period of time for which a disaster affects a country can be divided into some or all of the following phases:

a. Warning phase
b. Period of impact
c. Rescue phase
d. Relief phase
e. Rehabilitation period

a. Warning phase

With the aid of satellites and networks of weather stations using sophisticated electronic equipment, bodies such as the World Meteorological Organisation and the World Weather Watch can now predict many meteorological disasters (e.g. cyclones and hurricanes) well enough in advance in order to allow adequate precautions to be taken. Such warnings often relayed by radio, television, siren or even the ringing of church bells will only be of value if the community has been previously taught how to respond to such signals.

Table 1.1 Summary of events in East Pakistan/Bangladesh 1970–1972

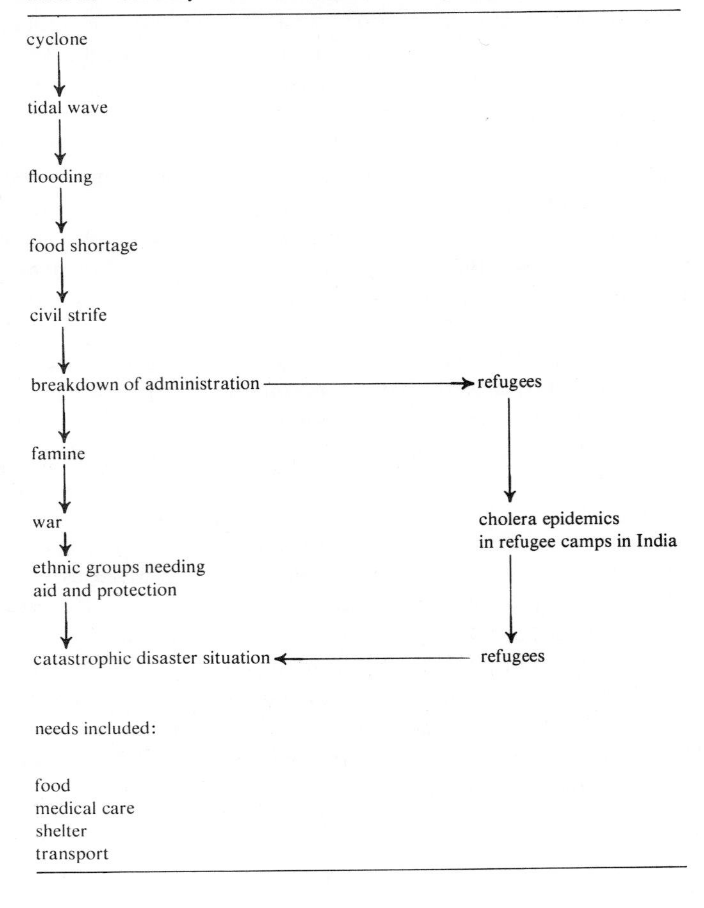

Most disasters are preceded by some sort of warning although the time permitted for evasive action may vary from seconds to months. For example, it took between six and seven successive years of drought before the Sahelian zone of Africa was declared a famine area by the League of Red Cross Societies in May 1973. Volcanoes often emit clouds of black smoke before erupting thus permitting the evacuation of the danger zone. Victims of a nuclear explosion might be aware of a blinding flash immediately before being struck by its impact.

b. Period of impact

This is the period when the disaster actually strikes and when very little can be done to lessen the effects or aid the survivors. The period of impact may only last for a few seconds (during an explosion or an earthquake) or days (floods) or even several months (droughts and epidemics). People within the affected area will be aware that there has been a disaster but this may not be apparent to neighbouring communities or nearby countries which will eventually be summoned to provide aid and rescue services.

c. Rescue phase

The rescue phase starts immediately after the impact and continues until organisation and authority have been restored to the affected community. During this period survivors will start to render first-aid to the victims, especially members of their own families. Limited uncoordinated assistance will start to arrive from neighbouring regions as news of the disaster spreads. This may take some considerable time in remote regions or in developing countries where communications are normally poor. Eventually the survivors will be located, the disposal of the dead organised and emergency feeding and shelter provided.

d. Relief phase

The confusion of the rescue period submerges into the next phase when professional teams of relief workers start to evaluate the damage, assess the most urgent needs and prepare an operational plan. Communication with donor communities will be restored, provisions will be made to receive and store relief supplies at airports, ports and railheads, food, clothing and other personal needs will be distributed in an orderly manner and medical and nursing services provided. Temporary accommodation or evacuation will be arranged and procedures established for the tracing of missing friends and relatives.

Depending on the severity of the disaster the government or some other coordinating body such as a civil defence force or the National Red Cross Society will assume authority of the situation. The effectiveness of this relief operation not only depends on the availability of the right resources but on the state of disaster preparedness within the community before the onset of the actual disaster.

e. Rehabilitation phase

Most of the relief workers will have left before the final and longest phase begins as it includes the rebuilding of damaged property, the replanting of crops and the restoration of all public services. It will only be seen to be over when the day-to-day pattern of life within the community returns to a state similar to that existing before the disaster. The assistance required during this phase will be in the nature of long term financial and technical help as provided by foreign governments, the World Bank and the International Monetary Fund.

4. Frequency of disasters

Although disasters can happen anywhere it is known that most natural disasters occur along two geographical patterns, one running along the Mediterranean basin to the Middle East, Afghanistan, Pakistan, India, Bangladesh down to Indonesia and then North through the Far East to Japan, the other along the Andes through the Caribbean into the United States of America.

The needs created by most disasters are met by the governments of the countries in which they occur. In large countries such as the U.S.A., which is often afflicted by a high number of different natural disasters in any year, most of these are managed by the local or state authorities. However, the majority of the countries in the above mentioned disaster belts are developing nations in the main relying upon international assistance when confronted with a large disaster situation. During the last decade the League of Red Cross Societies has, on average, launched a worldwide appeal every third week for the victims of natural disasters whose governments and National Red Cross Societies could not provide the total amount of aid required.

The U.S. Agency for Foreign International Developments (AID) Report on Foreign Disaster Emergency Relief for the fiscal year ending 30th June 1971, shows that during that year 51 disasters (excluding war) requiring foreign aid had occurred throughout the world. These catastrophes killed 522 212 persons and directly affected over 68 million people. An analysis of these incidents by type and region of the world affected is given in Table 1.2.

According to the U.S. AID Report, the total foreign assistance in favour of the victims of these 51 disasters reached the total of $472 304 000 against the reported assistance provided by the afflicted countries themselves of $744 837 000.

Table 1.2 Analysis of major disasters adapted from the U.S. AID Report for the fiscal year ending June 1971

Disaster	Latin America	Africa	Near East & South Asia	East Asia	Europe	Worldwide	Total
Border clash	—	—	1	—	—	—	1
Cholera epidemic	—	3	1	—	—	1	5
Civil disturbance	—	—	2	—	—	—	2
Crop failure	1	—	—	—	—	—	1
Cyclone	—	—	1	—	—	—	1
Drought	1	11	2	—	—	—	14
Earthquake	2	—	1	—	—	—	3
Flood	9	1	3	1	1	—	15
Food poisoning	1	—	—	—	—	—	1
Mine disaster	—	1	—	—	—	—	1
Refugee movement	—	—	1	—	—	—	1
Storm	2	—	—	—	—	—	2
Typhoon	—	—	—	3	—	—	3
Volcanic disruption	1	—	—	—	—	—	1
Total	17	16	12	4	1	1	51

5. The effects of disasters

The magnitude of a disaster can be assessed by its effects:

a. Size of area devastated
b. Number of people affected—dead, injured and homeless
c. Number of buildings, roads, railways, bridges and airports damaged and destroyed
d. Disruption of public services—telephones, electricity, gas, water and sewerage system
e. Spread of communicable diseases
f. Loss of crops and livestock
g. Effect on normal activities both commercial and social

There are two other factors which, although somewhat less tangible, should also be taken into consideration when evaluating a disaster situation, i.e. the psychological effects on the survivors and the overall consequence of the disaster on the community's economy.

a. Psychological effects

Cultural, religious and political beliefs exert differing influences on the human reactions to any disaster situation but the signs of a condition which has become known as the 'disaster syndrome' are usually present amongst its victims anywhere in the world. This response is very similar to the state of shock experienced by people who have just lost a close relative.

The immediate reaction is of abandonment and apathy as the individual is convinced that he is a lone sufferer. This state passes gradually when it is realised that others are equally involved. Old prejudices are then momentarily forgotten as a period of 'brotherly love' prompts him to join in the emotional solidarity which has enveloped those united into the rescue operation. Eventually, as life returns to normal, the victim will start to comprehend the full extent of the devastation and total human losses, whereupon the established social relationships will reassert themselves.

Natural disasters do not usually cause any long-term psychological problems whereas the horrors of war more commonly result in prolonged mental disturbances such as shell shock which are more difficult to treat.

b. Economic effects

The figures previously quoted from the U.S. AID Report for 1971 show that it is the recipient country which has to bear the overwhelming burden of the costs of any catastrophe and to provide most of the resources in manpower to alleviate its effects. It therefore follows that the efficiency of a relief operation will vary enormously according to the strength of a country's economy and the level of development reached before the disaster struck.

The following hypothetical situation illustrates this point. If a tectonic earth movement destroyed several large office buildings in the commercial area of any European city the damage expressed in monetary terms would appear to be astronomical. Insurance arrangements would, however, prevent the possibility of an ensuing financial crisis leading to the eventual breakdown of the country's economic viability. The appropriate resources would soon be concentrated on repairing the damage and the resumption of normal business activities would rapidly recommence.

The cost of rebuilding several thousand uninsured locally built houses in an African or Asian developing country affected by a similar disaster might seem insignificant when compared to the costs of replacing a few skyscrapers in an European capital. The long term economic effects on this community together with the personal losses sustained would in fact create far more serious repercussions. It is unlikely that the victims in these circumstances would have access to either the necessary cash or raw materials needed to rebuild their homes. The local government would, therefore, have to render assistance to such an extent that an insupportable pressure might be imposed on the nation's funds with a consequent adverse effect on the planned rate of economic growth. Several consecutive disaster-free years would then have to follow before a recovery could be effected. For example, the United Nations Food and Agricultural Organisation recently estimated that the severe drought which had plagued the Sahelian zone of Africa (Senegal, Mauritania, Mali, Upper Volta, Niger and Chad) between 1968 and 1974 reduced the average gross national product of the countries involved by at least 50 per cent.

Approximately two thirds of the world population live on this thin margin of subsistance where poverty, disease, chronic malnutrition and lack of education make them vulnerable to any disruption of their normal way of life. The problems for the governments of these people have since 1972 been further aggravated by the vicious spiral of rain, increasing energy, fertiliser and food costs together with uncontrolled and rapid population growth.

Developing nations often experience a rapid rate of political evolution which can lead to the eruption of armed conflict. A trend has developed during the last decade whereby the major world powers have engaged in indirect conflict through the medium of an internal war of liberation, e.g. Indo-China, the Middle East, Nigeria, Bangladesh, Angola. Such an outlet of aggression has to some extent aided the negotiation of strategic arms limitation treaties and, to date, the prevention of a nuclear holocaust but has simultaneously created severe economic difficulties and human suffering in the countries where the battles have actually been fought. The continual fighting in the Lebanon during 1975 and 1976 may be cited as a case in point as many months of continual strife reduced one of the most important banking centres in the Middle East to a 'ghost town' where people were too frightened to appear on the streets.

6. Future trends

There is no evidence to suggest that the frequency of natural disasters will alter significantly in the immediate future. But if current trends of high population growth and the movement to urban districts continues at the present rates, the effect of these will be far more serious. The number of major accidents occurring in areas of large concentrations of people will also increase dramatically with more cars, bigger aircraft, airports, etc.

The severity and number of man-made disasters will probably increase as technological achievements produce more nuclear power plants and factories for the processing of dangerous chemicals (e.g. Nypro plant at Flixborough which exploded on 1st June 1974 killing 28 people and causing extensive damage to the surrounding villages). Greater affluence and more leisure time in the Western World have also led to more adventurous pastimes which will further add to the risk of man-made disasters or accidents. For example, 108 people, mainly women from four Somerset villages on a day shopping trip to Switzerland, were killed when a British charter flight crashed near Basle on 10th April 1973. During August of the same year 49 people also lost their lives when fire partially destroyed the Summerland Entertainment complex at Douglas, Isle of Man.

The needs created by disasters in developing nations have been recognised by the United Nations and other inter-governmental bodies which are now prepared to include plans for dealing with emergencies when drafting long term development programmes. Being aware of the possible effect of disasters on these programmes they are also now prepared to concentrate more initial resources when disasters occur.

The effect of disasters will only be minimised when adequate methods of warning and plans for dealing with them have been drafted, notified and understood by those involved in every country in the world.

2. Disaster preparedness

Adequate procedures to deal with disaster situations should be formulated in every country of the world as no country is completely immune from both natural and man-made catastrophes. The activities related to such pre-disaster planning procedures can be broadly grouped into two categories under the headings of prevention and preparation. Very few natural disasters can be totally prevented but experience has shown that certain preventive measures such as the strengthening of buildings in earthquake zones or the introduction of irrigation systems in drought areas can considerably reduce their effects.

On the practical level, disaster preparation means the contingency planning necessary for the management of the situation from the time of the initial warning, through the relief phase, to the final period of reconstruction. Continuous preparedness to provide quick and effective relief, together with the adoption of such preventive measures as are possible, saves lives, lessens personal suffering and loss and reduces the destruction of property when a calamity strikes. It is the responsibility of government to ensure that legislative steps are taken to permit certain precautions to be enforced and to guarantee that an efficient national organisation exists for the provision of relief.

The relief plan

The purpose of a national disaster relief plan is to provide a clear and precise set of guidelines for government departments and other bodies which might be called upon to render service to the victims. The plan should be specifically designed so as to be able to coordinate the country's entire resources to meet the needs resulting from accidents likely to occur within its territory and, at the same time, be so flexible that it can be put into force in whole or part as circumstances require. The plan should be based on an analysis of information obtained from records concerning the causes, frequency, effects and management of major disasters which have previously occurred within the country and surrounding area. An assessment of the potential hazardous areas, e.g. airports and industrial manufacturing plants, should also be carried out during the drafting of the plan.

It is essential that the plan clearly defines the terms of reference of a central coordinating body chaired by the Head of State, Prime Minister or other senior official with a secretariat for the planning and implementation of any relief operation. The composition of this central coordinating body will be discussed in the next section. Its secretariat should be placed within an existing government department whose daily work is closely related to the services required following a serious disaster and the structure of which will provide established administrative links to regional and local authorities throughout the country.

During the emergency period the central coordinating body might have to assume the responsibility for the normal day-to-day services usually controlled by the central government and which might easily become part of the relief effort. It is important, therefore, that the authority of the central coordinating body and its secretariat is ratified by national laws and is readily accepted by the people. The responsibilities of governments during emergency situations included:

When disaster becomes imminent

1. Ensure national stockpiling of emergency reserves.
2. Open and staff a disaster coordination centre (operations centre).
3. Issue official warnings to those in danger and to neighbouring governments who might also be affected or asked to provide assistance.
4. Place relief services on alert.
5. Designate hazardous zones.
6. Enforce evacuation from threatened areas.
7. Open shelters and evacuation centres.

After disaster strikes

1. Mobilise rescue services (ambulance, fire, police, military, civil defence, coastguard, etc).
2. Provide immediate assistance to victims in the form of:
   Medical care (first aid, nursing and hospital treatment)
   Food
   Clothing
   Shelter
   Welfare services, including tracing of missing persons.
3. Make a detailed survey of the affected area.
4. Coordinate relief actions of government departments, UN Agencies and other voluntary organisations.
5. Keep the United Disaster Relief Coordinator informed of all developments of operation if international aid is requested.
6. Coordinate public information on effects of the catastrophe and resultant needs.
7. Restore communications.
8. Maintain law and order, including control of traffic.
9. Safeguard public health, especially care and prevention of communicable diseases.
10. Arrange for the identification and burial of the dead.
11. Repair and restore electricity, gas, water and sewerage systems.
12. Repair or replace public buildings (e.g. schools, hospitals).
13. Allocate grants for rehabilitation projects and compensation payments.
14. Plan reconstruction programmes for permanent housing.
15. Plan economic recovery of disaster area.

(Adapted from: *Your country could have a disaster:* Pamphlet produced by the League of Red Cross Societies, Geneva.)

In addition to the government's mandate to carry out these responsibilities legal arrangements should be made to enable the relief coordinating body to perform other functions which should also be included in the national disaster relief plan, such as:

1. Requisition of land, supplies, services, vehicles, labour, etc. for emergency relief operations.
2. Releasing of foreign exchange for the purchase of relief materials.

3. Authorisation of the exemption of purchase tax and customs duties and the provision of free transportation for relief supplies.

4. Rationing and the fixing of food prices.

The central coordinating body should meet at regular intervals between disasters to review the various contingency procedures contained in the national relief plan. It should also promote frequent propaganda campaigns to guarantee that the plan will be properly understood by everyone when it is activated because, as a result of warnings given too late, misunderstood or even completely ignored.

The central relief coordinating body

It is the function of the central coordinating body to centralise all available information relevant to a particular situation so as to allow the numerous agents in the field to operate as efficiently as possible under the terms of the national relief plan without any duplication or wasted effort. The central relief coordinating body should comprise the senior representatives from the following:

Government Ministries/Departments

Head of State/Prime Minister's Office
External Affairs
Treasury
Relief and Rehabilitation
Planning/Development
Meteorological
Health and Welfare
Public Works
Telecommunications
Public Information
Transportation (including national airline, port and airport authorities)
Public Services (electricity, water, gas and sewerage)
Food and Agriculture
Industry and Supply
Education and Culture
Defence (armed forces)
Police
Fire Brigade
Ambulance
Civil Defence
Coastguard
Judiciary
Others

Non-governmental organisations

National Red Cross

Voluntary agencies with trained personnel or equipment which might be useful, e.g. St John Ambulance, Amateur Radio Clubs, Youth Organisations, etc. News media—newspapers, television, radio

Transport authorities
Others

Regional/local relief committees

Where appropriate, regional and/or local relief committees with due competence and authority to prepare and organise the actual relief operations should be established. These operational committees should resemble the national plan in composition with the addition of local specialists where appropriate, for example a veterinary surgeon in a farming community.

The best way of achieving the objective of an effective relief force is to delegate specific duties to qualified and experienced leaders who are capable of organising the community's resources and training the nucleus of a team which can be expanded with volunteers or, in due course, with relief personnel from neighbouring districts.

Responsibilities of a local disaster committee

The local preparedness plans within a country may differ greatly from one area to the next as they will have taken into account such factors as the size and density of the population, the surrounding terrain, the most frequent types of major accidents and disasters and the ethnic cultural and social traditions. Nevertheless every local committee should:

1. Appoint a suitable chairman such as the local mayor.
2. Develop a set of procedures outlining a clear chain of command in order to be able to maintain the services listed as responsibilities of government, p. 11.
3. Prepare and maintain resource data files on the location and availability of supplies (food, clothing, drugs and other useful equipment), trained medical personnel (doctors, nurses, pharmacists, etc.), vehicles, contractors' machinery (e.g. cranes) for use in rescue operations and buildings for temporary hospitals and evacuation centres, etc.
4. Open an operations room with two way communications both with relief personnel on the scene and with the central relief coordinating centre. A back-up communications system with an independent power supply, e.g. radio with a petrol generator, should be on hand in case of power failures.
5. Pre-print disaster survey forms to ease overall assessment of catastrophe.
6. Establish a system whereby the officer-in-charge calls out a few key personnel and they in turn send for several others as required and so word spreads along the chain until everyone is informed. This obviates telephone congestion at any one level. Every emergency plan must of course list the names, telephone numbers and addresses of key personnel.
7. Send frequent situation reports to the national relief coordinating centre.
8. Organise frequent Press conferences in order to disseminate factual information to suppress rumours and resulting panic.
9. Formulate regulations with due authority for the requisitioning of supplies, etc.
10. Implement precise administrative and accounting routines needed to support relief teams.
11. Hold practical disaster relief exercises and constantly review operational plans.
12. Write a final report and submit it to the national disaster coordinating body at the end of the operation.

Summary

All disaster preparedness plans should be fully comprehensive and kept under constant review in order that they can be easily adapted to meet any unforeseen calamity. The effectiveness of the pre-disaster planning measures will exert a direct influence on the longer term rehabilitation programmes and it is therefore most important that accurate reports of the relief operation are prepared and given to the appropriate authorities.

National governments within a given region of the world should work together and, in conjunction with United Nations Agencies, to develop regional disaster preparedness programmes as many serious catastrophes, such as droughts, often effect entire geographical regions paying no respect to territorial boundaries.

3. Disaster relief operations

The preceding chapter outlined the rudiments of a national disaster preparedness plan. This chapter will begin by considering the survey and assessment processes and the arrangements for the provision of the basic necessities—feeding, clothing and shelter. Aspects relating to the coordination of the relief effort are then discussed and an alternative management structure capable of running the relief operation in the absence of a national or local disaster coordinating body suggested.

Although the procedures for establishing the facts in a standardised form, so that direct comparisons can be made, ought to be the same whether performed by either a local or experienced foreign survey team, it will, for the time being, be assumed that following a catastrophe in a country with a developed pre-disaster plan the rescue services have been mobilised. The first priority is, therefore, to carry out a survey.

The survey

As soon as it is safe to proceed, multidisciplinary survey teams (comprising administrators, medical and nursing staff, environmental health inspectors, engineers, sanitarians, etc.) as defined in the national relief plan should be dispatched to the disaster zone to prepare a report containing the following data:

Basic facts

Type of disaster
Cause
Exact time and date of occurrence
Place

Background information

Geographic location
Topography (e.g. hills, valleys, rivers, lakes)
Climate
Number of inhabitants, population density and average family size
Ethnic groups—language, religion and other distinguishable customs
Characteristics of houses and normal diet
Nature of economy (e.g. agricultural or industrial)
Communications
Economic, natural and material resources.

Extent of damage

Number of victims:

dead
injured (i.e. in need of medical attention)
homeless
in need of assistance (food, clothing)
affected

Houses damaged indicating approximate number of families involved in each category:
totally destroyed
extensive damage
minor damage (i.e. easily repairable)

Public buildings (schools, hospitals, etc.) damaged or destroyed

Condition of communications—roads, railways, bridges, dikes, airports

State of public utilities—electricity, gas, water, sewerage and telephone services

Effects on economy due to damage to crops, foodstocks, industries and the immediate consequences (e.g. food shortages and unemployment).

Assessment of immediate needs

Medical care—doctors, nurses and first-aiders with equipment

Food—daily requirements of meat, fish, flour, rice, wheat, oil, vegetables, tea, etc.

Clothing—thickness, type and size for men, women, boys, girls and babies—also blankets if needed

Shelter for homeless

Vehicles and fuel

Personnel—specify nature of job to be carried out and qualifications required

Finance—cash for the local purchase of supplies and operational expenses.

The survey report should also describe the type and effectiveness of the aid already provided together with an estimate of time for which the emergency relief help will have to be continued. The reports must be presented promptly to the disaster coordinating body in order that an operational plan can be agreed and initiated without delay. The essential requirements for the rehabilitation period ought to be taken into account when preparing the plan and the details with projected budgets included in any national or international appeals. It is important that every effort is made to restrict the aims of the relief and rehabilitation programmes to restoring the quality of life within the area to that which existed immediately before the disaster struck. If resources are limited it should be remembered that it is usually better to provide a minimum quantity of succour to a large number of people rather than concentrating all assistance on a small selected group.

Supporting relief services

Whilst most of the actual rescue work will be conducted by government teams such as engineers, fire brigade and civil defence, voluntary agencies are frequently asked to assist or even assume responsibility for the provision of food, shelter and clothing. It is most important that whenever possible each individual is visited in his dwelling and his needs established before relief vouchers are actually issued.

Some simple guidelines for those who might suddenly become involved in such programmes are set out in the following pages.

Feeding programmes

Immediately the disaster plan is activated the personnel responsible for mass catering and the distribution of food should proceed to the shelters where they will be prepared to provide hot beverages. After the period of impact they will also set up mobile feeding centres in the disaster zone to serve hot snacks to both the victims and the rescue workers.

If families are capable of cooking for themselves the most straightforward method of organising a feeding scheme is to issue vouchers which can be exchanged for food at local shops or ration centres established by the relief services. The scope of the feeding programme will be determined by the extent of the destruction, for example:

1. Supplementary—provision of certain items temporarily unobtainable or commonly protein food for vulnerable groups, e.g. small children.

Fig. 3.1 Cloth being used to receive rice when no utensils are available (Bangladesh, 1971). Courtesy of J. J. Kurz.

2. Short-term—basic feeding of population for several weeks when normal patterns of life re-emerge.

3. Medium-term—basic feeding of population until next harvest, i.e. several months.

4. Long-term—basic feeding of population for more than one year, usually because of war or severe drought.

The responsibilities of the staff administering the mass feeding operation will include:

1. The checking of pre-determined sources of supply (warehouses, shops, markets) and the designated places for the preparation of hot meals (schools, church halls, restaurants);

2. The calculation of the quantity of foodstuffs required each day according to the required number of kilojoules necessary for each person. During protracted operations such calculations should be used to allow the staggered delivery of goods in bulk thus avoiding the extra expense of warehousing and additional transportation;

3. The establishment of cooking and distribution centres (canteen style) in evacuation centres or as close as possible to where the people are living;

4. Ensuring that there are plentiful supplies of fuel and drinking water;

5. The preparation of simple varied menus according to the local feeding habits;

6. The supervision of suitable places of storage;

7. The printing of ration cards or meal tickets;

8. Warning people to bring their own food containers and maintaining a spare supply for those who have lost everything;

9. Issuing special instructions on the use of strange foods such as corn soya milk (CSM) or wheat soya blend (WSB) which might be introduced into the country for the first time during the relief operation;

10. Upholding standards of cleanliness and hygiene;

11. Overseeing the fair distribution of food by controlling queues, etc.

Clothing/blanket distributions

When a need for blankets or clothing has been confirmed by the survey team, stocks should either be released from emergency reserves or collected from merchants with whom previous contracts have been negotiated, and moved to distribution points in the refugee centres or near the living quarters of the disaster victims. The quantity and type of clothing released will be dictated by the prevailing climatic conditions, the number of those in need and the local traditions of dress. The distribution centre should be so arranged as to provide three distinct areas for reception, sorting and collection. It should, however, be noted that garments tailored to Western tastes and temperatures are quite commonly found to be unacceptable in developing countries. This is usually the case with women's clothing. In this type of situation the best solution is to issue lengths of cloth which can be either wrapped around the body according to local tradition or made up into the type of article preferred.

Care should be taken before launching appeals for clothing as this frequently results in a mountain of clothes being received which have to be screened for suitability and then cleaned, mended and finally sorted according to sex, type and age. This operation could easily waste valuable man-hours and take up space which could be utilised by more important supplies. Clothing and blanket stores tend to attract pilferers so tight security measures must be enforced.

A recent analysis of the League of Red Cross Societies records from 1965 to 1974 has shown that clothing and blankets were required in 60 per cent of its relief operations.

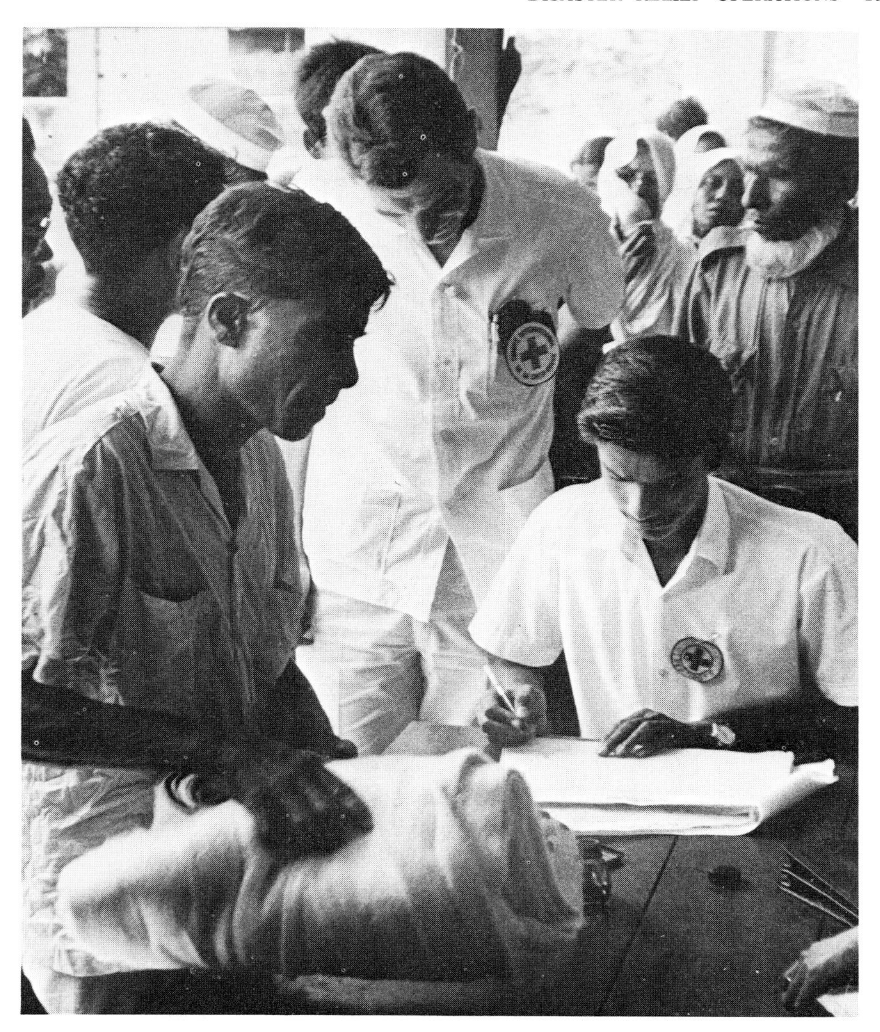

Fig. 3.2 Distribution of clothing (Bangladesh, 1971).

Shelter

A large number of people made homeless by disasters are normally absorbed into the homes of friends, relatives or neighbours whose houses have not been affected. This practice should be encouraged as not only does it promote a sense of community spirit but it lessens the burden placed on the relief services during a critical period of the operation. Nevertheless, the extra needs for clothing, blankets, cooking pots, etc. should not be ignored.

An organised inspection of buildings (e.g. large halls, gymnasiums, colleges) and land suitably situated and well-drained, already earmarked as potential mass shelters and camp sites respectively, should be started once the existence of a sizeable number of homeless has been identified. The general criteria for such establishments will be:

1. A safe location within a communicable distance of damaged homes;

2. A fresh and plentiful water supply;
3. Adequate toilet, washing and laundry facilities;
4. Sufficient space for family and single person sleeping quarters, kitchen and dining areas, dispensary, administrative offices, stores and recreational/educational activities for children;
5. Satisfactory fire precautions;
6. Good discipline and regular policing;
7. Maintenance of an individual registration system.

Whilst every effort should be made to satisfy the need for accommodation, certain refugees, notably those afflicted by war, should not be over-pampered as there is a definite tendency, in certain circumstances, for such people to become completely dependent on relief handouts. The Palestinian refugees, for example, are now well into their second generation and still reliant on the help provided by an international agency.

The most positive way to ease the acute housing problem after a disaster is to provide large amounts of cash for the purchase of local building materials and corrugated iron shedding which the local people will be able to use to repair or replace the damaged buildings. Alternatively, strong military-type canvas tents could be supplied as temporary housing units. They have the advantages of being relatively cheap, easily transportable and fairly durable. When sent to areas which experience sudden severe falls in temperature at night they should be accompanied by a kerosene stove whereas, in hot humid climates, extra ventilation apertures should be installed.

Coordination

In normal circumstances either the local, regional or national relief coordinating body can be expected to isolate the needs and manage the relief operation successfully. Problems only start to occur when the magnitude of the disaster exceeds the local resources and an appeal for international assistance is launched. Representatives of governments and aid agencies might then start to arrive and probably wish to conduct their own independent surveys thus causing a certain amount of anxiety and confusion. There is quite often much competition between such agencies for funds in donor countries and, unfortunately but not too surprisingly, this has often resulted in too few programmes for the elderly or very young which were originally allocated a very low priority. Sometimes there are too many agencies involved in similar activities resulting in duplication of effort, wastage and chaos.

The best way to avoid such pandemonium is for the government concerned to call regular coordinating meetings with foreign agencies and, if possible, to assign either specific programmes or areas to particular agencies. It is doubtful whether such a level of coordination would be possible in any country without a comprehensive legally endorsed set of disaster relief procedures.

It is, however, most encouraging to note that the Charities forming the British Disasters Emergency Committee (British Red Cross Society, Christian Aid/CAFOD, OXFAM, Save the Children Fund and War on Want) have been successfully launching joint appeals for disaster victims for over 10 years. This co-operation has brought about a high degree of internal coordination, many joint survey missions and multi-sponsored relief consignments. For example, 24 four-ton trucks were supplied to drought victims in Niger during 1974.

The United Nations Disaster Relief Office (UNDRO) has, since it increased its establishment in 1975, become extremely proficient in providing accurate information with regard to the exact emergency needs to potential donors. Their recent handling of the Guatemalan earthquake disaster is worth particular mention.

It is occasionally necessary due to the lack of a government relief coordinating office or the sheer enormity of a disaster for a relief agency to establish a secretariat within the country to assess and coordinate the relief operation.

Organisation of relief agency headquarters

An administration of this nature can only be established at the request of the host government. In order to avoid any complications it is most important that the government issues clear and concise terms of reference when deputing the responsibilities of a relief operation to a particular agency or group of agencies.

An organisation chart for such an establishment is shown in Figure 3.1. This chart is only intended to be a general indication of the functions to be performed as any such structure would, of course, have to be adapted to meet the needs of a given situation.

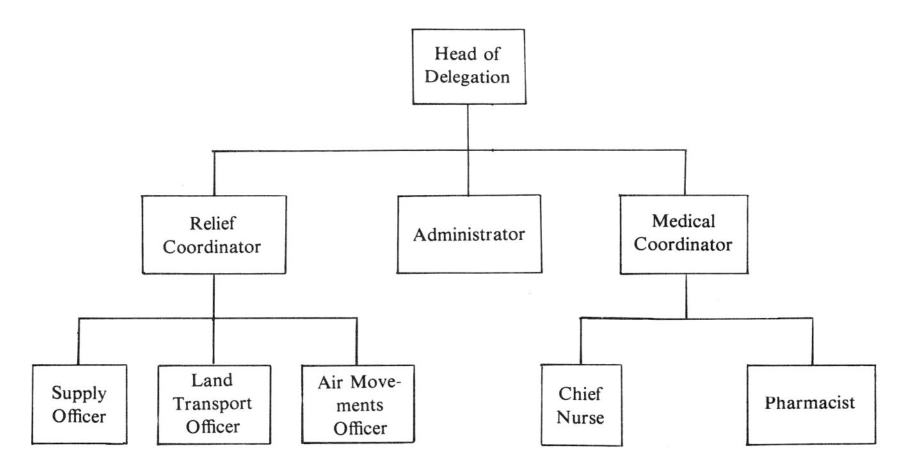

Fig. 3.3 Organisation chart for disaster relief headquarters.

The responsibilities of the key personnel include:

Head of Delegation

1. Maintains liaison between the government of the afflicted country and the headquarters of the relief agency,
2. Regularly reviews and adapts the sections of the relief operation delegated to him by the authorities,
3. Directs personnel, cash and relief supplies at his disposal within the framework of the operational plan,
4. Organises a secretariat to assist with the management of the relief programme,
5. Exerts budgetary controls,
6. Formulates a public relations policy,

7. Keeps in regular contact with U.N. voluntary agencies and government missions also working in the country,
8. Prepares job evaluations for his relief staff,
9. Chairs regular staff meetings,
10. Sends a monthly report to agency headquarters.

Relief Coordinator

1. Has the day-to-day direction of the relief operation,
2. Works closely with the supply officer and transport officer in order to keep relief teams, feeding centres, etc. supplied with equipment for their work,
3. Monitors the work of other agencies to avoid duplication,
4. Makes frequent trips into the field to visit teams and to assess the situation,
5. Prepares a monthly report for the Head of Delegation.

Supply Officer

1. Arranges receipt of supplies from abroad and the local purchase and storage of supplies when necessary,
2. Maintains records of supplies received, in stock and distributed,
3. Hires warehouses, recruits and trains local staff in accordance with personnel policies established for the operation,
4. Takes preventive measures to ensure against loss of supplies by theft, vermin or climatic conditions,
5. Monitors the food prices on the local market,
6. At end of operation liquidates surplus stocks and hands back rented or borrowed property,
7. Prepares monthly report for Head of Delegation.

Land Transport Officer

1. Prepares a cost effective analysis of available transport systems within the country to ensure the efficient movement of supplies from port of entry to warehouses and distribution points,
2. Determines the number of vehicles (trucks and personnel carriers) needed for the operation,
3. Where possible develops regular delivery schedules,
4. Recruits, trains and supervises local drivers,
5. Organises a motor pool and routine vehicle maintenance,
6. Purchases supplies of fuel and spare parts,
7. Keeps documents relating to vehicles,
8. Investigates all accidents and makes a report for insurance purposes,
9. Prepares a monthly report for Head of Delegation.

Air Movements Officer

1. Oversees the loading and unloading of aircraft,
2. Controls staff and use of loading equipment,
3. Prepares flight schedules for submission to civil aviation board,
4. Keeps records of all goods received and despatched,
5. Prepares a monthly report for Head of Delegation.

Administrator

1. Has the daily management of the secretariat—procurement of stationery and office machines,
2. Maintains a central filing system and arranges distribution of communications,
3. Employs local personnel, maintains their records, arranges payment of salaries and organises holiday rota,
4. Keeps senior staff informed of current policies and terms of contracts for local employees under their control,
5. Maintains the delegation's financial records and makes arrangements with a local bank for the depositing, transfer and payment of money,
6. Takes out insurance policies to cover all buildings and vehicles being used and sufficient cover against accident and loss of life for all staff and employees according to the local business practice,
7. Keeps a record of the location of field personnel and equipment,
8. Makes hotel and travel arrangements for incoming and outgoing delegates,
9. Prepares a plan for the liquidation of assets at the end of the operation,
10. Prepares a monthly financial and narrative report for the Head of Delegation.

Medical Coordinator

1. Advises the Head of Delegation on all medical and public health matters,
2. Determines the scope of medical services to be provided,
3. Liaises with government and local health officers,
4. Regularly visits refugee camps, evacuation centres, feeding schemes and checks water supply, drainage, sanitary facilities and general standards of hygiene,
5. Works closely with the Chief Nursing Officer and Pharmacist,
6. Monitors health of staff,
7. Recruits local medical personnel,
8. Monitors health of delegation staff,
9. Analyses nature, frequency and sequence of local diseases and/or epidemics,
10. Works closely with the relief coordinator to establish routines for medical/nutritional teams,
11. Prepares a monthly report for the Head of Delegation.

Chief Nurse

1. Determines with the medical coordinator the extent of the nursing programme within the operation,
2. Liaises with the government nursing adviser and other senior members of the local nursing profession,
3. Assesses the number of nurses required, recruits local nursing staff and deploys them within the programme according to their professional training and experience,
4. Inspects standards of nursing care provided by teams in refugee centres,
5. Supervises nursing staff in order to maintain professional standards,
6. Prepares a monthly report for the Head of Delegation.

Pharmaceutical Officer

1. Coordinates the receipt, storing and supply of drugs and medical equipment and maintains records accordingly,

2. Runs a medical store,
3. Arranges the local procurement of medical supplies,
4. Maintains quality control,
5. Supplies prudent information,
6. Works closely with government medical supply department,
7. Prepares a monthly report for Head of Delegation.

Some principles for disaster relief

Every country should have a pre-disaster plan.

Senior relief personnel should be well trained, experienced and should remain in station for long periods.

There must be a constant flow of information to and from the scene of disaster.

Maximum use should be made of local resources only essential foreign supplies and personnel should be sent to the disaster and only upon request.

Supplies should be purchased locally as they are usually cheaper and more acceptable.

Voluntary agencies should work closely with governments but retain their independence. A certain loss of sovereignty should, during joint operations, be accepted.

4. Special considerations in nursing administration in disasters

Definition

The Oxford English Dictionary states that a disaster is a great or sudden misfortune. The police use the phrase 'major incident'. Some regard a stated number of seriously injured casualties as the distinguishing feature, but Rutherford (1970) defines a disaster as an emergency of such magnitude as to require extraordinary mobilisation of the emergency services. This of course has the advantage that it depends upon what is needed, whereas any definition based on numbers can be little more than speculation. In practice, it soon becomes evident that extraordinary measures are required even though there may have been no formal declaration of a disaster and it is important to recognise that what constitutes a disaster depends upon the size and the competence of the organisation that is to deal with it. The main purpose of defining a disaster is to enable the police, fire, ambulance and hospital services to agree upon how best to cope with the additional calls made upon them.

Planning

Disasters can occur at any time, in any place, in any weather and, indeed, may owe as much to the circumstances as to the scale of the event. With the exception of the man-made disaster of war, the worst disasters follow natural events. Not all require medical action but rescue and medical services of any town, city, region or nation should draw up, practice and review arrangements for dealing with disaster. However well conceived such plans may be, unless there are frequent opportunities to put them into practice there will always be shortcomings owing to the fact that no two disasters are quite the same. The police, fire and ambulance services have certain advantages over doctors and nurses in that they are equipped, staffed and organised with more attention to the possibility of disaster than is the case with many hospitals.

Nursing administration in the event of disaster falls into two main groups:

1. Enabling existing hospitals to deal with disasters;
2. Providing nursing services to go to assist at the scene of a disaster, perhaps hundreds or thousands of miles away.

Nursing administration in hospital

Planning should start with clear recognition of the fact that however a disaster is defined and whatever arrangements are made for notifying those concerned, the circumstances may be such that a hospital with perhaps a secondary role in a carefully drawn up plan will suddenly find itself inundated with casualties. Chaos is inevitable if there is no warning and the scale of the event is large. Chaos that persists when resources have been mobilized is evidence of poor organisation or of overwhelming casualties. It is likely to persist when a hospital is not accustomed to emergency work.

Although the nursing services need special attention their general plans are inseparable from those of the medical and administrative staffs, so that close collaboration is as important in planning as it is in the face of disaster. An important practical expression of this is the fact that whereas the administrator and senior doctors go home, there is always a senior member of the nursing staff on duty in the hospital, so that it may fall to her to recognise that as far as the hospital is concerned a disaster has occurred and to set in motion the arrangements to deal with it. It is thus essential that nurses who will from time to time be in charge of a hospital should be properly versed in what they should do.

The immediate task when a disaster occurs at night is to dispose the available staff to the best advantage while calling in all those who can be reached; whereas during the day it will include suddenly interupting routine work at perhaps the busiest times.

Rehearsals

It may seem self-evident that rehearsals are essential, but in practice rehearsals are usually arranged at times that will disturb the normal activities of the hospital as little as possible. They are unrealistic in many other ways.

What is essential is that those in positions of authority should be able to act usefully in even the most taxing conditions and this is much better done by the equivalent of the 'Army's Tent' (tactical exercise without troops) than by rehearsals. In this way fire, explosion of noxious substances, interruption of supplies of water and electricity, impediment of access to the hospital and other complications of accidents causing many casualties, can be considered at leisure with the use of few staff and no material resources.

If those in command know what to do initial confusion rapidly gives way to order. It cannot be stated too strongly that one of the best ways to cause chaos is to require that unfamiliar procedures be adopted in cases of disaster. What is essential, for example, is that telephonists know who to call in, and in what order, and that registration staff can quickly switch from the usual procedure to a much more simplified one. 'Action Cards' setting out the principal duties of key members of staff (Savage, 1972) are a good way of ensuring the correct actions, but because the duties may not be committed accurately to memory the cards must be available and their whereabouts must be known. It is also desirable that staff be called upon from time to time to produce equipment set aside for use in disasters.

Principal tasks

1. To prepare a reception area for casualties.
2. To deploy existing staff and to summon extra help, if necessary.
3. To establish a joint headquarters for nurses, doctors and administrators.
4. To clear beds and operating areas for incoming patients and to augment existing facilities for resuscitating severely injured casualties.
5. To organise and integrate voluntary work.
6. To accommodate relatives and deal with enquiries. Rutherford (1970) graphically refers to the need for a 'weeping room'. Medical social workers have a valuable role to play here.
7. To organise with the police means of providing information for bona fide enquiries and dealing effectively with others.

8. To arrange for the temporary accommodation of the dead, if the hospital's mortuary should become full.

Mobile teams

There is a growing tendency to provide doctors and nurses to go to the scene of a serious accident and it may happen that a hospital is called upon to send out a team. A readiness to do so should be part of the responsibility of any district general hospital, although the occasions on which a team is called for are likely to be very few, and the value of the team is questionable. Such readiness should exist in the event of a disaster, as well as for less serious accidents, but it is to be hoped that if medical assistance were required at the accident it would not be sought from the hospital already busily occupied with casualties; and it should be accepted that in such a case the hospital concerned would have the right to urge that a team be sought elsewhere. In such circumstances the need for medical assistance may not be so urgent that a team cannot be from another hospital further away. In many parts of the country a better source of medical assistance may be a general practitioner's emergency scheme, which has the advantage of providing doctors who already have experience of giving medical aid in difficult circumstances. This cannot be said for many hospital teams.

If a mobile team is available its equipment should be stored near the point of departure. It should be examined at regular intervals and reviewed from time to time, especially in the light of practical experience. It should include protective clothing for the team which should be warm and waterproof, easily seen in poor light and clearly labelled. Colour coding is impractical. It is best for rescue services to collect the medical team and their equipment: this makes it easier for them to arrive at the right place and gain prompt admission. The team will usually consist of two doctors, one of whom is an anaesthetist, and two or more nursing staff, preferably with theatre experience and some degree of

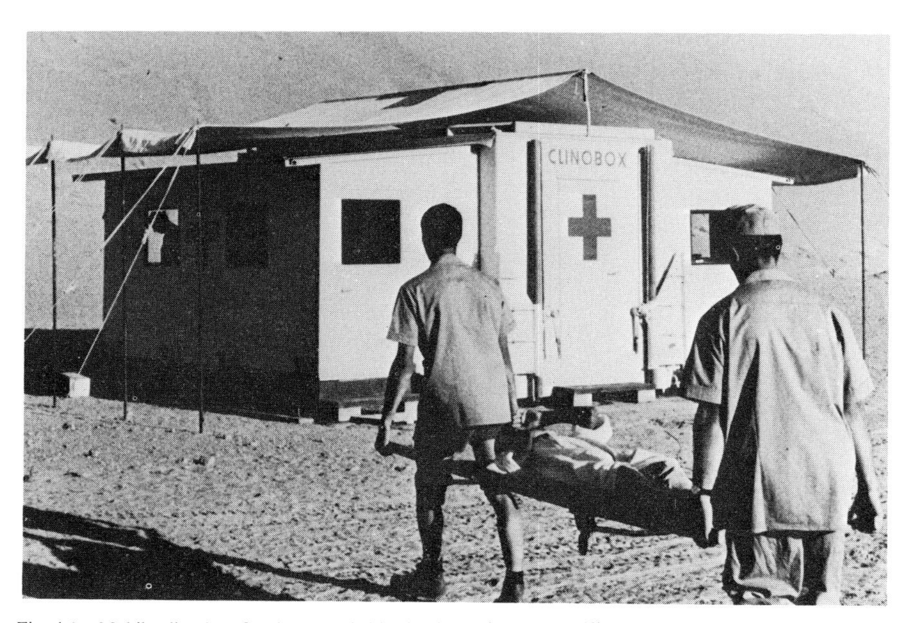

Fig. 4.1 Mobile clino-box for the wounded in the desert (Yemen, 1963).

anaesthetic training, but the precise composition may have to be varied. Before entering a disaster area the emergency team should be told of any dangers that they might have to face and the precautions they should take. Their main function is the resuscitation of the victims on the site. A medical team must keep its limitations in mind. Firemen are trained and equipped to free trapped casualties and to protect them while they do so. Ambulance men are trained and equipped to move injured persons. Doctors may have to advise on certain matters and perhaps to look after an injury of particular importance when a casualty is moved, but their most useful role is to resuscitate others before they are moved to hospital. Clearing air passages, stopping accessible bleeding, replenishing the circulation and relieving pain (which is not necessary in all cases), applying dressings and splints are some of the abilities likely to be required of them. Amputation is occasionally necessary to enable a person to be released.

It is important to distinguish between courage and folly in disaster conditions and to recognise the difficulties and dangers of trying, for example, to pass an endotracheal tube or setting up an intravenous infusion in poor light with little room to work. It is not possible to practice these activities, but there is much to be said for practicing preparing equipment for use in difficult and unfamiliar conditions and for members of a team going through the emergency equipment and its layout. Anything more than simple life-saving measures may be required only when casualties have to be carried a long way—as from a coalmine—and when local conditions are favourable. In such cases the team can order at once whatever it will require to be sent. It is unrealistic to try to anticipate remote surgical possibilities and carry an unnecessarily large amount of equipment.

Essential requirements

Surgical bag
Instrument roll
Syringes and needles
Portex tracheostomy tubes × 3 (assorted sizes)
Suture material and ligatures
Esmarchs bandage
3 towels and macintosh sheets
Crepe 6 inch bandages
Wool rolls 8 inch × 40 inch × 24
Wool balls—20 packets—10 per packet
Gauze dressings 4 inch × 3 inch × 5—20 packets
Gauze dressings 4 inch × 6 inch × 5—20 packets
Tincture of Chlorhexidine
1 per cent lignocaine
Cetrimide is useful for cleaning if not asepsis

Instruments carried in surgical bag
2 of each 15 and 23 blades with handles
2 sponge holders
1 pair 6 inch PB scissors
1 pair 7 inch and 5 inch Mayo scissors
6 pairs 6 inch Spencer Wells Artery forceps

2 pairs 5 inch dissecting forceps, untoothed
1 pair toothed Gillies dissecting forceps
1 pair 6 inch toothed dissectors
1 Mayo needle holder
2 double hooks
1 sharp single hook
1 tracheal dilator
1 self retaining retractor
3 pairs straight Mosquito forceps
1 Lion bone holding forceps
1 Liston's bone cutter
2 bone elevators
1 amputation saw
1 amputation knife

Two 'extra dressings' bags
Each containing:
Gauze dressing
Wool rolls
Conforming bandages 6 inch and 3 inch
Triangular bandages
2 boxes Band Aid dressings
1 pair dressing scissors
1 small traction kit
1 large traction kit
½ inch strapping
3 inch Elastoplast

Intravenous infusion bag
Cut down sets × 3
Assorted cannulae and intravenous catheters, e.g. Venflon
Angiocath's 5¼ inch Abbot drum cartridge catheters
Ligatures
Sutures ready threaded
Gauze swabs 4 inch × 3 inch × 5—18 packets
Swabs impregnated with 70 per cent isopropyl alcohol
1 per cent lignocaine
Syringes and needles
Plasma and water
Dextran 70 in 0·9 per cent saline
6 normal saline
12 Baxter blood administration sets

Summoning help and deploying staff

The telephonists' action cards will show which key nurses are to be called, but as conditions develop the Chief Nursing Officer may have to go beyond the usual sources of nursing and supply and turn to other hospitals, nursing agencies and the voluntary aid societies. One of her principal concerns will be to secure the staff she needs to deal with conditions as they are and yet keep in reserve the staff she needs to maintain the functions of the hospital until conditions are back to normal. Enthusiasm and devotion may well have to be restrained if exhaustion is to be avoided. Here numbers are not enough; staff working in unfamiliar conditions may be at a grave disadvantage and turn out to be more of a hindrance than a help.

Quite apart from her nurses, the Chief Nursing Officer knows only too well the importance of support by, for example, pharmacists, store-keepers, linen room staff, sterile supply department and catering staff. A general notice should, if possible, be issued by radio and television. Adequate reserves of stock are of fundamental importance. Extra stock carried by operating theatres in readiness for a disaster should include the following:

Linen packs

20 basic packs each containing:

3 wrapping layers, one of which should be waterproof, enabling it to be used as a working surface

3 rolls of wool

1 packet of dressing gauze 10 inch × 4 inch × 5

1 large sheet

6 dressing sheets

6 dressing towels

2 green sheets with waterproof paper backing

6 bundles 5 swabs 4 inch × 3 inch

4 inch cotton bandage

20 gown packs

20 tape mops × 10

20 Burns mops—large Raytec gauze rolls

20 4 inch × 3 inch swabs × 20

20 6 inch × 4 inch swabs × 20

10 disposable basic packs

50 wool and dressing packs

10 Pentothal packs

At least 6 dozen conforming bandages of each size

Disposable packs

6 boxes Mayo covers

6 boxes medium drapes

6 boxes orthopaedic split sheets

6 boxes gowns

6 boxes large drapes

30 general sets

20 Major Burn sets

10 neurosurgical sets

10 arterial sets

10 abdominal sets

10 chest sets
10 eye sets

Preparation of a reception area

On being notified of a disaster a suitable nurse should be dispatched with one or more porters to clear or create a reception area, to which all casualties, regardless of the severity of their injuries, should be directed on arrival. Here, one or more doctors will at once assess each patient's condition and direct him into one of three streams:

1. Severely injured patients to the intensive care unit;
2. Moderately severe injuries to a receiving ward;
3. Minor casualities for suturing, etc. through the normal casualty process.

A suitable area for this type of assessment is a large out patients' waiting hall, but this may cause serious difficulties in the middle of busy outpatient clinics.

Each patient should be provided with a set of notes and clearly identified with respect to those notes. Some will at first be known only by their sex and serial number, which should be marked on a suitable area of skin or attached by a band round a wrist or ankle. This will be most simply done if a batch of folders is kept in readiness, each with its identification band.

Difficult decisions

There is not likely to be any difficulty in deciding to which category each patient belongs, but if there is a large number of gravely injured persons it may be impossible to provide for each the standard of care that would be possible in less hectic conditions, and any attempt to do so may lead to less serious casualties being deprived of treatment that could mean the difference between recovery and deterioration. The decision that some of the casualties are beyond aid can properly be taken only by an experienced doctor, but the reasons for such a decision must be understood by the nurses concerned if loyalty and morale are to be maintained. In some cases, the doctor will decide that a patient is to be resuscitated, but subsequent events may make it clear that the outlook is hopeless. In such cases an experienced nurse may be the first to recognise this and she should be permitted to express her opinion to the assessing or other responsible doctor. For doctors and nurses who are used to working together, such a situation may not be unusual.

At the other end of the scale an experienced nurse may be able to assist a junior doctor in recognising the possibly serious significance of something which might otherwise be overlooked when a patient is being undressed and examined.

Those working in the receiving area have a duty to keep the hospital's disaster headquarters informed of the number of casualties received, their degrees of injury and the manner of their disposal, so that overloading of departments can be anticipated and suitable steps taken to avoid it.

Patients needing special care

District general hospitals can be expected to have units for the special care of the severely ill and injured, but they may be overtaxed or, in the case of smaller hospitals, they may find the need to create special wards with inadequate means of so doing. In such cases it may seem best to admit the most needy and more or less neglect the rest of the patients. It is, in fact, better to set aside an area that can be used for special care and to place in it those nurses that are best suited to it by training or temperament. It may be thought that special care is still more heavily dependent on personal attention than on mechanical and other aids. It is worth remembering that over twenty years ago many lives were saved in the Danish epidemic of poliomyelitis by relays of doctors, medical students and others who provided artificial respiration for paralysed patients by squeezing anaesthetists' bags for days on end.

The foregoing further emphasises the importance of having a headquarters or control room where a senior nurse, doctor and administrator can receive reports on current conditions and can plan ahead for likely needs. This is not to deny the value to morale of having senior staff visiting the different departments, but personal appearances of this sort are desirable rather than essential to the successful conduct of affairs.

Establishing a hospital headquarters

A suitable place for the headquarters should have been prepared with staff boards and bed boards, so that up-to-date knowledge of means and needs is easily visible. It must also have an outside telephone line for its own use independent of the hospital switch board. Hospital switch boards become blocked very soon after a disaster, but there must be a means of enabling the hospital to keep in touch with rescue services so that due warning can be given of the need to stop admitting patients, of the need to transfer patients to other hospitals or to send them home.

Another important task of headquarters is to decide how best to make use of the large number of volunteers that present themselves; particularly valuable among them being former members of the hospital.

Removal of patients to other hospitals or home

One of the advantages of the closed wards in many hospitals today is that they provide spare accommodation and, in times of actual or possible civil disturbance, or in case of warning of a natural disaster such as a cyclone, accommodation can be made ready for occupation. Unfortunately, under normal conditions, it soon becomes used as an unofficial rubbish dump or store. It is easier to move in staff or extra beds than to move patients from one hospital to another at short notice. Deciding which in-patients should be transferred or discharged is best left to the Sisters or the Senior Resident Medical Staff of the wards concerned, but the whole operation stands or falls by the ability of the ambulance service and other means of transport to take on the additional burden. If patients are to be moved in this way it is important to keep the patients being transferred separate from those that are still arriving, but given a good ambulance service and clear roads it may well be the case that the last of the casualties will have arrived long before it is possible to start evacuation.

Making use of volunteers

Arrangements should be made to identify those volunteers that could be useful. Those with medical or nursing experience need to be allocated with special care and tact because if they are unfamiliar with the hospital they may have to accept a subordinate role.

Unskilled volunteers may be useful for moving patients about. Blood donors should be requested to report to the blood transfusion service during working hours.

In many cases there is little need for volunteers because hospital staff soon learn what has happened and quickly return to duty. If radio and television are used to notify hospital staff that their services will be required, suitable instructions for volunteers should be broadcast at the same time.

Accommodation of relatives and friends

If a disaster produces large numbers of walking wounded many of these will arrive at hospital with relatives or friends and they will be followed by the relatives or friends of local residents wanting to know what has happened to them. Although many can be reassured and sent away, they have to be dealt with. Others will be related to badly injured patients and will have to be accommodated and looked after. Medical social workers are particularly useful for this purpose because of their skill in handling anxious relatives and it gives the advantage of making a prompt start on tasks that they would in any case be called upon to undertake. They should be encouraged to be present at meetings between doctors, nurses and relatives of patients, so that they know just what was said and can, if necessary, answer any subsequent questicns about it. It is not easy for anxious relatives to grasp what they have been told and they need time and an opportunity to talk about it. Time that doctors and nurses can ill afford.

Information centre

It is normal policy for the police to set up an information centre at the scene of a disaster and lesser posts at the receiving hospital(s). When possible, they will issue a list of the names of those injured and their condition. It is essential that there is a free flow of information to the information post and this is one of the most important tasks for the hospital's headquarters; otherwise medical and nursing staff will be waylaid and detained by anxious relatives. It is the responsibility of the police to establish, if possible, the identity of victims. Therefore, it is important that, no matter how badly damaged, all clothing and property removed from the victim should be carefully labelled and passed on to the police. Once identity has been established and a member of the hospital staff is ready to interview relatives, the information centre should be notified so that relatives may be directed to the interviewing area.

Accommodation of bodies

The disposal of bodies found at the place of a disaster is no concern of the hospital, but if many gravely injured casualties survive to reach hospital there may be more bodies than the mortuary can accommodate. It should not be necessary for the hospital to provide more than temporary accommodation because the Coroner's Office or comparable authority will remove the excess bodies, but if there have been so many deaths that even public mortuaries are overloaded, it may be possible to make use of industrial cold storage and refrigerated rooms. The hospital would not be expected to make any such arrangements without the authority of the police.

Lessons learnt and conclusions

No matter how well organised they are on paper people will be caught out by a major disaster occurring in their area with no advance warning of casualties. This is the crucial test and the ability to cope with it in an orderly manner, without prolonged chaos, is proof that all grades of staff are carrying out their roles efficiently.

It is imperative that patients are identified numerically as soon as they reach hospital by a suitably simplified version of the normal procedure.

It is important that team leaders of all grades keep themselves free from any specific duty, in order to ensure the coordinated effort of all the available resources under their control. When laying down any plans for a major disaster, they must be flexible because events do often take an unexpected turn.

The roles of the doctor, nurse and administrator have no clear lines of demarcation. When dealing with a major incident they must become blurred if the casualties are not to suffer as a result of divided counsel.

5. Surgical care of mass casualties

In any emergency situation the initial care of badly injured casualties is of limited use unless there is a sensible second line treatment and care service available to receive the casualties. Most disasters in developed countries occur within reach of well-equipped hospitals, so the relief tasks are those of rescue and first-aid whilst the hospitals implement their own disaster plans to cope with the flow of casualties. Disasters in less well developed areas may occur where hospital facilities are sparse and they may even be put out of action by the incident causing the disaster. In these circumstances, relief work includes the provision of surgery. To be worthwhile surgery must be backed by adequate manpower and material resources and it is with the consideration of these resources that part of this chapter is concerned.

The aim of surgery and of second line care must be to support the casualty until he or she can be looked after by the community or is fit enough to be self-supporting. The tasks of the surgical unit are, therefore, to admit, resuscitate, operate on, provide postoperative care for, and discharge the patient. There are two distinct ways of viewing the use of the resources of the provided unit and the leader of the team must be clear about the policy to be adopted and make such policy clear to his colleagues. Firstly, there is a situation where the unit will accept only the number of cases that it is equipped to deal with. The team must then be confident that other casualties will be cared for by other teams. Secondly, there is the situation where the unit will provide as much care as possible for all the casualties that arrive at that unit. This will often mean deliberately not spending a long time operating on one casualty but dividing the resources available to save the lives of as many as possible whilst giving good opportunities of survival. Decisions of this nature are never easy to make, but leaders should appreciate that they may have to be made and that this is a responsibility they must accept.

The division of resources to meet the task requires, firstly, the identification of possible tasks and, secondly, the apportioning of manpower and equipment.

It would be easy to go through each department in a hospital and make suggestions as to equipment and staffing. However, it is unrealistic to do so as no two situations are the same. At the end of this chapter is a chart showing the breakdown of departments and personnel based on the organisation of a Military Field Hospital (Table 5.1). It is included as one example and to serve only as a guide. There is sufficient manpower in this military unit to carry out several hundred operations and to look after 200 patients well at any one time. If necessary, many more than 200 may be catered for but as the quantity of care rises so must the quality decline. The equipment for this hospital, including tentage, fills 30 four-ton lorries.

The manpower required is about 160. Of these 36 are directly concerned with the four operating theatres; the 50-bed wards each have a nursing team of 14; reception, resuscitation and the other clinical departments take another 41. The remaining 37 are involved with the running and maintenance of the hospital. The team leader is responsible for the smooth running of the whole unit, and has also to fit the unit into the overall casualty plan for the disaster and do the necessary liaison work involved. There are four key administrative workers: the senior clinician, the Chief Nursing Officer, the hospital administrative officer and the quartermaster. The senior clinician (often a surgeon) has the overall clinical responsibility requiring the most experience and the finest clinical judgement available, for in a mass casualty situation he will have to select the cases to be operated on immediately and assign others to expectant treatment. The functions of the senior nursing sister are those of the Chief Nursing Officer of any hospital, but in addition, she may possibly have to be more versatile and flexible for in the periods of moving and setting up she has a more acute leadership which, as always, can best be solved by example. The administrative officer will be responsible for the day-to-day running of the hospital, making arrangements for admissions and discharges and for dealing with the day-to-day management of the staff. The quartermaster is responsible for the equipment, forecasting usage and wastage, demanding replacement and replenishment. He will also be responsible for supervising the kitchens providing the meals for both staff and patients.

Whatever the size of surgical unit deployed the duties of the Commanding Officer, chief medical officer, administrator and quartermaster must all be carried out, whether by one man or many. The larger the unit the more people must be employed on administration. However, the proportion of manpower so employed will fall as the self-supporting unit gets larger. Employment of local skilled and semi-skilled labour will lessen the administrative burden on the medical staff, and jobs such as those of interpreter, clerk, stretcher bearer, cook, kitchen orderly and cleaner should, where possible, be carried out by locally recruited labour.

The problem of equipment is as great as that of the deployment of the available manpower. Departments have to be manned and equipped. Standard equipment for an operating theatre is often best as it provides familiarity and allows training which makes for efficiency right from the start. In an emergency a surgeon may carry out up to fifteen operations a day. He has to be supplied with the specialised tools of his profession and sufficient dressings, drugs and parenteral fluids to allow his patients maximum chance of survival and meaningful recovery. In support of his skill, provision of blood, X-rays, laboratory pre- and post-operative nursing and sterilisation will increase his chances of success.

Besides the surgical cases there will be other casualties; disease, minor injuries and dental troubles will occur and have to be dealt with. Appropriate departments may have to be set up, equipped and manned and naturally their validity for a particular situation depends upon the overall response made to the disaster.

Some aspects of the work must be identified and considered early in order to minimise any loss of efficiency. Two important examples are the job of stretcher bearing and the need for shift work. Probably the physically most exhausting job in a mass casualty situation is the sheer effort of 'humping' stretchers. Teams must be identified, given areas of responsibility and controlled so that their efficiency is maintained. Each team should be led by a person who understands the task and can ensure that the instructions are accurately carried out. With this sort of guidance stretcher bearing is a task which can be undertaken largely by local labour.

The need for shift work is probably more readily understood. There is a limit to the length of time that skilled medical care can be given by anyone before the effects of fatigue lead to slowness and, possibly, errors. Good management will allow all-out effort to meet a crisis but will insist that a portion of the skilled team is rested early so that it can resume work when the remainder of the team is resting. This leads to the necessity for an early introduction of shift work and if the problem is assessed as a lengthy one then greater efficiency will be achieved in the long term. Suggested shifts are eight hours on duty and eight hours off duty.

When the leader arrives on location he will be allotted an area in which to set up his unit. Once again his requirements will depend upon the size of unit to be established and the local resources available. Normally, existing buildings are better than tents, but they must be clean, cool, well lit and have rooms large enough to facilitate nursing and provide space for operating theatres. An appreciation of the space required must be firmly in the leader's mind before he arrives at the disaster location and practice at disposing theoretical units on various sites is valuable training. For example, the 200-bed hospital described in Table 5.1 requires a space the size of three football pitches when fully laid out under canvas.

Fig. 5.1 Field hospital (Beirut, 1971).

The next question is the supply of services—water, electricity, other fuels and sewage. Is there piped water? Is it potable? Is there a sufficient supply? If the answer to any of these questions is 'no', then arrangements for the delivery of supplies have to be made (or a new site chosen). Similar questions arise in the case of electricity which is required for light, X-ray machines, laboratory machines and so on. Is it available? If not, can generators be supplied, or will the team have to downgrade its care to the limits set by the fuels available? Finally, if proper disposal facilities are not available for sewage, an incinerator, properly constructed latrines, disposal pits and soakage pits will have to be provided.

The unit leader should also consider two other concerns. These are the twin problems of how the patients get to the unit and where they go when they are fit to be discharged.

A field hospital cannot usually be established close to a disaster site for without sorting, trivial cases would swamp the reception facilities and downgrade the quality of care which could be offered to the serious cases. In some circumstances it may be necessary for the unit to send forward an element to do the sorting and to identify the cases which need evacuation. Any team given this task must be clear as to its duties. Rescue and first aid will have been completed and this team will provide a central collecting point for casualties which need onward transmission. At this point first aid will be checked, the casualties assessed and given a priority for evacuation. Normally, there will be a shuttle service of stretcher bearers and ambulance vehicles bringing rescued casualties from the disaster to this central point and a second shuttle service from this point to the hospital.

Any team so detailed must have authority so that all the rescuers know of its existence and work to it. The team needs shelter, food and drink, enough manpower and equipment to identify, document and check the casualties and sufficient communications to enable it to keep the hospital informed of the situation at the disaster site and the expected flow of casualties. Liaison with police, government and other authorities will be made at this point and it is wise to expect to deal with the Press and a mass of relatives here as well. Thus, when necessary, the support of expert interpreters is vital. In the consideration of the evacuation of casualties the principle of taking the casualty to the surgeon is followed. Any deviation from this will locate the surgical potential at a small focus of activity,

Table 5.1 A field hospital (200 beds)

		Commanding Officer		
		Chief Nursing Officer		
	Administrative Officer		Quartermaster	
Cleaners and orderlies 10	Administrative assistants and clerks 8	Technical support electricians, mechanics 2	Cooks 10	Stores and dispensary 7
Reception and minor treatments 16	Resuscitation 14	4 Wards (including post op) 14 each	4 Theatres 1 Surgeon 1 Anaesthetist 1 Resuscitation officer 1 Theatre sister 3 Operating theatre technicians 1 Transfusion assistant	Specialist departments
Medical specialist 1	Physiotherapy 2	Dental department 3	X-ray department 2	Laboratory

This chart is based on a Military Unit, but has been modified.

possibly poorly equipped and much less able to provide the greatest care for the greatest number.

After care of casualties is another concern of the team leader and it is appropriate that early negotiations should take place on the problems of discharge. The local community may have to be taught the responsibilities incumbent upon them and encouraged to make provision for after care so that the work of the rescue team is not wasted on the scrap heap of apathy.

6. Nursing severely injured patients

If a team is experienced, the roles of the doctors and nurses become integrated. Rightly so, if they are to function successfully as a team. An effective team requires a knowledge of the ways in which life is seriously endangered, the means of dealing with them and an organisation which enables them to be dealt with without delay. No amount of equipment can save lives unless it is used properly.

Relevant experience can only be gained by medical and nursing students through following a comprehensive syllabus in a good reception and resuscitation unit. With the guidance of senior staff their training must enable them to apply in practice what they have learnt in theory. Against the harrowing background of mutilation and suffering they must be able to recognise the need for urgent and life-saving treatment and be able to control their own fears and emotions, thus instilling confidence into the patients, relatives and junior colleagues.

Immediate needs

The over-riding need is for specially trained nurses to be available at all times and they, in turn, then must be assured of prompt medical support. Sudden, urgent demands and rapidly changing conditions call for a high standard of nursing, with the support to ensure that the best nurses of all grades are readily avilable. This means that the team must be permanent and only in extreme emergencies should it be supplemented by nurses with less experience, drafted from other departments of the hospital. It is most important that medical staff should be available at all times and that, as far as possible, the same group of doctors look after a given patient. It is increasingly recognised that in the caring for severely injured persons a consultant should be in charge and be among the first on the scene of disaster.

The reception and resuscitation area

Despite the many and varied types of injuries that patients may suffer, the principles of their care are the same in every case. Effective reception and resuscitation depend on design, site and policy, coupled with equipment that is immediately available and in working order.

Design. Privacy is not the first consideration so that although the beds can be screened from one another, the area should be capable of being made into an open space, thus allowing ease of movement of persons and equipment. It must be possible for several patients to be reached and attended from all sides and the equipment must be sufficiently mobile to allow this. Although a reception area will have been designed to take a certain

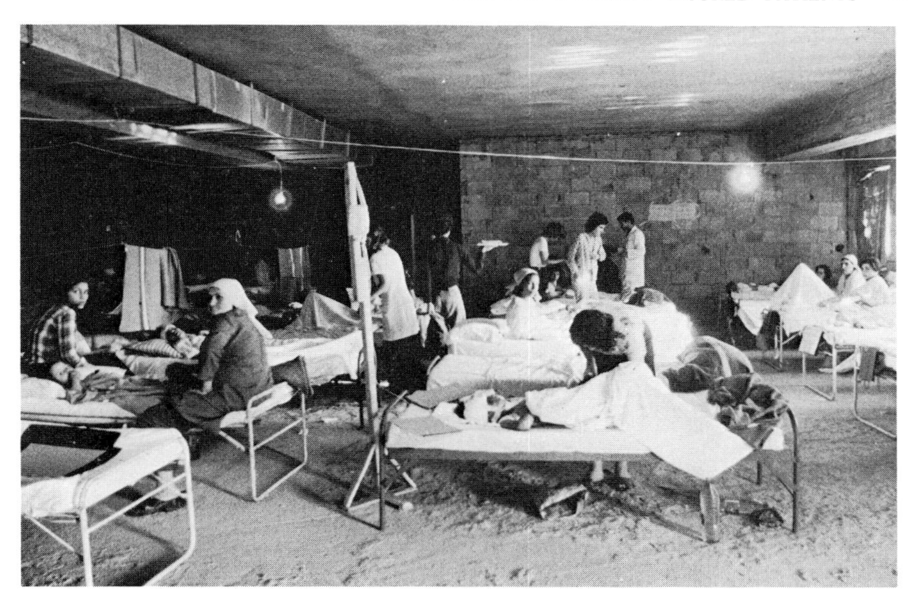

Fig. 6.1 Emergency ward accommodation (Lebanon, 1976).

number of patients, it may be necessary to accept many more patients than the maximum intended, so that other reception areas should have been selected beforehand.

Dressings and instruments should be sterile, ready for use and displayed to facilitate identification, removal and preparation for use. A wide range of drugs for urgent use has to be kept in stock and the cupboard for controlled and scheduled drugs kept within easy reach of the patient. Drugs that are not so frequently required should be available in a central pharmacy, so that a large stock of drugs need not always be carried.

Severely injured patients will require immediate intravenous infusion.

It is essential that any reception area can be quickly and effectively cleaned. The efficiency of a team includes the ability to promptly return the working area to a state of readiness.

Site. There must be adequate facilities for unloading large numbers of casualties directly into the reception area, thus enabling a rapid turn-round of emergency vehicles. The reception area should be within easy reach of the operating theatres and intensive therapy unit but it must be equipped to cope with all sorts of emergencies, so that if the patient is so severely injured that he cannot be moved it will be possible to carry out major life-saving operations within the reception area.

Policy. The necessary high standard of care by nurses cannot be maintained unless the staff are permanent. Learners can be integrated and trained if they are under constant supervision. Responsibility for the immediate and continuing care of a patient rests with the surgeon, anaesthetist and sister-in-charge, and the success of the unit depends to a very large extent on the relationship between them. Who should be in charge is a vexing question but suitability of personality and ability is much more important than rank, status or special skills. The consultant on duty in the reception area exercises general

Fig. 6.2 Wounded being carried to the operating room of a field hospital (Lebanon, 1976).

supervision and accepts ultimate responsibility. The anaesthetist is responsible for many of the immediate life-saving measures and, increasingly, for dealing with many of the respiratory consequences of serious injuries. The sister-in-charge disposes her nursing team to assist medical staff and to comfort and reassure patients and relatives.

The sister-in-charge has an overall responsibility inasmuch as her nurses are always in the unit and it therefore falls to her to ensure that sudden changes in a patient's condition are recognised and that the necessary steps are promptly taken to deal with them. She must, therefore, be given the discretion to act as she thinks best when no doctor is present. Traditional and legal niceties of responsibility have to be borne in mind but they are much less important than a system that is designed for the well-being of the patient and is successful. The relationship beween nurses and doctors that makes a system operate successfully eases possibly one of the most difficult tasks—that of deciding which patients should have priority in receiving special care when there are too few staff or facilities to meet the special needs of all.

Prior warning of the arrival of severely injured patients helps their efficient reception and is always desirable; it is best achieved when there is direct communication between ambulance crews or their control centres, and the receiving room of the hospital to which they are going. Arriving in the reception area the patient immediately becomes like a honeypot surrounded by diagnostic and therapeutic flies. All unnecessary movement of the patient should be eliminated. It is not always necessary to remove all clothing as soon as the patient is received; there may be more important things to do. Any clothing removed, or patient's possessions, should be clearly listed, labelled and taken into safe custody by the hospital until the patient or relatives are able to reclaim them.

X-ray plays an increasing part in emergency diagnosis but during the early stages of diagnosis and treatment it may be dangerous to the patient to subject him to the journey to the main X-ray department where conditions for supervision and treatment are likely to be inadequate. It can be more dangerous to move a badly injured person on a hospital trolley than in an ambulance. Portable X-ray films are usually sufficient to support or dispel the suspicions that are the hallmark of an experienced team of nurses and doctors. Other methods of investigation must also be used with due regard for the balance of benefit and risk.

Equipment

The following equipment must immediately be available and in working order:

1. Bed/trolley which tips head down, enables the patient to sit up and has cot sides.
2. Adequate suction apparatus, complete with selection of widebore catheters and water to flush the catheters once they have been used.
3. Boyle's anaesthetic machine. Equipment kept permanently on this machine should include:

   Laryngoscope, with a selection of blades and with the bulbs and batteries in working order
   Magill 'laryngoscope forceps'
   A selection of cuffed portex endotracheal tubes
   A selection of connections to fit endotracheal tubes (e.g. Cobb's or Wosworthy's)
   Catheter mounts
   20 ml syringe to inflate cuff of endotracheal tube
   Artery forceps to clamp cuff to endotracheal tube once it is inflated
   A selection of Guedel's oral airways
   Mouth gag
   Mouth peg
   Tape for securing endotracheal tube in position

4. A trolley prepared for the commencing intravenous infusion. This should carry a cutting down set; a selection of cannulae and intravenous catheters ready for use; 10 ml and 20 ml syringes with appropriate bottles for grouping and cross-matching blood, estimation of haemoglobin, and any other relevant investigations that may be required.
5. Gastric lavage tray.
6. Beside each bed/trolley there should be kept at all times a stethoscope, sphygmomanometer, pen-torch, tape measure, patella hammer, ophthalmoscope, a stout pair of scissors for cutting tough clothing (Fig. 6.3) and a receptacle for patient's clothing and property.

Any severely injured patient should, ideally, be received by two nurses: one to assist the anaesthetist and carry out observations of the patient's vital signs, and the other to assist other medical staff and prepare trolleys or equipment for procedures to be carried out.

First steps in managing patients

Recognise any threat to life presented by breathing, circulation and unconsciousness; if there is no doctor immediately available a nurse must be prepared to take steps to mitigate the threats. This is not a question of 'having a go'. It requires detailed training in how to carry out emergency measures—and when.

Fig. 6.3 Scissors for cutting tough clothing.

Breathing
The patient may choke to death because the air passages* are blocked, or may suffocate because of other conditions that prevent adequate ventilation of his lungs.

Choking
The correct posture of patient and his jaw may be all that is required to clear the air passages but in the presence of multiple injuries it is usually necessary to have a patient on his back with the result that suction and intubation must be carried out. Emergency tracheotomy is now reserved for upper respiratory obstruction that cannot be immediately relieved and must be by-passed. Examples are obstruction of the glottis by impacted molar or by oedema. The passage of an endotracheal tube can be one of the most urgently necessary and difficult procedures that any doctor is called upon to undertake and the skill of the nurse assisting him may make the difference between success and the disaster of having the contents of the stomach enter the lungs. The nurse should also be aware that most endotracheal tubes are so long that they can be passed beyond the bifurcation of the trachea. The right bronchus is more in line with the trachea than the left. If a tube is passed too far it enters the right bronchus and when the cuff is inflated the left lung is cut off from its supply of air. The effect is easily recognisable: if the patient is breathing spontaneously, the left side of the chest is drawn in during inspiration; if artificially, only the right side moves. It is sufficient to pull the tube out an inch or so. As soon as the tip is in the trachea both sides of the chest will regain normal movement.

Suffocation
This can result from wounds or fractures of the chest wall, from rupture of the diaphragm or from pneumothorax or haemothorax or both, which are most often found accompanying serious injuries of the chest. The treatment is artificial ventilation and in an emergency a bag and mask or even mouth to mouth (or nose) inflation may be used.

* This term is preferred to the other more usual airways, which is also used for pieces of equipment.

The circulation

If neither heart beat nor pulsation in the large arteries can be felt, circulation must be restored. This can easily be done by intermittent depression of the sternum (external cardiac massage), preceded by and alternating every 4 to 6 depressions with artificial inflation of the lungs. It is rarely necessary to open the chest to squeeze the heart (internal cardiac massage) but it may be necessary to abolish ventricular fibrillation by electric shock and it will be necessary to counteract the acidaemia of circulatory arrest with 8.4 per cent sodium bicarbonate; drugs such as lignocaine 2 per cent may be needed to deal with arrhythmia of the heart. It needs to be remembered, however, that if the heart stops beating after severe injury it is often because the patient is exsanguinated and the prospect of revival is very poor. If the heart stops beating for other reasons there is a better chance of making it beat again.

Most accessible bleeding can be stopped by applying firm external pressure and elevating the injured limb, but nurses must be on the lookout for an ill-applied tourniquet and should not hesitate to remove it if it is obviously causing congestion and promoting bleeding. Severe internal bleeding can require an emergency exploratory operation to find the bleeding point, but some benefit may be derived from the use of 'antishock trousers', which are inflatable splints that encase the abdomen, pelvis and lower limbs.

While the anaesthetist is ensuring adequate ventilation of the lungs another doctor should be available to commence an intravenous infusion. At the same time, blood should be taken for grouping and cross-matching and estimation of haemoglobin. The amount of blood ordered will depend on the degree and severity of the injuries sustained (Fig. 6.4).

Intravenous infusion. Up to 2 litres of normal saline, Hartman's Solution, or dextran 70 may have to be given to any one patient within half an hour or so of arrival in hospital. Rheomacrodex has no proven advantage over the other solutions for expanding the volume of blood in the circulation and plasma has the double disadvantages of having first to be mixed and of not always running well, in addition to carrying the risk of hepatitis and jaundice.

If the main blood bank is a long way from the reception and resuscitation unit this should have its own small stock of group O, Rhesus negative blood, in which case the staff of the unit must be clearly aware of their responsibilities while looking after what can be a very dangerous substance. It must also be stressed that group O, Rhesus negative blood must not be used because it is conveniently accessible, but because the patient's very survival depends on it. Administration of any but group O blood without prior knowledge of the patient's group is never justifiable. It is always preferable to give rhesus negative blood to girls and women of childbearing age until their rhesus group is known, but if the choice is between waiting until blood is available and giving what may be unsafe blood because life is at stake, rhesus positive blood may have to be given. Fortunately, provided that anti D serum is given within a day or two, the antigenic effects of rhesus positive blood in rhesus negative recipients can be neutralised.

It cannot be emphasised too strongly that the strictest attention to detail is necessary if errors of identification are to be avoided when large quantities of blood are being ordered for several patients. The commonest errors are to label specimens with the wrong name and to give blood to the wrong person: names are less reliable than hospital numbers, which must be checked with great care.

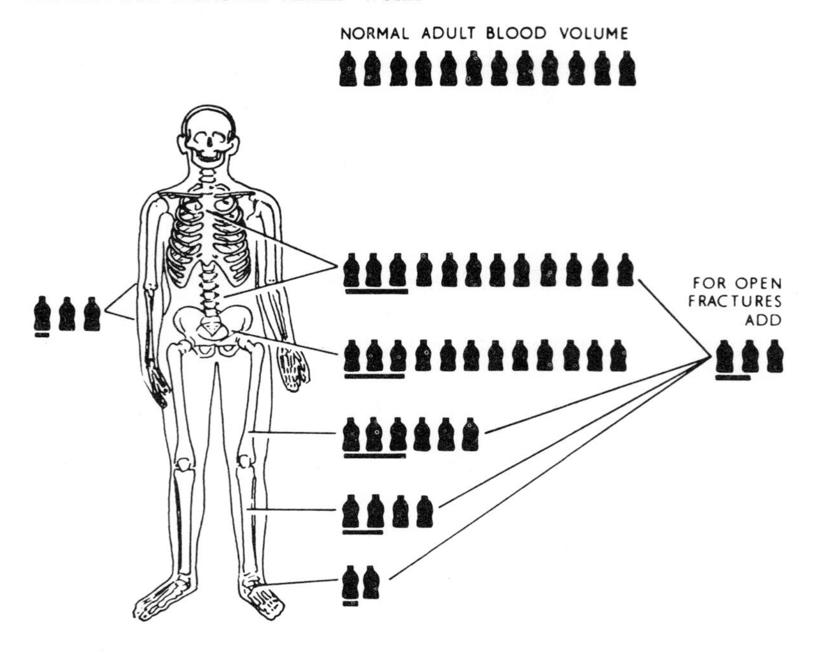

Rough equivalence between site and severity of injury and blood required for replenishment.
Bottles underlined represent the usual order of loss, the whole row the possible need.
With multiple injuries the individual losses have to be added and may considerably exceed a blood volume.

Fig. 6.4

Giving large quantities of blood (more than the patient's blood volume) may so alter the composition and properties of the blood in circulation that special restorative steps will have to be taken. These include the administration of platelets of fresh blood and of fresh frozen plasma. The advice of an haematologist is therefore necessary.

Unconsciousness

A distinction needs to be drawn between the cause of unconsciousness which may or may not be treatable, and the unconscious state which must always be treated, irrespective of its cause.

Obvious injury of the head in an unconscious person is not necessarily the cause of unconsciousness. Treatable causes of unconsciousness accompanying head injury include:

1. Expanding intracranial haematoma (which is rather rare);
2. Cerebral hypoxia caused by choking, suffocation and exsanguination;
3. Hypoglycaemia.

It is well-known that unconscious persons are sometimes restless but it is necessary to be aware that restlessness may be the result of severe cerebral hypoxia. This should be suspected if the restlessness has an aggressive element that is unprovoked. So-called 'air hunger' is, in fact, very rare; hypoxia restlessness in more common. Unconsciousness may mask the effects of other injuries and it increases the need for accurate examination and careful observation of the patient. The possibility of spinal injury should be kept in mind when handling the patient, and the presence of any injury of the face and forehead of an unconscious person must arouse suspicion of a broken neck until this has been ruled out by X-rays.

Observation and records

The fact that it may become urgently necessary to take steps to save life does not diminish the need for making an early start to recording pulse rate, blood pressure, respiratory rate, etc. At the same time it is desirable that someone should seek all relevant information from anyone accompanying the patient. Ideally, this should be done by someone who is not engaged in the hurly-burly of diagnosis and treatment; the task may well fall to a nurse if the ambulance crew cannot wait for a doctor.

Once the patient has been completely undressed the general nature of his injuries can be established and an estimate can be made of the amount of blood that may be required. Many seriously injured persons require $2\frac{1}{2}$ to 5 litres of blood for resuscitation and another $2\frac{1}{2}$ to 5 litres during any operations that may have to be performed, with a further litre or so to make good any postoperative bleeding. In some cases, total requirements have amounted to 8 to 10 times the normal blood volume (5 to 6 litres in an adult) (Fig. 6.5).

Nurses should be able to recognise (and must report) the following conditions:

Cyanosis

Venous congestion in the face and neck, or beyond a tourniquet on a limb

Distressed breathing

Asymmetry of shape and movements of the chest

Surgical emphysema, which usually starts on the chest or at the base of the neck. These last three peripheral signs may be present at the time of admission, or may not appear until hours, or even a few days, after admission.

Pattern bruising on the abdominal wall

Rapidly increasing swelling

These and certain characteristic postures may give early warning of damage to the brain or spinal cord.

As the pace slows, the task becomes that of establishing a working diagnosis and planning treatment. Wounds are dressed and injured limbs comfortably supported. For immediate use, inflatable splints and the hare traction apparatus are very successful. Later Plaster of Paris and Thomas' splints are used. Analgesia is not often required but there may be a need for drugs to quell anxiety.

As well as the measurements previously mentioned the following should be recorded every fifteen minutes at first:

Size and reaction of pupils

Responsiveness to speech and other stimulation

Abdominal girth

Temperature

Other records including output of urine, usually after passing a catheter

Central venous pressure

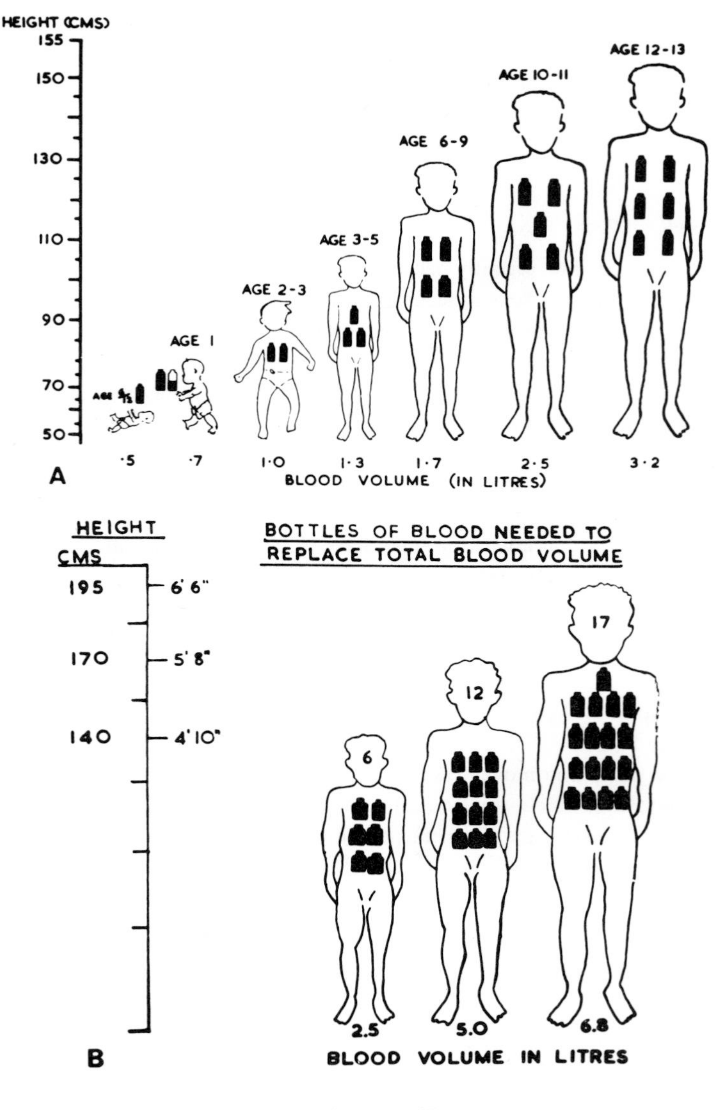

The blood volume at different ages.

Fig. 6.5

Electrocardiography
Echoencephalography
Arterial $P\text{O}_2$, $P\text{CO}_2$ and pH
Artificial ventilation and relevant details

Other investigations

Radiography plays a very important part in diagnosis. Plain films may be supplemented by cerebral and other angiograms, excretion urography and opaque swallows.

Peritoneal irrigation. A litre of saline is run into the peritoneal cavity through a dialysis catheter inserted below the navel and with the aid of local analgesia. It is then syphoned back and examined for staining by blood or faecal matter. This is a very useful test in case of suspected abdominal injury, particularly when there are other injuries or unconsciousness. This investigation may only be carried out after the bladder has been emptied.

Primary and later definitive care:

Breathing

Continual attention is required to keep the air passages clear, the lungs adequately ventilated and the blood gases within an acceptable range of values. Oxygen sedation and analgesia may often be required and radiography may have to be carried out several times a day.

Respiratory failure after injury

Respiratory failure means that the uptake of oxygen or the excretion of carbon dioxide in the lungs is inadequate. It can be said to have occurred if the $P\,O_2$ falls below 60 mmHg or the $P\,CO_2$ continues to rise above 50 mmHg when breathing at rest.

Signs of respiratory failure

1. Apnoea
2. Cyanosis
3. Flushed face and sweating
4. Drowsiness and lethargy but in some cases the patient is confused and excitable
5. Irregularities of the pulse

Causes of respiratory failure

This list is by no means complete but gives the more common causes seen after injury:

The air passages are commonly blocked, by the tongue when the patient is unconscious, and at any time by debris, blood, vomit, severe facial and oral swelling from burns or other injury.

The brain may be damaged by head injury, or depressed by an overdose of barbiturates or opiates or by inhalation of noxious fumes.

The spinal cord: fracture of the cervical spine above the level of C5 deprives the patient of nearly all his ability to breathe.

Respiratory muscles: poor reversal of muscle relaxants after operation or before removing from a ventilator. Tetanus affects the respiratory muscles directly.

Rib and diaphragm: multiple fractures of the ribs are much more frequent than ruptures of the diaphragm.

Pleura: pneumothorax and haemothorax cause the lungs to collapse.

The lungs are affected by severe bronchitis, pneumonia, inhalation pneumonitis, Mendelsohn's syndrome (if this is the result of inhaling gastric juices), severe pulmonary contusion, fat embolism, burning by inhalation of smoke, 'shock lung'.

Treatment of respiratory failure

1. Support ventilation by administering oxygen and keeping the air passages clear, by intubation if necessary.
2. Remove the cause of failure, if possible; i.e. relieve pneumothorax, reverse the effects of opiates, bypass any upper respiratory tract obstruction by endotracheal intubation or tracheotomy.
3. Oxygen may be all that is necessary if the $P\ O_2$ is low but the $P\ CO_2$ is normal, as happens with pulmonary shunt.
4. Artificial ventilation is used if the above measures are insufficient, or while the cause of the condition is being investigated.
5. Respiratory stimulants are now seldom used because they are brief in action and the effective dose is close to the toxic dose. Artificial ventilation is carried out by pumping air into the lungs via an endotracheal tube, whereas during spontaneous ventilation the chest expands and the air is drawn into the lungs. Pumping air into the lungs raises the pressure in the pleural space to above atmospheric pressure during inspiration and impedes the flow of blood back to the heart, thus reducing the efficiency of the heart. Normally the patient is able to compensate for this, but if the heart is already embarrassed by inadequate replacement of shed blood, the blood pressure will drop when ventilation starts.

The special care of patients attached to ventilators

In most specialised units one nurse will be made responsible for the total care of a patient with respiratory failure and the attached machinery. She should be constantly at the bedside, because if the patient becomes disconnected from the machine, he will not be able to breathe for himself as he is under the influence of paralysing drugs such as Pancuronium Bromide, Tubocuraine, aided by Phenoperidine, Papaveretum or Diazepam. Normally the nurse will be required to keep hourly records of:

Pulse, blood pressure and temperature;
Respiratory rate;
Inflation pressure;
Tidal and minute volume;
Amount of oxygen delivered to the patient via the machine.

The middle three observations are to ensure that the machine is working efficiently.

Care of an endotracheal tube

Whether it passes through the nose or mouth or through a tracheotomy, an endotracheal tube should be secured firmly to the patient by a non-elastic bandage or tape. The cuff should be inflated to create an air seal but using only the minimum amount of air necessary to do so. With plastic tubes and soft cuffs, regular inflation and deflation of the cuff is not necessary and in inexperienced hands it can be harmful. Dressings around the tracheotomy tube should be changed at regular intervals, to ensure that the wound stays as clean and as dry as possible. This may be helped by using a dressing impregnated with silver nitrate or chlorhexidine or both. Tapes should be changed only when necessary and there must be two nurses present to carry out this procedure. One holds the tube firmly in position while the other changes the tapes.

Physiotherapy

Whilst attached to the ventilator the patient will require chest physiotherapy every 2 to 4 hours. Two nurses are required and should work in conjunction with the physiotherapist. One nurse manually inflates the lungs with 100 per cent oxygen. The second nurse sucks the secretions from the endotracheal tube, using an aseptic technique. While physiotherapy is being carried out, the nurses should take the opportunity to observe that:

1. The water level in the humidifier does not need refilling;
2. There is not excessive water in the patient's inspired and expired air tubes because this can offset the pressure readings on the ventilator;
3. All tubing is firmly connected to the ventilator before reconnecting the patient to it.

If the ventilator is worked by electricity, and if there is any reason for switching off the current on removing any plugs from the sockets, great care must be taken to see that they are correctly reconnected. It is wise to label the plugs with the apparatus they supply and to label the sockets with the name of the patients they serve.

If the nurse is worried about the patient's condition or the efficiency of mechanical ventilation, she should disconnect the machine from the patient, inflate the lungs by hand and then summon help.

General care of helpless patients

Accurate observation and recording is necessary at all times and the records should be made and arranged so that trends as well as the patients' condition can be easily seen. When there are many conditions to be kept in mind, it is very helpful to have a clear statement of conditions and refer to each as the occasion requires. This is the 'problem orientated medical record' system as devised by Weed. As in so many other respects, the keeping of good records is the joint task for nurses, doctors, physiotherapists, social workers and others.

There should be a daily X-ray examination of the chest and a specimen of sputum should be sent for identification of the organisms in it and their sensitivity to antibiotics. Urine should be sent for culture twice a week, tested for pH, specific gravity and abnormal constituents every two hours and the amount produced measured every hour.

Care of the eyes

If the patient is unconscious it will be necessary to clean the eyes every two hours, irrigating gently with normal saline and then applying a bland lubricant such as sterile liquid paraffin. If the eyelids are not closed, the eyes should be covered with *tulle gras* to prevent dust particles causing corneal ulceration; this is especially important if the patients are receiving paralysing agents. Although it is highly desirable to examine the pupils frequently, this may have to be abandoned if the lids are so swollen that conjunctiva bulges out as soon as they are parted and cannot be replaced.

Oral hygiene

If the patient is conscious but unable to drink, frequent mouth washes should be given to ensure that his mouth stays fresh and clean. If the patient is unconscious, or has an endotracheal tube *in situ*, it will be necessary to clean the mouth every two hours, removing any debris or excessive secretions. The mouth is best cleaned and refreshed with a dilute solution of sodium bicarbonate, followed by a rinsing solution of any proprietary mouth wash. If the lips are dry, they should be moistened with either glycerine or vaseline; this is especially important when an endotracheal tube is in place, because the lips are very vulnerable to the pressure of the tube and its connections. Lack of attention to the mouth in an inert patient will lead to infection and further debilitation.

Pressure areas

All patients, whatever their condition, can be moved to have pressure areas attended to. This must be done every two hours. It often requires four to six people but it must be carried out and help must be summoned as necessary. It is not necessary to rub the skin with spirit or creams; as long as it is kept dry and clean, a light dusting of talcum powder is sufficient. If this is not available, skin covering bony prominences should be gently massaged to stimulate the circulation. The sheets should be kept taut and without creases. Once the patient has been placed in an appropriate position, pillows should be used to prevent skin surfaces coming into contact, to elevate limbs and generally to reduce pressure on any vulnerable surfaces. When there has been profuse sweating or incontinence of faeces or urine, the soiled areas should be washed and dried thoroughly and the sheets changed.

Codes

LEVELS OF RESPONSE

9. Alert, rational and fully orientated.
8. Automatism. (Appears fully awake, and alert, but gives incorrect information, e.g. name, address, next of kin. Often seen soon after a short period of loss of consciousness.)
7. Drowsy but answers all questions. Mild impairment of orientation.
6. Answers simple questions but confused and irritable, obeys most commands.
5. Answers only "Yes" or "No". Disorientated, restless and confused. Obeys only simplest commands.
4. No obedience to any commands but responds to pain purposefully.
3. No obedience to commands and responds to pain without purpose.
2. Unrousable by any means.
1. Unrousable, no cough reflex and requires artificial respiration.

PUPIL SIZE

L = Large
M = Medium
S = Small

PUPIL REACTION

B = Brisk
Sl = Sluggish
F = Fixed

Fig. 6.6 Code listed levels of response, used on some hospitals' observation charts.

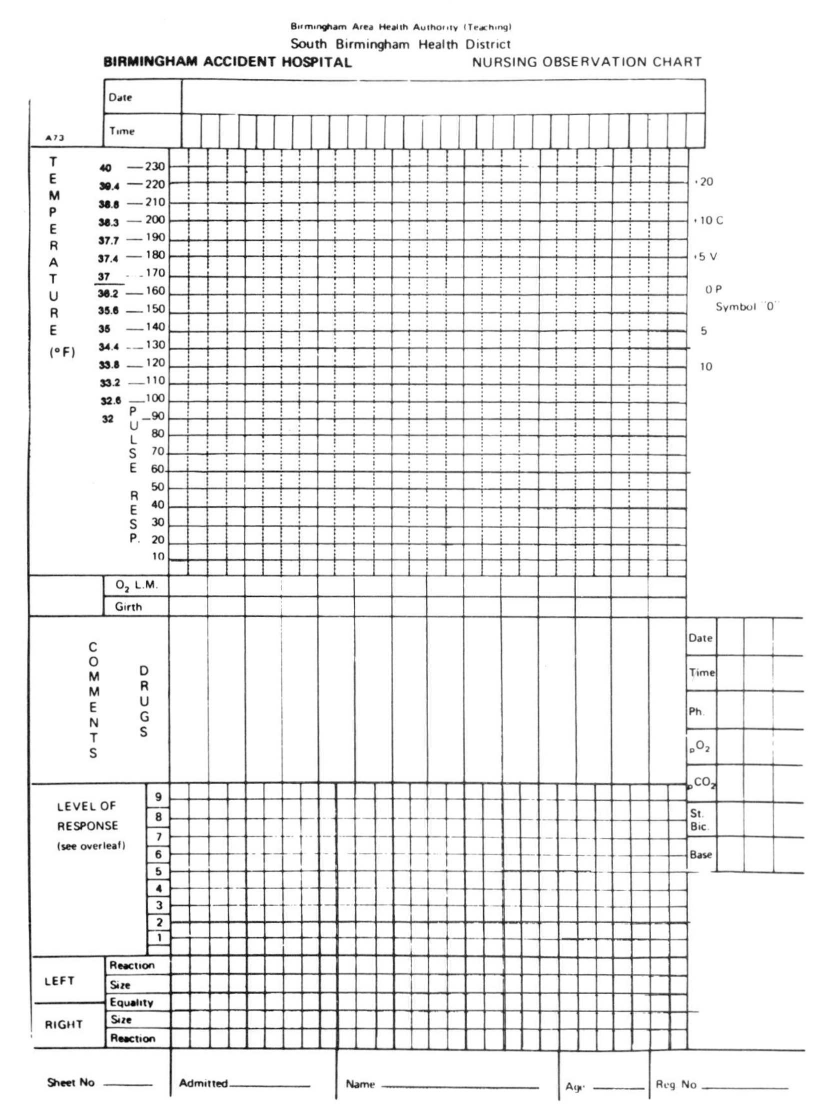

Birmingham Area Health Authority (Teaching)
South Birmingham Health District
BIRMINGHAM ACCIDENT HOSPITAL NURSING OBSERVATION CHART

A73

Date
Time

TEMPERATURE (°F)

Temperature	Pulse / Resp.
40	230
39.4	220
38.8	210
38.3	200
37.7	190
37.4	180
37	170
36.2	160
35.6	150
35	140
34.4	130
33.8	120
33.2	110
32.6	100
32	PULSE 90
	80
	70
	60
	RESP. 50
	40
	30
	20
	10

+20
+10 C
+5 V
0 P
Symbol "0"
5
10

O_2 L.M.
Girth

COMMENTS
DRUGS

Date			
Time			
Ph.			
$_pO_2$			
$_pCO_2$			
St. Bic.			
Base			

LEVEL OF RESPONSE (see overleaf)
9
8
7
6
5
4
3
2
1

LEFT
Reaction
Size
Equality
RIGHT
Size
Reaction

Sheet No ______ Admitted ______ Name ______ Age ______ Reg No ______

Fig. 6.7 Nursing observation chart (Birmingham Accident Hospital).

General hygiene

The patient should have a blanket bath every day (or twice a day), and a complete change of bed linen. Finger and toe nails should be kept clean and short. Hair should be washed once a week.

Feeding

If the patient is unconscious or attached to a mechanical ventilator, feeding will have to be carried out by artificial means until the patient is capable of feeding himself. A naso-gastric tube should be passed soon after admission; feeding should not be commenced until bowel sounds can be heard; most severely injured patients have a period of gastric stasis.

Start with 30 ml water hourly and aspirate the stomach 2- to 4-hourly for 6 hours. If the aspirate is only a small amount, increase to 60 ml water hourly and aspirate 4-hourly for a further 6 hours. If the stomach is absorbing the liquid, give 90 ml water hourly and aspirate 4-hourly. After a further 6 hours, give 90 ml water and 90 ml milk every 2 hours, aspirate every 4 hours. Flush the tube with 5 ml water before and after feeding. After a further 6 hours, increase the 2-hourly intake to 180 ml undiluted milk with 30 mls water to flush the tube. Aspirate the contents of the stomach 8-hourly and make sure that the tube is in place each time before feeding. After a further 6 hours, give 90 ml feed and 90 ml water with 30 ml water to flush the tube. Aspirate 8-hourly and make sure that the tube is in place before each feed is given. After twelve hours, give 180 ml full-strength feed with 30 ml water to flush the tube. It should then be necessary only to make sure that the naso-gastric tube is in position, not to aspirate. For feeding programme see Table 6.1.

Table 6.1 Standard feed mixture fed to patients by intragastric tube, Major Injuries Unit, Birmingham Accident Hospital (1973)

Mix together:	Quantity	Protein
'Carnation' Instant Breakfast Food	1 packet	8.75 g
Milk	250 ml	*8.5 g
Water	200 ml	
'Heinz' Strained Baby Food, Main meal	1 can	*4.9 g
Vitamin Compound (A, C, D)	10 drops	
Marmite	½ teaspoon	
Glucose (powder)	1 oz (28.45 g) (wt)	
	500 ml	*22.15 g
For twenty-four hour requirement multiply by 5.		
Patient regime		
Volume of feed every 2 hours	180 ml	
Volume of feed every 24 hours	2,160 ml	
Water (15 ml) to flush tube before and after feed	360 ml	
Total intake in 24 hours		
Fluid volume	2,530 ml	
Energy value	13.5 megajoules	
Protein	*96 g range 92–99 g	
Sodium Na^+	166 mmol range 121–212 mmol	
Potassium K^+	113 mmol range 95–130 mmol	

*mean values

Bowels

Because the naso-gastric feed contains large amounts of glucose, the bowels usually function normally. If it should be necessary to stimulate bowel action, suppositories should be tried first, followed by an enema. Occasionally it is necessary to perform a rectal washout. If the patient has a tendency to become constipated, suppositories should be used twice a week. If the patient develops diarrhoea which is not spurious or the result of enteritis, the glucose should be omitted from the feed until the diarrhoea stops.

Circulation

The effects of oligaemia

The picture of what is widely referred to as oligaemic shock is well-known. With prompt resuscitation, the circulation in most cases can rapidly be restored to normal merely by replacing the blood that has been lost and then keeping pace with further loss. Provided that the period of oligaemia has been less than an hour or so, the self-regulating systems of the body will still be in working order and able to deal rapidly and effectively with the acidaemia of peripheral hypoxia and stored blood (which may have a pH of 6.5), with the additional calcium and potassium; and even with the reduced affinity of stored blood for oxygen. The greatest danger from giving large quantities of stored blood in a short time is not that of biochemical disturbance, but that it will cool the heart below 28°C and cause ventricular fibrillation. It is for this reason that the blood is now warmed when large amounts are given.

A person suffering from the effects of oligaemia who becomes pink, warm, perhaps more alert and is excreting more than 20 to 30 ml of urine an hour with a specific gravity of either more or less than 1010, has good circulation and needs no specific tests or treatment.

If oligaemia is not corrected in time, mere replenishment of the circulation is not enough. A great deal of work has been done to identify the cause and treatment of what used to be called irreversible shock but there is still a certain amount of variation of opinion and practice from one unit to another. In principle, however, if a patient remains pale and cool and produces little urine in spite of having a normal central venous pressure and perhaps a blood volume that has been measured and found to be as much as 20 to 25 per cent above the expected normal, a vasodilator drug such as Phenoxybenzamine may be used, or massive doses of Methyl-prednisolone (20 to 30 mg/kg body weight). In either case, the intention is to relax blood vessels and allow the blood to flow again. If these measures are unsuccessful it may be because the patient has passed into a state of consumption coagulopathy or disseminated intravascular coagulation. Platelets become clumped and thrombi begin to form throughout the circulation. This leads to the consumption of clotting factors to such an extent that the patient is in danger of widespread bleeding. Fresh blood, platelets, fresh frozen plasma, E-aminocaproic acid (EACA) and even heparin may be needed to deal with this very serious state of affairs.

Renal failure following oligaemia occurs rarely except after burning and it is usually a sign of delayed or inadequate resuscitation.

The sickle cell syndrome

This condition may well have its origin in oligaemia, in hypoxaemia or in bad infection or septicaemia. It is characterised by a failure of the walls of the cells of the body to keep sodium ions and potassium ions in. This brings about redistribution of the body's water and the urine contains abnormally large amounts of potassium and little or no sodium, i.e. the reverse of normal. There is often evidence of renal failure as well. It may be possible to restore the functional integrity of the cell walls by giving 100 to 120 units insulin, with a sufficient quantity of 25 per cent or 50 per cent glucose intravenously to prevent hypoglycaemia.

Methods of investigation

In most cases it is sufficient to record blood pressure, pulse rate, central venous pressure, the electrocardiogram, output of urine and the biochemical state of the blood and urine, but in special units many additional measurements are made such as cardiac output, cardiac index, stroke volume, pulmonary arterial pressure together with frequent or even continuous recording of oxygen intake and consumption, carbon dioxide output, pH, $Pa\ O_2$, $P\ CO_2$, and blood lactate. These measurements have uses for research and, in difficult cases, they can mean the difference between death and the survival of the patient.

Responsibilities of the nurse

Apart from these special considerations, the nurse has a number of routine responsibilities to:

1. Ensure that the correct infusion is being given.
2. Regulate the flow in accordance with instructions.
3. Record accurately what infusions are given and when.
4. Warm blood, if large quantities are given rapidly.
5. Take care of infusion cannula or catheter. If a superficial vein is being used signs of phlebitis must frequently be looked for and reported at once.
6. Read central venous pressure.
7. Keep such other records as required.
8. Ensure that electrodes are correctly attached and connected.
9. Note and report any abnormality in the electrocardiogram.

Dangers

1. Infection, if poor aseptic techniques are used.
2. Air embolism—when venous air embolism is suspected the patient should be turned onto his left side allowing the air to rise in the right ventricle in an attempt to prevent it from being pumped into the pulmonary artery.
3. Mismatched blood.
4. Drugs incompatible with infusion.

Unconsciousness

For all the advances in the care of the victims suffering injury of the brain, the simple processes are still as important as ever. The first is to recognise any change in the patient's responsiveness. For this it is necessary to establish the level of responsiveness as soon as possible and thereafter to record it frequently. The second process is to treat the unconscious state by careful attention to respiration, circulation, nutrition, posture, skin, output of urine, and bowels, etc.

Deterioration of responsiveness

The cause of unconsciousness is often intrinsic damage to the brain caused at the moment of injury and not amenable to treatment, but the nurse must be continually alert for evidence that a treatable cause of deterioration has started to occur.

Hypoxia

Pneumonia, collapse of lung, pulmonary embolism by fat or thrombus can all cause hypoxia and lower the level of responsiveness, but the most dangerous may be epilepsy.

Epilepsy

The tonic phase of convulsions can cause such severe cerebral hypoxia that the patient's condition deteriorates rapidly, and may show some permanent loss of recoverability. Such fits may have to be controlled by paralysing the patient and carrying out artificial ventilation.

Pneumonia and atelectasis

Should be prevented by good nursing and physiotherapy but this becomes increasingly difficult if prolonged intubation is necessary and leads to tracheobronchitis.

Pulmonary embolism

Pulmonary embolism can occur even in young persons and after only a few days in bed. Although anti-coagulants offer a high degree of protection they are not given after head injury for fear of provoking intracranial bleeding.

Fat embolism

Fat embolism is an invariable consequence of many types of injuries, particularly fractures. It is a likely cause of the hypoxia that can be found within minutes of the injury but is usually not clinically evident. Clinical evidence of fat embolism includes an increased respiratory rate, obvious flaring of the nostrils, an anxious expression, cyanosis, mental confusion (sometimes mounting to uncontrollable restlessness), and a faint pink punctate rash that is usually scanty and most often found on the chest and shoulder. An experienced nurse will often suspect the condition and then look for the rash, which is not always present. Other features of cerebral fat embolism include falling of the level of response and unequal pupils, so that it may mimic an intracranial haematoma, with which it has been known to coincide.

Raised intracranial pressure

One of the classical causes of diminishing responsiveness after head injury is rising intracranial pressure because of bleeding within the skull, but swelling of the brain is more frequent and less easy to treat. Now that it has become possible to measure and record intracranial pressure continuously it has become clear how unreliable both the physical signs and the results of lumbar puncture are, and how sensitive the intracranial pressure is to even milk and transient respiratory obstruction. The injured brain swells, the swelling all too easily compresses blood vessels, so causing hypoxia, which leads to more swelling and sets off another cycle of deterioration that may become progressively worse. The value of traditional steps taken to lower intracranial pressure has been called into question and it has to be acknowledged that if the pressure cannot be measured, doctors and nurses can only hope that Mannitol, urea, caffeine, steroids or hyper-ventilation are having the desired effect. It is probably true to say that if the disabling effects of cerebral injury are to be reduced this will depend upon being able to prevent the intracranial pressure from rising and, by measurement, to know that this is so.

Meningitis

This is one of the less frequent and more insidious causes of deterioration; it is most likely to be thought of when there is known to have been a fracture of the base of the skull, and particularly if there has been a persistant leak of cerebrospinal fluid, but it can occur in the absence of any known fracture of the skull and in spite of a prophylactic course of sulphonamide and an antibiotic. It is a condition to be suspected, after which a lumbar puncture will uphold or dispel the suspicion. This is perhaps the only justification for carrying out a lumbar puncture after head injury. Once the diagnosis has been made by lumbar puncture, meningitis can usually be treated by large doses of a suitable antibiotic, given intravenously if possible.

Special investigations

Lumbar puncture is rarely required and intracranial pressure measured only in special units, but there are other methods of wider applicability.

Radiography. Plain X-ray films show fractures, air, or foreign bodies within the skull and they may show liquid levels in the sinuses. If the pineal gland is calcified, X-rays will show whether or not it is exactly in the midline, as it should be.

Angiography shows whether or not the vessels are filling normally and whether they are displaced by swelling or a clot. It is the most generally available, accurate way of locating intracranial bleeding.

Echoencephalography. Ultrasound waves passed through the head are reflected at the various interfaces; these are timed and recorded photographically and it is possible to tell whether or not the structures that should be exactly in the midline have been displaced. It is simpler, cheaper and safer than angiography, but less accurate.

Electroencephalography. Although much attention has been paid to the significance of a completely flat record of electrical activity of the brain as evidence of irrecoverable damage, this cannot be relied upon and other criteria of a hopeless prognosis must be used.

Brain scanning. The distribution in the brain of a minute dose of a radioactive substance can be of some diagnostic value but the most dramatically successful and most expensive (the apparatus costs over £150 000) type of scanning provides a cross sectional diagram of the patient's brain without any injections or invasive technique. The EMI scanner uses a computer to record as a diagram the degree to which the brain absorbs electromagnetic impulses, but it has the important disadvantage that the patient must be brought to it.

Emergency operation
It occasionally happens that deterioration occurs so rapidly that there is no time to move the patient into a proper operating room and burr holes have to be made in the reception and resuscitation area. Once the clot has been found and let out, the patient can be moved for any further surgical steps that may be required.

Special considerations in management

Apart from the general care of the patient there are special features in the care of victims of cerebral injury.

Restlessness
This may be severe enough to require sedation, but apart from what is often referred to as cerebral irritation, restlessness may be caused by fat embolism or a full bladder, headache or pain and concussion, all of which should be excluded or dealt with. Physical restraint should be avoided, if possible, because it often makes things worse and a moderate amount of restless activity may be a convenient supplement to physiotherapy. If there are fractures, restlessness can nullify the effects of splintage and it can even result in a closed fracture becoming open, especially if it is encased in plaster. Formal splintage may have to be abandoned if the fracture, or the patient's condition, is not suitable for internal fixation. In this case deformity has to be corrected later.

Spasticity
This is an occasional cause of serious difficulty in treating fractures. If it does not yield to simple measures such as passive movements, traction or splintage, tenotomy is sometimes used to prevent severe and perhaps permanent contractures. A less well known result of spasticity is the formation of bone in the muscles.

Contractures
Quite apart from spasticity, it is important to anticipate contractures by careful positioning and splinting of limbs. The hands, in particular, are at risk from a combination of intravenous infusions, restraint, posture and dependency.

Unrecognised awareness
Unless all members of staff clearly understand the difference between unconsciousness (which robs the patient of both awareness and recollection of events) and unresponsiveness (which may leave both these faculties unimpaired—as with the paralysis induced by curare and other paralysing drugs) they may cause avoidable distress and resentment by what they say and do within earshot of the patient.

There is no harm (and there may be some benefit) in behaving as though even 'deeply unconscious' patients are aware of their surroundings and visitors as well as nurses may find it easier to talk to the patient than to keep silent at the bedside. Careful observation may suggest that the patient is responsive to light, to sounds, to certain visitors or nurses or to certain nursing procedures. Any such responsiveness should be thoroughly tested by occupational therapists or clinical psychologists with a view to 'exercising the mental muscles' at the earliest opportunity. Patients undergoing modern intensive care, even

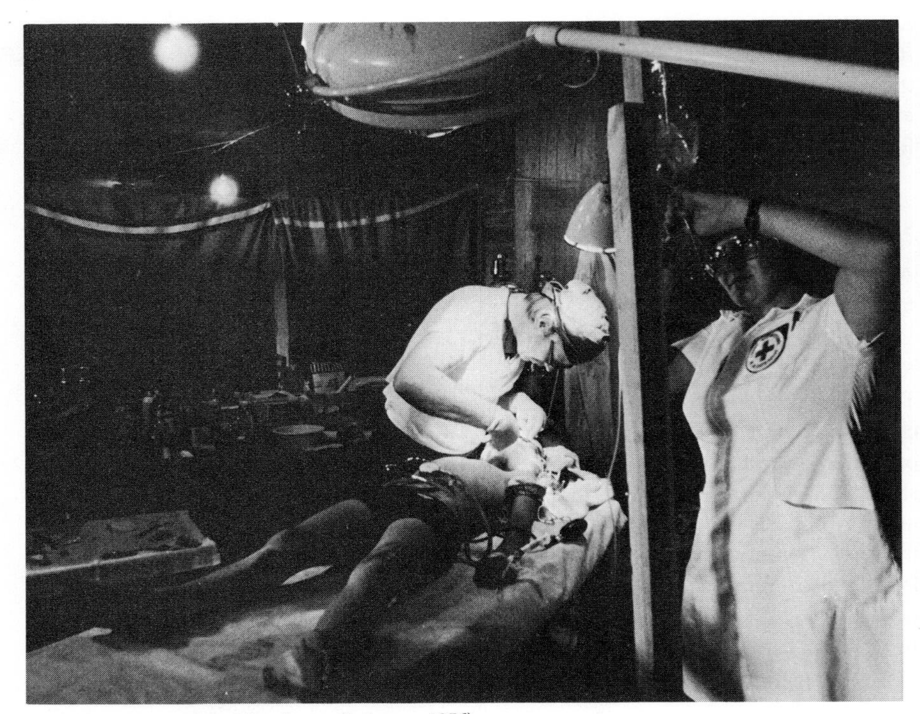

Fig. 6.8 Emergency operating theatre (Lebanon, 1976).

without impairment of consciousness, suffer more or less a sensory privation, the effects of which can seriously damage the personality. Proper care takes a great deal of time but it can make the difference between manageability and the uncontrollable restlessness that may be treated by drugs, but is really a sign of frustration in a patient who can perhaps see and hear and experience normal appetites and desires without being able to give comprehensible vent to his thoughts and feelings.

Spinal injuries

There has already been reference to the occasional association of injuries of the spine, particularly the neck, with injuries of the brain and it is enough to emphasise here the importance of handling the patient as though such injury has in fact occurred for as long as there is any possibility that this may be so.

Comprehensive care

In general, the patient should be looked after from the beginning in such a way as to make as much therapeutic use as possible of whatever mental, emotional and physical powers he has at any given time. This can be taught, but there are those with an instinctive grasp of what is needed by the variously deprived and handicapped persons. Such simple necessities as false teeth, hearing aids or glasses may make a great deal of difference to a person's self-respect as well as to his awareness of and responsiveness to his surroundings but for those who can only feel, a new language and understanding is necessary if they are to be given reassurance, comfort and understanding.

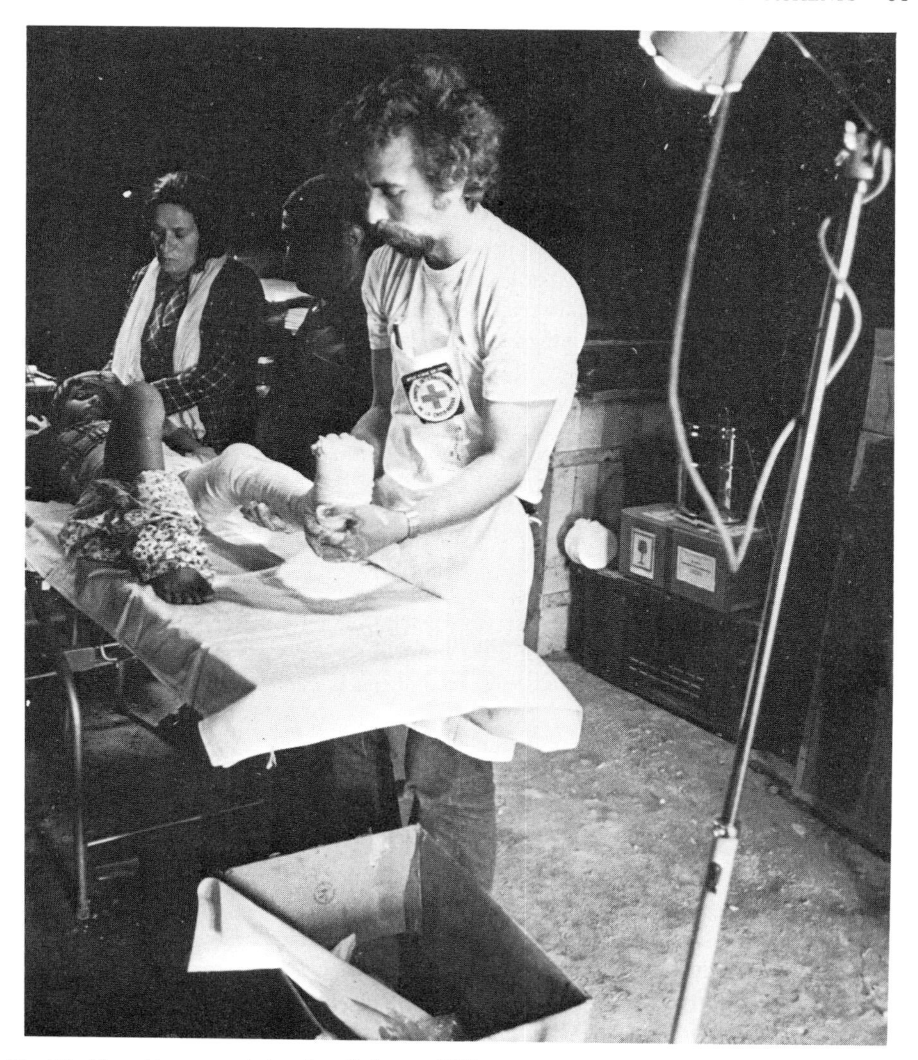

Fig. 6.9 First aid treatment being given (Lebanon, 1976).

The most frequent danger is that care will be concentrated upon the unconscious state, respiratory failure or metabolic disturbance and preventable complications will go unprevented. Patients may nowadays take it for granted that their lives will be saved and be understandably resentful if they are left with a disability that could have been avoided.

Difficult decisions

Now that patients are surviving cerebral injury with very severe mental and physical handicaps it is sometimes necessary for the staff to decide when to abandon the utmost efforts to sustain life at all costs. The decision is much more difficult for some than for others; nurses must at least be able to acquiesce and therefore to understand the point of view of doctors and relatives if they are to stand the strain of looking after those whose fate hangs in the balance. It is perhaps most helpful to regard artificial ventilation and other methods of keeping a person alive as part of an attempt to tide him over until the means of survival are restored. If they are not, the attempt can reasonably be regarded as having failed, and the natural course of events should no longer be interfered with.

These decisions are not necessarily for doctors and nurses alone. Some relatives are sufficiently realistic and compassionate to wish that a loved one should not survive as a pathetic human wreck and should not have his existence artificially prolonged but be allowed to die with dignity. Whether it is possible to be frank with relatives and ask them to share in the making of decisions, or necessary to be tactful and restrained and keep the decision in medical hands, medical social workers have an important part to play in comforting and otherwise assisting relatives at a time of acute anxiety and in the period of distress or mourning that follows.

Abdominal injuries

In most cases the decision that there is or is not an injury that needs to be explored is taken within the first few hours. It is based upon signs of bleeding and peritoneal irritation such as increasing pallor, pain, tenderness and rigidity, disappearance of bowel sounds, pattern bruising and the evidence of radiography. Peritoneal irrigation can much reduce the number of negative laparotomies that may result from relying on a purely clinical basis for decision. Conditions that are most often overlooked until complications set in are incomplete ruptures of spleen, gut and pancreas but this is minimal if the initial diagnostic zeal is good.

The main role of continuing care is the management of paralytic ileus and its accompanying metabolic disturbances, and the use of artificial feeding. Whenever possible, patients should receive natural foodstuffs by mouth or through a nasogastric tube, but if this is not possible for more than 2–3 days, then intravenous feeding must be adopted.

Intravenous feeding

The simplest foodstuff is glucose but to provide 8.25 megajoules a day requires nearly five hundred grams of glucose, or a litre of 50 per cent solution. Glucose provides energy, and to some extent it spares protein, but patients quickly lose flesh if they do not receive protein-building materials.

A suitable mixture will provide amino acids, glucose, fat and vitamins, the amount of water and joules being adjusted to need (Table 6.2).

In spite of all its advantages, intravenous feeding as a means of maintaining weight has complications such as chemical phlebitis; thrombosis at the tip of the catheter in a large vein, with the risk that it will break off and lodge in the lungs; and septicaemia caused by gram-negative organisms or yeast that can flourish in the unusually nutritious solutions.

The urinary tract

Haematuria frequently accompanies injuries of the abdomen but may indicate nothing worse than bruising of the bladder by a fractured pelvis. Investigation by pyelography, cystography and renal angiography allows very acurate diagrams to be made and shows the remarkable powers of recovery possessed by the kidneys. Even serious damage can be successfully treated by repair or partial nephrectomy and few kidneys have nowadays to be removed. These investigations also show whether or not there are two functioning kidneys.

Fracture of the pelvis
The two most serious complications are profuse and continuing bleeding and rupture of the urethra. Bleeding may amount to several times the patient's own blood volume; inflatable splints in the form of special trousers may stop it, but it is sometimes necessary to operate. Such profuse bleeding is usually arterial. A torn urethra can be repaired surgically and splintered by a urethral catheter but it is simpler to insert a suprapubic catheter and deal with the urethra later.

Infection

Prolonged intensive care certainly saves lives but, with equal certainty, can endanger life, most often by causing septicaemia, particularly by Gram-negative organisms. They gain entry at the bedside through intravenous tubes and by way of urinary catheters.

There is no simple preventive measure. Prophylactic antibiotics have been shown to play a large part in eliminating the usual hospital bacteria and giving free rein to resistant Gram-negative organisms that otherwise are rarely encountered. There should be an agreed policy that states when antibiotics will not be used and aims at keeping in reserve those that are most likely to combat potentially fatal infections by the most resistant organisms. Too often there is early resort to the latest 'broad spectrum' antibiotics in the belief that they will offer the best protection. Most infections reach patients directly by contact; nurses are the chief carriers, for the simple reason that they are with, and do most for, the patients. It behoves them, therefore, to take particular care to protect their clothes, hair and hands by means of aprons, masks and gowns, but all other attendants must be prepared to adhere to the policy drawn up in consultation with the Control of Infection Committee.

Reducing cross infection depends upon unrelenting attention to detail by all members of the staff and its incidence is an indication of the standard of discipline in the unit. In most cases, an indwelling catheter will be inserted soon after a badly injured person is admitted. This must be done with due regard for asepsis and the drainage system must be sealed and remain sealed. Clamping the catheter or blocking it with a spiggot is a certain way of infecting the bladder. In the case of spinal paralysis, intermittent catheterisation is generally preferable to an indwelling catheter. If it must be used it should be fine, such as Gibbon's or Foley's.

Wounds and fractures
Wounds and fractures of the trunk, head and neck can, like other injuries of these parts, have total results, usually because of damage to large blood vessels or vital organs. In the limbs, however, they carry a threat to function rather than to life. The surgeon's task is to prevent infection, to facilitate healing of the injured tissues and to enable the patient to regain function of the injured part. Antibiotics are in many ways less important for preventing infection than prompt and effective surgical treatment.

Preventing infection
Wounds should be promptly covered by a dressing sufficient to absorb blood without soon

Table 6.2 Basic requirements of energy and protein

Nutrition solution	Total volume ml	Water ml	Calories cal (mJ)	Carbo-hydrate g	Amino acids g	Fat g	Alcohol g	Electrolytes mEq
Aminosol 10%	500	460	165 (0.75)		50			80 Na^+ 65 Cl^-
Intralipid 20%	500	375	1000 (4.00)			100		
Fructose or glucose 20%	1000	875	820 (3.50)	200				
Total	2000	1710	1985 (8.25)	200	50	100		
Per kg bodyweight (50–70 kg)			28–40 (125–175 kJ)	3–4	0.7–1.0	1.5–2.0		
Increased requirement of energy and protein (required by severely injured patients)								
Aminosol-fructose-ethanol	1000	850	900 (3.75)	150	33		25	210 Na^+ 170 Cl^-
Aminosol 10%	1000	925	330 (1.37)		100			
Intralipid 20%	1000	450	2000 (8.33)			200		
Total	3000	2525	3230 (13.45)	150	133	200	25	
Per kg bodyweight (50–70 kg)			46–65 (191.6–270.3 kJ)	2–3	1.9–2.7	3–4	0.4–0.5	

40% solutions of fructose or glucose may be used if extra kilojoules are required.

becoming soaked through and the dressings should be kept securely in place. Plain, dry gauze can safely be applied to any wound but there may be advantage in using a dressing impregnated with silver nitrate or chlorhexidine or both, as they do not induce bacterial resistance. No other antibacterial substance should be used on the wound, but it is customary to give an antibiotic by intravenous or intramuscular injection and to give tetanus toxoid to those that have already received an immunising course, or human anti-tetanus immunoglobin to those who have not, and to initiate a curse of tetanus toxoid.

Repairing of wounds

Having removed dead and damaged tissues and foreign matter from a wound the surgeon will decide whether or not to close the wound. If it is less than about six hours old and is not likely to have been heavily contaminated, and if the surgeon is confident that the wound will heal without complication, he may decide to carry out immediately a careful repair, even of nerves, tendons, bones and blood vessels and close the wound by sewing it up or by means of skin grafts. If, on the other hand, there has been a delay or heavy contamination and the surgeon thinks that there may be a complication, he will not do more than carry out surgical toilet (without repair) and then loosely pack the wound and leave it open. A few days later the wound is inspected and is usually found to be suitable for at least closure and even repairs that could not be safely undertaken on the first day. This policy of delaying primary closure is particularly necessary with the severely disruptive injuries inflicted by modern high velocity bullets.

The twin hazards of wounds of former years were gas gangrene and tetanus. Both have been for all practical purposes abolished by prompt and effective surgical treatment of large wounds, but tetanus still occurs in persons who have wounds which seem too small to require medical attention and who have not been actively immunized against tetanus.

Fractures

The conscious patient's first requirements are comfortable supports for his fractures. These may be provided by formal splintage but must be clearly understood that the mere application of a splint, with however good an intention, may be anything but comfortable and may provide no support.

Relaxation induced by careful explanation may much reduce the discomfort of a fracture. Deformity is corrected if this can be done simply, safely and without adding to the patient's distress. Otherwise, if it is not endangering the skin, circulation, or nerves, it can be left until the patient can be given a suitable analgesic or anaesthetic substance.

Immediate comfortable support may be provided by pillows, sandbags, inflatable splints, Plaster of Paris slabs, Thomas' splints (or one of its modifications).

Definitive care of fractures includes the care of the associated wounds and of bleeding, which can be fatal if there are several fractures, and is based upon Plaster of Paris, traction or internal fixation. Internal fixation has an important place in facilitating the care of a severely injured patient who might otherwise be encumbered by having more than one limb in splints. In the case of the restless or unconscious patient the nurse must be constantly looking for evidence of dangerous pressure by splints. The appearance of a stain on a plaster some days after it was applied requires investigation and the suspicions that it should arouse will be increased if the stained area is odorous or warm to the touch.

Burns

In any catastrophe resulting in many casualties it is advisable that the severely injured are grouped together to allow a central pool of essential facilities near the place of greatest need.

It is rarely possible for severely burned patients to be admitted directly to a specialised unit. Even if one were conveniently near by the sheer numbers of injured would swamp existing facilities, staff and space would be totally inadequate, dressing, drugs, etc. would be insufficient.

It may be necessary to designate whole hospitals, clinics and school buildings as reception areas until more detailed sorting can be carried out.

Essential materials such as plasma, dextran, antibiotics and analgesics must be strictly conserved and used only for those patients who will most benefit. Dressings are not essential and may be reserved for other injuries.

Trained medical and nursing staff must not be involved in first aid or minor treatments; paramedical staff and volunteers can attend to these, leaving the trained staff free to attend to the severely injured. Priority of treatment must go to those who have a favourable prognosis, however difficult a decision this may prove to be morally. It is essential for people to return to duty as soon as possible so that they are no longer a drain on time, space and materials and so that any particular talents may be utilised. Ambulant patients can be treated as out-patients, even if they have quite extensive burns. Those with both hands and face burned, however, will probably be unable to care for themselves and can be admitted to self-care wards where paramedical staff and ancillary staff can attend to their basic needs.

Many of these patients with burn injuries of up to one fifth of the body surface may be successfully treated by an oral solution of salt 3 gm and bicarbonate 1.5 gm in a litre of water. Out-patients could be provided with packets of these powders to be made up at home.

Dressings do not need to be applied to hospitalised patients, but out-patients need some protection. Plastic bags placed over hands provide a comfortable cover, a barrier against infection, freedom of movement and a degree of independence. They are held on at the wrist by a bandage or strip of linen.

Reception of the severely burned

A reception area should be designated for the admission of patients where burned clothing can be removed and a very cursory estimate made of injuries before the patient is transferred to the appropriate group or ward to be weighed and placed on a clean bed.

Ideally, each patient requires a heated room and a nurse to 'special' him, but where this is not feasible one nurse can be responsible for an area of the ward.

As soon as possible, the doctor must perform a venous cut-down, preferably into the arm, as the long veins of the leg tend to go into spasms during the rapid transfusion of colloid.

A wide-bore cannula is required and can be fashioned in an emergency by fastening a 5 inch length of fine plastic tubing to a size 1 intramuscular needle. This is preferable to a 'stab' cannula which is not adequate and will probably fall out or pierce the wall of the vein before long. Subcutaneous infusions are not indicated, nor are rectal infusions because of the poor peripheral circulation. They may of course, provide limited use in extreme emergency situations.

The depth of burns is estimated by pin-prick. Using a sterile hypodermic needle, the doctor proceeds to prick the burns. Deep burns are painless, but other burns are sensitive to the pin pricks. This is of limited value when dealing with children. The area of the burn can be estimated by using the 'Rule of Nines' where an upper limb is nine per cent of the body surface; the surface of the trunk or a lower limb is 18 per cent; the palm equals one per cent. This is a guide which in extensive burns can be used to estimate the areas not burned, thus giving the areas burned. Generally, a burned area of a tenth of the body surface in children and fifteen per cent in adults is considered a 'shock case' but, particularly in adults, larger areas will need out-patient treatment when hospital facilities are at a premium.

Having estimated the area of the burn, the doctor can then calculate how much fluid is required by multiplying the extent by the weight in kilograms and dividing this total by two. This gives the amount of fluid required in the first period of four hours, starting at the time of the injury. It can be quite a large amount.

At this early stage the airway is usually clear, but sooty nasal hairs or mouth warn of possible inhalation trauma. A bright pink, flushed appearance may be due to carbon monoxide poisoning. Oxygen is given for these cases, but may be of limited value. Carbon monoxide poisoning responds well to treatment in a hyperbaric oxygen tank, but it is unlikely that one would be available in a catastrophe. Smokey plugs should be removed from the nostrils and mucus sucked out of the airways.

At this early stage, the patient will be in a state of primary shock and shout for pain relief. Deep burns are almost painless and often it is fright rather than pain which causes the distress. Therefore, a small amounts of analgesics such as morphine 5 to 10 mg or 25 mg Pethidine given intravenously are adequate. Care must be given not to give repeated amounts in spite of the apparent distress. Most effective analgesics are also respiratory depresssants. It is difficult to believe that these deep burns are comparatively painless, but the skin is dead and with it the nerve endings.

Burns which are sensitive to pin-pricks, however, the partial skin loss or second degree burns, can be very painful. When analgesics are not available the patient can be truthfully assured that the pain will ease within a few hours.

Restlessness is not usually due to pain, but may be caused by lack of oxygen and/or lack of fluid. These should be corrected rather than give the patient sedatives which will mask the signs of shock.

Patients with extensive burns require to be catheterized, using a balloon or other type of indwelling catheter. This allows accurate monitoring of renal function. The urine should be collected and measured hourly and placed in order in small containers so that the doctor can see at a glance the colour and quantity of the urine. It should be tested for sugar, ketones, albumen, blood, pH and specific gravity. Sugar may be present, at first due to the stress and later due to the type of intravenous fluid. Dextran may cause sugar to be present and also alter the specific gravity.

An adequate average hourly amount of urine is 20 ml. Less than this gives cause for concern.

Oral fluids must be restricted. An extensively burned patient will cry out for more to drink. It must not be given, as vomiting will certainly result. A solution of salt and bicarbonate in water, or plain water, may be given, but not more than 200 ml hourly for an adult and smaller amounts for a child. The amount given must be calculated from the amount allowed both orally and intravenously for each period.

Unless the burn was caused by electricity it is not necessary to record the blood pressure nor the central venous pressure. The pulse rate and volume should give any information required as to the patient's general condition.

The temperature should, if possible, be recorded hourly, as should the pulse rate. It will probably be advisable to take the temperature rectally as this will give a more accurate reading. For the first few hours it will remain normal or even subnormal, but will soon rise. It is very important to keep the room hot even when the patient's temperature seems high at 38.5°C or more. Unless this rises to 39.5°C or more, the patient ought not to be cooled. The high room temperature is needed to slow the metabolic rate and thus prevent the body metabolising its own tissue protein.

Respirations must be observed and are an important guide to respiratory trauma. Their nature and rate ought to be recorded. If dressings are available, they should not be applied for at least four hours: this gives the patient a chance to become accustomed to his surroundings and prevents the onset of secondary shock. When possible, all burned patients should be barrier nursed for the first 48 hours. At all times strict hygienic standards must be maintained, gloves should be worn, when available, and changed after each handling; gowns, masks and boots are desirable and also a covering for the hair. Infection is the biggest danger that the burned patient has to face and carries a high mortality rate.

Airway

Many burns involve the face and neck and the patient may have inhaled hot air, steam or noxious gases.

Oxygen may be required, preferably through a humidifier. The ordinary steam kettle is very useful. The bed can be canopied with a sheet so that the patient sitting inside this 'tent' breathes in the warm, moist air.

Where there is damage to the pharynx and lungs a tracheostomy is indicated.

Indications for performing tracheostomy

Stridor
Burned tongue
Soot in the nostrils and around teeth
Red posterior pharynx
Deep burns of the neck

Occasionally a patient may respond to intubation with the endotracheal tube kept in position for about 48 hours or so, until the oedema subsides. This is not appropriate where there are deep neck burns as the respiratory restriction will last for some weeks. Where tracheostomy is not adequate, mechanical ventilation on a respirator will be needed. The prognosis is very poor.

Intravenous infusion

Adequate replacement of intravenous fluid as soon as possible is essential. A wide bore plastic venous catheter is advisable. It allows for a limited amount of movement. This catheter must be well anchored. The infusion can be a fairly long-term treatment and there are few sites for infusions in a burned patient. Drugs such as antibiotics and anaesthetics sometimes need to be given intravenously. Blood transfusion and blood samples will be necessary later.

Solutions to be given are:

During shock phase

Human Plasma Protein Fraction
Freeze Dried Plasma
Frozen Plasma
Dextran in Saline
Plasmalyte
Ringer Lactate (Hartmann's Solution)
Saline

Later

Intralipid 10 or 20
Aminoplex 5
Aminosol Fructrose Ethanol
Dextrose or Lacvulose 10 or 20
Dextrose Saline
Blood will be required after the first week and at weekly intervals during treatment.

The shock phase requiring large amounts of replacement fluid is divided into six periods covering 36 hours. They are 4/4/4/6/6/12 hour periods and the amount of infusion fluid to be given should be reviewed at the end of each period. The first four-hour period begins at the time of injury, not at the time of admission or at the time that the infusion is begun.

The amount to be given may be calculated by a simple sum. The extent of the burn multiplied by the weight of the patient in kilograms is divided by two. This figure equals the amount, in millilitres, to be given in each period. Changes in amount may be governed by the general condition of the patient, the haematocrit readings, if available, and the urine output. Partial skin loss burns (second degree) tend to lose far more fluid than full scale skin loss burns (third degree). Burns of over a third of the body area may need a pint of blood per 10 per cent if the burn is very deep.

Blood investigations

Blood group and cross-match. Where the patient is being infused with dextran solutions it is important to take blood for these investigations before the treatment is started.

Haematocrit. This is a useful guide to the concentration ratio of red cells to plasma and aids the doctor's calculations as to the amount of intravenous fluid to be given. This is, however, only a guide as the result will be affected by the patient's haemoglobin at the time of injury. This occurs particularly in mothers and infants.

Electrolytes. Sodium, chloride and potassium are the most often affected and may need supplementing later in the treatment.

Blood-gases. These need only be estimated where there is evidence of inhalation trauma.

Haemoglobin. This is often very low in mothers and small children. If so, the loss of serous fluid will show as apparently normal haemoglobin, although there will be a higher concentration of blood cells to fluid than previously.

Blood volume. This is estimated by injecting tagged red cells and removing a sample of blood after a given period. It is unlikely that facilities will allow for this.

Drugs

Doses of analgesics should be comparatively small to avoid side-effects and to avoid masking the signs of shock.

Morphine 5–10 mg
Pethidine 25–50 mg
Pentazocine 30–60 mg

Tetanus toxoid. This is very necessary.

Antibiotics. There are several opinions about these but, generally speaking, antibiotics, if available, should be given prophylactically. They may be given orally if tolerated, otherwise intramuscularly for the lesser burns and intravenously for the severely burned. Absorption is poor both for oral and for intramuscular drugs, an important point. A broad spectrum antibiotic should be chosen; invading bacteria rapidly become resistant.

In the small hospital any of the penicillins will almost certainly be adequate. Otherwise the erythromycins or flucloxacillin can be used. The tetracyclines are not generally advised because of the rapid resistance of bacteria.

Where supplies are limited it must be decided who is to have the available antibiotics. It may be that out-patients would benefit most but as they cannot be relied upon to make full use of these drugs, it may be advisable to preserve them for the hospitalised patients who will benefit. Infection is the biggest danger, but as burns of over 50 per cent have a poor prognosis from many other factors they might be omitted. *Pseudomonas aeroginosa* and the haemolytic *streptococci* are the infecting organisms to be avoided.

Sedation. Sedatives should not be given during the shock phase as they will mask the signs of shock and delay any corrective treatment which may be needed.

Barbiturates may be given to children with cerebral symptoms where there is danger of convulsions, but not otherwise.

Vitamins. Even with a high protein, high carbohydrate diet, orally and intravenously, supplementary vitamins are required.

I.V. Parentrovite for extensive burn patients.

Vitamin C .50 mg, Vitamin B complex, halibut liver oil capsule, and ferrous sulphate are needed daily.

Itching. This can be very troublesome later. Chlorpheniramine 4 mg six-hourly will help relieve this condition.

Anticoagulants. The prothrombin is lost via the serous leakage together with the other plasma proteins. This, plus the immobilisation of the severely injured patient, will increase the dangers of thrombosis. Warfarin (Marevan) may be given to prevent this, but it requires regular checks on clotting and bleeding times. The urine and faeces should also be tested daily for blood.

During the emergency stage, it is desirable that some method of marking patients as they receive drugs is determined. An M for morphine, or T for tetanus could be written, preferably on the brow, but if burned, on the hand, arm, foot or leg. Marking the bed is not advised as mistakes can occur if patients are moved from area to area.

Dressing

Wound toilet. Burned clothing and chemicals are first removed.

The burned area and its surrounds are cleaned with a mild soapy solution such as Cetrimide 1 per cent, Chlorhexidine, 1/2000 or Savlon (ICI) or even with soap flakes. This removes soot, soil, crusts, etc.

Blisters which are broken are best removed using fine-toothed forceps and scissors, if time permits. Those which are still intact should be left unless they cause discomfort. Then they may have to be pricked and the excess fluid gently expressed. These blisters form a natural barrier against infection and pain and hasten healing. Desirable though it would seem, cleaning a burn wound at this early stage is not essential.

If dressings are available and are to be applied, it is wise to wait at least four hours after admission to allay the danger of second shock.

1. Well padded dressings using gamgee or cotton wool spread with an antibiotic cream:

Flamazine (Smith & Nephew)
Silver nitrate 0.5 per cent
Sulphamylon (Bayer)
Various tulles impregnated with antiseptics and antibiotics.

These are intended for daily change of dressing, but can safely be left much longer.

2. Op-Site (S & N) is a purpose-designed 'plastic' dressing.

3. Leofoam (Leo International) is a very comfortable foam dressing which does not stick to the burn wound. Melolin (S & N) non-adhesive dressing is not absorbent.

4. Cling-film: a plastic sheeting intended for food storage and therefore does not require sterilizing. It is cheap and readily available. Gauze or cream may be used under this.

5. Plastic bags: extremely useful for hands; large ones can cover the whole arm or leg. They provide protection from bacteria and dust, ease pain and allow a considerable amount of independence.

Exposure

In hot climates and where the sheer number of patients is too great for existing facilities to cope, burns are best treated by the exposure method. Dressing materials can then be released for other injuries.

Preferably, there should be facilities for barrier-nursing but, where this is impossible, every attempt must be made to avoid contaminating the burn wound.

A fly-screen may be required.

The patient should be turned every two hours, to allow the air to circulate and reach all areas.

Solutions such as silver nitrate 0.5 per cent or providone iodine, if available, may be applied frequently. (If silver nitrate is used the patient will possible need supplements of sodium chloride and potassium.) It must be remembered that exposure does not reduce the risk of infection, in fact it increases it. Bacteria thrive beneath the surface of the dry and apparently sterile eschar.

Without dressings, heat is lost and unless the room is warm (28–32°C) dehydration will occur and the metabolic rate increase, resulting in the breakdown of tissue protein.

Identification

Badly burned patients are often unrecognisable, even to their close relatives. Objects not destroyed in the fire, such as rings, watches and gold teeth can sometimes be used to identify individuals. Often relatives are so distressed that they will 'identify' anyone vaguely fitting the qualities of their beloved ones, resulting in confusion and distress.

As soon as identified, bodies should be labelled. Writing their names on any available area of the skin with a laundry marker or other indelible pen is suitable as a temporary measure. Most patients will be too shocked by their experience to resent this. The notes and charts should be kept near the individual. A list of the injured should be made as soon as possible and given to the person who is responsible for dealing with all outside enquiries.

1. Complications: shock

Clinical features:

- Ashen pallor
- Cold clammy skin
- Rapid pulse, becoming weak and thready
- 'Air hunger'
- Hypotension
- Inadequate urine output
- Hyper-alert mental state progressing to:
  - disorientation
  - confusion
  - irritability
  - extreme restlessness
- Feeling shivery and cold
- Intense thirst
- Vomiting
- Oedema
- Moribundity

Treatment:

Restoration of the circulation by intravenous cannula will reverse all these symptoms if instituted early enough. If not treated, the patient will die.

2. Complications: renal failure

Signs:

Anuria. Absence of urine is extremely rare and the catheter should be checked for blockage or kinking in the tube.

Oliguria. A small volume of concentrated urine hourly is usually caused by inadequate intravenous infusion.

Concentrated urine. This can be deceptive as dextran and other infusion liquids can affect the specific gravity of the urine.

Haemoglobinuria. This is caused by the degradation of the haemoglobin in the cells damaged by the heat.

Haemoglobinuria with oliguria. This is very serious and is a sign of renal failure.

The urine output should be measured hourly and tested, particularly for sugar, ketones and blood. Samples should be set up in small pots, in order of the time at which they were passed so that the colour change can be noted immediately. At times the urine will be bright red or plum coloured. An average of 20 ml hourly is adequate and within the normal range.

If diuretics, such as frusemide 20–40 mg intravenously, do not increase the urine output, peritoneal dialysis may be necessary.

3. Complications: respiratory tract

Adult respiratory syndrome—this is pulmonary oedema with left ventricular failure
Trauma caused by hot air or steam
Inhalation of toxic fumes

Signs and symptoms:

Increased respiratory rate
Laboured breathing
Air hunger
Hoarseness
Cough with sooty sputum

Treatment:

Mild respiratory distress can often be relieved by propping the patient up and placing in a steam tent, with or without oxygen. Tincture of benzoin added to the boiling water seems to ease the bronchial spasm a little.

Oxygen via a mask is usually badly tolerated. However, given via nasal spectacles after the nostrils have been cleared of sooty plugs, oxygen is better tolerated if introduced via a humidifier. It is important that the airways are kept warm and moist.

When facilities and time allow, the blood gases should be estimated. Pulmonary oedema may possibly be due to over transfusion. When an anaesthetist's examination can find no other cause it is useful to remove the excess fluid by giving Lasix (frusemide) or other diuretics.

Indications for tracheostomy

Hoarseness
Strider
Deep burns of the neck
Singed nasal hairs and soot in the nostrils
Burns of the tongue and/or soot around the teeth
Reddened posterior pharynx

Mechanical ventilation will be required when tracheostomy proves inadequate.

Extra special care must be taken to prevent contaminating the airways where there are burns of the neck and a tracheostomy.

4. Complications: burn encephaly

This is a neurological syndrome affecting children. It can be fatal.

Signs and symptoms:

Cerebral irritability
Vomiting
Twitching
Convulsions
Hyperpyrexia
Coma

Causes:

Sudden over-transfusion, particularly of water, leads to a change from hyper-osmolality to hypo-osmolality of the blood. This leads to cerebral oedema and convulsions.

The body temperature control is affected and the peripheral vasoconstriction prevents heat loss; the 'core' temperature remains very high resulting in hyperpyrexia which, again, leads to convulsions and coma.

Treatment:

Obviously, prevention is better than cure, but where the syndrome has already developed it is essential that treatment is slow and careful.

Review the IV fluid administration.

Give barbiturates to control the convulsions.

Heat the room to body temperature and then reduce temperature very slowly. The body temperature ought to come down with it.

Do not apply tepid sponge or ice-packs.

Aspirin 81 mg for infants; 1 g for adults.

Chlorpromazine in 5 mg for infants, 25 mg for adults.

Fan.

5. Complications: constriction of the circulation

Where there is a circumferential deep burn of a limb, it can have a tourniquet effect. If untreated, gangrene of the extremity will result. Deep burns of the neck and chest can inhibit respiration.

Treatment:

Decompression of the deep burn needs to be carried out urgently, and can have a dramatic result.

The deep burn is incised longitudinally, down through the burn until bleeding occurs freely. It does not hurt, therefore no analgesic need be given. Circulation will be restored immediately if the incision has been sufficiently deep and long.

6. Complications: septicaemia

Infection is a serious problem with the extensively burned patient and is often fatal. It is almost impossible to prevent some infection even under the most ideal conditions, but everything must be done to keep it under control and so prevent the development of septicaemia.

Dressings act as a limited barrier against bacteria and, although exposed burns look clean and dry, there are often pathogenic bacteria beneath the eschar. The bacteria to be avoided are the haemolytic *streptococci* and *pseudomonas aeroginosa.*

Systemic antibiotics, when available, should be given as soon as possible as a prophylactic measure. Out-patients should be convinced that it is important that they do take the medicine; often they will not bother.

Extensively burned patients with over 50 per cent of their body surface injured have a poor prognosis, therefore where supplies are limited the less extensive burns should receive priority. Special burn creams such as silver nitrate 0.5 or silver sulphadiazine (Flamazine) can be applied with or without dressing materials. Bathing the patient, if the staff situation allows, in soap flakes or mild antiseptic solution will help to clean off detritus and also encourage the patient to move his limbs which will make him feel better.

Types of burns

Chemical burns

Profuse dousing with large quantities of water to wash away the chemical is the most appropriate first aid measure.

Some chemicals, such as phenol, are absorbed by the skin and can cause renal failure and have toxic effects on the liver.

A buffer solution consisting of monobasic potassium phosphate and dibasic sodium phosphate can be used safely to irrigate even the mouth and eyes. Sodium bicarbonate can be used to neutralise acids. Phosphorus ignites when exposed to air. The area must be kept wet until all the particles have been removed or a small remaining particle could ignite dry dressings and result in a more severe burn than the patient suffered originally.

Lime requires brisk brushing-off before applying copious amounts of water.

Molten metal

These burns are almost always very deep and can be excised and then grafted early, within thirty-six hours if possible.

Burns involving the face

Gross oedema distorts the features. The lips become swollen and stiff preventing, or at least making difficult, routine oral hygiene and drinking.

A nasogastric tube may be passed. This is particularly useful for young children, but adults often find the procedure distressing. Most larger children and adults manage to take adequate fluids through a 'straw'. Short lengths of plastic tubing are ideal for this.

Frequent cleaning of the tongue and mouth using irrigations will help keep the mouth fresh and prevent ulcers and much discomfort.

Because the lips are so distorted and the nostrils often blocked with soot and/or exudate the patient breathes through his mouth. This quickly becomes dry and foul if not regularly attended to.

No application to the face wound is necessary and dressings are generally contraindicated. Silver nitrate solution 0.5 per cent may be applied but is not essential.

Flesh burns usually heal within 21 days.

Eyes

Even minor and superficial burns of the face can result in gross oedema. The eyelids swell quickly and it very quickly becomes impossible to examine the eyes.

Although rarely damaged it is advisable to examine the cornea. Fluorescin can readily be removed with saline after the instillation of cocaine drops; Fluorescin 2 per cent drops will show any abrasions or opacities when instilled. An ophthalmologist's advice is advisable as soon as possible, but meanwhile the cornea can be kept moist by Homatropine

1 per cent and chloramphenicol 1 per cent 4-hourly. If the eyelids are deeply burned they will require urgent skin grafts to prevent ectropion developing. This is when the lids shrink and turn back so that the cornea is not covered when the eyes are meant to be closed. Ulcers very rapidly result and can lead to blindness. When surgery is not available, pads well smeared with chloramphenicol or similar eye ointment can be placed over the eyes. The drops should be continued and every attempt made to ensure that the cornea is kept moist.

It is important to reassure the patient whose eyes are not damaged that the oedema will subside within three or four days and that he will then be able to see.

Electrical burns

It is important that the electricity source is cut before any attempt is made to rescue the patient or patients.

Non-conducting materials such as dry wood may be used to move the injured as he may still be alive.

Dangers: cardiac and/or respiratory arrest may occur and require prompt action. Artificial respiration and external cardiac massage will be needed.

Contact burns

These are often deceptively deep. Where high voltage is involved there is usually a small entry burn and a large, destructive, exit burn. Muscle and bone may be destroyed. These burns often require amputation and major reconstructive surgery.

Low voltage burns are comparatively small, but almost always deep. They require excision and grafting within 36 hours.

Flash burns

These injuries are usually sustained by an electrical flash lasting barely a fraction of a second. The most commonly injured areas are the hand and face, the rest of the body being protected by clothing. Generally they will heal spontaneously within three weeks. However, if the clothing catches fire there will be other much deeper burns.

Observations: ECG, BP, pulse, renal function.

Radiation flash burns. The majority of people injured will suffer from flash burns of exposed areas, i.e. face and hands. Where the clothing has caught fire there will be deeper burns.

The secondary effects of the radiation will not show for some time. The burns are treated as any other burns, except that they may take longer to heal.

Obstetric complications

Extreme emotional and physical stress can cause premature labour, therefore any woman of childbearing age who is involved in a disaster situation, whether injured herself or associated with the injured, is in danger of losing her baby.

Later, if the burn or other injury requires surgery or becomes infected there is a possibility that the patient might abort or begin labour. Signs and symptoms of abortion (miscarriage) are:

Vaginal bleeding: this may, however, be from a delayed period.

Intermittent pain in the lower abdomen and/or back.

Dilation of the cervical os.

It is, of course, desirable that the mother does not lose the fetus. However, the other injuries may constitute a danger to her life and must be attended to, sometimes precluding treatment to prevent a miscarriage. Airways must be cleared, haemorrhage arrested and limbs splinted into a position which prevents further injury and distortion.

It is when the pregnancy is about twelve weeks that abortion is most likely to occur.

The patient will require a great deal of reassurance. In addition to her involvement in a major accident, the threat of losing her baby can cause severe emotional upset, hysteria and mental trauma.

When there are signs of threatened abortion, the patient must be sedated and kept in bed.

Pulse should be recorded every quarter of an hour, and blood pressure ½ to 1-hourly. The nature of the pains and vaginal loss should be recorded. When bleeding persists, and if the membranes rupture, shown by a trickle or small gush of clear fluid, abortion is inevitable. Intramuscular erogometrine 0.5 mg and morphine 10 mg, or pethidine 100 mg may be given.

It is inadvisable to perform a vaginal examination unless full aseptic precautions can be assured. Infection is a very real problem.

If the bleeding persists, it will be necessary to evacuate the uterus and if theatre facilities are not available, this can be performed digitally by a nurse or doctor.

Before attempting digital evacuation intramuscular ergometrine 0.5 mg must be given, in addition to sedation such as pethidine 100 mg. Blood should be grouped and cross-matched and an infusion of dextrose or similar begun. Blood can then immediately be substituted, if required.

Preferably it is a doctor's task to perform the evacuation but it may be necessary for the nurse to take responsibility in circumstances where any delay would put the mother's life at risk.

Strict aseptic technique is of the utmost importance.

The nurse must wash and soak her hands thoroughly, in antiseptic such as Chlorhexidine or Dettol. The patient's vulva, thighs and abdomen must also be washed and, if time allows, she might also be shaved. The nurse wears gloves and gown, if they are available. The patient lies in the left lateral or dorsal position. Liberally smeared with obstetric or mild antiseptic ointment cream, the hands are placed in the vagina. The left hand attempts to antevert and press down on the uterus while the right index finger hooks out any products of conception from the uterus. This procedure will be greatly hindered by vulval oedema and lacerations and by pelvic fractures.

When clear, the vagina is packed tightly up to the fornices with linen or gauze which has been soaked in antiseptic solution. It should be packed so tightly that the vulva bulges.

A perineal pad firmly fastened will increase the pressure.

The foot of the bed should be raised and a strict watch kept of pulse rate and blood pressure. This is a greatly shocking and traumatic experience and there is a danger of cardiac arrest and haemorrhage. If trickling continues, 250 ml water may be given rectally to provide further pressure against the uterus. Ergometrine may be repeated.

This is, at best, a temporary measure until such time as expert medical advice can be obtained.

Some of the main problems when a woman at term, or in the last two months of pregnancy, goes into labour will be associated with the injuries which she has obtained in the disaster. Her labour and delivery can possibly be carried out in a modified routine manner, adapting the usual methods to available resources. Positioning of the patient in the dorsal position often will need to be straight legged and a modified lithotomy position can be satisfactorily obtained by propping the legs, which have been splinted in Thomas' splints to immobilize the fracture, on chairs, lockers, peoples' shoulders, oildrums, etc. This position is also suitable for delivering breech babies and performing forceps deliveries. The mother would then be placed at the edge of the bed or table so that there is room to manoeuvre the infant as he is born.

A multiparous woman will usually progress more rapidly than the primipara who has not had a baby before.

The contractions vary from woman to woman, but come towards the end of the first stage of labour, will be very strong and every two to four minutes.

Signs that the second stage of labour has begun and the birth imminent are:

a. No cervical ring felt on vaginal examination;
b. No cervical ring felt on rectal examination;
c. Mother has bearing-down pains;
d. Slight trickle of blood;
e. Membranes rupture—a gush or trickle of clear fluid;
f. Anus pouts and gapes;
g. Tenseness between the coccyx and anus;
h. Vulva gapes;
i. Baby becomes visible;
j. Perineum bulges.

The only definite sign among these is the first. Even being able to see the baby's head can be caused by 'moulding' where there is a large swelling of the scalp which may be visible at the vulva quite early.

The patient should be encouraged to pass urine. This is extremely important as many serious problems can arise when the bladder remains full in the second and third stages of labour. Catheterisation may be required.

To prepare for the delivery, the following are required:

Plastic apron
Gown
Gloves
Mask
  For the nurse
  For the delivery
Bowl of antiseptic lotion for rinsing the hands
Bowl of antiseptic lotion for swabbing the vulva
Drapes, including leggings
Waterproof sheet for under the patient's buttocks
Perineal pads
Gauze swabs

Gallipot for obstetric cream
Gallipot for saline to bathe the baby's eyes
Kidney dish for urine
Catheters
Kidney dish for the placenta (afterbirth)
Measuring jug for blood loss
2 swab-holding forceps
Towel clips
2 Mucous extractors
2 Mayo forceps or other large self-locking clamps
1 Kochers toothed forceps
1 pair blunt ended scissors to cut the cord
1 pair curved scissors for episiotomy
Cot
Warm towels for the baby to be wrapped in
Name tape for baby
Suture materials
Cord ligature or clamps

The mother is placed in the dorsal position with her knees up. Her thighs, abdomen and perineal area are throughly washed with soap and water. Her clothes are first changed if possible, or at least hitched up to above her waist. It is a good idea to give her long warm socks if these are available.

The cot with warm towels and blanket is ready, the foot end tipped up and mucous extractor to hand.

Wearing a plastic apron, the nurse scrubs her hands, paying particular attention to nails and finger webs. She then swabs the vulva using the swab holding forceps, giving extra attention to the labial folds.

She then puts on gown and gloves.

A sterile plastic sheet should be positioned under the patient's buttocks and she should be draped with sterile towels. The nurse should stand on the patient's right side and the patient should be lying on her back with her knees flexed and legs widely separated. Thus there should be good vision and control.

As soon as she feels a contraction begin, the mother should be encouraged to hold her breath and bear down. She must be encouraged to give long steady pushes rather than short bursts which would only exhaust her.

The wide aspect of the head will gradually emerge and then the mother must be told not to push but to 'pant like a little dog'. Too rapid expulsion can tear the perineum and cause brain damage in the infant. If the perineum appears tight and shiny and resists the stretching effect of the descending head, episiotomy may be required to prevent a tear. No anaesthetic is required at this stage as the pressing down of the baby numbs the tissues. The cut should be made diagonally backwards to avoid the anal sphincter and the other vascular areas. Two fingers slipped between the head and the perineum allow blunt-ended scissors to be positioned without damaging either the baby or the mother. A cut of about 2½ inches should be made: less is insufficient and may tear out of control.

When the wide aspect of the head appears, whether episiotomy is necessary or not, the nurse places her spread fingers of the left hand over the vertex. This is to prevent sudden expulsive movement. Immediately the face appears the eyes must be cleaned by wiping them outwards with separate cotton wool balls soaked in saline. This is to prevent contamination from the non-sterile secretions of the vagina. The cotton wool balls should be large enough to avoid the nurse's fingers touching the eyes. At this time, nostrils and mouth may also be cleaned.

Many babies are born with the umbilical cord around their neck. Therefore, a finger should be slipped in to feel and, if possible, to slip the cord up over the infant's head. It is very important not to pull the cord. If tight, it will be necessary to divide the cord before the next contraction. The two Mayo forceps are clamped around the cord, about an inch apart. It is then divided between them and the loop unwound. The blunt-ended scissors should be used for this procedure.

If the baby continues to slip out before the cord can be dealt with, the cord should be slipped over the first shoulder and arm as they appear.

There may be a few minutes to wait after the baby's head has been delivered before another contraction allows the body to slide out. Should the face become blue, not the congested redness of the almost born baby, the mother can be asked to push gently. The baby's head ought not be pulled, twisted, or otherwise manhandled but may be carefully depressed towards the anus to facilitate delivery of the shoulders.

Ergometrine 0.5 mg intramuscularly with Hyaluronidase 1000 units may be given as the body slithers out or when the baby is delivered. In emergency conditions it is not always wise to give this with the birth of the anterior shoulder because of the danger of retained placenta.

Sometimes perineal tears and lacerations are unavoidable but can be minimised by careful control of the delivery.

As soon as the baby is born, even if he cries immediately, the airways must be cleared. The mouth, pharynx and bronchi may be filled with liquor amnii (the 'waters') and will be inhaled with the first breaths if the infant is not placed head downards to allow any fluid to drain out of the lungs.

If he doesn't cry at once, active removal of the mucous must be instituted. A mucous extractor which has two lengths of tubing divided by a small container, can be used. If this is not available, a rubber catheter, gauze swab, or even finger can be used. Excessive suction is dangerous. It deprives the baby of his oxygen and will cause fetal shock.

When breathing adequately, the baby should be labelled with his mother's name. A tape or piece of strapping may be used or the details written on his foot with Bonney's Blue or a surgical pencil.

The umbilical cord may then be cut, the two Mayo forceps are placed about an inch apart and the cord divided using the blunt-ended scissors. It is advisable to cut about five inches from the baby. Some authorities advocate waiting until the cord ceases pulsating, but this is not really necessary.

Various materials may be used as cord ligatures: five stranded twisted thread, small elastic bands or special cord clamps. They are fastened 3 to 4 inches from the infant, taking care not to cut into the soft jelly-like tissue. The Mayo forceps are best left in position for at least twenty minutes as a precaution against cord shrinkage and the ligature slipping. A second ligature may then be applied.

When the airways are cleared, the cord divided and everything apparently satisfactory, the baby is wrapped in a warm towel and placed in the cot on his side and with his head slightly downwards.

Meanwhile, the placenta may have separated and been delivered. It is quite normal for separation to take up to an hour although about ten minutes is more usual. Nature must be allowed to take its course and it is extremely important not to interfere.

Ergometrine 0.5 mg with Hyaluronidase, if available, will have been given as the baby was being delivered, and this should control any bleeding. However, constant observation of blood loss is vital. This is one of the most dangerous stages of the whole delivery; bleeding can be sudden and massive.

The mother should be kept warm with a blanket and her pulse recorded every minute.

The nurse now washes her hands and changes her gloves. The lotions are replaced and a fresh supply of perineal pads and swabs supplied. A large kidney dish may be placed between the mother's legs with the clamped end of the cord resting on it.

Strict aseptic techniques are essential.

Signs of placental separation

a. The fundus (top of womb) feels hard and round;
b. The fundus rises to the umbilicus and is obvious;
c. The uterus can be 'ballotted' from side to side, gently using two fingers;
d. The cord lengthens as the placenta slides down the vagina;
e. There is a gush of blood, 30 to 60 ml;
f. The placenta appears at the vulva.

Most women can expel the placenta with a contraction by lying on their backs with knees drawn up and legs flopped outwards.

If the abdominal muscles are lax the nurse may place her hands flat against the abdomen as a brace for her to push against.

If the mother fails to expel the afterbirth herself, the nurse may take active measures. She stands on the right side of the bed, and with her left hand gently presses the palm against the fundus in a backward and downward movement. The right hand at the vulva catches the placenta as it emerges.

Before this is done, the following points should be observed:

Empty bladder, catheterise if necessary;
Uterus is hard and contracted;
Use one hand only and no undue force;
The uterus must not be pushed down into the pelvis.

Unless an experienced midwife, the nurse ought not to pull the cord. It may be fragile and break causing haemorrhage.

All blood clots and loss should be measured. More than 250 ml would be excessive. A second dose of Ergometrine may be given. Examination of the placenta and membranes to ensure that they are complete is very important. There should be no raw edges on the liver-like maternal surface and the membranes should be large enough to accommodate a baby and a pint of fluid. Any small pieces left behind prevent complete contraction of the uterus and cause bleeding. Later they may form sites for infection. Ergot given orally twice a day may be sufficient to expel small pieces, but larger fragments will necessitate manual removal, preferably under an anaesthetic.

After the baby and the afterbirth have been safely delivered the nurse should stay with the mother for an hour, recording blood pressure, temperature and pulse, and checking the fundal height and consistency and any blood loss.

A hot drink such as tea and a few biscuits may be given. After the hour has passed and all is well, the mother should be washed all over, the vulva swabbed with antiseptic and a clean perineal pad supplied. Before transferring her to another area checks should be made again on pulse, blood pressure, fundal height and any bogginess of the uterus as well as any bleeding. The baby should be examined, his temperature taken rectally, weight and length recorded and, lastly, another ligature affixed to the umbilical cord.

Retained placenta. This occurs when the placenta has separated from the upper uterine segment, but cannot be expelled.

The most common cause is faulty technique. The other causes are a full bladder, and, rarely, a constriction ring.

Faulty technique: this occurs when an inexperienced midwife attempts to push out the placenta before it is completely separated and/or by pressing downwards rather than back and down.

Full bladder: it is advisable to encourage the mother to pass urine before the delivery of her baby and, if she cannot, catheterisation should be carried out.

Constriction ring: otherwise known as an hourglass contraction. Occurs when Ergot has been given too early and the placenta is trapped behind the constriction ring, or when the nurse has massaged the fundus too vigorously thus causing spasm of the circular muscle fibres at the level of upper and lower segments.

Treatment. A relaxing drug is given such as the inhalation of an ampoule of amyl-nitrate followed by IV injection of 20 ml magnesium sulphate 10 per cent. The bladder should also be emptied by use of a catheter.

Haemorrhage is a very real danger and Ergometrine should be given afterwards, if available. The pulse should be checked at least every quarter of an hour and the fundus checked to make sure it is not filling with blood.

Forceps delivery and Caesarean section

There will be many cases where, because of other injuries, vaginal delivery is impossible, dangerous to mother and baby, or unwise. She may be too weakened by blood loss, shock, emotional distress and physical exhaustion.

Where there are severe injuries to the spine or pelvis it will be advisable to perform a Caesarean section, but in other cases forceps delivery will suffice.

If there are extensive burns, severe blood loss and/or multiple injuries it is very possible that the fetus will be dead, therefore the treatment will be modified in the best interests of the mother.

Preparation for operation

The customary preparation for operation may be much modified in case of multiple injury.

Consent to operation

Unconsciousness may prevent a patient giving consent, but this does not in any way interfere with the primary duty of nurses and doctors to do what is best for the patient. It is, however, advisable to inform relatives of what is intended and, in the case of children, the parents' consent should be obtained, in writing whenever possible. If the patient is conscious, but unable to write, it is sufficient to record that verbal consent was witnessed by two named persons, who should sign the document. Difficulties may arise if qualified consent is given as, for example, when a Jehovah's Witness agrees to be operated on, but refuses to be given blood when the doctor believes it to be necessary. If, in such a case, the surgeon were to decide to save the patient's life by giving blood while the patient was anaesthetised, a court might find him technically guilty of assault and battery, but impose only a nominal sentence.

Preparation of the site of operation
It is usually both more inconsiderate and, indeed, unnecessary to shave or wash a patient until the patient is anaesthetised.

Emptying the stomach
Because many victims of serious injury have quite possibly had a meal before being injured, their stomachs should be emptied as much as possible before they are subjected to general anaesthesia. The disturbance that accompanies the passage of a large stomach tube is capable of setting off profuse bleeding and it is therefore wise to have blood running into the patient before passing the tube if there is any reason to think that this will initiate or aggravate bleeding.

Public relations

Nurses and doctors retain something of the respect and awe with which the public and their patients used to regard them but they are now, rightly, expected to be able to sit down and discuss matters and to answer questions instead of making brief and perhaps misinformed but reassuring statements.

Patients and relatives should be given as much information as they can usefully want, but it is important that the dangers of misunderstanding and of possibly conflicting statements be acknowledged and care taken to ensure that nurses, doctors and medical social workers are all aware of what each has said so that differences of working are not interpreted by anxious and perhaps distracted listeners as differences of opinion and therefore cause further anxiety. Visitors able and willing to play a part in the care of patients should be allowed to do so, with due safeguards. When there is a serious possibility that the patient will die it may be decided to seek the relatives' permission for organs to be taken for transplantation. This is a doctor's responsibility but nurses may be involved by relatives who wish to discuss it. While a nurse is entitled to her own opinions about the propriety of the procedure, if relatives have already given their consent she should not say anything to call their decision in question.

The police have custodial as well as investigatory duties and are usually on particularly good terms with nurses. The press, radio and television reporters are increasingly associated with serious accidents and at other times they may require material for articles and programmes. In such circumstances, nurses will be guided by administrators and their employing authority, but they should be encouraged to contribute to responsible informative undertakings.

Conclusion

For someone to suffer a severe injury and survive may be the most devastating thing he and his family ever have to face. The results of the accident may mean a complete upheaval of their lives, living standards and accommodation. It is the responsibility of the people treating the patient not only to repair where possible the injuries sustained, but to try to put back into society someone who can lead as nearly as possible a normal life. Support and guidance must be given to the patient and his family to help them readjust their outlook on life and, when possible, to prevent mental and behavioural disturbance as a result of physical disability.

Anyone who undertakes to look after the severely injured must realise that the work can be long, arduous and as much a source of strain as of satisfaction. It requires someone who is not only a 'jack of all trades', but also a master of life, understanding and implementing the ways of preserving it.

7. Communicable diseases

Introduction

Communicable diseases of man are caused by the attempted colonisation of his body by parasites of various species, the progeny of which can, in several different ways, be transferred to another human host. This concept of disease as a manifestation of parasite involves its study as a biological phenomenon rather than as a clinical one.

Some definitions

Immunity comprises all those natural processes in the host which prevent infection, re-infection or super-infection; which assist in destroying the invading parasites or restrict their metabolism or multiplication; or which modify the physical effects of the invasion.

Natural immunity is an inherent or species characteristic which is independent of existing or previous infection.

Acquired immunity is produced as a result of a natural existing or part infection. It can also be induced *artificially* by the injection of parasites or their products. Immunity of this nature is called *active.*

Passive immunity results from the transplacental transference from the mother or (artificially) from inoculation of specific protective antibodies obtained from another host with an active immunity. It is usually of short duration.

Tolerance is a form of immunity dependent on, and conditioned by, the presence, or recent presence, of the parasite in the host and manifests itself as an ability to limit the clinical effects of a given quantum of infection. It differs from simple immunity in which the host has the additional ability to destroy infecting parasites.

Premonition (normally used about malaria infections) is a partial or incomplete immunity in which there is tolerance to the clinical effects of the parasite in the body and is associated with an ability to resist super-infection with the same strain of parasite, so long as the individual continues to harbour parasites of that particular strain.

Herd immunity is the protection afforded to a community against an infectious disease by the gradual increase of the number of individuals who have acquired immunity, up to a point where the causative parasite of the disease has great difficulty in finding a non-immune or susceptible host. The immunity may result from recognisable attacks of the disease, from subclinical or inapparent infection, or artificially by vaccination.

Abortive or modified cases are those in which the interaction between host and parasite does not produce a reaction of characteristic intensity or duration. Clinical diagnosis may not be possible except by inference from the association of frank cases.

In some instances the reaction may be so slight as to pass unnoticed. The term *subclinical cases* covers them as well as abortive and modified cases.

Latent infections are those in which clinical symptoms do not develop or, if they do, they subside, although the parasites themselves continue to exist in the body for variable periods. Later they may become active and the symptoms will appear.

A carrier is a person who harbours and disseminates the causative organisms of a disease, yet shows no clinical evidence of infection.

An incubating carrier is one who is actually in the incubation period of disease.

A convalescent carrier is one who has recovered from the clinical attack of the disease, but continues to harbour the organism.

A chronic carrier is one in whom the above condition persists more than three months.

An intermittent carrier is one who excretes the progeny of the organism at irregular intervals.

Sporadic: a disease which occurs in occasional unconnected cases.

Endemic: a disease which is constantly present to a greater or lesser degree in a community or locally over a period of time.

Epidemic: a disease which is common to, or affects, a large number of persons in a community in a short time (involving a concept of number, place and time). It may be a new experience or an incident of an endemic disease beyond the usual experience.

Pandemic: a disease which affects a majority of the community within a short period and tends to spread beyond ethnographic and geographic boundaries.

Epidemiology: the study of the behaviour, spread and control of epidemic diseases.

(*Note:* Although the above terms are most often used in connection with communicable disease they are not necessarily so limited).

Fomites: inanimate articles which may retain infective matter and afford means whereby the disease is transferred.

Vehicle: the means by which infectious material is transferred.

Vector: a living creature which acts as an agent of dissemination or inoculation, or both.

Biological carriage: transmission by a vector in the body in which an essential part of the life-cycle of the parasite occurs.

Mechanical carriage: transmission by a vector which is not essential to the life-cycle of the parasite.

Intrinsic incubation period: the period which elapses between the infection of man with a parasite and the appearance of symptoms or signs of the disease.

Extrinsic incubation period: the period which elapses between the time a vector becomes infected and the time when it is able to transmit the parasite to another host. (During this period the parasite is continuing its development and making its way to the point of exit from the vector.)

The problems of communicable diseases are not easily solved unless the multitude of facts concerning their aetiology, transmission and natural history are first arranged in a logical order.

The train of transmission has five links.

1. *Source of infection*
2. *Exit portal*
3. *Route of transmission*
4. *Entry portal*
5. *Target* (susceptible individual)

1. Sources of infection

a. Human

i. Cases: Overt and cover. Mild and 'missed' cases are of particular importance.
ii. Contacts: These may be incubating the infection and about to become true sources.
iii. Carriers: Convalescent carriers
Chronic carriers (persisting over three months)
Intermittent excretors.

b. Animal

The zoonoses: plague, brucellosis, scrub typhus, etc.

For continued existence of the species the infecting organism must, from time to time, be transferred from one host to another. Therefore, for a time, the colonisation of the host by the organism must be at a site from which it can be disseminated, and this is the period of illness. In respect of many communicable diseases, patients are most infectious during the early stage of the illness, often at the end of the incubation period and before the illness is clinically detectable.

2. Exit portals

The infecting organism may be set free naturally, or it may be extracted by an insect.

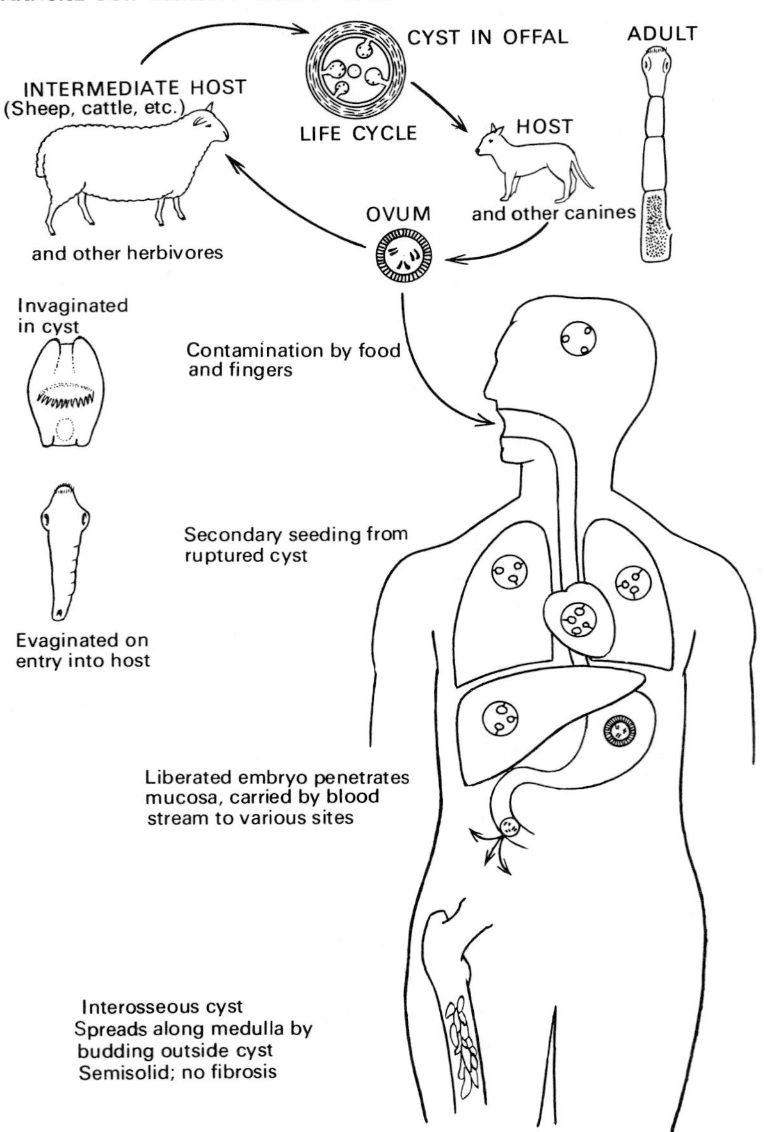

Fig. 7.1 *Echinococcus granulosus*, causing hydatid disease. Geographical distribution world-wide (sheep raising areas).

a. 'Natural' methods

i. By droplets (from the respiratory tract);
ii. By discharges (from mucous and cutaneous surfaces);
iii. By excretions (from the alimentary and urinary tracts).

b. Extracted method

The aspiration of pathogenic organisms in blood or tissue fluids by arthropods: mosquitoes and malaria, lice and epidemic typhus, etc.

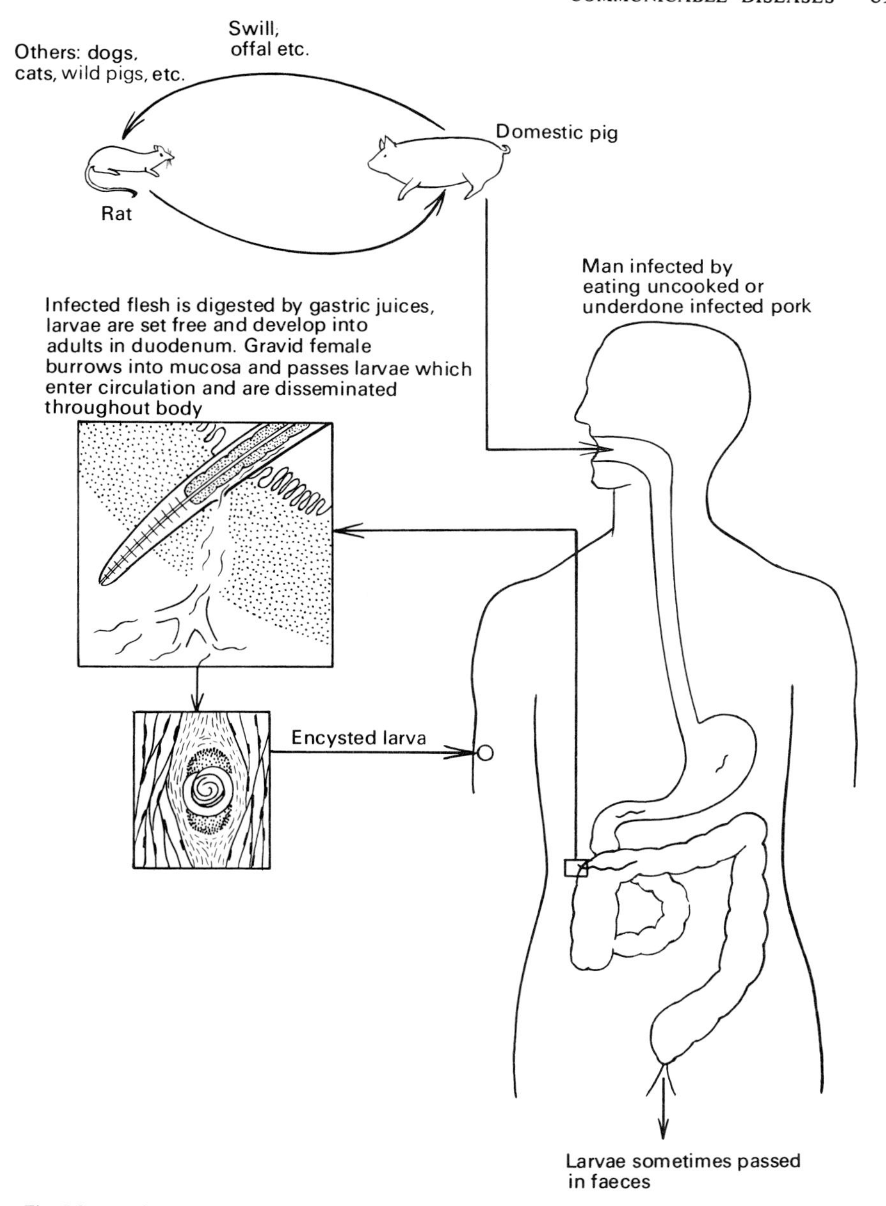

Fig. 7.2 *Trichinella spiralis*. Geographical distribution: cosmopolitan (frequent in temperate climates).

Each species of parasite tends to use a particular portal of exit from the host, a particular route of transmission and a particular portal of entry into a new host. During transfer, the organism is exposed to unfavourable environmental conditions both chemical and physical (e.g. temperature, humidity, solar radiation), and comparatively few survive to reach a new host.

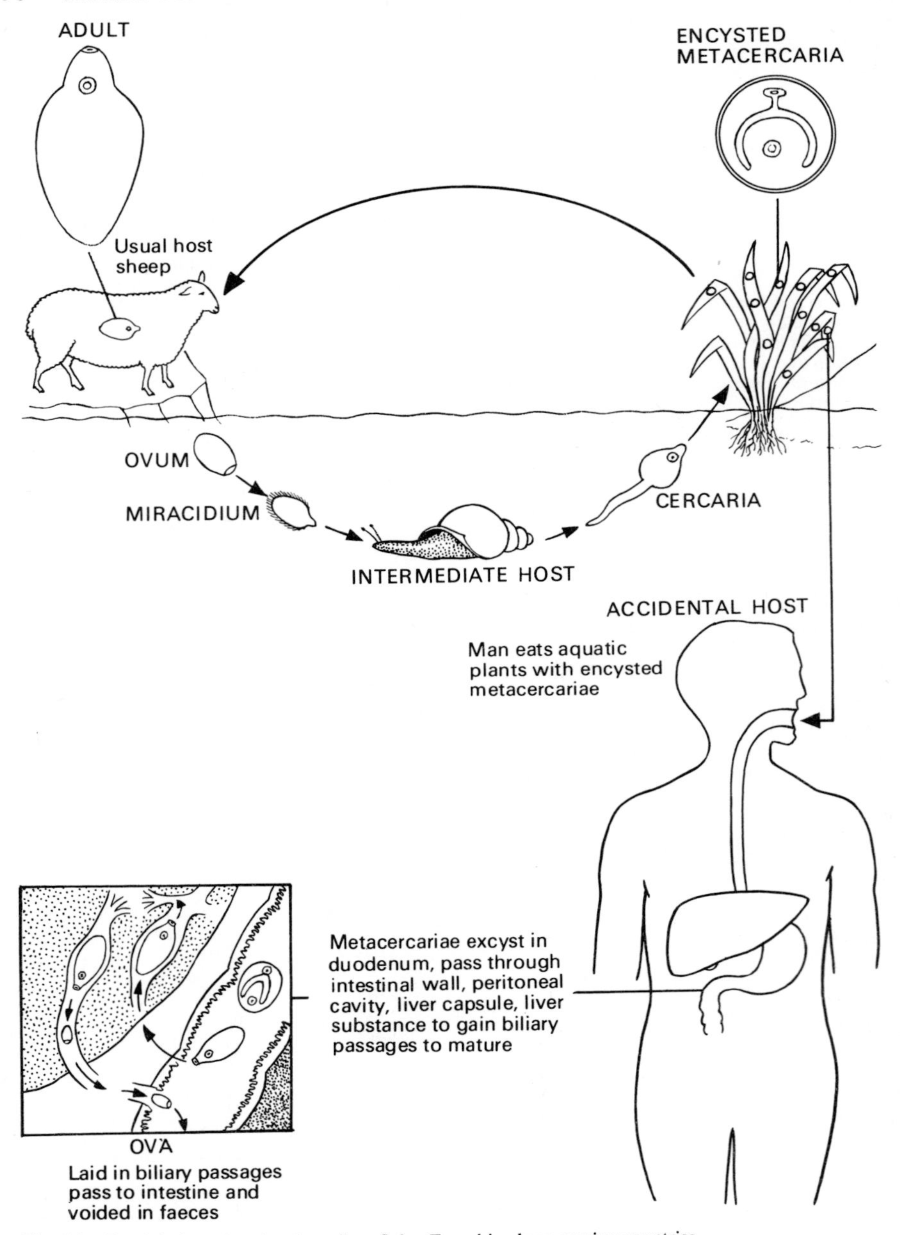

Fig. 7.3 *Fasciola hepatica*, the sheep liver fluke. Found in sheep rearing countries.

3. Routes of transmission

a. Contact infections

Infections spread either by direct contact between source and target or by indirect contact through the medium of fomites such as towels and toilet articles (e.g. skin infections and venereal disease).

b. Airborne infections

Some infections are spread through the air, either directly by the propulsion of droplets from source to target, or indirectly through the medium of fomites. These release infective material into the air when disturbed by such procedures as dry sweeping of floors or bed-making. (Respiratory infections such as pulmonary tuberculosis and influenza may be spread in this way.)

c. Insect-borne infections

These infections are spread by means of an insect vector (e.g. malaria).

d. Ingestion infections

These infections which gain access to the body during ingestion, usually of food or drink (e.g. cholera, typhoid and food poisoning).

4. Entry portals

There are various ways in which infecting organisms can enter a new host:

a. Ingestion: portal of entry through the mouth to the alimentary tract (dysentry, cholera, food poisoning);

b. Inhalation: portal of entry through the nose and mouth to the respiratory tract (influenza, common cold, smallpox);

c. Injection: portal of entry is a break in the skin made by the mouth of an arthropod (e.g. mosquito and malaria), or by the mouth of an animal (e.g. dog and rabies);

d. Inoculation: portal of entry through the skin. Organisms implanted on intact skin into which they are inoculated by scratching (epidemic typhus) or on wounds (pyogenic infection) or on mucous membrane (gonorrhoea).

e. Penetration: the organism penetrates intact skin itself (e.g. schistosomiasis).

5. The target

This is the susceptible individual, the new host, and successful colonisation by the infecting organism depends upon several factors. Those relating to:

a. The organism are

i. Its pathogenicity (infectivity, invasiveness and virulence);

ii. The size of the 'infecting dose'.

b. The host are

i. Immunity. Whether innate or acquired, natural or artificial, active or passive;

ii. Non-specific resistance. This is based on genetic factors; age, sex, occupation, state of mucous and cutaneous surfaces, effect of trauma, chill, fatigue, malnutrition, concomitant diseases, etc.

The reaction of the new host to attempted colonisation by the organism may or may not constitute disease. There will be a delay between the invasion and the appearance of symptoms.

This incubation period has a range of time within fairly constant limits: yellow fever 2 to 6 days; typhoid 3 to 38 days. A knowledge of the incubation period is important regarding retrospective surveys (contact tracing, etc.) and regarding the segregation of surveillance of contacts.

Prevention of communicable diseases

a. The target

i. Immunisation
ii. Increase of non-specific resistance
iii. Health education
iv. Chemo-prophylaxis

b. The entry portal

i. *Contact infections.* Attention to personal hygiene and care of the skin; provisions of adequate facilities; avoidance of contact; protection of skin (especially feet).
ii. *Airborne infections.* Wearing of surgical masks for those attending patients. Avoidance of infected persons and places.
iii. *Insect-borne infections.* Wearing of suitable clothing. Use of nets and insect repellents. Screening of buildings.
iv. *Ingestion infections.* Attention to hygiene of food service; avoidance of unhygienic sources of food.

c. The routes of transmission

i. *Contact infections.* Attention to cleanliness of floors (especially where persons may walk barefoot); laundering arrangements and hygiene of hairdressing and barber shops.
ii. *Airborne infections.* Prevention of overcrowding; bed spacing; ventilation; dust suppression and preventive measures against fomites.
iii. *Insect-borne infections.* Measures directed against the vector. (Prevention of vector breeding and destruction of larvae and pupae; destruction of adult forms; use of insecticides; alteration of environment to make it unsuitable for the vector.)
iv. *Ingestion infections.* Attention to hygiene and food production, storage, transportation, preparation and cooking; the health and behaviour of food handlers; regular food inspection; selection and protection of sources of drinking water; water purification. Antihousefly measures. Attention to sanitation with particular regard to waste disposal (especially faeces and urine).

d. The exit portal

Current and terminal disinfection of infective excretions and discharges from human sources and soiled articles.

e. The sources

i. *Human.* Isolate, notify, treat; carefully dispose of excreta.
ii. *Animal.* Isolate, notify, treat; carefully dispose of excreta, carcases, etc.

Control of communicable diseases

a. Source

i. *Human.* Search for cases, especially those that are 'missed', mild and ambulatory. Early diagnosis, isolation, treatment, notification and contact tracing are important.
ii. *Animal.* Probably destroy.

b. Exit portal *c. Route* *d. Entry portal* *e. Target*	Action similar to that detailed under these headings above.

A rapid and thorough investigation will be necessary to trace the spread of the disease and to determine what specific action is to be taken at various points along the chain of infection.
Fluctuations in incidence may be:

General trends
Periodic cycles, e.g. epidemics of measles every two years.
Seasonal outbreaks. Related to climate, habits, customs, prevalence of insect pests, etc.
Irregular fluctuation. Caused by population movements, refugees, pilgrimages, changes in social conditions, wars, exceptional weather conditions.

The balance

There will tend to be a balance between the hosts on the one hand and the parasites on the other. The factors which may upset this balance are:

Hosts. Alterations in immunity and resistance.
Parasites. Alterations in prevalence, infectivity, invasiveness and virulence.
Herd environment. Changes in regard to such factors as climate, sanitary conditions, social conditions, population density, movement, occupation, malnutrition, insect population, poverty and housing.

It is the last factor which causes outbreaks of communicable diseases in disaster areas. Important factors likely to result in the genesis of epidemics are:
a. Increased numbers of sources (perhaps imported);
b. Increased dispersion of the infecting parasite;
c. More favourable environment for transmission;
d. Increased accessibility of new hosts to the parasite;
e. Increased numbers of susceptibilities;
f. Increased infectivity of parasite.

Some of the communicable diseases most frequently occurring in disaster areas (groupings in alphabetical order) are listed on the following pages.

ACTINOMYCOSIS

1. Identification. A chronic suppurative or granulomatous disease most frequently localised in jaw, thorax or abdomen; rarely limited to skin and subcutaneous tissues. The lesions are firmly indurated granulomata; they spread slowly to contiguous tissues and break down focally to form multiple draining sinuses which penetrate to the surface. Discharges from sinus tracts contain 'sulphur granules' which are colonies of the infectious agent.

2. Occurrence. An infrequent disease of man, occurring sporadically throughout the world. All races, both sexes, and all age groups may be affected; greatest frequency at 15 to 35 years of age and the ratio of males to females is approximately 2 : 1. Occurs also in cattle, swine, horses and other animals.

3. Infectious agent. Actinomyces israelii and *A. bovis*, Gram-positive, non-acid-fast, anaerobic fungi.

4. Reservoir and source of infection. The natural reservoir is man. In the normal oral cavity *Actinomyces* grows as a saprophyte in and around carious teeth, in dental plaques, and in tonsillar crypts, without apparent penetration or cellular response of adjacent tissues. Sample surveys in the USA, Sweden and other countries have demonstrated *A. israelii* microscopically in granules from crypts of 40 per cent of extirpated tonsils; and isolation in anaerobic culture from as many as 60 per cent of specimens of saliva or material from carious teeth. No external environmental reservoir such as straw or soil has been demonstrated. The source of clinical disease is endogenous. Presumably a similar endogenous reservoir exists in cattle and is similarly related to bovine actinomycosis, but transmission from animals to man has not been demonstrated.

5. Mode of transmission. Presumably the fungus passes by contact from man to man as a part of the normal oral flora. From the oral cavity the fungus may be swallowed, inhaled, or introduced into jaw tissues by injury or at the site of neglected or irritating dental defect. Transmission by human bite has been reported but is a rare event.

6. Incubation period. Irregular: probably many years after appearance in the normal oral flora, and days or months after precipitating trauma and actual penetration of tissues.

7. Period of communicability. Time and manner in which *A. israelii* becomes a part of the normal oral flora unknown and not pertinent. Origin and development of clinical actinomycosis is endogenous and except for the rare instances of human bite not dependent upon exposure to an infected person or animal.

8. Susceptibility and resistance. Natural susceptibility is low. Immunity following attack has not been demonstrated. Patients quickly develop recognisable symptoms; acute cases tend to become chronic. Malnutrition contributes to severity and frequency. Recent immigrants to endemic areas often contract clinical disease. Immunity to reinfection has not been clearly established in man.

9. Methods of control

A. Preventive measures:

i. Sanitary disposal of human faeces.

ii. Protection of public water supplies against faecal contamination; boiling of drinking water where necessary. Chlorination of water supplies as generally practised does not destroy cysts. Sand filtration removes nearly all cysts, diatomaceous earth filters completely. Avoid cross-connections between public and private auxiliary water supplies and of back-flow connections in plumbing systems. Small quantities of water as in Lyster bags and canteens are best protected by tetraglycine hydroperiodide tablets.

iii. Health education of the general public in personal hygiene, particularly as to sanitary disposal of faeces; hand-washing after defaecation and before preparing or eating food; and of the risks in eating moist foods raw.

iv. Fly control and protection of foods against fly contamination by screening or other appropriate means.

v. Supervision by health agencies of the health and sanitary practices of persons preparing and serving food in public eating places; also general cleanliness of the premises. Routine examination of food handlers as a control measure is impractical.

vi. Disinfectant dips for fruits and vegetables have no proven value.

B. Control of patient, contracts and the immediate environment:

No isolation. Exclusion of patient from preparation, processing and serving of food until treatment is completed.

AMOEBIASIS

1. Identification. The colon is the primary site of infection. The disease may be asymptomatic, or with mild abdominal discomfort and diarrhoea alternating with constipation; or a chronic diarrhoea with mucus and some blood; or an acute dysentery with profuse blood and mucus, usually little pus. Infection may be spread by the blood stream or by direct extension to produce amoebic hepatitis, abscess of liver, lung or brain, or ulceration of skin. Amoebiasis is not a common cause of death. Synonym: Amoebic dysentery.

Diagnosis is by identifying trophozoites or cysts of *Entamoeba histolytica* in faeces, or trophozoites in smears or sections from lesions.

Differential diagnosis includes shigellosis, appendicitis, ulcerative colitis, balantidial and giardial diarrhoea (balantidiasis, giardiasis). Other intestinal protozoa also are associated with diarrhoea in man or exist concomitantly with *Ehistolytica.*

2. Reservoir and source of infection. Reservoir is usually a chronic or asymptomatic patient. Acute disease is of little menace because of fragility of trophozoites. Source of infection is cysts from faeces of infected persons. An amoebic disease of dogs occurs but has not been identified as a source of human infection.

3. Mode of transmission. In epidemics, mainly by contaminated water. Endemic spread is by water, by hand-to-mouth transfer of fresh faeces and by contaminated vegetables, especially those served raw; by flies and by soiled hands of food handlers.

4. Incubation period. From five days to several months. Commonly from three to four weeks.

5. *Period of communicability.* During intestinal infection, which may continue for years.

6. *Susceptibility and resistance.* Susceptibility to infection is general; relatively few persons harbouring the organism develop recognised symptoms; acute cases tend to become chronic. Malnutrition contributes to severity and frequency. Recent immigrants to endemic areas often contract clinical disease. Immunity to reinfection has not been clearly established in man.

7. *Methods of control*
A. Preventive measures: *see* Actinomycosis.
B. Control of patient, contacts, and the immediate environment:

1. Isolation: none. Exclusion of patient from preparation, processing and serving of food until treatment is completed.
2. Concurrent disinfection: sanitary disposal of faeces. Terminal cleaning.
3. Quarantine: None
4. Immunisation of contacts: not applicable.
5. Investigation of contacts and source of infection: microscopic examination of faeces of suspected contacts, supplemented by search for direct contamination of water.
6. Specific treatment: acute amoebic dysentery: tetracyclines and emetine hydrochloride. Emetine hydrochloride will relieve symptoms but usually not eliminate the infection. Both should be accompanied or followed by a standard amoebicide, such as diodoquin, carbarsone, milibis, or humatin to eliminate infection from lumen of the intestine. These amoebicides also serve in treatment of mild and asymptomatic infections. Emetine-bismuthiodide is highly regarded. Entamide furoate has been reported effective.

Amoebic hepatitis and liver abscess: chloroquine, aralen or emetine hydrochloride. If abscess requires aspiration, precede by chloroquine or emetine to limit infection. Broad spectrum antibiotics should be administered to control possible bacterial infection. Repeated faecal examination at intervals up to three months is necessary to ensure that amoebae have been eliminated.

C. Epidemic measures:
Any grouping of several cases from a single area or in an institution requires prompt epidemiologic investigation to determine source of infection and mode of transmission. If a common vehicle is indicated, such as water or food, take appropriate measures to correct the situation. If the epidemiologic evidence points to person-to-person transmission, the emphasis is on personal cleanliness, sanitary diposal of faeces, and fly control.
D. International measures: None.

ARTHROPOD-BORNE VIRAL DISEASES

Summary

A large number of arboviruses are known to produce disease in man and the number is growing rapidly. The diseases are principally within three clinical syndromes and, for convenience, are discussed under these major headings. Encephalitis is the first syndrome. These diseases frequently exhibit encephalitis in their normal spectrum but range in severity and manifestations from mild aseptic meningitis to coma, paralysis and death.

The second syndrome includes principally a group of acute benign fevers of short duration. Many resemble dengue, some with and others without an exantham. On occasion a few may give rise to a more serious illness, with central nervous system involvement or haemorrhages. The third syndrome, haemorrhagic fever, includes acute febrile diseases with conspicuous haemorrhagic manifestations, frequently serious, and associated with shock and significant fatality. One of them, yellow fever, also have severe liver damage and sometimes jaundice. Milder forms may resemble the second syndrome (benign fever) and a few may also have an encephalitic component.

Most of these diseases are zoonoses, accidently acquired by man through an arthropod vector, with man an unimportant host in the cycle. In the presence of a suitable vector a few may become epidemic, with man the principal source of vector infection. Still others are not at present recognised as basically dependent on an animal-arthropod cycle. Most of the viruses are mosquito-borne, several are tick-borne, two are known to be phlebotomus-borne, and though the vector is unknown, two are possibly transmitted by mites. Laboratory infections occur.

Many common epidemiologic factors in transmission cycles (principally in relation to the vector) are of importance in respect to methods of control. Consequently, the several selected diseases under each clinical syndrome are arranged in four groups: Mosquito-borne, tick-borne, phlebotomus-borne and unknown (possibly mite-borne). Certain diseases of major importance in many countries are described individually or in groups if clinical and epidemiological similarities exist. Some of the less important or less well studied diseases are presented only in the following table.

Approximately 75 known arthropod-borne viruses produce either infection or infectious disease in man. Most of them are classified by haemagglutination or complement fixation into antigenic groups, of which A and B are the largest and best known. Both contain agents predominantly causing encephalitis and agents predominantly causing other febrile illnesses. Group A includes only mosquito-borne viruses, group B both mosquito and tick-borne agents. Viruses of Group C and of six other groups produce principally febrile diseases resembling the dengue syndrome. Several human pathogens for which no common antigens have been demonstrated remain in a miscellaneous category.

All viruses associated with human disease are listed in Table 7.1 by type of vector reasonably established or suspected, predominant character of recognised disease and geographical area where found. In some instances observed cases are too few to be certain of the usual clinical reaction. None is included where evidence of human infection is based solely on serological survey. Otherwise the number would be much greater.

ARTHROPOD-BORNE VIRAL ENCEPHALITIDES

I. Mosquito-borne
of Eastern Equine, Western Equine, Japanese B, Murray Valley, and St Louis Encephalitis

1. Identification. A group of acute inflammatory diseases of short duration, involving parts of the brain, spinal cord and meninges. Signs and symptoms are similar but vary in severity and rate of progress. Mild cases often occur as aseptic meningitis. Severe infections usually have acute onset, high fever, meningeal signs, stupor, disorientation, coma, spasticity, tremors, occasionally convulsions in infants, and spastic but rarely flaccid paralysis. Fatality ranges from 5 per cent to 60 per cent, that of Japanese B and Eastern Equine types being highest. With most viruses, conspicuous sequelae are rare except in infants; more with Eastern Equine and Japanese B than others; no parkinsonism. Mild

Table 7.1 Diseases in man caused by arthropod-borne viruses

Virus group	Name of virus	Vector	Disease in man	Where found
Group A	Chikungunya (TH-35)	Mosquito	Fever, haemorrhagic fever	Africa, SE Asia
	Eastern equine	Mosquito	Encephalitis	Americas
	Mayaro (Uruma)	Mosquito	Fever	S America
	Mucambo	Mosquito	Fever	S America
	O'nyong-nyong (Gulu)	Mosquito	Fever	Africa
	Ross River	Mosquito	Fever	Australia
	Semliki Forest	Mosquito	Fever	Africa
	Sindbis	Mosquito	Fever	Africa, India, Malaysia, Philippines, Australia
	Venezuelan equine	Mosquito	Fever, encephalitis	S America, Mexico, USA
	Western equine	Mosquito	Encephalitis	Americas
Group B	Bat salivary gland	Unknown	Fever, aseptic meningitis	USA
	Dengue 1, 2, 3, 4	Mosquito	Fever	
	Dengue 3, 4, 5, 6 or 1, 2	Mosquito	Haemorrhagic fever	
	Diphasic meningoencephalitis	Tick	Haemorrhagic fever, encephalitis	USSR, Europe
	Ilheus	Mosquito	Fever, encephalitis	S America, C America
	Japanese B	Mosquito	Encephalitis	Asia
	Kyasanur Forest	Tick	Haemorrhagic fever	India
	Langat	Tick	Fever, encephalitis	Malaysia
	Louping ill	Tick	Encephalitis	G Britain
	Murray Valley	Mosquito	Encephalitis	Australia
	Negishi	Unknown	Encephalitis	Japan
	Omsk haemorrhagic	Tick	Haemorrhagic fever	USSR
	Powassan	Tick	Encephalitis	Canada, USA
	Russian spring summer	Tick	Encephalitis	USSR
	Spondweni	Mosquito	Fever	Africa
	St Louis	Mosquito	Encephalitis	Americas, Jamaica
	Uganda S, H 336	Mosquito	Fever	Africa
	Wesselsbron	Mosquito	Fever	Africa
	West Nile	Mosquito	Fever, encephalitis	Africa, India, Israel
	Yellow fever	Mosquito	Haemorrhagic fever	Africa, S America

Group C	Apeu	Mosquito	Fever	S America
	Caraparu	Mosquito	Fever	S America
	Itaqui	Mosquito	Fever	S America
	Marituba	Mosquito	Fever	S America
	Murutucu	Mosquito	Fever	S America
	Oriboca	Mosquito	Fever	S America
Bunyamwera Group	Bunyamwera	Mosquito	Fever	Africa
	Germiston	Mosquito	Fever	Africa
	Guaroa	Mosquito	Fever	S America
	Ilesha	Unknown	Fever	Africa
Bwamba Group	Bwamba	Mosquito	Fever	Africa
California Group	California	Mosquito	Encephalitis	USA, Canada
	Tahyna	Mosquito	Fever	Europe
Guama Group	Catu	Mosquito	Fever	S America
	Guama	Mosquito	Fever	S America
Sandfly Fever Group (Phlebotomus fever)	Candiru	Unknown	Fever	S America
	Chagres	Unknown	Fever	C America
	Naples type	Phlebotomus	Fever	Europe, Africa, Asia
	Sicilian type	Phlebotomus	Fever	Europe, Africa, Asia
Simbu Group	Oropouche	Mosquito	Fever	S America
Tacaribe Group	Junin (Machupo)	Unknown ?Mite	Haemorrhagic fever	S America
Miscellaneous and Ungrouped	Colorado tick fever	Tick	Fever	USA
	Crimean haemorrhagic fever	Tick	Haemorrhagic fever	USSR
	Haemorrhagic fever with renal syndrome	Unknown ?Mite	Haemorrhagic fever	Asia, Europe
	Quaranfil	Tick	Fever	Africa
	Rift Valley	Mosquito	Fever	Africa
	Semunya (Nakiwogo)	Unknown	Fever	Africa
	Vesicular stomatitis, New Jersey type (Cocal)	Unknown ?Mosquito	Fever	USA, S America

leucocytosis is usual; leucocytes in spinal fluid from 50 to 200 per mm^3, occasionally 1000 or more in infants.

Specific identification is by demonstrated titre changes in antibody between early and late specimens of serum, by neutralisation, complement fixation, and haemagglutination inhibition; group reactions may occur. Virus may be isolated from the brain of fatal cases, rarely from blood or cerebrospinal fluid, histopathological changes are not specific for individual viruses.

These diseases require differentiation from encephalitic and non-paralytic poliomyelitis, rabies, mumps, meningoencephalitis, lymphocytic choriomeningitis, aseptic meningitis due to enteroviruses, herpes encephalitis, post-vaccinal or post-infection encephalitides, bacterial, protozoal, leptospiral and mycotic meningitides or encephalitides; also the von Economo type of encephalitis (encephalitis lethargica) of unknown etiology and of frequent occurrence just before and after 1920, but now rarely reported. These diseases should be reported to official health agencies under the appropriate disease; or as Encephalitis, other forms; or as Meningitis, other forms; or as Aseptic Meningitis, with etiology or clinical type specified when known. Venezuelan equine virus, primarily producing an arthropod-borne viral fever is increasingly responsible for cases of encephalitis.

2. *Reservoir and source of infection.* True reservoir or means of winter carry-over unknown, possibly bird, rodent, bat, reptile, amphibian or surviving adult mosquito. Source of infection for man is an infective mosquito.

3. *Mode of transmission.* By bite of mosquitoes. Mosquitoes usually acquire the infection from wild birds but pigs are of some importance for Japanese B. For others, occasionally a mammal, e.g. horse. Virus is not usually demonstrable in the blood of man after onset of disease. Horses develop active disease with the two equine viruses and Japanese B, but viraemia is seldom present for long periods or in high titres. Therefore, men and horses are uncommon sources of mosquito infection. Most important vectors are: Eastern equine in USA, probably *Culiseta melanura*; Western equine in USA, *Culex annuliorostris*; St Louis in USA, *Culex tarsalis*, *C pipiens-quinquefasciatus* complex and *C nigripalpus*.

4. *Incubation period.* Usually 5 to 15 days.

5. *Period of communicability.* Not directly transmitted from man to man. Mosquito remains infective for life. Viraemia in birds usually lasts two to five days but may be prolonged in bats, reptiles and amphibia, particularly during hibernation.

6. *Susceptibility and resistance.* Susceptibility to clinical disease usually highest in infancy and old age but varies with type, particularly St Louis, which tends to spare young children. Inapparent or undiagnosed infection is more common at other ages. Infection results in homologous immunity. In highly endemic areas adults are largely immune to local strains by reason of mild and inapparent infections, and susceptibles are mainly children.

7. Methods of control

A. Preventive measures:

1. Destruction of larvae and elmination of breeding places of known or suspected vector mosquitoes.

ii. Killing of mosquitoes by space and residual spraying of human habitations.

iii. Screening of sleeping and living quarters; use of mosquito bed-nets.

iv. Avoiding exposure to mosquitoes during hours of biting, or using repellents.

v. Education of the public as to mode of spread and control.

vi. Active immunisation of persons at great risk (laboratory workers and others), with experimental or commercially prepared equine formalinised vaccines (not recommended for general use). Mouse brain inactivated vaccine is used for children in Japan.

vii. Passive protection of accidentally-exposed laboratory workers by human or animal immune serum.

B. Control of patient, contacts, and the immediate environment:

i. Isolation: None. Virus not usually found in blood, secretions, or discharges during clinical manifestations.

ii. Concurrent disinfection: None.

iii. Quarantine: None.

iv. Immunisation of contacts: None.

v. Investigation of contacts and source of infection: Search for missed cases and presence of vector mosquitoes—primarily a community problem.

vi. Specific treatment: none.

C. Epidemic measures:

Identification of the disease among horses or birds and recognition of human cases in the community has epidemiological value to indicate frequency of infection and areas involved. Immunisation of horses does not limit spread of the virus in the community.

D. International measures:

Insecticide spray of aircraft arriving from recognised areas of prevalence.

II. Tick-borne

Russian Spring-Summer Encephalitis, Diphasic Meningoencephalitis, Louping ill, and Powassan Encephalitis

1. Identification. A group of diseases clinically resembling mosquito-borne encephalitides, except that Russian spring-summer type is often associated with flaccid paralysis, particularly of shoulder girdle with residua. Diphasic meningoencephalitis (Diphasic milk fever or Central European tick-borne encephalitis) has a longer course averaging three weeks. Initial febrile stage is unassociated with symptoms referable to central nervous system. A second phase of fever and meningoencephalitis follows four to ten days after apparent recovery. Fatality and severe residua are less than for the Russian spring-summer disease. Louping ill in man also has a diphasic pattern and is relatively mild.

Specific identification is by serological tests or by isolation of virus from blood during acute illness. Serological tests cannot be expected to differentiate members of this group, but do distinguish the group from most other similar diseases.

2. Reservoir and source of infection. The tick or a combination of tick and mammal appears to be the true reservoir; transovarian passage of some USSR viruses has been demonstrated. Sheep are the hosts most involved in louping ill. Rodents, sometimes other mammals and birds, rarely man, give rise to tick infection. The source of infection for man is usually an infective adult tick.

3. Mode of transmission. By the bite of infective ticks, or consumption of milk from certain infected animals. *I. persulcatus* is the principle vector in eastern USSR and *I. ricinus* in western USSR and other parts of Europe; the latter is also the vector of louping ill of sheep in Scotland. Dermacentor ticks are suspect in Canada and USA. Larval ticks usually obtain virus by feeding on rodents, sometimes other mammals and birds. Man may be responsible for occasional infection of adult ticks. Raw milk may be a vehicle for diphasis meningoencephalitis.

4. Incubation period. Usually 7 to 14 days.

5. Period of communicability. Not directly transmitted from man to man. A tick infected at any stage remains infective for life. Viraemia in a variety of vertebrates may last for several days; in man, up to a week or 10 days.

6. Susceptibility and resistance. Both sexes and all ages are susceptible, but the age pattern varies widely in different regions as influenced by exposure to ticks, consumption of milk from an infected animal, or previously acquired immunity.

7. Methods of control. International measures: none.

ARTHROPOD-BORNE VIRAL FEVERS

I. Mosquito-borne

A. Dengue Fever

1. Identification. An acute febrile disease of sharp onset, occasionally with two periods of short duration; fever for about five days and rarely more than seven, intense headache, postorbital pains, joint and muscle pains, and eruption. Early general erythema in some cases; eruption usually appears three to four days after onset of fever, either maculopapular or scarlatiniform; petechiae may appear on feet, legs, axillae, or palate on last day of fever or shortly thereafter. Dark-skinned races frequently have no visible rash. Recovery associated with prolonged fatigue and depression. Leucopenia and lymphadenopathy are usual. Epidemics are explosive and fatality exceedingly low. Synonym: Breakbone Fever.

Differential diagnosis includes all diseases listed in Section B below, Colorado Tick Fever, the Sandfly Fevers and others.

Haemagglutination, complement-fixation or neutralisation tests, using specific types of virus, are diagnostic aids. Virus isolated from blood by inoculation of suckling mice or by tissue culture techniques.

2. Reservoir and source of infection. Man, together with the mosquito, is one reservoir;

the existence of an added animal-mosquito reservoir, possibly monkey, is suspected but not demonstrated. The immediate source of infection is an infective mosquito.

3. *Mode of transmission.* By the bite of mosquitoes, *Aëdes aegypti, A. albopictus*, or one of the *A. scutellaris* complex, infected by biting a patient.

4. *Incubation period.* 3 to 15 days, commonly five to six days.

5. *Period of communicability.* Not directly transmitted from man to man. Patients are usually infective for mosquitoes from the day before onset to the fifth day of disease. The mosquito becomes infective from 8 to 11 days after the blood meal and remains so for life.

6. *Susceptibility and resistance.* Susceptibility is apparently universal, but children usually have a milder disease than adults. Homologous type immunity is of long duration; heterologous immunity, though present, is brief and may permit mild febrile illness without rash.

7. *Methods of control*

A. Preventive measures:

i. Elimination of vector mosquitoes and, where practicable, their breeding places.

ii. Public health education on personal measures for protection against mosquitoes, including use of repellents.

B. Control of patient, contacts, and the immediate environment:

i. Isolation: patient should be kept in screened room for at least five days after onset, or in quarters treated with insecticide with residual effect, such as DDT.

ii. Concurrent disinfection: none.

iii. Quarantine: none.

iv. Immunisation of contacts: none.

v. Investigation of contacts: place of residence of patient during the two weeks previous to onset. Search for unreported or undiagnosed cases.

vi. Specific treatment: none

C. Epidemic measures:

i. Community survey to determine density of vector mosquitoes, to identify breeding places, and to promote plans for elimination.

ii. Search for and destroy *Aëdes* mosquitoes in places of human habitation.

iii. Use of moquito repellents by persons exposed to bites of vector mosquitoes.

D. International measures:

Enforcement of international agreements designed to prevent spread of the disease by persons, and mosquito transfer by ships, aircraft and land transport from areas where an epidemic exists.

B. Bunyamwere, Bwamba, Chikungunya, Mayaro, O'Nyong-Nyong, Rift Valley, Venezuelan Equine, West Nile, and Group C Viral Fevers

1. *Identification.* A group of acute febrile dengue-like illnesses of a week or less. Usual onset is with headaches, malaise, arthralgia or myalgia and occasionally nausea and vomiting; generally some conjuctivitis and photophobia. Temperature may or may not be

of the saddleback type; rashes common in West Nile, chikungunya and o'nyong-nyong disease, possible haemorrhages in chikungunya fever in Southeast Asia; leucopenia common; convalescence frequently prolonged. Meningoencephalitis is an occasional feature of West Nile. Venezuelan equine virus in recent years has been responsible for increasing numbers of encephalitis. It is still included under Viral Fevers because most cases are of that nature. The several demonstrated related viruses within the Venezuelan equine complex make indefinite the proportion of fevers and encephalitis attributable to that virus itself. Several group C viruses reported to produce weakness of lower limbs. Rarely fatal, except encephalitis from Venezuelan equine.

Serological tests differentiate other fevers of viral or unknown origin, but chikungunya, o'nyong-nyong and Mayaro fevers are difficult to distinguish from one another. Specific diagnosis is possible by virus isolation from blood during febrile period; Venezuelan equine also from nasopharyngeal washings. Laboratory infections occur with many of these viruses.

2. Reservoir and source of infection. Reservoirs are unknown. All appear to be tropical dependent, with a continuous vertebrate-mosquito cycle essential. Chikungunya, O'nyong-nyong, and possibly others, may be maintained by a man-mosquito cycle but other vertebrates may well be involved. Birds are important hosts for West Nile; sheep, other domestic ruminants, game, monkeys and rodents for Rift Valley. The source of human infection is usually an infective mosquito.

3. Mode of transmission. In most instances by bite of mosquitoes. For Chikungunya: *A. aegypti* and possibly others. For Rift Valley: *Aëdes caballus, A. circumluteolus* and *A. theileri*; species of Eretmapodites probably important in forest cycles. West Nile: *Culex univittatus* in Egypt, *C. pipiens molestus* in Israel. O'nyong-nyong: *Anopheles sp.* Mayaro: *Masonia venezueluensis*. Bunyamwera: *Aëdes sp.* Group C viruses: isolated from species of *Aëdes, Mansonia, Psorophora* and *Sabethini.* Viruses of the Venezuelan equine complex isolated from many genera and species, many of them susceptible in the laboratory, including *Mansonia, Psorophora, Aëdes, Culex, Haemagogus, Sabethinin* and *Anopheles*. Most human infections with Rift Valley are associated with handling infective material of animal origin during necropsy and butchering.

4. Incubation period. Usually 3 to 12 days.

5. Period of communicability. Not directly transmitted from man to man except possibly Venezuelan equine. Infective mosquitoes probably transmit virus throughout life. Viraemia, essential to vector infection, present for many of these viruses during early clinical illness in man.

6. Susceptibility and resistance. Susceptibility appears general, in both sexes and throughout life. Inapparent infections and mild undiagnosed disease are common. Infection leads to immunity and susceptibles in highly endemic areas are mainly among young children.

7. Methods of control

A. Preventive measures:

An experimental attenuated virus vaccine for Venezuelan equine has been used effectively to protect laboratory workers and others at high risk. An experimental inactivated tissue culture vaccine is used similarly for Rift Valley.

B. Control of patient, contacts, and the immediate environment:

i. Isolation: Keep patient in screened room for at least five days after onset, or in quarters treated with insecticide with residual effect, such as DDT.

ii. Concurrent disinfection: none

iii. Quarantine: none

iv. Immunisation of contacts: none

v. Investigation of contacts: place of residence of patient during two weeks previous to onset. Search for unreported or undiagnosed cases.

vi. Specific treatment: none.

C. Epidemic measures:

i. Community survey to determine density of vector mosquitoes, to identify their breeding places, and to promote plans for their elimination.

ii. Use of mosquito repellents by persons exposed to bites of vector mosquitoes.

Identification of the disease among horses (Venezuelan), or sheep and other animals (Rift Valley), serological survey of birds (West Nile), or rodents (Group C viruses); has epidemiological value to indicate frequency of infection and areas involved.

D. International meaures:

For Rift Valley fever, restrict movement of animals from enzootic areas to those free from disease. Others, none except enforcement of international agreements designed to prevent transfer of mosquitoes by ships, aircraft and land transport.

II. Tick-borne

Colorado Tick Fever

1. Identification. An acute febrile dengue-like disease usually without rash; a brief remission is usual, followed by a second bout of fever, each lasting two or three days. Characteristically mild but may be severe in children, occasionally with encephalitis or tendency to bleed. Deaths are uncommon.

Laboratory confirmation is by isolation of virus; complement fixing and neutralising antibodies do not appear until two weeks or more.

2. Reservoir and source of infection. Reservoir is small mammals; ground squirrels, porcupine, chipmunk and peromyscus have been identified; also nymphal and larval ticks. Source of infection is the adult vector tick.

3. Mode of transmission. Immature ticks, *Dermacentor andersoni*, acquire infection through feeding on infected animals during viraemia; they remain infected through the various moults and transmit virus to man by feeding as adult ticks.

4. Period of communicability. Not directly transmitted from man to man; the wild life cycle maintained by ticks is the important consideration. Ticks remain infective throughout life. Virus is present in man during the course of the fever, from one to ten days after onset.

5. Susceptibility and resistance. Susceptibility apparently universal. Second attacks are unknown; experimental reinfection unsuccessful.

6. Methods of control

A. Preventive measures:
No available vaccine.

B. Control of patient, contacts, and the immediate environment:
i. Isolation: none.
ii. Concurrent disinfection: none; destroy ticks on patient.
iii. Quarantine: None.
iv. Immunisation of contacts: none.
v. Investigation of contacts and source of infection: identification of ticks and tick infested areas.
vi. Specific treatment: none.

C. Epidemic measures: not applicable.

D. International measures: none.

III. Phlebotomus-borne

A. Sandfly Fever

1. Identification. Three or four days' fever clinically not unlike influenza except for absence of inflammation of the respiratory tract. Headache, fever of 38.3° to 39.5°C (101°F to 104°F), retrobulbar pain on motion of the eyes, infected sclerae, malaise, nausea and pain in limbs and back are characteristic. Leucopenia is usual on fourth or fifth day after onset of fever. Temperature occasionally exceeds 104°F, may present alarming symptoms, but death is unknown. Diagnosis is clinical and by epidemiological means, through occurrence of multiple and similar cases. Synonyms: Papataci Fever, Phlebotomus Fever, Three-day Fever.

Diagnosis may be confirmed by neutralisation test, using mouse adapted viruses, or by isolation of virus in newborn mice.

2. Reservoir and source of infection. One reservoir is in man and the sandfly; an animal reservoir is suspected but not demonstrated. For agents adequately studied, the immediate source of infection is in infective sandfly.

3. Mode of transmission. The vector of the classical viruses is a small, hairy, bloodsucking midge, *Phlebotomus papatasii*, the common sandfly, which bites at night and has a limited flight range. Sandflies of genus *Sergentomyia* have been found infected and may be vectors.

4. Incubation period. Up to six days, usually three to four days, rarely less.

5. Period of communicability. Virus is present in the blood of an infected person at least 24 hours before and 24 hours after onset of fever. Phlebotomus becomes infective about seven days after biting an infected person and remains so for life.

6. Susceptibility and resistance. Susceptibility is essentially universal; homologous acquired immunity is possibly lasting. There is no heterologous immunity. Relative resistance of native populations in sandfly areas is probably attributable to infection early in life.

7. Methods of control

A. Control of patient, contacts, and the immediate environment:

i. Report to local health authority: In most countries with endemic areas; this is not a reportable disease.

ii. Isolation: none. Protect infected individual from bites of sandflies for first few days of illness, by screening or mosquito bed nets (25 to 30 mesh to the inch) or by spraying quarters with insecticide.

iii. Concurrent disinfection: none; destruction of sandflies in the dwelling.

iv. Quarantine: none.

v. Immunisation of contacts: no measures currently available.

vi. Investigation of contacts and source of infection: search for breeding areas of sandflies around dwellings, especially in rubble heaps, masonry cracks, and under stones.

vii. Specific treatment: none.

B. Epidemic measures:

Community use of insecticide to destroy sandflies in and about human habitations; public health education on conditions leading to infection; and necessity to avoid bites of sandflies by use of repellents while in infected areas, particularly after sundown.

C. International measures: none.

ARTHROPOD-BORNE VIRAL HAEMORRHAGIC FEVERS

Mosquito-borne

Yellow Fever

1. Identification. An acute infectious disease of short duration and varying severity. The mildest cases are clinically indeterminate; typical attacks are characterised by sudden onset, fever, headache, backache, prostration, nausea and vomiting. As the disease progresses, the pulse rate slows in relation to temperature and albuminuria becomes pronounced, anuria may occur. Leucopenia appears early, most pronounced about the fifth day. Common haemorrhagic symptoms include epistaxis, buccal bleeding, haematemesis, and melaena. Jaundice is moderate early in the disease, later is intensified and post-mortem icterus may be pronounced. The fatality among indigenous populations of endemic regions is less than five per cent; for persons of other origin, rates of 30 per cent to 40 per cent are common.

Laboratory diagnosis is by isolation of virus from blood, demonstration of a rising titre of antibodies in paired acute phase and convalescent serums, and demonstration of typical lesions of the liver.

2. Reservoir and source of infection. In urban areas the reservoir of infection is man and *Aëdes aegypti*; in forest areas, vertebrates other than man, mainly monkeys, marmosets, possibly marsupials and forest mosquitoes. Man has no essential part in transmission of jungle yellow fever, nor in maintaining the virus. The immediate source of infection for man is an infective mosquito.

3. Mode of transmission. In urban and certain rural areas, by the bite of the mosquito, *Aëdes aegypti.* In forests of South America, by the bite of several species of forest mosquitoes of the genus *Haemagogus,* and *A. leucocelaenus.* In tropical Africa, *A. africanus* is the vector in the monkey population, while *A. simpsoni*, a semi-domestic mosquito, and probably other *Aëdes* transmit the virus from monkey to man.

4. Incubation period. Three to six days.

5. Period of communicability. Blood of patients is infective for mosquitoes shortly before onset of fever and for the first three days of illness. Highly communicable where many susceptible persons and abundant vector mosquitoes co-exist. Not communicable by contact or common vehicles. The extrinsic period of incubation before *A. aegypti* becomes infective is commonly 9 to 12 days at the usual summer temperatures. *Aëdes aegypti* mosquitoes, once infected, remain so for life, but transovarian passage does not occur.

6. Susceptibility and resistance. Recovery from yellow fever is followed by lasting immunity; second attacks are unknown. Mild, inapparent infections are common in endemic areas. Transient passive immunity in infants born to immune mothers may persist up to six months. In natural infection, antibodies appear in the blood within the first week.

7. Methods of control

A. Preventive measures:

i. Urban yellow fever, by eradication of *A. aegypti* mosquitoes. In the Americas this has been accomplished in Mexico, all of Central America and most of South America. In continental USA, in the Caribbean and in Africa much remains to be done.

ii. Sylvan or jungle yellow fever, transmitted by *Haemagogus* and forest species of *Aëdes*, cannot be controlled by any known method except vaccination, which is recommended for all persons living in rural areas whose daily occupation brings them into forests in yellow fever areas, and for persons who intend to visit those areas.

iii. Active immunisation of all persons necessarily exposed to infection because of residence, occupation, or travel. A single subcutaneous injection of a vaccine containing viable 17D strain of virus cultivated in chick embryo is effective. Antibodies appear from 7 to 10 days after vaccination and persist for at least 17 years, probably much longer. This is the only vaccine used in the Americas. A second method employs a living neurotropic yellow fever virus (Dakar strain prepared in mouse brain) administered by cutaneous scarification to persons 10 years of age and over; used extensively in Africa. Reactions are more frequent and a fatal encephalitis is an occasional complication.

B. Control of patient, contacts, and the immediate environment:

i. Report to local health authority. Case report universally required by International Sanitary Regulations, Class 1.

ii. Isolation: none. Prevent access of mosquitoes to patient during first three days by screening sickroom or by spraying quarters with insecticide having residual effect, or by using a bed net.

iii. Concurrent disinfection: none; home of patient and all houses in vicinity should be sprayed promptly with a residual insecticide such as DDT, benzene hexachloride, chlordane, or dieldrin.

iv. Quarantine: none.

v. Immunisation of contacts: Family and other contacts and neighbours not previously immunised should be vaccinated promptly.

vi. Investigation of contacts and source of infection; inquiry about all places, including forest areas, visited by patient three to six days before onset, to locate focus of yellow fever; observe all persons visiting that focus. Search of premises and place of work for mosquitoes capable of transmitting infection. Attention to mild febrile illnesses and unexplained deaths suggesting yellow fever.

C. Epidemic measures:

i. Urban or *Aëdes aegypti*—transmitted yellow fever:

a. Mass vaccination beginning with persons most exposed and those living in *aegypti*-infested parts of the area.

b. Spray all houses in community with residual insecticide.

c. Application of larvicide to all actual and potential breeding places of *A. aegypti.*

ii. Jungle or sylvan yellow fever:

a. Immediate vaccination of all persons living in or near, or entering, forested areas.

b. Avoidance by unvaccinated individuals of those tracts of forest where infection has been localised and by vaccinated persons for the first week after vaccination.

iii. In regions where yellow fever may occur, a viscerotomy service should be organised to collect, for diagnostic purposes, small specimens of liver from fatal febrile illnesses of 10 days' duration or less. Many cases and outbreaks otherwise missed are discovered in this way.

iv. Deaths of howler and spider monkeys in the forest, when confirmed, are presumptive evidence of the presence of yellow fever. Confirmation by histopathological examination of livers of moribund or recently dead monkeys is highly desirable.

v. Immunity surveys by mouse neutralisation test of wild primates captured in forested areas are useful in defining enzootic areas. Serological surveys of human populations are practically useless nowadays because of the wide use of yellow fever vaccination.

D. International measures:

i. Telegraphic notification by governments to WHO and to adjacent countries of the first imported, first transferred, or first non-imported case of yellow fever in a local area previously free of the disease, and of newly discovered or reactivated foci of yellow fever infection among vertebrates other than man.

ii. Measures applicable to ships, aircraft, and land transport arriving from yellow fever areas are specified in International Sanitary Regulations, WHO, second annotated edition, Geneva 1961.

iii. Animal quarantine: Quarantine of monkeys, marmosets and other wild primates arriving from yellow fever areas may be required until seven days have elapsed after leaving such areas.

iv. International travellers: A valid international certificate of vaccination against yellow fever is required by many countries for entry of travellers coming from or through recognised yellow fever zones of Africa and South America; otherwise, quarantine measures are applicable. The international certificate of vaccination is valid from 10 days after date of vaccination and for six years; if revaccinated within that time, from date of that revaccination and for six years.

Haemorrhagic fevers of the Philippines and South East Asia

1. Identification. A group of epidemic acute haemorrhagic fevers recognised thus far principally in children under 5 years of age, though higher ages affected in Singapore and Calcutta. Sudden onset with high fever, prostration, headache, malaise, frequently nausea and vomiting. Conjuctivitis, epistaxis and abdominal pain soon appear, along with an early petechial rash first noted on extremities and not infrequently involving face and trunk but not axillae or chest. Purpuric lesions may appear early and extensive ecchymoses later. Many patients have gastrointestinal haemorrhage and serious shock on the second to fifth day; blood platelets reduced, bleeding time prolonged, usually no leucopenia or leucocytosis in severe cases. Significant differences in clinical manifestations are observed in different countries, hepatomegaly conspicuous in Thailand and absent in Philippines; epistaxis more frequent in Philippines. Duration is usually five to eight days with prompt uncomplicated recovery. Fatality is about 1 per cent with death mainly during period of shock.

Serologic tests give a rise in titre with the responsible viruses and others closely related; virus isolation from blood during acute febrile stage.

2. Reservoir and source of infection. Reservoir unknown; probably man and *A. aegypti.* Immediate source of infection is an infective *A. aegypti.*

3. Mode of transmission. By bite of an infective *Aëdes aegypti* mosquito. Viruses isolated from this mosquito during epidemics.

4. Incubation period. Unknown.

5. Period of communicability. No evidence of transmission from man to man.

6. Susceptibility and resistance. Modal age of attack in epidemics thus far recognised, except Singapore and Calcutta, is about 3 to 5 years, with range from 4 months to young adulthood. Prevalence of dengue antibodies in the general population is high in older children and in adults. Many mild cases recognised by serological tests. Absence in most areas of haemorrhagic disease in Caucasians not understood; classical dengue has been observed in Caucasians during epidemic of haemorrhagic disease in Orientals.

ASCARIASIS

1. Identification. A chronic nematode disease of the intestine. Symptoms are variable, often vague or absent, and ordinarily mild; live worms passed in stools or vomited are frequently the first sign of infection. Heavy infection may cause digestive disturbances, abdominal pain, vomiting, restlessness, and disturbed sleep. The result is sometimes serious complications and occasional deaths among children in tropical countries.

2. Reservoir and source of infection. Reservoir is an infected person discharging eggs in faeces. The immediate source of infection is soil containing embryonated eggs, in and about houses where facilities for sanitary disposal of human excreta are lacking or not used.

3. Mode of transmission. By direct or indirect transmission of embryonated eggs from soil or other contaminated material to mouth; embryonation requires about a month after passage of the egg. Salads and other foods eaten raw are vehicles. Contaminated soil may be carried long distances on feet, or footwear, into houses and conveyances; infection also transmitted by dust.

4. Incubation period. Worms reach maturity about two months after ingestion of an embryonated egg.

5. Period of communicability. As long as mature fertilised female worms live in intestine. Most adult worms live less than six months; maximum life under one year. The female produces about 200 000 eggs a day. Embryonated eggs under favourable conditions remain viable in soil for months and even years.

6. Susceptibility and resistance. Susceptibility is general.

7. Methods of control

A. Preventive measures:

i. Provision of adequate facilities for proper disposal of faeces and prevention of soil contamination in areas immediately adjacent to houses, particularly in play areas of children.

ii. In rural areas, construction of privies in such manner as to obviate dissemination of ascarid eggs through overflow, drainage, or similar circumstance. Composting is practised to advantage where such facilities are lacking.

iii. Education of all persons, particularly children, to use toilet facilities, and to wash hands after defaecating. Encouragement of satisfactory hygienic habits on the part of children, especially washing hands before handling food, and not to eat food which has been dropped on the floor.

B. Control of patient, contacts, and the immediate environment:

i. Report to local health authority: official report not ordinarily justifiable.

ii. Isolation: none.

iii. Concurrent disinfection: sanitary disposal of faeces.

iv. Quarantine: none.

v. Immunisation of contacts: none.

vi. Investigation of contacts and source of infection: individual and environmental sources of infection should be sought, particularly in persons and premises of family.

vii. Specific treatment: A piperazine derivative for ascariasis alone or associated with enterobiasis; biphenium or hexylresorcinal for co-existing ascariasis and hookworm disease; dithiazamine for ascariasis with strongyloidiasis or trichuriasis.

C. Epidemic measures:

Surveys for prevalence in highly endemic areas, education in sanitation of environment and in personal hygiene, and provision of treatment facilities.

D. International measures: none.

BRUCELLOSIS

1. Identification. A systemic disease with acute or insidious onset characterised by continued, intermittent or irregular fever of variable duration, headache, weakness, profuse sweating, chills or chilliness, arthralgia, and generalised aching. The disease may last for several days, many months, or occasionally for several years. Recovery is usual but disability is often pronounced. The fatality is 2 per cent or less; higher for *B. melitensis* infections than for other varieties. Clinical diagnosis is often difficult and uncertain. Synonyms: Undulant Fever, Malta Fever, Mediterranean Fever.

Laboratory diagnosis is by isolation of the infectious agent from blood, bone marrow or other tissues, or from discharges of the patient. The agglutination test is valuable, especially with paired serums to show rise in antibody.

Vibriosis, primarily a disease of animals, on rare occasions produces a clinical disease of man that may suggest brucellosis, as does leptospirosis.

2. *Reservoir and source of infection.* Reservoirs of human infection are cattle, swine, sheep, goats and horses; in USA, primarily swine. The sources of infection are tissues, blood, urine, milk and especially placentas, vaginal discharges, and aborted fetuses of infected animals.

3. *Mode of transmission.* By contact with infected animals, dairy products from infected animals. Air-borne infection may occur among animals in pens and stables, and also in laboratories and abattoirs.

4. *Incubation period.* Highly variable and difficult to ascertain; 5 to 21 days, occasionally several months.

5. *Period of communicability.* Rarely communicable from man to man although the infectious agent may be discharged in urine and other excretions for long periods.

6. *Susceptibility and resistance.* Severity and duration of clinical illness are subject to wide differences. Children are less likely to have manifest disease than are adults. Mild and inapparent infections are frequent. Duration of acquired immunity is uncertain.

7. *Methods of control.*

Ultimate control of brucellosis in man rests in the elimination of the disease among domestic animals.

A. Preventive measures:

i. Education of farmers and workers in slaughter houses, packing plants, and butchers' shops as to the nature of the disease and the danger of handling carcasses or products of infected animals.

ii. Search for infection among livestock by the agglutination reaction—eliminate infected animals by segregation or slaughter. Infection among swine usually requires slaughter of the drove. Calf immunisation is recommended in enzootic areas.

iii. Pasteurisation of milk and dairy products from cows, sheep or goats. Boiling of milk is practical when pasteurisation is impossible.

iv. Care in handling and disposal of discharges and fetus from an aborted animal. Disinfection of contaminated areas.

v. Meat inspection and condemning of carcasses of infected swine; not a useful procedure for cattle.

B. Control of patient, contacts, and the immediate environment:

i. Report to local health authority: case report obligatory in most states and countries.

ii. Isolation: none.

iii. Concurrent disinfection: of body discharges.

iv. Quarantine: none.

v. Immunisation of contacts: none.

vi. Investigation of contacts and source of infection: trace infection to the common or individual source, usually infected domestic goats, swine, or cattle, unpasteurised milk or dairy products from cows and goats. Test suspected animals, remove reactors. Diseased are slaughtered.

vii. Specific treatment: the best results are with a combination of chlortetracycline and dihydrostreptomycin with or without addition of a sulphonamide. Treatment should be continued for at least three weeks. The relapse rate is high.

C. Epidemic measures:

Search for common vehicle of infection, usually unpasteurised milk or milk products from an infected herd. Stop distribution of pasteurisation.

D. International measures:

Control of domestic animals and animal products, especially feed stuffs, in international trade and transport.

CHICKENPOX

1. Identification. An acute generalised viral disease of sudden onset with slight fever, mild constitutional symptoms and an eruption of the skin which is maculopapular for a few hours, vesicular for 3 to 4 days, and leaves a granular scab. Lesions tend to be more abundant on covered than on exposed parts of the body; may appear on scalp, and mucous membranes of upper respiratory tract; commonly occur in successive crops, with several stages of maturity present at the same time: may be so few as to escape observation. Mild, atypical and inapparent infections occur. Rarely fatal. A primary viral pneumonia is the commonest cause of death in adults and septic complications and encephalitis in children. Synonym: Varicella.

Herpes zoster is a local manifestation of recurrent infection with the same virus. Vesicles with an erythematous base are restricted to skin areas supplied by sensory nerves of a single or associated group of dorsal root ganglia. Lesions may appear in crops in irregular fashion along nerve pathways, are deeper seated and more closely aggregated than chickenpox; histologically they are indentical. Severe pain and paraesthesia are common. Occurs mainly in older adults. Occasionally a vericelliform eruption follows some days after zoster, and rarely a secondary eruption of zoster type after chickenpox.

Laboratory tests, such as isolation of the virus by tissues culture or identification by serological means, are useful but not generally available.

2. Reservoir and source of infection. Reservoir is the infected person. Source of infection is secretions of the respiratory tract of infected persons; lesions of the skin are of little consequence and scabs of themselves are not infective. Susceptibles may contract chickenpox from patients with herpes zoster.

3. Mode of transmission. From person to person by direct contact droplet, or air-borne spread; indirectly through articles freshly soiled by discharges from the skin and mucous membranes of infected persons. One of the most readily communicable of diseases, especially in the early stages of the eruption.

4. Incubation period. From two to three weeks; commonly 13 to 17 days.

5. Period of communicability. Probably not more than one day before the eruption of chickenpox, appears not more than six days after the first crop of vesicles.

6. Susceptibility and resistance. Susceptibility to chickenpox is universal among those not previously attacked; ordinarily a more severe disease of adults than of children. One attack confers long immunity; second attacks are rare. Infection apparently remains latent and recurs years later as herpes zoster in a small proportion of older adults, sometimes in children.

7. Methods of control

A. Preventive measures:

i. Cases reported as chickenpox in persons over fifteen years of age, or at any age during an epidemic of smallpox, should be investigated to eliminate possibility of smallpox.

ii. Several investigators have noted fatal chickenpox in patients receiving steroid therapy. If susceptible to chickenpox, efforts should be made to protect such persons against exposure; and, if exposed, to reduce the dose of steroid to physiological levels as rapidly as possible.

B. Control of patient, contacts, and the immediate environment:

i. Report to local health authority: official report is not ordinarily justifiable. Case report of chickenpox in adults may be required where smallpox is infrequent.

ii. Isolation: none. Exclusion from school for one week after eruption first appears and avoidance of contact with susceptibles.

iii. Concurrent disinfection: articles soiled by discharges from the nose and throat and from lesions.

iv. Quarantine: none.

v. Immunisation of contacts: none.

vi. Investigation of contacts: of no practical importance except under suspicion of smallpox.

vii. Specific treatment: none.

C. Epidemic measures: none.

D. International measures: none.

CHOLERA

1. Identification. A serious, acute intestinal disease characterised by sudden onset, vomiting, profuse watery stools, rapid dehydration, and collapse. Severity differs greatly from place to place and within epidemics. Mild cases show only diarrhoea; in others, death may occur within a few hours of onset. Case fatality is from 5 to 15 per cent in endemic cholera to as much as 75 per cent in explosive epidemics, the number of deaths being determined by adequacy of the rehydration provided.

Laboratory confirmation is by isolation of cholera vibrios from faeces or rectal swabs.

2. Reservoir and source of infection. Reservoir is an infected person; source of infection is faeces and vomitus of patients, to a lesser extent faeces of persons incubating the disease and of convalescents.

3. Mode of transmission. Transmission in the initial wave of an epidemic of cholera is commonly by contaminated water, less commonly by food. Later cases usually occur by direct contact, by foods contaminated by soiled hands or utensils, and by flies. In sporadic and endemic cholera, carriers are a significant factor, especially in spread of infection within families, through contaminated food and by contact. Water plays a less important part.

4. Incubation period. From a few hours to five days, usually, two to three days.

5. Susceptibility and resistance. Susceptibility is variable and related to nutritional state. Recovery from clinical attack affords some short-term protection. Immunity artificially induced by vaccines is of unknown degree and short duration, not more than six months.

6. Methods of control

A. Preventive measures:

i. Sanitary disposal of human faeces.

ii. Protection and purification of water supplies.

iii. Boiling of milk or pasteurisation of milk and dairy products.

iv. Sanitary supervision of processing, preparation and serving of foods, especially those eaten moist and raw; special attention to provision and use of hand-washing facilities.

v. Destruction of flies, control of fly breeding, and screening to protect foods against fly contamination.

vi. Education of the public in personal hygiene, especially washing of hands before eating and after defaecation.

vii. Active immunisation with cholera vaccine of persons subject to unusual or continued risk.

B. Control of patient, contacts, and the immediate environment:

i. Report to local health authority: case report universally required by International Sanitary Regulations.

ii. Isolation: preferably in hospital during communicable period.

iii. Concurrent disinfection: of faeces and vomitus and of articles used by patient. Practice by attendants of scrupulous cleanliness; disinfection of hands each time after handling articles contaminated by faeces. Terminal cleaning.

iv. Quarantine: surveillance of contacts for five days from last exposure, longer if faeces contain cholera vibrios.

v. Immunisation of contacts: no passive immunisation. Inoculation of contacts with cholera vaccine can be expected to do no more than protect against subsequent or continued exposure.

vi. Investigation of contacts and source of infection: search for unreported cases; investigate possibilities of infection from polluted drinking water or from contaminated uncooked foods.

vii. Specific treatment: Prompt and adequate replacement of fluid and electrolyte and other measures for shock are paramount. Current studies suggest that tetracyclines may reduce volume and duration of diarrhoea, and shorten period of excretion of vibrios.

C. Epidemic measures:

i. Emergency measures to ensure a safe water supply: boiling of water used for drinking, toilet purposes, washing dishes or food containers (unless water supply is treated adequately, as by chlorination, and protected from contamination thereafter). Water in accessible and sufficient supply for hygienic purposes is important.

ii. Inspection service for early detection of infected persons: provision of temporary emergency facilities, by requisition or otherwise, for isolation of patients and suspects. Identification and isolation of carriers is desirable, but usually impractical. Detention in suitable camps for five days of persons leaving the area.

iii. Immediate administration of cholera vaccine to exposed population groups, despite its limited value.

iv. Careful supervision of food and drink. After cooking or boiling, protect against contamination by flies and human handling.

v. Control of flies by limiting fly breeding, by use of appropriate insecticides, and by screening kitchens and eating places.

vi. Promulgation of temporary regulations to ensure proper execution of the above control measures.

D. International measures

i. Telegraphic notification by governments to WHO and to adjacent countries of the first imported, first transferred or first non-imported case of cholera in a local area previously free of the disease.

ii. Measures applicable to ships, aircraft, and land transport arriving from cholera areas are specified in International Sanitary Regulations, World Health Organisation, second annotated edition, Geneva, 1961.

iii. International travellers: Cholera patients or suspects are not permitted to depart for another country. Many countries require that travellers from an area where cholera is present possess a valid international cholera vaccination certificate for entry. The certificate is valid from six days until six months after the first injection of vaccine; or, in the event of revaccination within such period of six months, then as of that date and for six months thereafter.

FILARIASIS

1. Identification. Early acute manifestations include fever, lymphadenitis, retrograde lymphangitis of extremities, orchitis, epididymitis, funiculitis, and abscess. These are primarily allergic reactions, but secondary bacterial infection may result in death. Prolonged or repeated infection with obstruction to lymph flow often leads to hydrocele and elephantiasis of limbs, genitalia or breast, or to chyluria. Female worms give rise to larvae, microfilariae, which, in the absence of lymphatic obstruction, reach the blood stream. Many infected persons have no clinical manifestations but do have circulating microfilariae; many persons with clinical manifestations do not have circulating microfilariae. A nocturnal periodicity of microfilariae in the peripheral blood (10 p.m. to 2 a.m.) occurs in all endemic areas except those Pacific Islands where the vector is an *Aëdes* mosquito.

Microfilariae are best detected in blood at optimum daily periodicity, examined in thick-

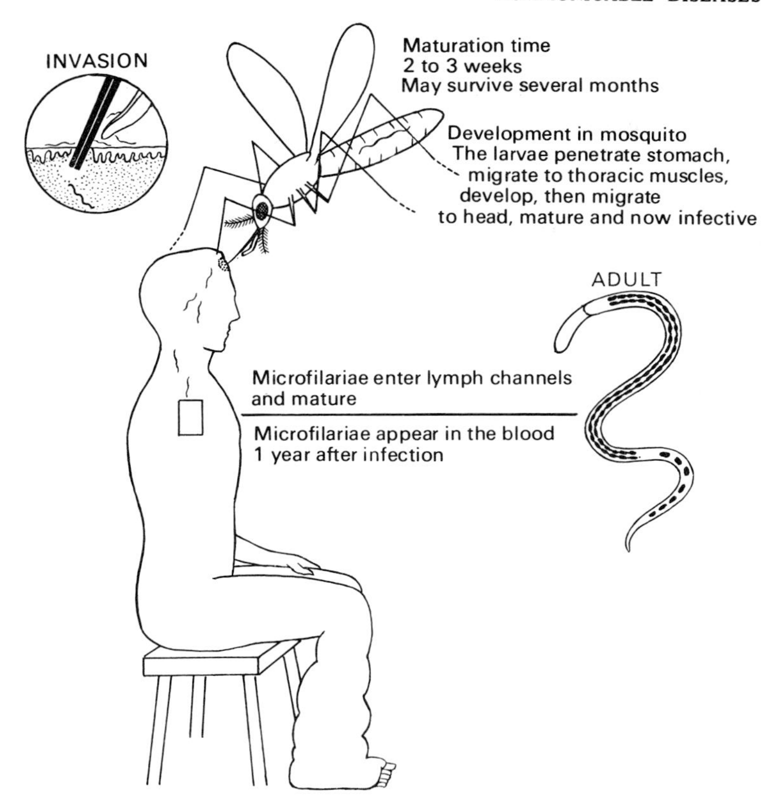

Fig. 7.4 *Wuchereria bancrofti*. Found in Asia, Africa, South America and Australasia.

film preparation or stained sediment of caked blood. Skin test is non-specific, of value in absence of microfilaraemia.

This classical filariasis requires differentiation from other filarial diseases, loiasis, onchicerciasis, dracontiasis, and others.

Infectious agents: *Wuchereria bancrofti* and *Brugia malayi*, nematode worms.

2. Reservoir and source of infection. Reservoir is man with microfilariae in the blood. Immediate source of infection is a mosquito.

3. Mode of transmission. By bite of a mosquito harbouring infective larvae. *W. bancrofti* is transmitted in nature by many species, the most important being *Culix fatigans, C. pipiens, Aëdes polynesiensis* (pseudoscutellaris), and several species of *Anopheles. B. malayi* is transmitted by various species of *Mansonia* and *Anopheles*. The microfilariae penetrate the stomach wall of the mosquito, lodge in thoracic muscles, develop into infectie larvae, migrate to the proboscis, and are transmitted to the new host as the mosquito bites.

4. Incubation period. Allergic manifestations may appear as early as three months after infection. Microfilariae do not appear in the blood until at least nine months.

5. Period of communicability. Not directly transmitted from man to man. Man remains infective for mosquitoes as long as microfilariae are present in the blood, which may be years. Communicability in the mosquito is from 10 days after blood meal until all infective larvae are discharged.

6. Susceptibility and resistance. Universal susceptibility.

7. Methods of control

A. Preventive measures:

i. Determine, by dissection, the vector or vectors; study times and places of feeding and locate breeding places. In most areas other than the South Pacific, attack adult mosquitoes by spraying buildings with an acceptable residual insecticide; screen houses, use bed nets and insect repellents. Attack larvae by eliminating small breeding places and treating others with larvicides. Each local situation requires individual study.

ii. Educate the public concerning mode of transmission and methods of mosquito control.

B. Control of patient, contacts, and the immediate environment:

i. Report to local health authority in selected endemic regions. In most countries not a reportable disease, Class 3C. Reporting of cases with demonstrated microfilariae provides data on potential transmissions. Cases of elephantiasis without microfilariae in the blood should not be reported as filariasis, but are usefully recorded in estimating prevalence or in planning control programmes.

ii. Isolation: not practicable. As far as possible, patients with microfilariae in blood should be protected from mosquito bites as a means of reducing transmission.

iii. Concurrent disinfection: none.

iv. Quarantine: none.

v. Immunisation of contacts: none.

vi. Investigation of contacts and source of infection: only as part of a general community effort.

vii. Specific treatment: diethylcarbamazine results in rapid disappearance of most or all microfilariae from the blood, but may not destroy the adult female worm; microfilariae usually reappear after several months. Sodium thiacetasamide (Caparsolate sodium) causes slow disappearance of microfilariae during treatment without subsequent increase over a 2 year period. Action of this compound apparently is against adult worms rather than microfilariae.

C. Epidemic measures:

The first essential of high endemicity is an appraisal of the local situation, particularly the bionomica of mosquito vectors, prevalence and incidence of disease, and environmental factors responsible for transmission. Vector control is the fundamental approach. Even partial control by anti-mosquito measures may reduce incidence and restrict the endemic focus. Measurable results are slow because of the long incubation period. Mass treatment of known infected persons with hetrazan contributes materially.

D. International measures:

Coordinated programmes by neighbouring countries where the disease is endemic with the purpose of limiting migration of infected persons across international boundaries, and instituting treatment and control measures near such boundaries.

HEPATITIS, INFECTIOUS

1. Identification. An acute, infectious disease with fever, anorexia, nausea, malaise and abdominal discomfort, followed by jaundice. Bilirubin may be detected in blood and urine. Convalescence may be prolonged. Many cases are mild, without jaundice, especially in children, and recognisable only by liver function or serum enzyme tests. Fulminating, and usually fatal, cases of acute necrosis of liver are rare. Usually a benign disease with case fatality under 1 per cent more severe in adults than children. Synonyms: Epidemic Hepatitis, Epidemic Jaundice, Catarrhal Jaundice.

No specific laboratory tests are available.

2. Reservoir and source of infection. Man is the reservoir; very rarely, chimpanzees. Sources of infection are faeces, urine and blood from infected persons. Presence of the infectious agent in nose and throat discharges not proved but commonly assumed on epidemiological grounds.

3. Mode of transmission. Through intimate person-to-person contact by faecal–oral route with respiratory spread possible; also transfusion of whole blood, injection of blood serum or plasma from infected persons, and by accidental contamination of syringes or needles with traces of blood. Transmissable to humans by ingestion or parenteral inoculation of blood or filtered faecal suspensions from patients with early disease. Epidemics have been related to contaminated water, milk and food, including oysters and clams.

4. Incubation period. From 15 to 50 days, commonly 25.

5. Period of communicability. Unknown infectious agent demonstrated in blood before clinically recognised disease. Clinical experience suggests greatest communicability from several days before to usually not more than seven days after onset of manifest disease.

6. Susceptibility and resistance. Susceptibility is general. Degree and duration of immunity after attack unknown, but second attacks of jaundice are rare.

7. Methods of control

A. Preventive measures:

i. Health education directed towards good sanitation and personal hygiene, with particular emphasis on disposal of faeces.

ii. Proper technical procedures to prevent transmission by blood, or blood products, from an infected blood donor or through use of improperly sterilised syringes, needles and other instruments.

iii. Where supplies permit, travellers with expected heavy brief exposure may be given immune (gamma) globulin in a dose of 0.05 to 0.1 ml per kg of body weight. Protection may be expected for five to six months.

B. Control of patient, contacts, and the immediate environment:

i. Report to local health authority: reporting advisable, though not required, in many countries.

ii. Isolation: during first week of illness.

iii. Concurrent disinfection: Faeces, and nose and throat secretions.

iv. Quarantine: none.

v. Immunisation of contacts: immune (gamma) globin, 0.02 to 0.05 ml per kg of body weight given intramuscularly and within one week after exposure provides passive protection against infectious hapatitis with jaundice for six to eight weeks. Should be given promptly, but is known to be effective when given after intervals longer than one week after exposure; larger doses, 0.1 ml per kg give longer protection. Prolonged exposure, as in institutions, requires a repeated dose. Usually to be limited to children and young adults in close household contact.

vi. Investigation of contacts: search for missed cases and surveillance of contacts.

vii. Specific treatment: none.

C. Epidemic measures:

i. Epidemiological investigation to determine possible transmission by water, food, blood or blood products.

ii. Special efforts to improve sanitary and hygienic practices, to reduce faecal contamination of foods and water and careless disposal of nose and mouth discharges.

iii. Focal concentration of disease in schools and institutions of limited population may warrant mass prophylaxis with immune globulin.

D. International measures: none.

HEPATITIS, SERUM

1. Identification. Clinically indistinguishable from infectious hepatitis. Chief differences are longer incubation period, lack of direct transmission from patients to contacts, and a higher fatality, varying from 6 to 12 per cent. Synonym: Homologous Serum Jaundice.

Absence of naturally-occurring infection among associates and history of injection of blood products 50 to 160 days previously are essential to differentiation from infectious hepatitis.

2. Reservoir and source of infection. Man is the reservoir. Sources of infection are blood or blood products from an infected person.

3. Mode of transmission. By parenteral (intravenous, intramuscular, or subcutaneous) inoculation of human blood, plasma, serum or thrombin from an infected person or by use of syringes, needles or other instruments contaminated with traces of such materials. Immune (gamma) globulin and heat-treated albumin, although blood derivatives, do not transmit the disease.

4. Incubation period. From 50 to 160 days, usually 80 to 100 days.

5. Period of communicability. Blood from experimentally inoculated volunteers, taken 89 days before first symptoms and as many as eight days after jaundice appears, has produced serum hepatitis. Blood donors are known to have been continuously or intermittently infective for many years. Some persons are carriers without having experienced a clinically recognised attack.

6. Susceptibility and resistance. Susceptibility high.

7. Methods of control

A. Preventive measures:

i. Limit administration of whole blood, and particularly pooled serum or plasma, to patients or others with clear indication of therapeutic usefulness or necessity. Pooling increases the likelihood that blood products will contain the infectious agent. Where feasible, use blood substitutes such as human albumin or dextran. Reject donors transfused within the previous six months, in known contact with hepatitis within preceding six months, with a history of previous attack whose blood is suspected of being responsible for a case of post-transfusion hepatitis, or with a history of addiction to narcotics.

ii. Thorough heat sterilisation of syringes and needles, and of stylets for finger puncture. A fresh sterile syringe and needle is essential for each person receiving parenteral inoculations or venipuncture. Sterilise needles between patients for intracutaneous testing to protect against inoculation of traces of blood from previous use. Use disposable equipment when possible. Discourage tattooing.

iii. Storage of liquid plasma for six months at a temperature of about 32°C (90°F) is the preferred method for destroying the infectious agent of serum hepatitis. Ultraviolet irradiation is not reliable.

iv. Evidence of the prophylactic value of immune (gamma) globulin for protection of persons receiving contaminated blood, by transfusion or otherwise, is conflicting.

B. Control of patient, contacts, and the immediate environment:

i. Report to local health authority. Official report is advisable, though not required in many places.

ii. Isolation: none. Not known to be communicable except by injection.

iii. Concurrent disinfection: of equipment contaminated with blood.

iv. Quarantine: none.

v. Immunisation of contacts: none.

vi. Investigation of contacts: search for groupings of cases among other persons who have attended a clinic or hospital where parenteral therapy is much employed, e.g. for diabetes mellitus or syphilis.

vii. Specific treatment: none.

C. Epidemic measures:

Surveys of persons receiving blood or blood products to determine incidence and to control techniques associated with parenteral injections.

D. International measures: none.

HOOKWORM DISEASE

1. Identification. A chronic debilitating disease with a variety of vague symptoms varying greatly according to extent of infection and nutritional state of the patient. The blood-sucking activity of the worm along with malnutrition leads to hypochromic microcytic anaemia, a major cause of disability. Infected children may be retarded in mental and physical development. Death is infrequent in both acute and chronic stages, and then usually in association with other infection. Light hookworm infection with egg counts of five hundred or less per gram of stool generally produce few or no clinical effects. Synonyms: Ancylostomiasis, Ucinariasis.

Hookworm infection is confirmed by the finding of the eggs of worms in faeces; species recognition is through microscopic examination of adult worms.

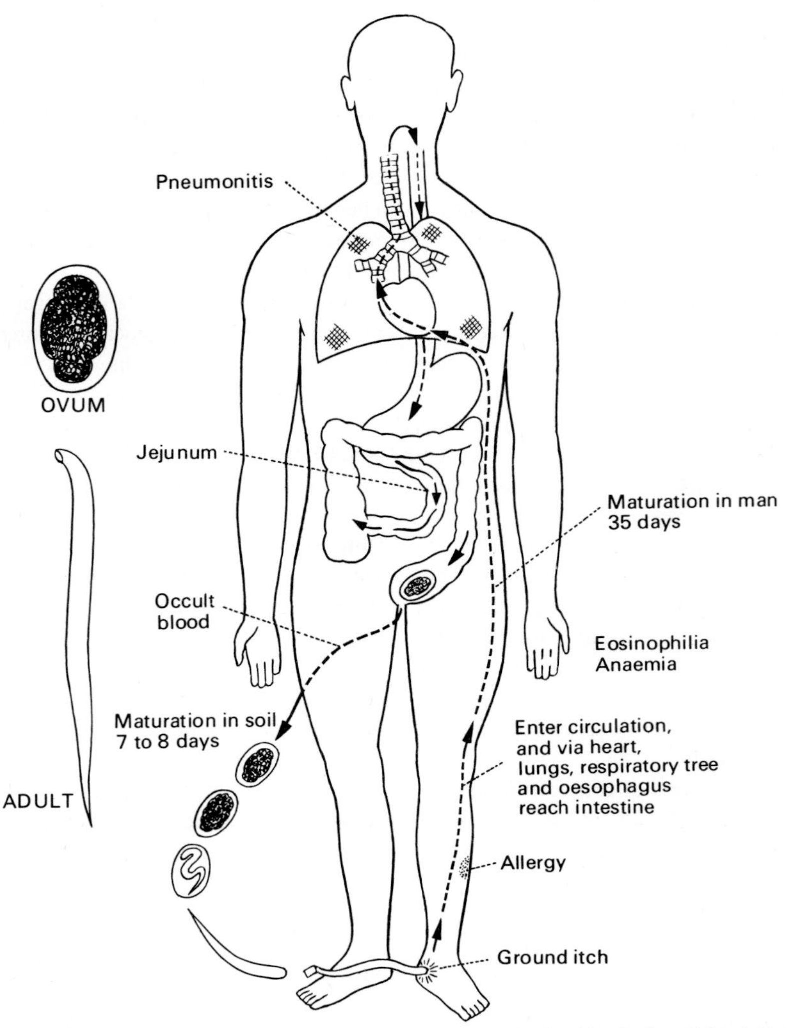

Fig. 7.5 The hookworm. *Ancylostom duodenale* is found in Europe, North Africa, India and South East Asia. *Necator americanus* is found in the United States, Central America, Central and South West Africa, Oceania and South East Asia.

Infective larvae of cat and dog hookworm (*Ancylostoma brasiliense* and *A. caninum*) cause a dermatitis in man called creeping eruption, a disease of refuse workers, gardeners, children and others in contact with contaminated sandy soil. The larvae are destroyed on the skin and do not otherwise affect man.

2. *Reservoir and source of infection.* Reservoir is an infected person discharging eggs in faeces. The usual source of infection is soil contaminated with infective larvae.

3. *Mode of transmission.* Eggs in faeces are deposited on the ground where they hatch; larvae develop to the third stage (becoming infective in 7 to 10 days) and penetrate the

skin, usually the foot, in so doing characteristically producing a dermatitis (ground itch). Infection by ingestion is possible, but rare.

4. Incubation period. Eggs appear in the faeces about six weeks after infection. Symptoms may develop after a few weeks to many months or even years, depending on the intensity of infection.

5. Period of communicability. Infected persons are potential spreaders of infection as long as they remain infected and continue to pollute soil, often for several years in the absence of treatment. Under favourable conditions third stage infective larvae remain alive in soil for several weeks.

6. Methods of control

A. Preventive measures:

i. Education of the public to dangers of soil contamination, and to the practice of personal hygiene, especially the wearing of shoes.

ii. Prevention of soil contamination by installation of sanitary disposal systems for human faeces.

B. Control of patient, contacts, and the immediate environment:

i. Report to local health authority: but in most countries not a reportable disease.

ii. Isolation: none.

iii. Concurrent disinfection: sanitary disposal of faeces to prevent contamination of soil.

iv. Quarantine: none.

v. Immunisation of contacts: none.

vi. Investigation of contacts: each patient and carrier is a potential or actual spreader of the disease.

Examine all family contacts if possible.

vii. Specific treatment: tetrachlorethylene or hexylrescorethylene or hexylrescorcinol; toxic reactions are infrequent so treatment can be repeated if necessary; communicability is shortened. Bephenium hydroxynapthoate is of value, especially for *A. duodenale* infections.

C. Epidemic measures:

Surveys for prevalence in highly endemic areas, public health education in sanitation of the environment and in personal hygiene, and provision of facilities for treatment.

D. International measures: none.

INFLUENZA

1. Identification. An acute, infectious disease of the respiratory tract characterised by abrupt onset of fever, chills, headache, myalgia and sometimes prostration. Coryza and sore throat are common, but more so in the later than in the early stages of the disease. Cough is almost universal, often severe and protracted. Usually a self-limited disease with recovery in two to seven days. Usually, recognition is by presence of an epidemic wave; sporadic cases can be identified only through laboratory means. Influenza derives its importance from the rapidity with which epidemics evolve, sufficient to threaten the normal functioning of a community, and also from the complications that follow—notably bacterial pneumonia. Deaths are concentrated in the elderly and persons debilitated by chronic cardiac, pulmonary, renal or metabolic disease. Case fatality is low, but epidemics are associated with a general mortality much in excess of non-epidemic expectancy.

Laboratory confirmation is by recovery of virus from throat washings or demonstration of a rise in antibody in serums obtained during acute and convalescent stages. Virus recovery is most successful if throat washings are obtained within 72 hours of onset.

2. Reservoir and source of infection. Man is the reservoir; souces of infection are discharges from the mouth and nose of infected persons.

3. Mode of transmission. By direct contact, through droplet infection, or by articles freshly soiled with discharges of the nose and throat of infected persons. Possibly airborne.

4. Incubation period. Short, usually 24 to 72 hours.

5. Period of communicability. Probably limited to three days from clinical onset.

6. Susceptibility and resistance. Susceptibility is universal. Infection produces immunity of unknown duration to the type and sub-type of the infecting virus. Repeated infection broadens the base of immunity. Immunisation produces serological responses specific for the subtypes present in the vaccine, with booster responses for those sub-types with which the individual has had prior experience.

Age-specific attack rates in any one epidemic reflect the past experience of various age groups in the population with strains of the epidemic sub-type and the degree of exposure which, in turn, depends on social and environmental conditions. In general, highest incidence is in childhood at about 10 years of age, less in pre-school children and progressively decreasing among adults of increasing age. Exceptions occur. In the 1962/3 epidemic in the USA, the third major recurrence of A2 influenza, incidence was uniform for all ages.

Immunity after attack with homologous or closely related sub-types may persist for several years but has not been accurately evaluated. The tendency for new sub-types to replace old ones and the existence of other viral agents capable of inducing an influenza-like syndrome confuse the clinical evaluation of duration of immunity, both natural and artificial.

7. Methods of control

A. Preventive measures:

i. Active immunisation is effective when at least one of the antigenic components of the vaccine closely matches the prevailing strain of virus. Vaccine should be given to people in categories with unusual risk of complications or death, and may be considered for those engaged in essential community services, such as policemen, firemen, hospital employees and transport workers, as well as in strategic industries and the military forces. It should be accomplished well before expected epidemic occurrence. Routine inoculation of whole populations is not recommended.

ii. Education of public in basic personal hygiene including the avoidance of crowds during epidemic periods.

B. Control of patient, contacts, and the immediate environment:

i. Report to local health authority: obligatory and prompt report of all epidemics resembling influenza. No individual case report required. Supplementary report of identity of epidemic as determined by laboratory examination.

ii. Isolation: during the acute illness (not as an official requirement but as directed by the attending physician), primarily for the protection of the patient.

iii. Concurrent disinfection: discharges from the nose and throat of the patient.

iv. Quarantine: none.

v. Immunisation of contacts: none—too late to be effective.

vi. Investigation of contacts: of no practical value.

vii. Specific treatment: none. Sulphonamides and antibiotics have no effect on the uncomplicated disease; they should be employed only if bacterial complications arise.

C. Epidemic measures:

i. The severe and often disrupting effects of epidemic influenza on community activities may be mitigated in part by effective health planning and education, particularly at the local level. Continued community surveillance by local health authorities of the extent and progress of outbreaks within their areas is essential, with prompt reports to state and national health agencies of the prevailing epidemic pattern. Such reports permit evaluation of the epidemic as a whole, and are useful to all local health officers as a guide in planning, to others responsible for the control of influenza, and to the public.

ii. Discourage the unnecessary congregation of large numbers of people during epidemic periods. Closing of schools is not an effective control measure but may be unavoidable in the face of excessive pupil or teacher absenteeism.

iii. Hospital administrators should anticipate the increased demand for space and staff during epidemic periods. Elective admissions as well as unnecessary hospitalisation of mild uncomplicated cases of influenza should be discouraged during these periods, and some curtailment of visiting privileges may be warranted.

iv. Vaccination of a community after recognition of the epidemic is of little, if any, value.

D. International measures:

i. Prompt report to WHO of epidemics within a country, with complete description of epidemiologic characteristics.

ii. Prompt identification of virus type and sub-type in individual epidemics with immediate report to WHO of the antigenic characteristics of isolates. Necessary throat washings and blood samples may be sent to one of the 65 WHO influenza laboratories located in 46 countries throughout the world. The World Influenza Centre, Medical Research Council, Mill Hill, London, England, and the International Influenza Centre for the Americas, Communicable Disease Centre, US Public Health Service, Atlanta, Georgia, USA, serve as reference centres in their respective areas.

iii. Continuing epidemiological studies and prompt identification of type and strain of virus by national health agencies. Exchange of information with WHO in order to increase understanding of the basic epidemiology of influenza, to establish the broad movements of an epidemic, and to aid in the early recognition of outbreaks in previously uninvaded territory.

iv. Continuing effort to ensure commercial or governmental facilities for vaccine production, in large volume and rapidly, should a new sub-type of influenza virus appear and threaten to become pandemic.

LEPTOSPIROSIS

1. Identification. A group of acute infectious diseases with fever, headache, chills, severe malaise, vomiting, muscular aches, meningeal irritation and conjunctivitis; infrequently jaundice, renal insufficiency, haemolytic anaemia and haemorrhage in skin and mucous membranes. Pretibial rash occurs occasionally. Clinical illness lasts from one to three weeks; relapses may occur. Fatality is low but increases with advancing age; may reach 20 per cent or more in patients with jaundice and kidney damage. Synonyms: Weil's Disease, Canicola Fever, Haemorrhagic Jaundice, Fort Bragg Fever.

Agglutination tests and culture of leptospires are useful in confirmation of clinical diagnosis.

2. Reservoir and source of infection. Reservoirs among farm animals include cattle, dogs and swine. Rats and other rodents are frequently infected, as are wild animals such as deer, foxes, skunks, racoons, opossums and even reptiles. The source of infection is urine of infected animals and possibly infected tissues.

3. Mode of transmission. Contact with water contaminated with urine of infected animals, by swimming or accidental or occupational immersion, and by direct contact with infected animals. Infection presumably results from penetration of abraded skin or mucous membrane, or possibly through ingestion.

4. Incubation period. Four to 19 days, usually 10 days.

5. Period of communicability. Direct transmission from man to man is negligible.

6. Susceptibility and resistance. Susceptibility of man is general.

7. Methods of control

A. Preventive measures:

i. Protection of workers in hazardous occupations with boots and gloves.

ii. Education of the public in modes of transmission, the need to avoid swimming or wading in potentially contaminated waters and for proper protection when work requires such exposure.

iii. Rodent control in human habitations, especially rural and recreational.

iv. Segregation of domestic animals, and prevention of contamination of living and working areas of man by urine of infected animals.

v. Vaccines for man have been used experimentally in Europe and Japan. They must represent the dominant local strain.

B. Control of patient, contacts, and the immediate environment:

i. Report to the local health authority: obligatory case report in many states and countries.

ii. Isolation: none.

iii. Concurrent disinfection: none.

iv. Quarantine: none.

v. Immunisation of contacts: none.

vi. Investigation of contacts: search for exposure to infected animals or history of swimming in contaminated waters.

vii. Specific treatment: penicillin, streptomycin and tetracycline antibiotics are leptospirocidal, but not yet of demonstrated value in treatment of human disease.

C. Epidemic measures:

Search for source of infection, such as a pond used for swimming. Eliminate contamination or prohibit use. Investigate industrial or occupational sources, including direct animal contact.

D. International measures:

Six leptospirosis reference laboratories operate throughout the world under WHO and FAO auspices.

MALARIA

1. Identification. A systemic communicable disease, acute, sometimes severe and often chronic, commonly beginning with indefinite malaise; soon followed by a characteristic shaking chill and rapidly rising temperature; usually accompanied by headache and nausea; ending with profuse sweating. After an interval free of fever the cycle of chills, fever and sweating is repeated, daily, every second day or every third day, depending on the species of malaria parasite. Duration of untreated primary attack varies from a week to a month or longer. Relapses are common and may occur at irregular intervals for several years. Fatality in untreated cases varies from less than 1 per cent to 10 per cent; rarely higher, depending on character of the parasite and degree of host resistance. In treated cases the fatality may be 0.1 per cent and rarely exceeds 0.5 per cent. Clinical diagnosis depends on characteristic intermittent chills and fever, enlargement of the spleen and secondary anaemia, often with mild icterus.

Laboratory confirmation should always be sought through demonstration of malaria parasites in blood films by microscopic examination. Repeated examinations may be necessary. The thick film method is most likely to reveal the parasite; it is often not demonstrable in films from patients recently or actively under treatment.

2. Reservoir and source of infection. Man is the only important reservoir of human malaria although higher apes may harbour *P. malariae.* The immediate source of infection is an infective mosquito.

3. Mode of transmission. Certain species of *Anopheles* ingest human blood containing plasmodia in the gametocyte stage and act as definitive hosts. The parasite develops into sporozoites in from 8 to 35 days depending on species of parasite and temperature to which the vector is exposed. Sporozoites concentrate in the salivary glands and are injected into man as the insect feeds. In the susceptible host, gametocytes usually appear in the blood within 3 to 14 days after onset of symptoms, according to species of parasite. Malaria may be transmitted also by injection of transfusion of blood of infected persons or by use of contaminated hypodermic syringe, e.g. by drug addicts.

4. Incubation period. Average 12 days for *P. falciparum*; 14 days for *P. vivax* and *P. ovale*; 30 days for *P. malariae.* With some strains of *P. vivax,* primary attack may be delayed for 8 to 10 months, the period of latency being known as protracted incubation period. With infection by blood transfusion, incubation is usually short.

5. Period of communicability. For mosquito infection, as long as infective gametocytes are present in the blood of patients. Varies with species and strain of parasite and with response to therapy. May extend indefinitely in quartan malaria; from one to three years in *vivax*; and rarely more than one year in *falciparum*. The infected mosquito remains infective for the rest of its life of a month or more; only the female takes blood meals.

6. Susceptibility and resistance. Susceptibility is universal, the degree sometimes lessened by previous infection. Tolerance to the effects of infection may develop in highly endemic primitive communities where exposure to infective anophelines is continuous over many years.

7. Methods of control

A. Preventive measures:

i. Application of residual insecticide (chlorinated hydrocarbons such as DDT, benzene hexachloride or dieldrin) in suitable formula and dosage on the inside walls of dwellings and on other surfaces upon which vector anophelines habitually rest will generally result in effective malaria control, except where resistance to these insecticides has appeared. When this occurs, the chlorinated hydrocarbons can be replaced by organophosphates such as malathion, or carbamate compounds such as sevin. These are effective in residual application. Ideally, entire communities should be included in a spraying project, to be carried forward year after year until malaria ceases to be endemic. Country-wide effort over four consecutive years has, in some instances, eradicated malaria in a particular region.

ii. Where residual insecticide is not available, nightly spraying of living and sleeping quarters with a liquid or an aerosol preparation of pyrethrum is useful.

iii. In endemic areas, install screens in living and sleeping quarters and use bed nets.

iv. Insect repellents (such as diethyltoluamide, 50 per cent solution, or dimethyl phthalate; or 2-ethylhexane-1,3-diol, commonly called '612') applied to uncovered skin and impregnated in the clothing of persons exposed to bites of vector anophelines, are useful.

v. Sanitary improvements, such as filling and draining to eliminate breeding places of vector anophelines, should not be neglected. Larvicides (such as oil and Paris green) are now not commonly used where residual spraying is effective, but may be useful under special conditions.

vi. Regular use of suppressive drugs in highly malarious areas has special value.

vii. Effective treatment of acute and chronic cases is an important adjunct to malaria control and essential in attempted eradication.

viii. Antimalarial projects profit materially from health education in modern drug treatment and suppression, and in practical measures of prevention.

B. Control of patient, contacts, and the immediate environment:

i. Report to local health authority: obligatory case report in non-endemic areas; limited to authenticated cases is the more practical procedure in endemic areas.

ii. Isolation: none. Patients are protected at night by screens or bed nets.

iii. Concurrent disinfection: a single concurrent residual spraying of the neighbourhood may be useful if a primary or relapsing case occurs in an area not under control, previously free from the disease and where potential vectors are active.

iv. Quarantine: none.

v. Immunisation of contacts: not applicable.

vi. Investigation of contacts: determine history of previous infection among household members or of exposure to anophelines. In advanced stages of eradication, attempt to determine source of infection in every detected case. Treat persons with pyrexia by 'presumptive' single dose therapy even before result of blood examination is known.

vii. Specific treatment:

a. Acute cases in non-immune subjects: Chloroquine diphosphate or sulphate, 600 mg base immediately, followed in 6 hours by 300 mg base, and 300 mg base on each of next two days; or amodiaquine dihydrochloride dihydrate, same regimen and dosage as above.

b. Acute cases: emergency treatment of adults: Chloroquine (hydrochloride, diphosphate or sulphate), 300 to 400 mg base intramuscularly, repeated after 6 hours if patient is unable to take additional drug by mouth (see 7a); or mepacrine methane sulphonate, 300 mg intramuscularly, repeated after 6 hours if necessary; or quinine hydrobromide or dihydrochloride, 600 mg well diluted in a litre of normal saline, glucose-saline or plasma, administered intravenously and slowly, and repeated after 6 hours if necessary; or chloroquine hydrochloride or diphosphate, 400 mg base in 500 ml saline administered intravenously and slowly, once in 24 hours. Parenteral treatment of children should be undertaken with caution, using accurate proportionate dosage in relation to child's weight.

c. Acute attacks in semi-immune subjects: Chloroquine diphosphate or sulphate in a single dose of 600 mg base or amodiaquine dihydrochloride dihydrate in a single dose of 600 mg base will often terminate the acute attack, but further treatment is desirable. Recent emergence of strains of *P. falciparum*, resistant to all except quinine, requires careful observation of response to treatment, and supplement with quinine if necessary.

d. Suppression or prophylaxis: For non-immune persons temporarily residing in endemic areas: chloroquine diphosphate or sulphate, 300 mg base, once or twice weekly, or amodiaquine dihydrochloride dihydrate, 300 mg base, once or twice weekly, depending on degree of endemicity and exposure; or pyrimethamine, 25 mg once weekly, always on the same day each week; or proguanil monohydrochloride, 100 mg daily. Suppressive treatment should be continued for about one month after leaving the endemic area. For semi-immune persons permanently living in malarious areas: chloroquine diphosphate or sulphate, 300 mg base once weekly or once every two weeks; or amodiaquine dihydrochloride dihydrate, 300 mg base once weekly or once every two weeks. In highly endemic areas, pyrimethamine or proguanil should not be used for treatment or suppression, unless these drugs are associated with chloroquine or amodiaquine.

e. Prevention of relapse in vivax infections: for persons who have been on suppressive drugs and are leaving an endemic area, primaquine diphosphate, 15 mg base daily for 14 days, beginning when suppressive drugs are discontinued; or in case of an acute attack may be given following standard treatment with chloroquine or amodiaquine.

The above doses are for adults. Children require lesser amounts in relation to age and weight.

C. Epidemic measures:

A field survey to determine nature and extent of the hyperendemic or epidemic situation is the point of departure. Intensify residual spraying, treat acute cases, and use suppressive drugs. Sometimes the breeding places of anophelines responsible for an epidemic can be eliminated.

D. International measures:

i. Disinsectisation of aircraft, ships or other vehicles on arrival in an area free from malaria or any of its vectors, if the health authority at place of arrival has reason to suspect importation of malaria vectors.

ii. Disinsectisation of aircraft before departure from an area where vectors have become resistant to a particular insecticide, using an insecticide of a type to which the vectors are still susceptible.

iii. Strong effort to maintain rigid anti-mosquito sanitation within the mosquito flight range of all ports and airports.

iv. In special circumstances, administration of antimalarial drugs to migrants, seasonal workers or persons taking part in periodic mass movement into an area or country where malaria has been eliminated.

MEASLES

1. Identification. An acute highly communicable viral disease with prodromal symptoms of coryza, bronchitis, fever and Koplik spots on the buccal mucosa. A characteristic dusky-red blotchy rash appears on the third or fourth day, beginning on face, becoming generalised, lasting four to six days, and sometimes ending in branny desquamation. Leucopenia is usual. In USA, death from uncomplicated measles is rare; such deaths as occur are from secondary pneumonia, mainly in children less than 2 years old, and occasionally from post-infection encephalitis. Measles is a severe disease among malnourished children of lesser-developed countries, with fatality of 5 to 10 per cent or more. Synonyms: Morbilli, Rubeola.

Virus isolation by tissue culture, or demonstration of a rise in specific haemagglutination inhibition, complement-fixing or neutralising antibodies is possible, but the necessary laboratory facilities are often not available.

2. Reservoir and source of infection. Reservoir is man. Source of infection is secretions of nose and throat of infected persons.

3. Mode of transmission. By droplet spread or direct contact with an infected person; indirectly through articles freshly soiled with secretions of nose and throat. One of the most readily transmitted of communicable diseases: in some instances probably air-borne.

4. Incubation period. About 10 days from exposure to initial fever, about 14 days until rash appears; rarely, longer or shorter. Late inoculation with measles immune globulin in attempted passive protection may extend incubation to 21 days.

5. Period of communicability. During catarrhal symptoms, usually about nine days: from four days before to five days after rash appears.

6. Susceptibility and resistance. Practically all persons are susceptible. Permanent acquired immunity is usual after attack. Babies born of mothers who have had the disease are normally immune for the first few months of life.

7. Methods of control

A. Preventive measures:

i. Live attenuated and inactivated measles virus vaccines have been tested and are available for use.

a. Live attenuated vaccine. Single injection induces active immunity in 95 per cent of susceptible children for a known five years. The majority have mild or inapparent non-communicable infection with minimal symptoms; 30 to 40 per cent develop fever, 103°F rectal, on the fourth to the tenth day, lasting two to five days but with little disability; of these 30 to 60 per cent have modified measles rash as fever subsides; a few have coryza, mild cough and Koplik spots. Symptoms are sharply reduced by measles immune globulin administered at the same time but at a different site with a separate syringe; fever, of shorter duration, exceeds 103°F in 15 per cent, rash is less frequent. Serological conversion the same but antibody level slightly less, persisting an observed four years and protecting against natural disease for a known three years. No reports of encephalitis or serious reactions in normal children; rare convulsions (without known sequelae), probably febrile.

b. Inactivated vaccine. Three doses intramuscularly at monthly intervals; reactions are rare; serological conversion in 90 per cent or more of susceptible children; antibody titres distinctly lower than with live vaccine and usually undetectable one year later; 80 to 95 per cent protected against natural disease for an observed two years, longer periods unknown.

c. Combined inactivated and live virus vaccines. One or two doses of inactivated vaccine followed in one to three months by one dose of live attenuated vaccine. Less than 10 per cent have fever exceeding 103°F (rectal), rarely rash, coryza and cough. Serological conversion in 95 per cent, persistence undetermined; protection against natural disease, 97 per cent for observed two years, longer periods unknown.

d. Indications for use. Primarily children with no history of measles, at 9 months of age or as soon thereafter as possible. Adult vaccination rarely indicated, nearly all immune; reactions approximate those of children. Recommended especially for institutional children and those with cystic fibrosis, tuberculosis, heart disease, asthma and other chronic pulmonary diseases. Contra-indications to use of live attenuated vaccine are pregnancy, leukaemia, lymphomas, other generalised neoplasms; resistance-depressing therapy (steroids, irradiation, alkylating agents, antimetabolites); severe illness; an immediately previous administration of large doses of protective immune globulin; egg sensitivity.

ii. Educate the public to special danger of exposing young children to those exhibiting any fever or acute catarrhal symptoms, particularly during years and seasons of epidemic measles.

iii. Health departments and private physicians should encourage the administration of measles immune globulin to susceptible infants and children under 3 years of age in families or institutions where measles occurs. This product carries no risk of serum hepatitis.

B. Control of patient, contacts, and the immediate environment:

i. Report to local health authority: obligatory case report in most states and in many countries. Early report permits better isolation and adequate care for the underprivileged child and provides opportunity for passive protection of contacts.

ii. Isolation: from diagnosis until seven days after apperance of rash, to reduce the patient's risk against secondary invaders and to minimise transfer of measles to susceptible contacts, especially children less than 3 years old.

iii. Concurrent disinfection: all articles soiled with secretions of nose and throat.

iv. Quarantine: impractical and of no value in large communities. Exclusion of exposed susceptible school children and teachers from school and from all public gatherings until 14 days from the last exposure may be justifiable in sparsely settled, non-endemic rural areas. If date of single exposure is reasonably certain, an exposed susceptible child may be allowed to attend school for the first seven days of incubation. Quarantine of institutions, wards or dormitories for young children is of value; strict segregation of infants if measles occurs in an institution.

v. Immunisation of contacts: administration of measles immune (gamma) globulin, especially indicated for children less than 2 years old. Given within three days after first exposure to known measles will avert the attack in most instances and almost certainly modify it; maximum duration of immunity about three weeks. Given between four and six days after first exposure, modification may be expected and probably the usual lasting immunity; given after the sixth day, little effect. For protection, the dosage of measles immune globulin is 0.25 ml per kg of body weight; for modification 0.05 ml per kg.

vi. Investigation of contacts: search for exposed susceptible children under 3 years of age is profitable. Carriers are unknown.

vii. Specific treatment: none. Treat complications with an appropriate antibiotic or sulphadiazine.

C. Epidemic measures:

i. Examine exposed children and known susceptible adult contacts daily and record body temperature. Isolate promptly susceptible persons exhibiting a rise of temperature of 0.5°C (1.0°F) or more, pending diagnosis.

ii. Schools should not be closed nor classes discontinued; provide daily observation of children by physician or nurse and remove sick children promptly.

iii. In institutional outbreaks, protective doses of measles immune (gamma) globulin should be given to all susceptibles to check spread of the disease and to reduce fatality. If new admissions are unavoidable protect them also. Exclude visitors under 16 years of age, whether the outbreak is in the institution or in the community. Removal of patients during the pre-eruptive period may prevent an outbreak.

iv. In non-immunised rural villages of lesser developed countries measles is a highly fatal disease. Characteristically it occurs in periodic epidemics, being absent in the intervals. Outbreaks progress slowly among pre-school children compared with school children and when the start is during a long school vacation. The course is frequently over several months. Prompt community immunisation by vaccination on first report of cases has the potentiality of restricting outbreaks, especially among young children where fatality is greatest.

D. International measures: none.

MENINGOCOCCAL MENINGITIS

1. Identification. An acute bacterial disease characterised by sudden onset with fever, intense headache, nausea and often vomiting, signs of meningeal irritation, and frequently a petechial rash. Delirium and coma often appear early; occasional fulminating cases exhibit signs of collapse and shock from onset. Meningococcaemia without extension to the meninges occurs occasionally and should be suspected in cases of otherwise unexplained acute febrile illness associated with petechial rash and leucocytosis. With modern chemotherapy a fatality of less than 5 per cent is usual, supplanting the former 40 to 50 per cent; this varies greatly under both endemic and epidemic conditions. Synonyms: Cerebrospinal Fever, Meningococcal Infection.

2. Reservoir and source of infection. Meningococci usually can be cultivated from the blood, the spinal fluid, and the nasopharynx. Stained smears from petechiae examined microscopically may reveal the infectious agent.

A group of purulent meningitides secondary to parameningeal or general infection, commonly related to nose, accessory nasal sinuses, ear or lung, present clinical signs and symptoms ordinarily indistinguishable from those of meningococcal meningitis. The differentiation is microbiologic. The commoner infectious agents are pneumococci, haemolytic and other streptococci, *H. influenzae, Staphylococcus aureus*, and less common, but of increasing frequency in recent years, are members of the colon-aerogenes-proteus group, *Salmonella, Pseudomonas aeroginosa* and others. A variety of mycoses occasionally and in meningitis. *H. influenzae* meningitis may also occur as a primary suppurative meningitis, i.e. without evidence of local or general disease other than cases. Carrier prevalence of 25 per cent or more may exist without cases. During epidemics more than half of a military organisation may be healthy carriers of the responsible strain of meningococcus.

3. Mode of transmission. By direct contact with infected persons and by droplet spread. Indirect contact has little significance because the meningococcus is highly susceptible to chilling and drying.

4. Incubation period. Varies from two to ten days, commonly three to four.

5. Period of communicability. Until meningococci are no longer present in discharges from nose and mouth. Meningococci usually disappear from the nasopharynx within 24 hours after administration of an appropriate chemotherapeutic agent.

6. Susceptibility and resistance. Susceptibility to the clinical disease is slight as shown by the low ratio of cases to carriers. Type, degree, and duration of immunity after attack are unknown. There are no generally accepted methods for inducing artificial immunity.

7. Methods of control

A. Preventive measures:

i. Health education as to personal hygiene and necessity of avoiding direct contact and droplet infection.

ii. Prevention of overcrowding in living quarters, public transportation, working places and especially in barracks, camps and ships.

B. Control of patient, contacts, and the immediate environment:

i. Report to local health authority. Obligatory case report in most states and countries.

ii. Isolation: for 24 hours after start of chemotherapy.

iii. Concurrent disinfection: of discharges from the nose and throat and of articles soiled therewith. Terminal cleaning.

iv. Quarantine: no complete quarantine; surveillance is profitable.

v. Immunisation of contacts: none.

vi. Investigation of contacts: impractical.

vii. Specific treatment: penicillin is the drug of choice, given intravenously for 24 hours, then orally. Sulphadiazine by mouth may be used if strains are sensitive.

C. Epidemic measures:

i. Increase the separation of individuals and the ventilation of living and sleeping quarters for such groups of people as are especially exposed to infection because of occupation or some necessity of living condition.

ii. Mass chemoprophylaxis with sulphadiazine (0.5 g for children, 1.0 g for adults, each 12 hours for four doses) will reduce the carrier rate and limit spread of the disease in control of outbreaks in institutional and military populations where all members of the community can be included, where medical supervision is practicable, and where sulphonamide-resistant strains are absent or few. Piecemeal use through limitation to direct contacts or selected segments of a population serves no useful purpose; it encourages development of resistant strains. No satisfactory prophylactic agent exists for populations harbouring a large proportion of resistant strains.

PLAGUE

1. Identification. A highly fatal infectious disease with toxaemia, high fever, shock, fall in blood pressure, rapid and irregular pulse, restlessness, staggering gait, mental confusion, prostration, delirium and coma. Conjunctival infection is common; haemorrhages may occur. Sporadic cases are mainly of two clinical forms:

a. Bubonic plague, the more common, with acutely inflamed and painful swelling of lymph nodes draining the site of original infection. Secondary invasion of the blood often leads to localised infection in diverse parts of the body. A secondary, often terminal, pneumonia has special significance as the means by which primary pneumonic plague is engendered.

b. Septicaemic plague, proved by blood smear or blood culture, is rare; it is a form of bubonic plague in which the bubo is obscure. During epidemics, two other forms are recognised:

c. Primary pneumonic plague and

d. Tonsillar septicaemic plague. Though uncommon, primary pneumonic plague occurs in localised and sometimes devastating epidemics among persons living under crowded conditions. Untreated bubonic plague has a fatality of 25 to 50 per cent, primary septicaemic plague and pneumonic plague are usually fatal. Modern therapy materially reduces the fatality of bubonic plague; pneumonic plague also responds if recognised and treated early.

Diagnosis is confirmed by demonstrating the infectious agent in fluid from buboes, in blood, or in sputum of pneumonic plague.

2. Reservoir and source of infection. Wild rodents are the natural reservoir of plague and numerous species in many parts of the world are subject to periodic epizootics. The infection may transfer to domestic rats in urban or rural areas where rats and wild rodents have common contact. The immediate source of infection in bubonic plague of man is an infective flea; in pneumonic infection, exhaled droplets and sputum of patients.

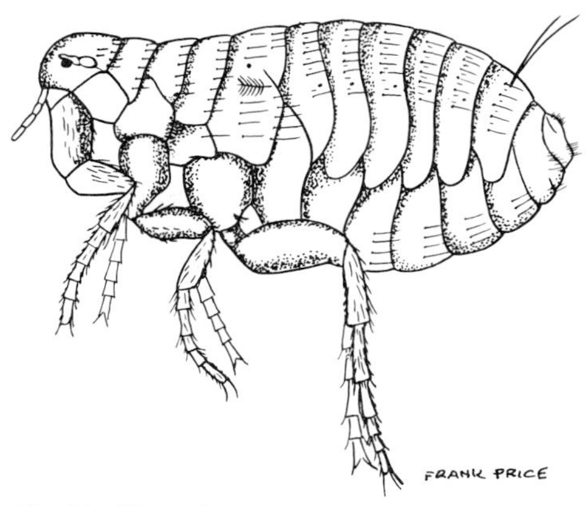

Fig. 7.6 The rat flea.

3. Mode of transmission. Bubonic plague is transmitted by bite of an infective (blocked) rat flea, *Zenopsylla cheopis* and other species. Pneumonic plague and tonsillar plague are spread by contact or by air-borne route from patients with primary pneumonic plague or from patients with bubonic plague who develop terminal plague pneumonia. Accidental infections occur among laboratory workers.

4. Incubation period. From two to six days in bubonic plague; three to four days in pneumonic plague. May be shorter, rarely longer.

5. Period of communicability. Bubonic plague is not directly transmitted from person to person except through terminal plague pneumonia. Fleas remain infected for days or weeks under suitable conditions of temperature and humidity, or may clear themselves of infection. Infective (blocked) fleas are short-lived (three to four days). Pneumonic plague is usually intensely communicable under climatic or social conditions which lead to overcrowding in unsanitary dwellings.

6. Susceptibility and resistance. Susceptibility is general. Bubonic infection is occasionally no more than a localised infection of short duration, pestis minor. Immunity after recovery is temporary and relative.

7. Methods of control

A. Preventive measures:

i. Active immunisation with a vaccine of killed bacteria may confer some protection for several months when administered in two or three doses at weekly intervals; repeated stimulating injections are necessary for continued protection. Vaccines prepared with living avirulent strains may confer satisfactory immunity in one dose, repeated once yearly. Vaccination of persons travelling or living in areas of high incidence and of laboratory workers handling plague bacilli is justifiable but not to be relied upon as the principal preventive measure.

ii. Periodic surveys in endemic and potentially epidemic areas to determine prevalence of rats and rat fleas; suppression of rats by poisoning or trapping in urban areas. Continuing inspection and survey of wild rodents and their ectoparasites in areas of sylvatic plague. Where plague is present or threatening, systematic search for infected fleas by pooling methods.

iii. Ratproofing of buildings and reduction of breeding places and harbourages, particularly in docks and warehouses.

iv. Rat control on ships by ratproofing or periodic fumigation, combined, when necessary, with destruction of rats and their fleas in vessels and cargoes arriving from plague localities.

v. Health education of the public in endemic areas on mode of transmission and protective measures against fleas and rats.

B. Control of patient, contacts, and the immediate environment:

i. Report to local health authority: case report of suspect and confirmed cases universally required by International Sanitary Regulations.

ii. Isolation: Hospitalise all patients if practicable; ordinary aseptic precautions suffice for patients with bubonic plague; strict isolation is required for patients developing primary pneumonic plague or plague pneumonia.

iii. Concurrent disinfection: sputum and purulent discharges, and articles soiled therewith; urine and faeces of patients. Terminal cleaning. Bodies of persons dying of plague should be handled with strict aseptic precautions.

iv. Quarantine: for contacts of bubonic plague, disinfestation with insecticide powder, such as 5 to 10 per cent DDT or pyrethrum in talc, and surveillance for six days; for contacts of pneumonic plague, dust with insecticide powder, quarantine for six days with close observation for developing illness, including recording of body temperature every four hours, start specific therapy as soon as fever appears.

v. Immunisation of contacts: none. The management of contacts should concentrate on quarantine and close observation with prompt institution of specific treatment at first appearance of fever. When circumstances or resources do not permit, chemoprophylaxis may be necessary, broad spectrum antibiotics at least 1.0 g per day, or sulphonamides 2.0 to 3.0 g per day, for six days.

vi. Investigation of contacts and source of infection: Search for infected rodents and fleas or exposure to plague pneumonia. Focal attack on fleas should precede anti-rat measures, using an appropriate insecticide powder with residual effect. Dust rat runs and harbourages in and about known or suspected plague premises or areas. Disinfest by dusting or spraying the houses, outhouses and household furnishings. Dust the persons and clothing of immediate contacts and all other residents in the immediate vicinity. Supplemental suppression of rat populations by poisoning or trapping then follows.

vii. Specific treatment: Streptomycin, tetracyclines and chloramphenicol used early are highly effective. Results are good even in pneumonic plague if therapy is begun within 24 hours of onset, but poor thereafter. Recurrence of fever during streptomycin therapy may indicate that the infectious agent is resistant, or that a complication has developed, such as secondary pneumonia due to other bacteria; penicillin or other appropriate antibiotic is then indicated. Penicillin is not effective against plague itself. When antibiotics are not available, use sulphonamides.

C. Epidemic measures:

i. Investigate all deaths, with autopsy and laboratory examinations when indicated. Develop case-finding facilities. Establish the best possible provision for diagnosis and treatment. Alert all existing medical facilities toward immediate reporting and toward utilisation of diagnostic and therapy services. Provide adequate laboratory services and supplies of antibiotics.

ii. Institute intensive flea control in expanding circles from known foci.

iii. Institute supplemental rat destruction within affected areas.

iv. Prophylactic administration of broad spectrum antibiotics or sulphadiazine to all medical, nursing and public health personnel exposed to definite and repeated risk of infection may be considered if they cannot be kept under close and frequent observation. Quarantine of hospital personnel to the premises is desirable when patients with pneumonic plague are under treatment.

v. Field workers should protect themselves against fleas by weekly dusting of clothing with insecticide powder. Daily application of insect repellents is a valuable adjunct.

vi. Widespread active immunisation of native populations with a single dose of avirulent living plague bacillus vaccine has proved valuable. Killed vaccines are less useful because of practical difficulties in administering repeated injections.

D. International measures:

i. Telegraphic notification by governments to WHO and to adjacent countries of the first imported, first transferred or first non-imported case of plague in a local area previously free of the disease. Report newly discovered or reactivated foci of plague among rodents.

ii. Measures applicable to ships, aircraft and land transport arriving from plague areas are specified in International Sanitary Regulations, WHO, second annotated edition, Geneva, 1961.

iii. All ships should be periodically de-ratted, or kept permanently in such condition that rat populations are reduced to a minimum.

iv. Buildings of ports and airports should be ratproofed, with application of appropriate residual insecticide every six months and de-ratting with effective rodenticide.

v. International travellers: plague-infected persons or suspects are not permitted to depart from a country. No country currently requires immunisation against plague for entry. Because protection by vaccines is brief, immunisation should be completed just before anticipated exposure.

POLIOMYELITIS

1. Indentification. An acute viral illness with wide range of severity including inapparent infection, nonparalytic and paralytic disease. Symptoms include fever, headache, gastrointestinal disturbance, malaise and stiffness of neck and back, with or without paralysis. The virus invades the alimentary tract; viraemia may then follow with invasion of central nervous system and selective involvement of motor cells resulting in flaccid paralysis, most commonly of lower extremities. Site of paralysis depends upon location of nerve cell destruction in spinal cord or brain stem; characteristically is asymmetrical. Nonparalytic poliomyelitis is a type of aseptic meningitis. Incidence of inapparent infection usually exceeds clinical cases by more than a hundredfold. Case fatality for paralytic cases varies from 2 to 10 per cent in epidemics and increases markedly with age. Synonym: Infantile Paralysis.

2. Reservoir and source of infection. Reservoir is man, most frequently persons with inapparent infections, especially children. Source of infection is pharyngeal secretions and faeces of infected persons.

3. *Mode of transmission.* Direct contact through close association with infected persons. In rare instances milk has been a vehicle. No reliable evidence of spread by other foods, insects or virus contaminated sewage; water is rarely, if ever, involved. Whether faeces or pharyngeal secretions have the greater importance in transmission has not been determined, and may vary according to environmental circumstances. Virus is more readily detectable and for a longer period in faeces than in the throat, but epidemiological evidence suggests that oral–oral spread may be more important than faecal–oral spread, especially where sanitation is good.

4. *Incubation period.* Commonly 7 to 12 days, with a range from 3 to 21 days.

5. *Period of communicability.* Poliovirus is demonstrable in throat secretions as early as 36 hours and in the faeces 72 hours after infection; it occurs in both clinical and inapparent cases. Virus persists in the throat for approximately one week and in the faeces for three to six weeks or longer.

6. *Susceptibility and resistance.* Susceptibility to infection is general but few infected persons develop paralysis. Type-specific resistance of long duration follows both clinically recognisable and inapparent infection. Second attacks are rare and result from infection with poliovirus of a different type. Infants born of immune mothers have transient passive immunity. Removal of tonsils, recent or remote, predisposes to bulbar involvement. Trauma, and injection of precipitated antigens or certain other substances, may provoke paralysis in an already infected but symptomless person, the paralysis tending to be localised in the affected limb or appearing there first. Excessive muscular fatigue in the prodromal period may likewise predispose to paralytic involvement. An increased susceptibility to paralytic poliomyelitis is associated with pregnancy.

7. *Methods of control*

A. Preventive measures:

i. Active immunisation of all susceptible persons against the three types of poliovirus. Give priority to ages with highest incidence and to selected groups at unusual risk. Two methods are available: immunisation by either method may begin as early as 6 weeks of age, although delay to 4 to 6 months avoids the depressive effect of maternal antibody on immune response.

a. Oral poliovirus vaccine provides a high level of immunity by means of an alimentary infection with an attenuated poliovirus. It is administered by mouth in one of two ways. One procedure is to give a separate dose of each of the three monovalent vaccines. In the USA, where incidence is low, a recent recommendation for order of administration is types 2, 1 and 3, with the interval between types 2 and 1 to be not less than eight weeks. The other procedure is to give two doses of a trivalent mixture of the three types. In both procedures an interval of six weeks should separate each dose of vaccine and regimen should be augmented by a later dose of the trivalent mixture after six months or more. In the United Kingdom, three doses of trivalent vaccine are given at four to six week intervals.

b. Formalin inactivated poliovirus vaccine also provides immunity but does not prevent, to the same degree, alimentary infection and excretion of virus by those subsequently infected. In the USA, a basic series of four injections, preferably initiated in early infancy, is recommended, the first three about six weeks apart, the fourth, six months or more after the third.

c. Additional booster inoculations with either the oral or inactivated vaccine are indicated with the threat of an epidemic, travel to a hyperendemic area and at the time of entering school. If not previously immunised at school, give a full series.

ii. Health education of the public on the advantages of immunisation in early childhood, on modes of spread and the desirability of avoiding excessive physical exertion during epidemic times.

B. Control of patient, contacts, and the immediate environment:

i. Report to local authority: obligatory case report in most states and countries. Each case is to be designated as paralytic or nonparalytic. Supplemental reports, giving vaccine history, virus type, severity and persistence of residual paralysis for more than 60 days after onset, are necessary measures for effective control in areas where incidence is low.

ii. Isolation: isolation precautions for not more than seven days in hospital management of the patient. Of little value under home conditions because spread of infection is greatest in the prodromal period.

ii. Concurrent disinfection: of throat discharges and faeces and of articles soiled therewith. In communities with modern and adequate sewage disposal systems, faeces and urine can be discharged directly into sewers without preliminary disinfection. Terminal cleaning.

iv. Quarantine: of no community value because of large numbers of unrecognised infections in the population.

v. Immunisation of contacts: vaccination of familial and other close contacts contributes little to immediate control. Usually the virus is widely spread among them by the time the first case is recognised. Passive protection with immune (gamma) globulin in amounts of 0.3 ml per kg of body weight may be expected to prevent only an occasional case in an exposed family. In instances of known single exposure at a susceptible age, it may have considerable value if given within two days of exposure. On occurrence of a single paralytic case in a community, children attending the same school or living on the same street as the patient may be offered oral vaccine.

vi. Investigation of contacts: thorough search for sick persons, especially children, to assure treatment of unrecognised and unreported cases. Foot drop, scoliosis and other deformities resulting in functional impairment may be late manifestations of initially mild or inapparent illness.

vii. Specific treatment: none. Attention during the acute illness to the complications of paralysis; may require expert knowledge, especially for patients in need of respiratory assistance.

C. Epidemic measures:

i. Institute mass vaccination with oral vaccine at the earliest indication of an outbreak. Use monovalent vaccine of the virus type causing the outbreak. If typing facilities are not available, use trivalent vaccine.

ii. Organise mass vaccination campaigns to achieve the most rapid and complete immunisation of epidemiologically relevant groups, especially young children. Locate vaccination centres in relation to population densities, taking advantage of normal social patterns. Schools often meet these criteria. Requiring individual records of each person vaccinated slows distribution markedly; a simple tally by age group is rapid and practical. Subsequent community sample surveys give adequate measure of the numbers immunised.

iii. With the use of mass immunisation, disruption of community activities such as closing schools and other places of population aggregation is no longer necessary.

iv. Postpone elective nose and throat operations until after the epidemic has ended.

v. Provide facilities in strategically located centres for specialised medical care of acutely ill patients and rehabilitation of those with significant paralysis.

D. International measures:

i. Susceptible international travellers visiting areas of hyperendemic prevalence, especially the tropics, should be adequately immunised.

ii. WHO-designated Enterovirus Reference Centres are ready to identify poliomyelitis and other enteroviruses sent to them from national virus reference laboratories, to provide laboratory diagnostic aid and to advise on control measures in epidemics. They have available information on current prevalence of different enterovirus types.

Q FEVER

1. Identification. Onset is sudden with chilly sensations, retrobulbar headache, weakness, malaise and severe sweats; there is great variation in severity and duration. A pneumonitis occurs in most cases, with mild cough, scanty expectoration, chest pain, minimal physical findings, and little or no upper respiratory involvement. Chronic general infections have been reported; inapparent infections occur. Fatality of untreated patients is about 1 per cent with treatment negligible, except in aged persons.

Laboratory diagnosis by complement-fixation or agglutination tests, with demonstration of rise in antibody between acute and convalescent stages; or by recovery of the infectious agent from blood of the patient, a procedure hazardous to laboratory workers.

2. Reservoir and source of infection. Ticks, wild animals (bandicoots), cattle, sheep and goats are natural reservoirs, with infection inapparent. The commonest source of human infection is dust contaminated by products of domestic animals, particularly placental tissues, birth fluids and raw milk. Other sources include animal carcasses, contaminated wool, straw, fertiliser and laundry.

3. Mode of transmission. Commonly by air-borne dissemination of rickettsiae in or near contaminated premises, in establishments processing infected animals or their by-products, and at necropsy. Raw milk from infected cows may be responsible for some cases; also contracted by direct contact with infected animals or other contaminated materials.

4. Incubation period. Usually two to three weeks.

5. Period of communicability. No evidence of direct transmission from man to man.

6. Susceptibility and resistance. Susceptibility is general.

7. Methods of control

A. Preventive measures:

i. Immunisation with inactivated vaccine prepared from *R. burnetii* infected yolk sac is so useful in protecting laboratory workers that it should be considered for others in hazardous occupations.

ii. Pasteurisation of milk from cows, goats and sheep at 62.9°C (145°F) for 30 minutes, or at 71·6°C (161°) for 15 seconds by the high-temperature short-time method, or boiling, inactivates rickettsiae.

iii. Public health education on sources of infection and the necessary hygienic practices of pasteurisation of milk and adequate disposal of animal placentas, also strict hygienic measures in cow sheds and barns (dust, urine, faeces, rodents) during epizootics.

iv. Control infection of animals by vaccination and by regulating movement of infected livestock. The control of Q Fever in man depends upon control of the disease in animals.

B. Control of patient, contacts, and the immediate environment:

i. Report to local health authority, in selected endemic areas (USA); in many countries not a reportable disease.

ii. Isolation: none.

iii. Concurrent disinfection: of sputum, excreta and blood, and articles freshly soiled therewith. Precautions at postmortem examination.

iv. Quarantine: none.

v. Immunisation of contacts: unnecessary.

vi. Investigation of contacts and source of infection: search for history of contact with cattle, sheep and goats, consumption of raw milk, or direct or indirect association with a laboratory handling *R. burnetii.*

vii. Specific treatment: the tetracycline antibiotics or chloramphenicol, administered orally and continued for several days after patient is afebrile; reinstitute if relapse occurs.

C. Epidemic measures:

Outbreaks are generally of short duration: control measures are essentially limited to observation of exposed persons and antibiotic therapy for those becoming ill. In hyperendemic situations immunisation should be considered for persons at greatest risk.

D. International measures:

Control of importation of domestic animals, especially goats, sheep and cattle.

RABIES

1. Identification. An almost invariably fatal acute encephalitis. Onset is with a sense of apprehension, headaches, fever, malaise, and indefinite sensory changes often referred to site of a preceding local wound resulting from bite of a rabid animal. The disease progresses to paresis or paralysis, with spasm of muscles of deglutition on attempts to swallow. Delirium and convulsions follow. Death is from respiratory paralysis. Usual duration is from two to six days, sometimes longer. Synonym: Hydrophobia.

Other diseases resulting from bites of animals include pasteurellosis from cat and dog bites, tularaemia, rat-bite fever, tetanus and cat-scratch fever.

2. Reservoir and source of infection. Reservoirs include many wild and domestic *Canidae,* including dog, fox, coyote, wolf, cat, skunk, raccoon and other biting mammals, vampire and fruit-eating bats in the USA, Canada, Europe and the Middle East. Source of infection in rabies of man is saliva of rabid animals.

3. Mode of transmission. By bite of a rabid animal or rarely by saliva of such animals entering a scratch or other fresh break in the skin. Transmission from man to man is possible but not confirmed; the saliva is known to be infectious. Air-borne spread from bats to man in caves where bats are roosting.

4. *Incubation period.* Usually four to six weeks, occasionally shorter or longer, depending on extent of laceration, site of wound in relation to richness of nerve supply, and other factors.

5. *Period of communicability.* In dogs and most biting animals, for three to five days before onset of clinical signs, and during the course of the disease. Bats may shed virus for many months.

6. *Susceptibility and resistance.* Most warm-blooded animals are susceptible. Natural immunity in man is unknown.

7. *Methods of control*

A. Preventive measures:

i. Specific prevention of rabies in man is by vaccination. Protection depends on administration soon after injury, usually on 14 consecutive days; in severe or multiple bites sometimes for 21 days. Vaccination often is supplemented by passive immunisation with hyperimmune serum. The following is a guide in different circumstances:

a. If the animal is apprehended, confine and observe for 10 days. Give vaccine to exposed person at first physical sign or laboratory evidence of rabies in the observed animal.

b. If animal is not apprehended and rabies is known to be present in the area, start vaccination immediately.

c. In severe bites, particularly in region of head, face and neck, when there is any likelihood of the animal being rabid, give a dose of rabies hyperimmune serum immediately, follow promptly with a full course of vaccine, with booster doses of non-nervous tissue vaccine at 10 days and again 20 days after initial series is completed. An intradermal sensitivity test should precede administration of serum.

d. Rabies vaccination carries a small risk of postvaccinal encephalitis. This must be weighed against the risk of contracting rabies. Vaccine should not be given unless the skin is broken. The schedule of inoculations may be reduced if the person has had previous antirabic inoculations. If severe sensitivity appears in the course of vaccination, either with suspensions of nervous tissue or avianised (duck embryo) vaccine, complete the series with the other type.

ii. Wounds caused by bite or scratch of an animal with rabies or suspected rabies should be cleaned promptly with soap or detergent solution. Hyperimmune serum may be infiltrated beneath the bite wound; do not suture for several days.

iii. Education of the public in the necessity of complying with restrictions on dogs, of vaccinating dogs, of seeking immediate medical attention if bitten by a dog, of confining and observing animals that have inflicted bites, of prompt reporting to the police of dogs manifesting strange behaviour, and of reporting rabies and bites by animals to the local health authority. Warn against picking up or handling sick or strangely-acting bats.

iv. Detention and clinical observation for 10 days of dogs, bats and other animals known to have bitten a person or having suspicious signs of rabies. Animals should not be killed until existence of rabies is established. Rabid animals usually have a change in behaviour, with excitability or paralysis, followed by death. Signs and symptoms appear within 10 days of being bitten, except by bats, when they may not appear for months.

v. Immediate submission to a laboratory of iced intact heads of animals dying of suspected rabies. Confirmation of rabies is by demonstration of Negri bodies in brain, by animal inoculation, or by demonstration of virus by fluorescent antibody test.

vi. Immediate destruction or six months' detention in approved pound or kennel of unvaccinated dogs or cats bitten by known rabid animals. If previously vaccinated, revaccinate and restrain for 30 days.

vii. Register and license all dogs. Owned dogs in congested areas should be kept on leash when not within homes of owners. Collect and destroy stray dogs by public authority. Emphasise preventive vaccination of dogs; attenuated live vaccines administered intramuscularly confer longer lasting immunity than inactivated vaccines.

viii. Co-operative programmes with wildlife conservation authorities toward reducing numbers of foxes, skunks, and other wildlife hosts in areas of sylvatic rabies.

B. Control of patient, contacts, and the immediate environment:

i. Report to local health authority: obligatory case report required in most states and countries.

ii. Isolation: for duration of the illness.

iii. Concurrent disinfection: of saliva and articles soiled therewith. Immediate attendants should be warned of hazard of inoculation with saliva and provided with rubber gloves and protective gowns.

iv. Quarantine: none.

v. Immunisation of contacts: contacts of a patient with rabies need not be vaccinated.

vi. Investigation of contacts and source of infection: search for rabid animal and for persons and other animals bitten.

vii. Specific treatment: for clinical rabies, none.

C. Epidemic measures:

Applicable only to animals: a sporadic disease in man.

i. Establish area control under authority of state laws, public health regulations and local ordinances, in co-operation with appropriate wildlife conservation and livestock sanitary authorities.

ii. Carry out widespread vaccination of dogs, preferably with an attenuated live vaccine, through officially sponsored intensified programmes providing mass immunisation at temporary and emergency stations.

iii. Strictly enforce regulations requiring collection, detention and destruction of ownerless or stray dogs, and of unvaccinated dogs found off owner's premises.

D. International measures:

Strict compliance by common carriers and by travellers with national laws and regulations that institute quarantine or require vaccination of dogs.

SCABIES

1. Identification. An infectious disease of the skin caused by a crab-shaped mite whose penetration is visible as papules or vesicles housing males and nymphs, or as tiny linear burrows containing females and their eggs. Lesions are prominent around finger webs, anterior surfaces of wrists and elbows, anterior axillary folds, belt line, thighs, external genitalia in men, nipples, abdomen and lower portion of buttocks in women. Itching is intense, especially at night, but complications are few except when lesions become secondarily infected by scratching.

Diagnosis may be established by locating the female in its burrow and identifying it microscopically.

2. Reservoir and source of infection. Reservoir is man. Sarcoptes of animals can live on man but do not reproduce in the skin.

3. Mode of transmission. Transfer of parasites is by direct contact and to a limited extent from undergarments or soiled sheets freshly contaminated by infected persons. The disease is frequently of venereal origin.

4. Incubation period. Several days, or even weeks, before itching is noticed.

5. Period of communicability. Until mites and eggs are destroyed by treatment, ordinarily after one or occasionally two courses of treatment a week apart.

6. Susceptibility and resistance. Anyone may become infected or reinfected.

7. Methods of control

A. Preventive measures:

Public health education on the need for maintaining cleanliness of person, garments and bedclothes.

B. Control of patient, contacts, and the immediate environment:

i. Report to local health authority: obligatory report of epidemics, no individual case report.

ii. Isolation: exclude infected children from school until treated adequately.

iii. Concurrent disinfection: proper laundering of underwear, sheets and blankets.

iv. Quarantine: none.

v. Immunisation of contacts: none.

vi. Investigation of contacts: search for unreported or unrecognised cases among companions or household members. Single infections in a family are uncommon.

vii. Specific treatment: a bath followed by application of 20 to 25 per cent emulsion of benzyl benzoate or 1 per cent benzene hexachloride ointment to the whole body. Medication is usually applied with a brush with particular attention to infected areas. The following day a cleansing bath is taken and a change made to fresh clothing and bed linen. Itching may persist for days and is not to be regarded as a sign of superinfection. This is important, for overtreatment is common. In perhaps 5 per cent of cases a second course of treatment is necessary after an interval of seven to ten days. Five per cent sulphur ointment is a time-honoured, effective treatment now little used; the regimen is similar to that just given.

C. Epidemic measures:

i. Treatments are undertaken on a co-ordinated mass basis.

ii. Case-finding efforts are redoubled in order to screen whole families, military units or institutions.

iii. Soap and facilities for mass bathing and laundering are essential.

iv. Health education of infected persons and of others at risk, as well as treatment. Co-operation of civilian and/or military authorities is needed.
D. International measures: none.

SCHISTOSOMIASIS

1. Identification. A blood-fluke (trematode) disease with adult male and female worms living in veins of the host. Eggs deposited there produce minute granulomata and scars in organs where they lodge. Symptomatology is related to the life cycle of the parasite: *Schistosoma mansoni* and *S. japonicum* give rise primarily to intestinal and *S. haematobium* to urinary manifestations. The complications that arise from chronic infection are the important considerations: liver involvement and portal hypertension in the intestinal form, obstruction and superimposed infection in the urinary disease. Synonym: Bilharziasis.

2. Reservoir and source of infection. Man is the principal reservoir of both *S. haematobium* and *S. mansoni*, although primates and other animals are naturally infected with both species. Dogs, pigs, cattle, water buffalo, horses, field mice and wild rats are epidemiologically important animal hosts of *S. japonicum*. Immediate source of infection is water contaminated with larval forms (cercariae) derived from snails.

3. Mode of transmission. The eggs of *S. haematobium* leave the body mainly with urine, those of *S. mansoni* and *S. japonicum* with faeces. The egg hatches in water and the liberated larva or miracidium enters a suitable fresh-water snail host. Free swimming, cercariae emerge from the snail after several weeks and penetrate human skin, usually while the person is working, swimming or wading in water. They enter the blood stream, are carried to blood vessels of the liver, develop to maturity, and then migrate to veins of the abdominal cavity. Adult forms of *S. mansoni* and *S. japonicum* usually remain in mesenteric veins; those of *S. haematobium* usually migrate through anastomosis into the pelvic veins. Eggs are deposited in venules and by necrosis of tissue escape into the lumen of bowel or bladder, or lodge in other organs.

4. Incubation period. Systemic manifestations usually begin when worms are reaching maturity, four to six weeks after infection. Eggs usually are found in faeces or urine a week or two after onset of symptoms.

5. Period of communicability. As long as eggs are discharged in urine or faeces of infected persons, which may be 25 years or longer. Infected snails may give off cercariae for several months.

6. Susceptibility and resistance. Susceptibility is universal; whether or not resistance develops as a result of infection is controversial.

7. Methods of control
A. Preventive measures:
i. Disposal of faeces and urine so that eggs will not reach bodies of fresh water containing snail intermediate host. Control of animals infected with *S. japonicum* is desirable, but usually not practical.

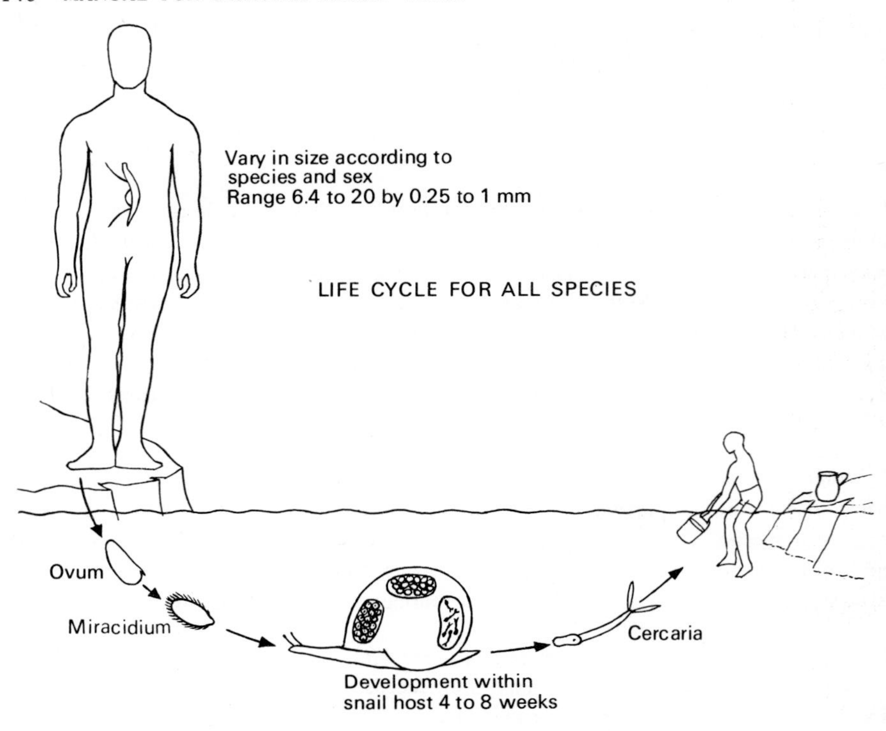

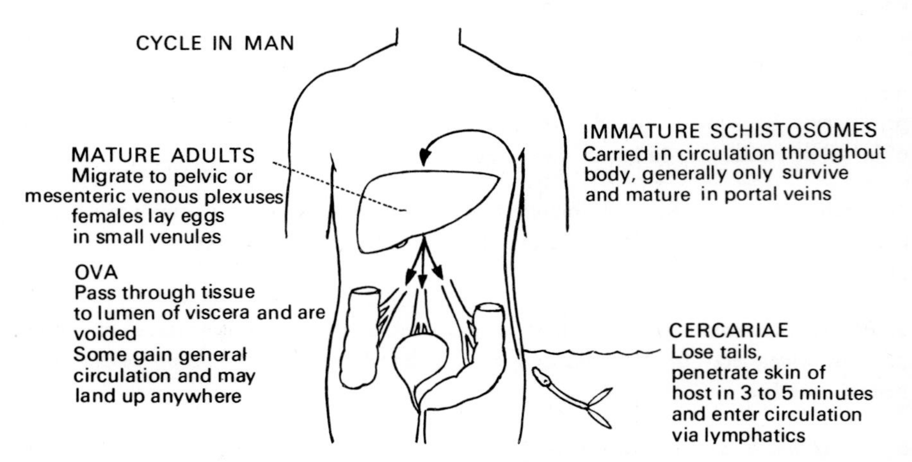

Fig. 7.7 *Schistosoma* species (the blood fluke). Three main species are to be found; *S. haematobium* in the area from Africa to Iran, *S. mansoni* in Africa and South America, and *S. japonicum* in the Far East.

ii. Improved irrigation and agricultural practices, drainage and reclamation of swamps.

iii. Treatment of snail breeding places with molluscicides, copper sulphate, sodium pentachlorophenate, copper pentachlorophenate and others.

iv. Provision of water for drinking, bathing, and washing clothes from sources free from cercariae.

v. Provision of cercaria-repellent or protective clothing for persons required to enter contaminated water.

vi. Education of people in endemic areas regarding mode of transmission and methods of protection.

vii. Mass treatment of infected persons in endemic areas may help to reduce transmission through lessened severity and duration of the disease; in the past this has not materially reduced prevalence.

B. Control of patient, contacts, and the immediate environment:

i. Report to local health authority in selected endemic areas; in many countries not a reportable disease.

ii. Isolation: none.

iii. Concurrent disinfection: sanitary disposal of faeces and urine.

iv. Quarantine: none.

v. Immunisation of contacts: none

vi. Investigation of contacts: examine contacts for infection from a common source. Search for source is a community effort.

vii. Specific treatment: for *S. mansoni* and *S. haematobium*, stibophen intramuscularly, for *S. japonicum* tartar emetic intravenously; toxic side effects occur. Also used for other species.

C. Epidemic measures:

In areas of high incidence, or in endemic areas where outside groups such as military forces become infected, determine snail breeding places and treat with molluscicides.

Snails have a high host specificity; expert aid is needed to determine which snails to control. Prohibit entering contaminated water. Provide clean water, examine population for infection, and treat diseased persons.

D. International measures: none.

SHIGELLOSIS

1. Identification. An acute bacterial disease of the intestine characterised by diarrhoea, accompanied by fever and often vomiting, cramps and tenesmus. In severe cases the stools may contain blood, mucus and pus. Under usual circumstances in temperate climates the disease is self-limited, complications are rare, mild cases and inapparent infections are numerous, and fatality is less than 1 per cent. In epidemics in tropical areas with much overcrowding and poor sanitation fatality is greater, sometimes as much as 10 to 20 per cent, for hospitalised patients. Synonym: Bacillary Dysentery.

Bacteriological diagnosis is by isolation of *Shigella* from faeces, or preferably from rectal swabs.

2. Reservoir and source of infection. Reservoir is man: the source of infection is faeces from an infected person.

3. Mode of transmission. By direct contact through faecal–oral transmission; indirectly, by objects soiled with faeces; by eating contaminated foods, or drinking water or milk contaminated by flies.

4. Incubation period. One to seven days, usually less than four.

5. *Period of communicability.* During acute infection and until the infectious agent is absent from faeces, usually within a few weeks. In rare instances the carrier state may persist for a year or two.

6. *Susceptibility and resistance.* Susceptibility is general but the disease is more common and more severe in children than in adults. The extent of type-specific immunity after attack is unknown. Second attacks are common.

7. *Methods of control*

A. Preventive measures:

i. Sanitary disposal of human faeces.

ii. Public health education in the hygiene of breast feeding, scrupulous cleanliness in preparation, handling and refrigeration of food, boiling of milk and water for infant feeding, and continuous supervision of diet.

iii. Protection and purification of water supplies, see Typhoid Fever.

iv. Pasteurisation of milk and dairy products or boiling of milk, see Typhoid Fever.

v. Sanitary supervision of processing, preparation and serving of all foods, particularly those moist and eaten raw; special attention to provision and use of hand-washing facilities. Protection of foods against contamination by flies.

vi. Fly control and control of fly breeding, see Typhoid Fever.

B. Control of patient, contacts, and the immediate environment:

i. Report to local health authority: case report obligatory in most states and countries. Recognition and report of epidemics has more than usual importance in schools and institutions.

ii. Isolation: during acute illness. Rigid personal precautions by attendants.

iii. Concurrent disinfection: of faeces and of articles soiled therewith. In communities with a modern and adequate sewage disposal system, faeces can be discharged directly into the sewer without preliminary disinfection. Terminal cleaning.

iv. Quarantine: contacts should not be employed as food handlers during period of contact nor before three cultures of faeces at daily intervals are negative.

v. Immunisation of contacts: no known satisfactory method.

vi. Investigation of contacts: search for unrecognised mild cases and convalescent carriers among contacts. For sporadic cases, this is time consuming and gives meagre results.

vii. Specific treatment: fluid and electrolyte replacement is the important consideration. Antimicrobial drugs to which the infectious agent is sensitive may be used.

C. Epidemic measures:

i. Groups of cases of acute diarrhoeal disorders should always be reported to local health authority at once, even in absence of specific identification of the disease.

ii. Investigation of food, water and milk supplies, general sanitation, and search for unrecognised mild cases and carriers.

iii. Prophylactic administration of antibiotics is not indicated.

D. International measures: none.

SMALLPOX

1. *Identification.* An exanthematous disease with sudden onset of fever, malaise,

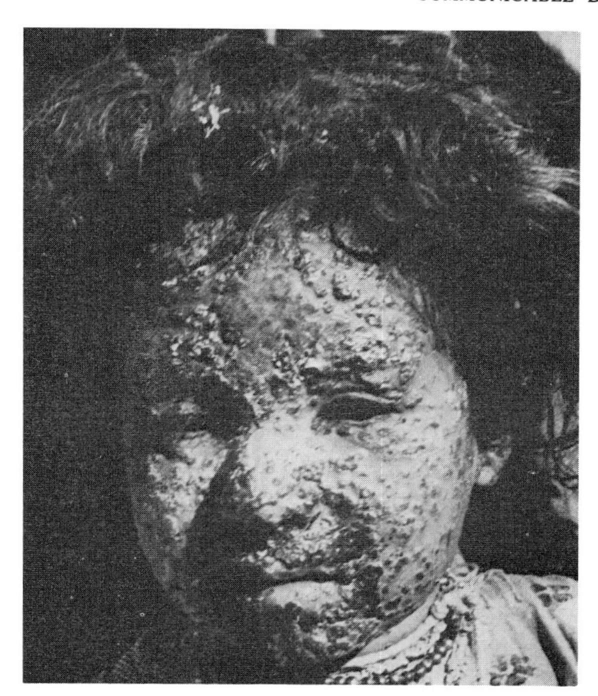

Fig. 7.8 A typical case of smallpox, in Afghanistan (World Health Organisation).

headache, severe backache, abdominal pain and prostration, normally of three to four days' duration with limits of one to five days. The temperature then falls, commonly to normal, and a rash appears which passes through successive stages of macules, papules, vesicles, and pustules, and finally scabs, which fall off at about the end of the third week. The lesions are deeper seated than those of chickenpox. The key to identification is the distribution of the lesions. This is usually symmetrical and general, more profuse on irritated areas, prominences and flexures. Most abundant and earliest on the face, next on forearms and wrists, and favouring the limbs more than trunk; more abundant on shoulders and chest than loins or abdomen. Lesions are sometimes so few as to be overlooked. Synonym: Variola.

Variola major (classical smallpox) is a severe disease which in recent years has run true to type with case fatality of about 30 per cent. An uncommon fulminating form, haemorrhagic smallpox, is characterised by haemorrhages into the skin or from orifices, and death within three or four days, usually before the typical rash appears. Variola minor (alastrim) is a milder form also running true to type, with fatality of less than 5 per cent, milder prodromal symptoms and a discrete or even scanty rash. Modification in clinical features of both mild and classical forms occurs in persons with waning immunity after vaccination.

Laboratory confirmation is by isolation of virus from blood during the febrile pre-eruptive stage or from fluid, scrapings or crusts of skin lesions. A rapid provisional diagnosis is often possible, using material from cutaneous lesions with antiviral serum in agar gel diffusion test or complement-fixation test. Fluorescent antibody test is also useful.

2. Reservoir and source of infection. Reservoir is man. Source of infection is respiratory discharges of patients and lesions of skin and mucous membrane, or materials contaminated therewith. Separated scabs can remain infectious for several years. Inapparent infections are rare, if indeed they exist.

3. Mode of transmission. By contact with persons sick with the disease; contact need not be intimate. Air-borne transmission occurs over short distances, especially within closed spaces. Indirect transmission occurs through articles or persons freshly contaminated.

4. Incubation period. From seven to 16 days, commonly nine to 12 days to onset of illness and three to four days more to onset of rash.

5. Period of communicability. From first symptoms to disappearance of all scabs, about two to three weeks. Most communicable in early stages, shortly before and during appearance of rash.

6. Susceptibility and resistance. Susceptibility is universal. Permanent immunity usually follows recovery; second attacks are rare.

7. Methods of control

A. Preventive measures:

i. Effective vaccination, where the height of reaction occurs before exposure, prevents the disease. Immunity gradually wanes, but revaccination with fully potent vaccine every three to five years maintains immunity. Communities and nations have been kept free of the disease for long periods by maintaining general vaccination programmes and national quarantine vigilance.

ii. In countries with little or no smallpox, routine primary vaccination is recommended at 6 to 18 months of age, with revaccination after about 5 years. In countries where smallpox is endemic or the risk great, primary vaccination within the first 3 months is advised, with revaccination at 18 months. Maintenance of immunity by repeated revaccination is desirable for all. It is essential for persons under special risk or likely to be exposed to newly introduced infection by reason of occupation or habits, such as military personnel; international travellers, particularly those coming from or visiting endemic areas; persons having frequent contact with international travellers, including transport personnel and workers at airports and seaports; hospital employees, including physicians, nurses, attendants, laboratory and laundry workers and morticians and others handling the dead. They should be vaccinated immediately upon employment and revaccinated every three years. Under conditions of sustained high risk, it may be desirable to revaccinate more frequently.

iii. Vaccination is accomplished by inserting potent smallpox vaccine into the superficial layers of the skin. The multiple pressure method is least traumatic, gives smallest reactions and few failures. Place a drop of vaccine on the dry, previously cleansed, skin. Using the side of a needle, make 10 rapid pressures through the vaccine drop for a primary vaccination, 30 for revaccination, in such a manner that the point is pressed into an area no more than 3 mm in diameter. Use firm pressure, avoiding the vascular layer by holding the needle parallel or tangential to the skin. Allow to dry. Keep site dry and cool without shields or dressing. The deltoid area of the arm is the preferred site: avoid leg vaccination. If the scratch method is employed, carefully avoid drawing blood and rub the vaccine into the scratch with the side of the needle for at least 15 seconds. Check a sample of primary vaccinations after about two weeks to establish successful reaction and normal healing. Dried vaccine, to be reconstituted at the time of use, is now generally available. Its use assures a potency otherwise often not possible under field conditions in endemic or tropical areas. Glycerinated vaccine must be kept below freezing during storage and shipment, and until used.

The use of vaccine fully potent at the moment of insertion is the most important and most neglected part of the vaccination procedure. To check potency of the vaccine used, observe and record reactions of a sample of revaccinated persons on the third and ninth days. When the maximum diameter of redness occurs in less than three days it represents an early reaction, formerly called immediate or immune reaction; between three and seven days, accelerated reaction or vaccinoid; and after seven days, vaccinia. Practically all primary vaccinations should result in vaccinia. At least 50 per cent of persons revaccinated after ten years or more should show the accelerated or vaccinoid reaction.

Vaccinia reactions indicate previous absence of immunity. Accelerated reactions with vesicle formation indicate some protection from previous vaccination. Early reactions indicate existing protection only if produced by a vaccine fully potent by the above test. Errors in interpretation of the early reaction are frequent. Partially or completely inactive vaccine can give the same response due to skin sensitivity; trauma also confuses and sometimes secondary infection. If there is any doubt, revaccinate; with no reaction, always revaccinate.

Complications and sequelae of vaccination are unusual. Most are rare, some extremely so. They include: (a) encephalitis, rare in the USA, somewhat more common in other areas particularly Northern Europe; (b) disseminated vaccinia, multiple vaccinial lesions in various parts of the body; (c) eczema vaccinatum, severe extensive vaccinial involvement of skin in eczematous persons, either vaccinated in error or contacts of vaccinees; (d) vaccinia necrosum or gangrenosum, an extremely rare host reaction to vaccinia virus; (e) secondary infection, including tetanus, staphylococcal sepsis, and other infections from improperly prepared vaccine or contamination of the site.

iv. Avoid primary vaccination throughout pregnancy unless exposed to smallpox. Eczema, leukaemia, hypogammaglobulinaemia, corticosteroid therapy and acute and severe illness are contra-indications to routine vaccination. In the presence of real danger from smallpox, perform vaccination with precautions. Concurrent injection of vaccinia-immune-globulin provides a safety factor. Recently vaccinated persons should not come into contact with unvaccinated persons who have eczema. Protect against secondary inoculation, particularly eyes of young children.

v. Education of the public on the desirability of universal immunisation against smallpox during early childhood and maintenance of immunity through revaccination every three to five years.

B. Control of patient, contacts, and the immediate environment:

i. Report to local health authority: case report universally required by International Sanitary Regulations.

ii. Isolation: until all scabs have disappeared, preferably under hospital conditions in screened wards or rooms. Strict precautions: infection can be carried outside the hospital by visitors, themselves immune, as well as by linen or dust.

iii. Concurrent disinfection: deposit oral and nasal discharges in a paper bag or other suitable container and burn. Sterilise articles coming in direct contact with patient by high pressure steam or by boiling. Terminal cleaning; sterilise mattresses, pillow and bedding.

iv. Quarantine: all persons living or working on the same premises as the person who develops smallpox, or otherwise definitely exposed, are to be considered intimate contacts and promptly vaccinated or revaccinated. If not vaccinated, quarantine for 16 days from date of last exposure. If vaccinated and considered immune by reason of prior attack or successful vaccination or revaccination within the previous three years, keep under medical surveillance until height of reaction to the recent vaccination has passed. If vaccinated and not considered immune, continue surveillance until 16 days have passed since last exposure. Surveillance may vary from twice daily medical examinations to daily report, depending upon time since exposure and estimated likelihood of developing the disease. Any rise of temperature during surveillance calls for prompt isolation until smallpox is excluded. Complete quarantine should be substituted for surveillance of intimate contacts whose cooperation is uncertain.

v. Immunisation of contacts: prompt vaccination of all contacts, casual as well as intimate. There is some evidence that either vaccinia-immune-globulin or methisazone affords additional protection.

vi. Investigation of contacts and source of infection: the immediately prior case should be sought assiduously. Adults with chickenpox or patients with generalised haemorrhages or pustular lesions of the skin, particularly fatal cases or those associated in time or place with known smallpox, need careful review for errors in diagnosis.

vii. Specific treatment: none of proved efficacy.

C. Epidemic measures:

i. Search for all cases and suspects, all intimate and casual contacts and others indirectly exposed to infection. Provide care for each as described in B above.

ii. Immediately publicise by all practical means, giving a simple, clear and frank statement of the situation, the control measures in force and the vaccination policies adopted.

iii. Provide potent vaccine to physicians and hospitals. Establish vaccination clinics as needed.

iv. Vaccination of an entire community is an emergency measure to be used only when contact tracing appears unlikely to control further spread of infection.

D. International measures:

i. Telegraphic notification by governments to WHO and to adjacent countries of first imported, first transferred or first non-imported case of smallpox in a local area previously free of the disease.

ii. Measures applicable to ships, aircraft, and land transport arriving from smallpox areas are specified in International Sanitary Regulations, WHO, second annotated edition, Geneva, 1961.

iii. International travellers: infected persons or suspects are not permitted to depart from a country. The USA and many other countries require arriving travellers to present evidence of a recent vaccination or of a previous attack of smallpox. The validity of an international certificate of vaccination against smallpox extends for three years, beginning eight days after a succcessful primary vaccination was performed or, in the event of revaccination, on the date of that revaccination.

In October, 1976, WHO stated that the Ogaden Desert was the focal point of a massive search for what is hoped will be the world's last known case of smallpox.

TETANUS

1. Identification. An acute disease induced by toxin of the tetanus bacillus growing anaerobically at site of an injury; characterised by painful muscular contractions, primarily of masseter and neck muscles, secondarily of trunk; rigidity is sometimes confined to region of injury. History of injury or apparent portal of entry sometimes lacking. Fatality varies according to age and length of incubation, average about 35 per cent.

2. Reservoir and source of infection. Reservoir is intestinal canal of animals, especially horses, also man. The immediate source of infection is soil, street dust, or animal and human faeces.

3. Mode of transmission. Tetanus spores enter the body through injury, usually a puncture wound, but also burns and trivial or unnoticed wounds. Tetanus neonatorum usually occurs through infection of the unhealed umbilicus.

4. Incubation period. Commonly four days to three weeks, dependent on character, extent and location of wound; also longer and shorter.

5. Period of communicability. Not directly transmitted from man to man.

6. Susceptibility and resistance. Susceptibility is general. Active immunity is induced by tetanus toxoid, passive immunity by tetanus antitoxin. Recovery from tetanus does not always imply immunity; second attacks are known.

7. Methods of control

A. Preventive measures:

i. Health education about the danger of the prescribed types of injury, the value of routine immunisation with tetanus toxoid and the need after injury for either a reinforcing (booster) injection, if previously actively immunised, or passive protection by tetanus antitoxin if not immunised.

ii. Active immunisation with tetanus toxoid gives solid protection. The initial inoculation is preferably in infancy or early childhood, together with diptheria toxoid and pertussis vaccine.

Tetanus toxoid is recommended for universal use but epecially for workers in contact with soil or domestic animals and for military forces, policemen, firemen and others with more than usual risk of traumatic injury. Pregnant women should be actively immunised in regions where tetanus neonatorum is prevalent. In the USA active immunisation is by two initial doses of alum precipitated (adult type) toxoid or three doses of fluid toxoid not less than four weeks apart, followed by a reinforcing (booster) injection about 8 to 12 months later; and thereafter, in the absence of injury, at intervals of 10 years; can be given at any age.

iii. If a person previously actively immunised against tetanus has an injury with danger of tetanus, a single reinforcing (booster) injection of tetanus toxoid is administered promptly on the day of injury; reactions are essentially absent. Such procedure has a great advantage over passive immunisation with tetanus antitoxin because it obviates the risk of horse serum reactions, of special importance to persons known to be allergic to a variety of substances. It provides a ready and simple means for protection against injuries erroneously considered to warrant no attention.

iv. With no previous active immunisation, including recovered cases, passive protection of injured persons is indicated through injection of 5000 units of tetanus antitoxin, providing the patient is seen on the day of injury and there are no compound fractures, gunshot wounds or other wounds not readily debrided. If delay is greater, or such complications exist, the recommended dose is 10 000 units. Half the stated dose suffices for children under 10 years of age. Protection lasts about 10 days. Because a serum reaction is far more likely should the emergency again arise, a full course of active immunisation should follow passive protection after several weeks.

In many localities, human tetanus-immune globulin is now commercially available. Administered in amounts of 500 units, it has advantages over horse antitoxin, mainly in an absence of serum reactions.

v. Under all circumstances, foreign matter is to be removed from wounds by thorough cleaning, with debridement where indicated.

vi. Licensing of midwives, with professional supervision and education as to methods, equipment and techniques of asepsis in childbirth.

vii. Health education of mothers, relatives and attendants in the practice of strict asepsis of the umbilical stump of newborn infants. Important in many lesser developed areas where ashes, poultices or other contaminated substances are traditionally applied to the cord.

B. Control of patient, contacts, and the immediate environment:

i. Report to local health authority: case report required in most states and countries.

ii. Isolation: none.

iii. Concurrent disinfection: none.

iv. Quarantine: none.

v. Immunisation of contacts: none.

vi. Investigation of contacts and source of infection: case investigation to determine circumstances of injury. In tetanus neonatorum, rigid inquiry into competence and licensure of attendants at birth, and methods of umbilical care employed by family.

vii. Specific treatment: tetanus antitoxin in a single large dose intravenously; penicillin in large doses intramuscularly. Maintain an adequate airway; employ sedation as indicated and actively immunise recovered patients.

C. Epidemic measures:

In uncommon hospital outbreaks, thorough search for inadequacies in sterilisation.

D. International measures:

Active immunisation against tetanus is advised for international travellers.

TRACHOMA

1. Identification. A chronic communicable disease of the eye, of insidious or abrupt onset; if untreated, of long or even life-time duration. It is characterised by conjunctival inflammation with follicular and papillary hyperplasia, followed by vascular invasion of the cornea (pannus) and later cicatrisation leading to gross deformity of the eye-lids, increasing visual disability and blindness. Associated bacterial infections, common in many areas, increase communicability and severity, and modify clinical behaviour.

Laboratory diagnosis is by finding cytoplasmic inclusion bodies in scrapings of epithelial cells, by isolation of the agent in chick embryo yolk sac, and by demonstration of characteristic cytological changes in expressed follicular material. The agent has not been clearly differentiated from that of inclusion conjunctivitis, although the two diseases are dissimilar epidemiologically.

A number of forms of follicular conjunctivitis of bacterial or viral origin may resemble trachoma and require differentiation.

2. Reservoir and source of infection. Reservoir is man. Source of infection is exudate from eyes and, possibly, mucoid or purulent discharges of nasal mucous membranes of infected persons; tears of such persons also carry infection.

3. Mode of transmission. By direct contact with ocular discharges of infected persons or materials soiled therewith. Flies, especially *Musca sorbens*, may contribute to spread of the disease, but transmission occurs in their absence. Communicability is relatively low.

4. Incubation period. 5 to 12 days, experimentally in volunteers.

5. Period of communicability. While active lesions are present in conjunctivae and annexed mucous membranes. Communicability is greatly reduced with cicatrisation but reactivation of the disease may occur, with reappearance of infective discharges.

6. Susceptibility and resistance. Susceptibility is general; affects children more frequently than adults, particularly persons of unclean habits and those whose eyes are irritated by exposure to sun, wind and sand. No effective immunity results from an attack of the disease.

7. Methods of control

A. Preventive measures:

i. Provision of adequate case-finding and treatment facilities, with emphasis on pre-school children.

ii. Health education of the public in the need for personal hygiene, especially the risk in common use of toilet articles.

iii. Improved basic sanitation, including availability of soap and water.

iv. Conducting of epidemiological investigations to determine important factors in occurrence of the disease in each specific situation.

v. Experimental vaccines are under trial but their efficacy has not been established.

B. Control of patient, contacts, and the immediate environment:

i. Report to local health authority: case report required in states and countries of low endemicity.

ii. Isolation: not practical in most areas where the disease occurs.

iii. Concurrent disinfection: of eye discharges and contaminated articles.

iv. Quarantine: none.

v. Immunisation of contacts: none.

vi. Investigation of contacts: members of family, playmates and schoolmates.

vii. Specific treatment: tetracycline antibiotics in oil or ointment applied locally are effective in most instances; oral sulphonamides for resistant cases or for collective treatment of special groups, under adequate supervision.

C. Epidemic measures:

In regions of hyperendemic prevalence, mass treatment campaigns have been successful in reducing frequency, when associated with health education of the people in personal hygiene and efforts toward an improved sanitary environment.

D. International measures: none.

TUBERCULOSIS

1. Identification. A chronic bacterial disease and an important cause of death in many parts of the world. Primary infection usually goes unnoticed clinically; lesions heal spontaneously, leaving no residual changes except pulmonary or tracheobronchial lymph node calcifications, but occasionally leads to pleurisy or to dissemination of bacilli with miliary, meningeal or other extrapulmonary involvement. May progress directly to pulmonary tuberculosis. Tuberculin sensitivity appears within a few weeks after infection. Serious manifestations develop most often in infants.

Pulmonary tuberculosis generally has a chronic, variable and often asymptomatic course, with exacerbations and remissions, and is capable of arrest or relapse at any stage. Three stages (minimal, moderately advanced, and far advanced) are distinguished according to extent of lung involvement; activity is determined by presence of tubercle bacilli, by progression or retrogression as detected in serial X-rays, or by symptoms. Abnormal X-ray densities indicative of pulmonary infiltration, vacitation, or fibrosis commonly occur in advance of clinical manifestations. Cough, fatigue, fever, weight loss, hoarseness, chest pain and haemoptysis may occur but often are absent until advanced stages.

Diagnosis by X-ray is confirmed by demonstration of tubercle bacilli in sputum or gastric washings, by stained smear, concentration and culture, or animal inoculation. Repeated examinations often are needed to find bacilli. The tuberculin test is positive except in critically ill persons, during certain intercurrent diseases (e.g. measles) and sometimes in old age.

Extrapulmonary tuberculosis is much less common than pulmonary. It includes meningitis, miliary tuberculosis, and involvement of bones and joints, lymph nodes, kidneys, intestines, larynx and skin. Diagnosis is by isolation of tubercle bacilli from lesions or exudates.

2. Reservoir and source of infection. Reservoir is primarily man; in some areas, diseased cattle. Source of infection is respiratory secretions of person with 'open' (bacillary-positive) pulmonary tuberculosis; occasionally milk from tuberculous cattle. Extrapulmonary tuberculosis usually is not directly communicable.

3. Mode of transmission. Contact with patients with open lesions. Prolonged household exposure to an active case usually leads to infection of contacts and frequently to active disease. Air-borne route may be a frequent mode of spread. Indirect contact through contaminated articles or dust is less important. Bovine tuberculosis results from ingestion of unpasteurised milk or dairy products from tuberculous cows, by air-borne infection in barns and from handling contaminated animal products.

4. Incubation period. From infection to demonstrable primary lesion, about four to six weeks; to progressive pulmonary or extrapulmonary tuberculosis may be years; the first 6 to 12 months after infection is the most hazardous period.

5. *Period of communicability.* As long as tubercle bacilli are discharged. Some patients are intermittently sputum-positive for years. The degree of communicability depends on numbers of bacilli discharged, coughing habits and hygienic practices of patient. Antimicrobial therapy commonly shortens communicability.

6. *Susceptibility and resistance.* Susceptibility is general: highest in children under 3 years, lowest 3 to 12 years; aboriginal races, and undernourished, neglected and fatigued persons and those with silicosis or diabetes are especially susceptible. Resistance conferred by healed primary infection is limited. Relapse of long latent infection, particularly in older males, accounts for a large proportion of active cases.

7. *Methods of control*

A. Preventive measures:

i. Health education of the public in the importance, mode of spread, and methods of control of the disease.

ii. Hospital, laboratory, X-ray and clinical facilities for examination of patients, contacts and suspects and for treatment of active cases.

iii. Public health nursing service for home supervision of patients and to encourage and arrange for examination of contacts.

iv. BCG vaccination of uninfected (tuberculin negative) persons confers definite, though partial, protection. Where risk of infection is low, mass vaccination has a small role but vaccine may be used for household contacts of active cases and for persons exposed to infection by reason of occupation, such as medical and nursing students. In areas of high mortality where economic resources do not permit other control measures to be widely practised, mass vaccination of nonreactors gives hope of partial control. Preliminary tuberculin testing is unnecessary for newborn infants. Proper vaccination induces tuberculin sensitivity in over 90 per cent of individuals; duration of protection is undetermined.

v. Elimination of tuberculosis among dairy cattle by tuberculin testing and slaughter of reactors; pasteurisation of milk.

vi. Measures to prevent inhalation of dangerous concentrations of silica dust in in dustrial plants and mines.

vii. Routine X-ray examination of groups that have a higher prevalence of tuberculosis than the general population, such as nurses, medical students, patients and outpatients in general and mental hospitals, and selected groups of industrial workers; also those who constitute a special hazard to others if infected, such as school personnel. When feasible, initial screening by tuberculin test may be substituted, with examination by X-ray restricted to reactors.

viii. X-ray screening of adult populations in communities where the prevalence of tuberculosis is excessive.

ix. Tuberculin-testing surveys, employing 5 TU of PPD intracutaneously, may be helpful in identifying groups at high risk of infection. Periodic retesting of tuberculin-negative persons, with close observation of those whose reaction converts to positive, and a search for their source of infection, may be of value.

x. Chemoprophylaxis, defined as prevention of active disease by administration of isoniazid in therapeutic dosage for one year, has been tried with promising results for household associates of active cases, and for circumscribed populations in which risk of tuberculosis is unusually great; may also be protective for persons who, during the previous year, have converted from a tuberculin-negative to a tuberculin-positive state, and for tuberculin-positive children under 3 years of age. A course of isoniazid has been proposed for arrested cases never previously treated with antibacterial drugs.

B. Control of patient, contacts, and the immediate environment:

i. Report to local health authority: obligatory case report in most states and countries. Health departments should maintain a current register of active cases.

ii. Isolation: control of infectivity best achieved by prompt specific drug therapy, which commonly produces sputum conversion within six months. Hospital treatment is highly desirable beginning at diagnosis and continuing at least until sputum has converted. For patients remaining at home, public health nursing supervision, including instruction in personal hygiene, especially the need to cover mouth and nose in coughing and sneezing; compulsory isolation of patients with open tuberculosis who do not observe necessary precautions.

iii. Concurrent disinfection: of sputum and articles soiled therewith, including handkerchiefs, cloth or paper napkins and eating utensils. Ordinary hygienic precautions suffice when patient is on specific therapy and demonstrated free from tubercle bacilli. Terminal cleaning.

iv. Quarantine: none.

v. Immunisation of contacts: BCG vaccination of tuberculin negative household contacts may be warranted.

vi. Investigation of contacts. X-ray examination of all members of the household and intimate extra-household contacts, especially adults. Alternatively, tuberculin testing of contacts with X-ray examination of reactors. Annual retest of tuberculin-negative persons, with intensive study of converters and their contacts, is sometimes useful.

vi. Specific treatment: most primary infections heal without treatment; if recognised in an early or active stage antimicrobial therapy is indicated.

Patients with active pulmonary tuberculosis should preferably be hospitalised. Prompt treatment with an appropriate combination of antimicrobial drugs; isoniazid, paraaminosalicylic acid (PAS) and streptomycin, continued for one or more years. Initial cultures of tubercle bacilli should be examined for drug sensitivity, with the test repeated in six months if sputum fails to become negative or reverts to positive after a series of negatives. Drug fastness necessitates change in antimicrobial agents. Thoracic surgery, chiefly pulmonary resection, used in selected cases.

In extrapulmonary tuberculosis, antimicrobial therapy is combined with specific measures, often surgical, suited to the form and type of disease. Miliary and meningeal infections require intensive antimicrobial treatment.

C. Epidemic measures:

Alertness to recognise aggregations of new cases resulting from contact with an unrecognised infection.

D. International measures:

X-ray screening of individuals prior to emigration.

TYPHOID FEVER

1. Identification. A systemic infectious disease characterised by continued fever, malaise, anorexia, slow pulse, involvement of lymphoid tissues, especially ulceration of Peyer's patches, enlargement of spleen, rose spots on trunk, and constipation more commonly

than diarrhoea. Many mild and atypical infections. A usual fatility of 10 per cent is reduced to 2 to 3 per cent by antibiotic therapy.
Synonyms: Enteric Fever, Typhus Abdominalis.

Typhoid bacilli are found in blood early in the disease and in faeces or urine after first week. Agglutination reaction becomes positive during second week.

2. Reservoir and source of infection. Reservoir is man: patients and carriers. The source of infection is faeces and urine of infected persons. Family contacts may be transient carriers; faecal carriers are more common than urinary. The carrier state is most common among persons infected during middle age, especially females; faecal carriers frequently have a typhoid cholecystitis.

3. Mode of transmission. Direct or indirect contact with patient or carrier. Principal vehicles of spread are contaminated water and food. Raw fruits and vegetables are important factors in some parts of the world; milk, milk products and shellfish in others.

4. Incubation period. Variable: average two weeks, usual range one to three weeks.

5. Period of communicability. As long as typhoid bacilli appear in excreta; usually from first week throughout convalescence, thereafter variable. About 10 per cent of patients will discharge bacilli three months after onset; 2 to 5 per cent become permanent carriers.

6. Susceptibility and resistance. Susceptibility is general, although many adults acquire immunity through unrecognised infections; attack rates decline with age after second or third decades. A high degree of resistance usually follows recovery.

7. Methods of control

A. Preventive measures:

i. Protection, purification and chlorination of public water supplies, construction of safe private supplies. For individual or small group protection and while travelling or in the field, water is preferably boiled; or chlorine (halazone) or iodine disinfecting tablets can be added directly to water, the number depending on turbidity and amount of water to be treated. The iodine preparation has the advantage that it kills amoebic cysts as well as bacteria.

ii. Sanitary disposal of human excreta.

iii. Fly control by screening, spraying with residual insecticides and use of insecticidal baits (such as diazinon) and traps. Control fly breeding by provision for adequate garbage collection; elimination of open garbage dumps and substitution of land-fill operations; provision for proper disposal of faeces.

iv. Boiling of milk or pasteurisation of milk and dairy products, including cheese. Sanitary supervision of commercial milk production, transport, processing and delivery. Proper storage and refrigeration in stores and homes.

v. Limitation of collection and marketing of shellfish to those from approved sources.

vi. Sanitary supervision of processing, preparation and serving of foods in public eating places, especially foods eaten raw; special attention to provision and use of hand-washing facilities. Protection of foods against flies by screening.

vii. Immunisation with a vaccine of high antigenicity, given in a primary series of two injections spaced by several weeks. Current practice is to vaccinate persons subject to unusual exposure through occupation or travel, those living in areas of high endemic incidence, and institutional populations where maintenance of good sanitation is difficult. Periodic single reinforcing injections are desirable, commonly once in three years, either 0.5 ml subcutaneously or 0.1 ml intradermally, the latter usually attended by lesser reaction.

viii. Discovery and supervision of typhoid carriers. Those exceeding duration of one year may be released from supervision and restriction of occupation only after six consecutive negative cultures of authenticated specimens of faeces and urine taken one month apart. Prolonged antibiotic therapy may end the carrier state; for faecal carriers, cholecystectomy is highly effective.

ix. Instruction of convalescents and chronic carriers in personal hygiene, particularly as to sanitary disposal of excreta, hand-washing after defaecation and before eating, and exclusion from acting as food handlers.

x. Health education of the general public and particularly of food handlers concerning sources of infection and modes of transmission.

B. Control of patient, contacts, and the immediate environment:

i. Report to local health authority: obligatory case report in most states and countries.

ii. Isolation: in flyproof room. Hospital care desirable for patients who cannot command adequate sanitary environment and nursing care at home. Release from supervision by local health authority should be by not less than three negative cultures of faeces and urine, taken at least 24 hours apart and not earlier than one month after onset; if any one of this series is positive, release should be by not less than three negative cultures at intervals of one month and within the 12 months following onset.

iii. Concurrent disinfection: of faeces and urine and articles soiled therewith. In communities with modern and adequate sewage disposal systems, faeces and urine can be disposed of directly into sewer without preliminary disinfection. Terminal cleaning.

iv. Quarantine: family contacts should not be employed as food handlers during period of contact nor before repeated negative faeces and urine cultures are obtained.

v. Immunisation of contacts: administration of typhoid vaccine to family, household and nursing contacts who have been, or may be, exposed to cases or carriers.

vi. Investigation of contacts and sources of infection: actual or probable source of infection of every case should be determined by search for common and individual sources, unreported cases and carriers, or contaminated food, water, milk or shellfish. Presence of Vi agglutinins in blood of suspected carriers is suggestive of the carrier state. Phage typing of organisms from patients and carriers and identification of the same type serves usefully in indicating a common origin.

vii. Specific treatment: Chloramphenicol. An initial oral loading dose is followed by oral doses every six hours until temperature is normal, then in smaller doses for a total of 14 days; use with caution because of side-effects. If chloramphenicol is contra-indicated or ineffective, promptly substitute a tetracycline antibiotic.

C. Epidemic measures:

i. Intensive search for case or carrier who is source of infection.

ii. Exclusion of suspected food.

iii. Boiling or pasteurisation of milk or exclusion of milk supplies or other foods suspected on epidemiological evidence, until safety is assured.

iv. Chlorination under competent supervision of suspected water supply or its exclusion. All water used for drinking must be chlorinated or boiled before use.

D. International measures:

Inoculation with typhoid vaccine is advised for international travellers unless they have had the disease; TAB (typhoid, paratyphoid A and B) vaccine is often used. Not a legal requirement of any country. The risk is minimal in the USA, Canada, Great Britain and northwest Europe.

WHOOPING COUGH

1. Identification. An acute bacterial disease involving trachea, bronchi and bronchioles. Initial catarrhal stage has insidious onset with irritating cough which gradually becomes paroxysmal, usually within one or two weeks and lasts for one to two months. Paroxysms are characterised by repeated violent coughs; each series has many coughs without intervening inhalation, followed by a characteristic crowing or high pitched inspiratory whoop; frequently ends with expulsion of clear, tenacious mucus. Young infants and adults often do not have the typical paroxysm. General fatality is low, less than 0.5 per cent; approximately 70 per cent of deaths are among children under 1 year of age, with further concentration in those under 6 months, where fatality of hospitalised patients is at times as high as 30 per cent. Synonym: Pertussis.

The infectious agent is readily recovered during catarrhal and early paroxysmal stages by nasopharyngeal swab and suitable culture; fluorescent antibody technique appears promising.

Parapertussis is an allied disease clinically indistinguishable from pertussis. It is usually milder and relatively infrequent. Identification is by immunological differences between *Bordetella parapertussis* and *B. pertussis.*

2. Reservoir and source of infection. Man is the reservoir. Source of infection is discharges from laryngeal and bronchial mucous membranes of infected persons.

3. Mode of transmission. By direct contact with an infected person, by droplet spread, or indirectly by contact with articles freshly soiled with discharges of such persons.

4. Incubation period. Commonly seven days, almost uniformly within 10 days, and not exceeding 21 days.

5. Period of communicability. Highly communicable in early catarrhal stage before paroxysmal cough. Thereafter communicability gradually decreases and becomes negligible for ordinary non-familial contacts in about three weeks despite persisting spasmodic cough with whoop. For control purposes, the communicable stage extends from seven days after exposure to three weeks after onset of typical paroxysms.

6. Susceptibility and resistance. Susceptibility is general; no evidence of temporary passive immunity in young infants born of immune mothers. Predominately a childhood disease, incidence being highest under 7 years of age. Numerous unapparent and missed atypical cases. One attack confers definite and prolonged immunity although exposed adults occasionally have second attacks. Fatality is higher in females than males of all ages.

7. Methods of control

A. Preventive measures:

i. Active immunisation of all susceptible pre-school children is an effective procedure for control of pertussis. Plain or alum adjuvant vaccines may be used alone or mixed with diphtheria and tetanus toxoids. In the USA three doses of a triple alum adjuvant vaccine (DTP), administered intramuscularly at four to eight week intervals, is commonly used for simultaneous immunisation. In general, routine immunisation can be started at 3 to 4 months of age. When primary immunisation is properly carried out in infancy, a single reinforcing dose of multiple antigen is advised one year later and again before entering school. Infants in institutions and in households with other susceptible children, particularly when whooping cough is prevalent in the community, should have active immunisation by 2 or 3 months of age.

ii. Educational measures to inform the public and particularly parents of infants of the dangers of whooping cough and of the advantage of immunisation in infancy.

B. Control of patient, contacts, and the immediate environment:

i. Report to local health authority: case report obligatory in most states and countries.

ii. Isolation: separation of patient from susceptible children and exclusion from school and public places for the recognised period of communicability. Isolation of children over 2 years of age is often impractical; even for those under 2 years it should not be practised at the expense of fresh air in the open if weather permits.

iii. Concurrent disinfection: Discharges from the nose and throat and articles soiled therewith. Terminal cleaning.

iv. Quarantine: exclusion of non-immune children from school and public gatherings for 14 days after last exposure to a household or similar case; may be omitted if exposed non-immune children are observed throughout each school day to detect the first sign of infection. It is especially important that children less than 3 years old are protected from contact with known or suspected whooping cough.

v. Immunisation of contacts: brief and limited passive immunity may be conferred on young children by administration of immune (gamma) globulin. Vaccination after effective exposure is of no proven value.

vi. Investigation of contacts: carriers in the exact sense of the term are not known; search for missed and atypical cases among contacts is indicated.

vii. Specific treatment: Tetracycline antibiotics and chloramphenicol, given early, shorten period of communicability but do not dramatically modify clinical manifestations.

C. Epidemic measures:

A search for unrecognised and unreported cases to protect pre-school children from exposure and to ensure adequate medical care for exposed infants.

D. International measures:

Active immunisation of susceptible infants and young children travelling to other countries, if not already protected; review need of reinforcing dose for those previously inoculated.

YAWS

1. Identification. An acute and chronic relapsing non-venereal treponematosis characterised by hypertrophic, granulomatous, or ulcerative destructive lesions of the skin, and by destructive and hypertrophic changes in bone. Three to six weeks after exposure an initial papule appears at the site of inoculation, eventually developing into a papilloma ('mother yaw'). In several weeks to months, and often before the initial lesion has healed, mild constitutional symptoms appear; also a generalised eruption of papules, some developing into typical frambesial lesions, in successive crops and lasting several months. Frambesial papillomata may appear on palms and soles, also hyperkeratoses in both early and late stages. The late stage often develops some years after the last early lesions, with characteristic destructive lesions of skin and bone. Early and late lesions tend to heal spontaneously, but may relapse. Between these active phases infection is latent, to give a latent early stage from which early relapses occur, and a latent late stage with late lesions and relapses. Central nervous system, eyes and viscera are not involved, nor does congenital yaws occur. It is rarely, if ever, fatal. Synonyms: Frambesia Tropica, Pian, Bouba, Parangi, and many others.

Diagnosis is confirmed by dark-field examination of exudates from lesions. Serological tests for syphilis are reactive with the same frequency in yaws as in syphilis, becoming positive during the initial stage, remaining positive during the early stage and tending toward nonreactivity after many years of latency, even without specific therapy.

2. *Reservoir and source of infection.* Man is the only reservoir. Source of infection is exudates of early skin lesions of infected persons.

3. *Mode of transmission.* Principally by direct contact. Indirect transmission by contaminated articles and flies is uncertain and probably of minor importance.

4. *Incubation period.* From two weeks to three months; generally three to six weeks.

5. *Period of communicability.* Variable. May extend intermittently over several years while relapsing moist lesions are present. The infectious agent is not usually found in late ulcerative lesions.

6. *Susceptibility and resistance.* No evidence of natural or racial resistance. Infection results in immunity to homologous and heterologous strains, of slower evolution for heterologous strains and probably not complete until one year. The part of superinfection in nature is not well defined, and may be unimportant.

7. *Methods of control*

A. Preventive measures:

The following are applicable to yaws and to other non-venereal treponematoses. The infectious agents in all of these disorders are morphologically and biologically identical and the resulting clinical syndromes come from epidemiologic rather than biologic differences.

i. General health promotional measures: health education about treponematosis, better sanitation, and improved social and economic conditions over a period of years will reduce incidence.

ii. Organisation of intensive control activities on a community basis, to include analysis of the specific local problem, clinical examination of entire populations, and mass treatment of patients with active lesions, latent cases and contacts. Periodic surveys and continuous surveillance are essential to successful results.

iii. Provision of facilities for early diagnosis and treatment on a continuing plan, whereby the mass control campaign is eventually consolidated into permanent local health services providing early diagnosis and treatment to patients, and contact investigation and health education to the community.

iv. Emphasis on control of infectivity should not preclude treatment of disfiguring and incapacitating late manifestations nor the discovery and treatment of latent cases, since many subsequently relapse with infective lesions to maintain the disease in the community.

B. Control of patient, contacts, and the immediate environment:

i. Report to local health authority in selected endemic areas: in many countries not a reportable disease. Differentiation of venereal and non-venereal treponematoses with proper reporting of each has particular importance in evaluation of mass campaigns and in the consolidation period thereafter.

ii. Isolation: none. Avoid intimate contact until lesions are healed.

iii. Concurrent disinfection: care in disposal of discharges and articles contaminated therewith.

iv. Immunisation of contacts: not applicable. Prompt institution of a course of treatment.

vi. Investigation of contacts: all familial contacts should be treated. Persons with no active disease should be regarded as latent cases and contacts, and treated. In areas of low prevalence, treat all active cases, all children, and close contacts of infectious cases.

vii. Specific treatment: Penicillin. For patients with active disease a single intramuscular injection of procain penicillin G in oil with 2 per cent aluminium monostearate (PAM or benzathine penicillin G); half doses for children under 15 and for latent cases and contacts.

C. Epidemic measures:

Active mass treatment programmes are under way in many areas of high prevalence. Essential features are (a) that a high percentage of the population be examined through field survey; (b) that treatment of active cases be extended to other segments of the population according to demonstrated prevalence of active yaws; and (c) that periodic surveys be made at yearly intervals for one to three years, with surveillance and integration of activities into the established rural public health activities of the country.

D. International measures:

To protect countries against risk of reinfection where active mass treatment programmes are in progress, adjacent countries in the endemic area should institute suitable measures against yaws. Movement of infected persons across frontiers may need supervision.

Epidemic diarrhoeas of natural disasters and newly aggregated populations

People crowded in unhygienic surroundings provide the basic setting for an epidemic of diarrhoea. The common situations are populations newly aggregated under unfamiliar ecologic conditions or following natural disasters. Such epidemics bring into play the same principles as in traveller's diarrhoea except that the process is on a larger scale. Similarly, some cases are due to recognised specific enteric agents. Most are not.

Natural disasters of flood, fire, earthquake and hurricane commonly precipitate an epidemic. The temporary aggregation of people where sanitation is elementary may result in multiple cases of simple diarrhoea. The longer a situation continues the greater the likelihood of an increase in such events. Noteworthy, however, is the need in such prolonged exposures to consider a possible specific intestinal disease, e.g. shigellosis, cholera and typhoid fever under appropriate circumstances.

Accidents in central water supply systems with gross sewage pollution bring explosive outbreaks of clinically mild diarrhoea, sometimes called acute sewage poisoning. They affect large proportions of a population and cases may be in the thousands. They may precede epidemics of water-borne infectious hepatitis.

Control measures are first preventive, through anticipating such outbreaks under the prescribed circumstances and instituting sanitary safeguards. The second need is a prepared plan for emergency action, based on local resources and designed to meet catastrophic situations where warning is likely to be brief. This includes advance consideration of administrative means for marshalling personnel and resources, and plans for the technical procedures to be followed in identifying sources of infection and remedying the environmental deficiency.

FOOD POISONING

Food poisoning is a generic term which by common practice has been applied to certain illnesses of abrupt evolution, usually enteric in nature and acquired through consumption of food.

The term applies to the food intoxications due to chemical contaminants (heavy metals, fluorides and others), to toxins elaborated by bacterial growth (staphylococcal toxins, botulinus toxins), and to a variety of organic substances that may occur in natural foods such as certain mushrooms, mussels, eels and other sea food.

By long tradition, acute salmonellosis has been commonly classed with food poisoning although it is more an acute enteric infection than an intoxication. Many other infectious diseases are spread occasionally through food, particularly milk. These include typhoid and paratyphoid fever, shigellosis, streptococcal pharyngitis (septic sore throat), diphtheria, brucellosis, infectious hepatitis, amoebiasis, trichinosis, and other helminthic infections. These latter examples of food-borne infections are not usually, and properly should not be, classed as forms of food poisoning. Epidemic nausea and vomiting of presumed viral origin also enters into differential diagnosis of food poisoning.

Food poisoning outbreaks are usually recognised by the sudden occurrence of a group of illnesses within a short period of time among individuals who have consumed one or more foods in common. The diagnosis is usually indicated by epidemiological findings. While single cases of food poisoning are undoubtedly common, they are difficult to identify unless as in botulism there is a distinctive clinical syndrome.

SALMONELLOSIS

The commonest clinical manifestation of Salmonella infections is an acute gastro-enteritis. Occasionally, the clinical course is that of an enteric fever or a septicaemia. Every Salmonella strain is potentially capable of producing any of these three main clinical types. A Salmonella infection also may begin as an acute gastro-enteritis and may develop into an enteric fever or a septicaemia. The infectious agent may localise in any tissue of the body by producing abcesses and causing arthritis, cholecystitis, endocarditis, meningitis, pericarditis, pneumonia, or pyelonephritis. Nevertheless, most salmonellosis arises directly from contaminated food, and presents as gastro-enteritis. Attention is here limited to these food infections.

1. Identification. Salmonella gastro-enteritis is an acute infectious disease with sudden onset of abdominal pain, diarrhoea and frequent vomiting. Fever is nearly always present. Deaths are uncommon but somewhat more frequent than for staphylococcal food poisoning. Anorexia and looseness of the bowels often persist for several days. Synonym: Salmonella Food Poisoning.

2. Infectious agents. Numerous serotypes of Salmonella of the group pathogenic for both animals and man. Primary human pathogens are excluded, also those producing disease only in animals. The types currently most common in the USA are *S. typhimurium, S. heidelberg, S. newport, S. oranienburg, S. infantis, S. derby* and *S. enteritidis*; in the United Kingdom, *S. typhimurium, S. enteritidis, S. thompson, S. newport* and *S. heidelberg*; there is much variation from country to country. On a world basis *S. typhimurium* is most common. Total serological types that may be involved in food poisoning approximate 800.

3. Reservoir and source of infection. Reservoir is domestic: wild animals and pets, e.g. turtles and chicks; also man, patients and convalescent carriers, especially mild and unrecognised cases. Sources of infection are faeces of animals and infected persons; whole eggs (particularly duck eggs) and egg products (frozen and dried whole egg, egg albumin and egg yolk), meat and meat products, poultry, animal feeds and fertilisers prepared from meat, fish meal and bones.

4. Mode of transmission. Epidemics are usually traced to foods such as meat pies, poultry or poultry products, raw sausages, lightly cooked foods containing eggs or egg products, unpasteurised milk or dairy products; foods contaminated with rodent faeces or by an infected food handler; or to utensils, working surfaces or tables previously used for contaminated foods such as egg products. Sporadic cases often originate through direct contact with an infected person or animal.

5. Incubation period. Six to 48 hours; usually about 12 to 24 hours.

6. Period of communicability. Throughout infection. Extremely variable, usually three days to three weeks. A carrier state occasionally continues for months, especially in young babies. Chronic carriers are rare.

7. Susceptibility and resistance. Susceptibility is general. Severity of disease is greatest at extremes of life and related to size of infecting dose and, to a slight extent, to species of infectious agent. No active or passive immunisation. Some type-specific immunity probably follows recovery.

8. Methods of control

A. Preventive measures:

i. Thorough cooking of all foodstuffs derived from animal sources, particularly turkeys and other fowl, egg products, and meat dishes. Prevention of recontamination within kitchen after cooking is completed. Avoidance of raw eggs, as in egg drinks. Pasteurisation of egg products. Refrigeration of prepared foods during storage before use.

ii. Education of food handlers and housewives in the necessity for protection of prepared food against rodent or insect contamination, in refrigeration of foods and in handwashing before and after food preparation.

iii. Recognition and control of Salmonella infection among domestic animals.

iv. Meat and poultry inspection with adequate supervision of abattoirs and butcher shops.

v. Adequate cooking or heat treatment, and protection of prepared animal feeds (meat, meal, bone meal, and others) against contamination by Salmonella.

B. Control of patient contacts, and the immediate environment:

i. Report to local health authority: obligatory report of epidemics; also suspected or confirmed cases with evidence of grouping or association with others in time and place.

ii. Isolation: exclusion of infected persons from food handling and occupations involving care of young children until cultures of faeces are free from Salmonella for three successive days.

iii. Concurrent disinfection: of faeces and of articles soiled therewith. In communities with a modern and adequate sewage disposal system, faeces can be discharged directly into sewer without preliminary disinfection. Terminal cleaning.

iv. Quarantine: none. Family contacts should not be employed as food handlers during period of contact.

v. Immunisation of contacts: none.

vi. Investigation of contacts: search for unrecognised mild cases and convalescent carriers.

vii. Specific treatment: none. Chloramphenicol and the tetracycline antibiotics have limited and irregular effect.

C. Epidemic measures:

Determine the extent of the outbreak. Identify the clinical features of the illness. Assemble evidence implicating a particular food as the vehicle of spread, nature of suspected food as a likely medium for bacterial growth, and laboratory examination of materials from cases and from samples of the suspected food or its ingredients. Intensive search for the source and means of contamination, including the infected person associated with preparation or distribution of the food. Do not destroy the remainder of suspected food until adequate samples are taken for laboratory examination.

STAPHYLOCOCCAL FOOD POISONING

1. Identification. An intoxication (not an infection) of abrupt and sometimes violent onset with severe nausea, cramps, vomiting, severe diarrhoea and prostration. Subnormal temperatures and lowered blood pressure are sometimes severe. Deaths are exceedingly rare. Duration of illness is not normally more than a day or two. Diagnosis is usually through recognition of a group of cases with the characteristic short interval between eating food and onset of symptoms.

Isolation of large numbers of staphylococci from stomach contents or suspected food, supports the diagnosis. Demonstration of ability of the organism to produce enterotoxin is essential to confirmation. Phage typing greatly aids epidemiological investigation.

Differential diagnosis includes other recognised forms of food poisoning, epidemic nausea and vomiting, and the food poisoning from gross bacterial contamination.

Toxic agent is several enterotoxins of staphylococci, stable at boiling temperature. Staphylococci multiply in food, producing toxin which causes poisoning.

2. *Reservoir and source of poisoning.* In most instances from staphylococci of human origin from purulent discharges of an infected finger, abscesses, nasal secretions or the apparently normal skin of hands and forearms; of bovine origin in outbreaks associated with milk.

3. *Mode of transmission.* By any of a wide variety of food products: pastries, custards, salads and salad dressing, sandwiches, sliced meat and meat products in which the toxin-producing staphylococcus has been introduced, with the food then prepared in a manner permitting growth of the organism and elaboration of toxin. In the United Kingdom, ham and bacon, pressed meat; milk from cows with infected udders; dried milk occasionally, sometimes in extensive outbreaks.

4. *Incubation period.* Interval between taking food and onset of symptoms is one to six hours, usually two to four hours.

5. *Period of communicability.* Not applicable.

6. *Susceptibility and resistance.* Most persons are susceptible, although individual reactions are variable.

7. *Method of control*

A. Preventive measures:

i. Prompt refrigeration of sliced and chopped meats to avoid multiplication of staphylococci accidentally introduced. Immediate disposal or prompt refrigeration of left-over foods.

ii. Temporary exclusion from food handling of persons suffering from pyogenic skin infections.

iii. Education of food handlers in strict attention to sanitation and cleanliness of kitchens, including refrigeration, hand-washing, attention to fingernails, and the danger of working while having skin infections.

B. Control of patient, contacts, and the immediate environment:

i. Report to local health authority: obligatory report of epidemics of suspected or confirmed cases.

ii. Control is of epidemics: single cases are rarely identified.

C. Epidemic measures:

i. Search for food contaminated with staphylococci and for food handlers with skin infections, particularly of the hands. Culture of all purulent lesions and the nose. Phage typing of strains of staphylococci isolated from foods and food handlers and from vomitus of patients.

ii. Do not destroy any remainder of suspected food until samples have been taken for laboratory examination.

D. International measures: none.

8. Some endemic disorders and conditions

Vitamin deficiency syndromes

Multiple deficiency states are common in the tropics. Clinical conditions are diagnosed by the predominant deficiency—for example, beriberi (thiamine deficiency) and xerophthalmia (vitamin A deficiency)—but often deficiencies of protein and energy are co-existent.

In addition there may be bacterial or viral infections and parasitic infestations to be treated.

XEROPHTHALMIA

This is a common cause of blindness among pre-school children aged 1 to 4 years throughout the tropics. It is more common in towns than in rural areas. It is often associated with protein energy malnutrition.

Deficiency causes a morphological change in epithelial cells which undergo squamous change, becoming dry, flat and heaped. In the conjunctiva this is called xerosis conjunctivae and in the cornea, xerosis corneae.

If the deficiency is severe and continues, necrosis occurs, resulting in permanent damage. Rupture of the eyeball may cause blindness.

Too often in disaster areas, large quantities of multi-vitamins are sent in for the medical teams to distribute. An accurate assessment of the specific vitamin deficiency, and its supply, is of paramount importance. In addition, supportive therapy for the general malnutrition is vital. This will include treatment of electrolyte imbalances, general infections and coincidental local eye infections.

Mortality in xerophthalmia is often high, due mainly to the accompanying protein energy malnutrition.

Treatment

In mild cases of xerophthalmia with no corneal involvement oral supplements should be adequate. The daily dose should be 25 000 units (7.5 mg) of retinol supplied in 30 ml cod-liver oil.

If the cornea is involved, water-dispersable Vitamin A palmitate should be given by intramuscular injection and by stomach tube if necessary. The daily dose should be 10 000 units (3 mg) of retinol per kg body weight.

BERIBERI

This is a disease with generalised oedema and peripheral neuropathy. Sometimes there is also heart failure. It is associated with thiamine deficiency often caused by the polished

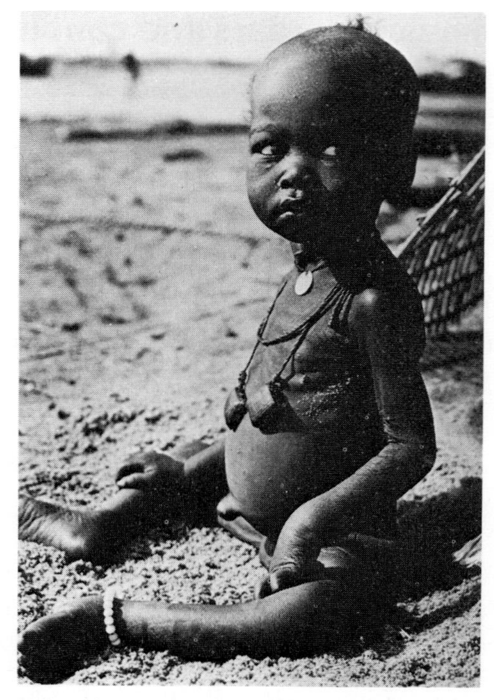

Fig. 8.1 Malnutrition: a child suffering from rickets (French Sudan) (WHO).

rice diet of the peoples of Asia. It can also be found in groups of people who eat highly milled wheat.

Acute infantile beriberi

This usually occurs in breast-fed babies aged 2 to 6 months when the mother is deficient in thiamine. The mother may not show signs of beriberi. The baby may be restless, vomit, cry unduly and have some puffiness of the face and feet. The infant is cyanosed, has an enlarged liver and sometimes neck vein distension. Breathlessness and convulsions are often the first signs and death from acute heart failure can occur rapidly.

An injection of 10 mg thiamine may be given intravenously to the baby. If he is in a moribund condition the injection should be intracardiac.

Intramuscular injections of 25 mg thiamine should be given to the mother and baby, and the former advised to eat green vegetables.

Chronic beriberi

This consists mainly of peripheral neuropathy and peripheral oedema. The heart may be involved. There is increasing heaviness and weakness of the lower limbs. There may be tingling of the toes, cramps in the legs, cold and burning feet. Swelling of the face and feet may be noticed.

The most useful signs for diagnosis are the inability to rise unaided from the squatting position, and marked tenderness to pressure of the calves.

Oedema responds quickly to oral thiamine hydrochloride 10 mg b.d. or t.d.s. If heart failure is present, the first dose (of 10 mg) of thiamine should be given by intramuscular injection. Intravenous injection should be avoided as it can precipitate hypertension and thus aggravate the heart condition.

KWASHIORKOR

The name means (approximately) 'the deposed one'. The syndrome occurs in most parts of the world, affecting children between the ages of 6 months and 4 years.

It is a disease of artificially-fed or early weaned children. The child who develops it has usually been living on an inadequate diet for some time and then, during weaning, is kept satisfied by being given bulky carbohydrate staples (such as cassava) which are almost devoid of protein and which, in order to provide sufficient joules, must be taken in impossibly large quantities. Kwashiorkor can appear in infants who are being breast fed but are also having a supplementary diet of carbohydrate staple foods.

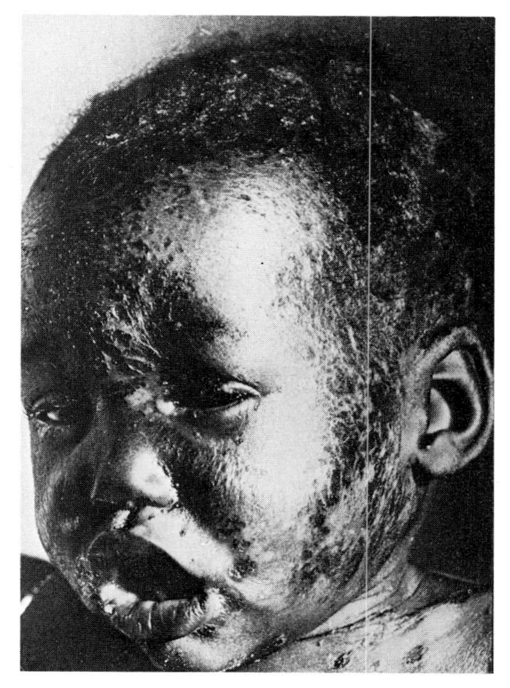

Fig. 8.2 Malnutrition: an example of kwashiorkor (Uganda) (WHO).

The clinical picture is usually a variation of the following: growth retardation, changes in pigmentation (hair and skin), alteration in texture of hair, oedema, apathy and irritability. Wasted muscles may be masked by oedema. There may be xerophthalmia, angular stomatitis, cheilosis, glossitis and photophobia. Diarrhoea is common, with porridgy or liquid stools containing undigested food. Offensive steatorrhoea may occur. Vomiting is often present and may be persistent. Where there is secondary gastro-intestinal infection, dehydration may be extreme.

Treatment

The diet must be adjusted as quickly as possible but too rapid feeding may exacerbate the diarrhoea, and worsen the electrolyte imbalance. Once anorexia has been overcome, the child becomes eager for food, and adjustment of his diet is comparatively easy.

In very sick children attention should first be given to life saving procedures such as rehydration. Small amounts of diluted dextrose saline should be given frequently. In addition, 1.0 g potassium chloride should be added to each litre of the mixture. The child should receive 120 to 200 ml per kg body weight per day. Parenteral replacement of fluid may be necessary if the gastro-intestinal disturbances are gross. The infusion should be given intravenously if possible; if not, intraperitoneally or subcutaneously (without sugars).

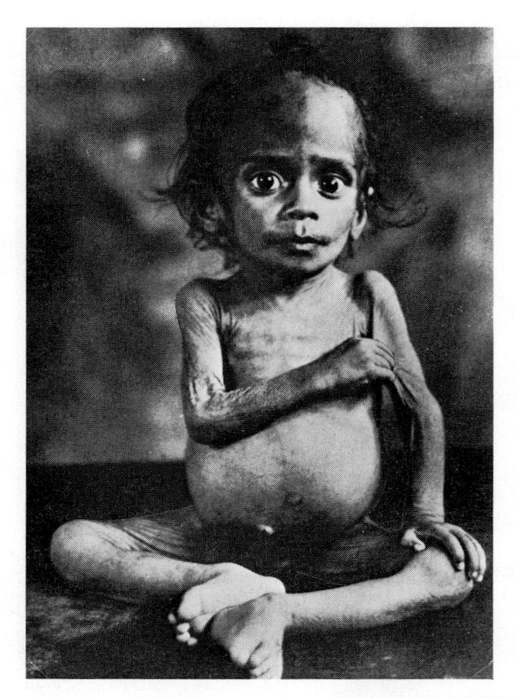

Fig. 8.3 Malnutrition: an example of marasmus (Venezuela) (WHO).

Suitable hypotonic fluids are Ringer lactate (1 part sodium lactate one sixth molar : 2 parts Ringer solution : 3 parts 5 per cent glucose solution) with dextrose or Darrow's solution (sodium chloride 3 g : potassium chloride 2.7 g : sodium bicarbonate 4.4 g) in each litre. If vomiting is severe, the lactate or the bicarbonate should be omitted.

The initial volume of fluid provided should be 40 to 50 ml per kg body weight per day. The infusion should be given quickly in the first instance at 40 to 50 drops per minute, gradually slowing the rate during the day. As soon as rehydration is established, and the urinary output improves, oral fluid should be substituted.

Diuretics should not be given. If blood is needed, it should be given very slowly to avoid circulatory embarrassment.

Very sick children may develop bacterial bronchopneumonia and to avoid this children

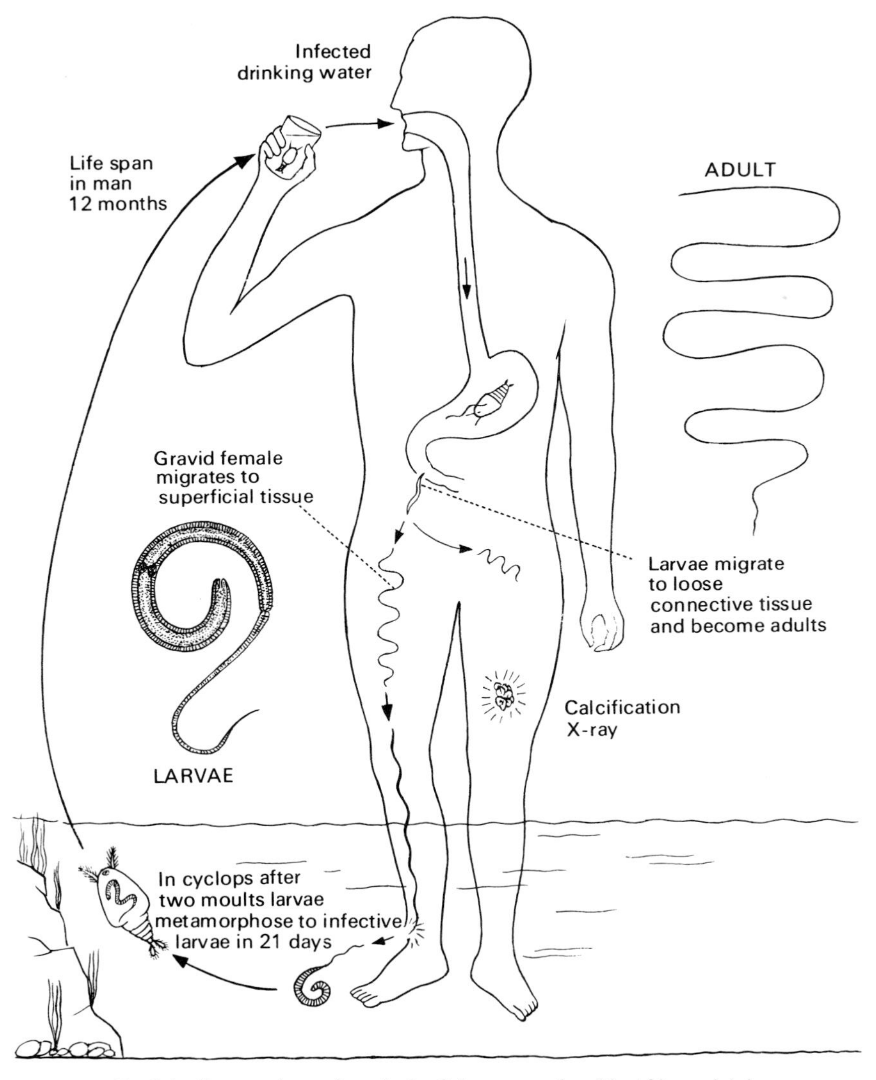

Fig. 8.4 *Dracunculus medinensis*, the Guinea worm, found in Africa and Asia.

with very severe kwashiorkor are usually given procaine penicillin over the first week. (Other antibiotics are sometimes recommended but the broad spectrum antibiotics can present side effects.) Streptomycin is sometimes given in addition to penicillin in the usual dosages.

Hypothermia may be a serious complication despite a tropical environment. The baby will be cold and cyanotic with a rectal temperature well below normal. Warmth, protection and shelter are essential.

Adjustment of diet

Once the life saving procedures are in operation, the adjustment of the diet should begin.

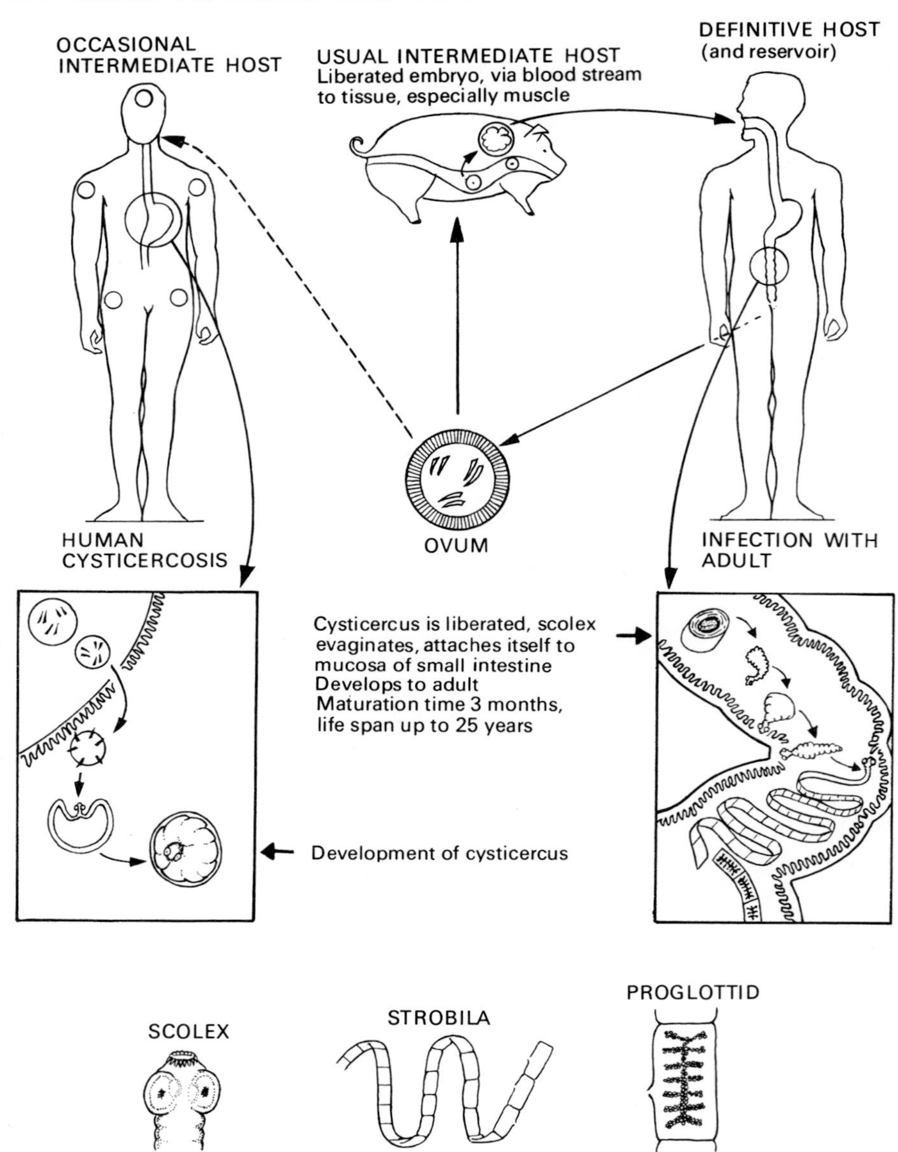

Fig. 8.5 The pork tape worm (*Taenia solium*) found world-wide.

The principle is to give a high protein, energy-adequate and easily assimilated diet, usually based on cow's milk. For the first few days the infant may be given food gradually on the basis of 100 to 250 kJ and 1 to 1.5 g protein per kg body weight per day. This may be given either in the form of the mixture or as milk diluted with an equal volume of 5 per cent glucose solution. This diet is increased to 400 to 500 kJ and 3 to 5 g protein per kg body weight per day.

Nursing supervision is essential in the early days with the family helping at first and then gradually taking over completely.

Vitamins may be given as multivite preparations or in local foods. If there are signs of xerophthalmia, Vitamin A should be given intramuscularly.

In severe cases, after rehydration, magnesium should be given in the form of a 50 per cent solution of the sulphate; daily doses of 0.5 ml intramuscularly for a child of 5 to 7 kg body weight increasing to 2.0 ml at 15 kg. Supplements of groundnuts, provided later, ensure adequate quantities of the mineral.

Protein is best supplied from animal sources, but for social and economic reasons this

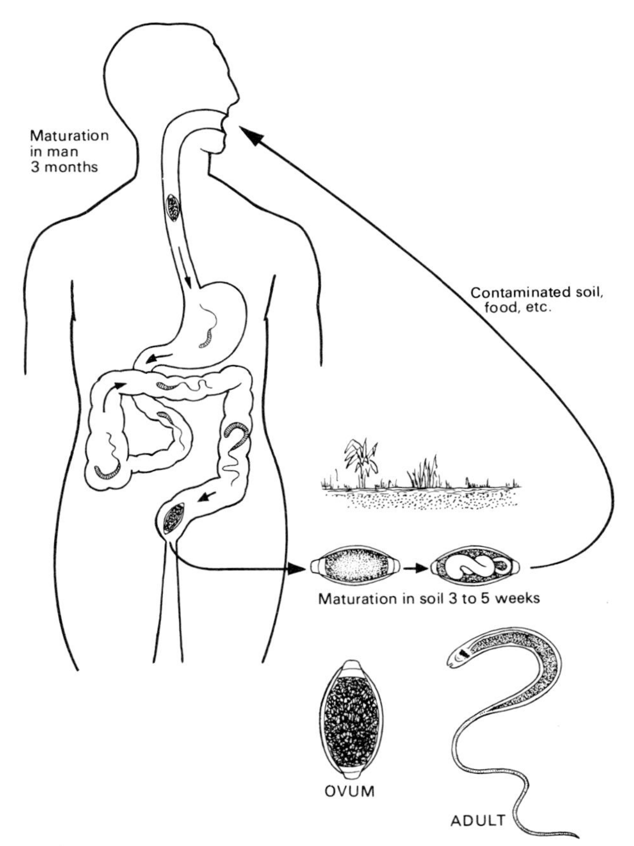

Fig. 8.6 *Trichuris trichiura* (the whip worm), also called *Trichocephalus trichiura*. Geographical distribution: cosmopolitan.

may not be possible. As an alternative, balanced vegetable protein mixture must be provided. It is to be hoped that very soon leaf protein will be accepted but, meanwhile, groundnut extract and soya bean are the most frequently used sources. The family must be taught to provide and prepare the diet, otherwise relapse is likely.

If there are co-existent parasitic and bacterial infections these must be treated immediately. Helminth infections, such as hookworm, should be left until convalescence unless causing severe anaemia.

MARASMUS

This syndrome is caused by the effects of extreme under-nutrition and presents with infection (especially ascariasis and hookworm infection) and gastro-intestinal disturbances associated with diarrhoea. The maximum age incidence is eighteen months. It is rare in the first few months of life.

The infant is grossly underweight and there is marked loss of subcutaneous fat. The skin is cold and flaccid. The features are sharpened and the eyes are wide and sunken.

The ribs and bony eminences are prominent, the muscles wasted and the limbs 'like matchsticks'. The abdomen is usually distended. There are no hair changes, no dermatosis and, usually, no oedema. The child is miserable and sucks his fingers continuously.

Marasmus is difficult to treat and in severe cases the mortality rate is high. The advanced syndrome should be treated similarly to kwashiorkor.

9. Other medical treatments in disaster situations

EMERGENCY RESUSCITATION

The vital needs are:

1. Airway: open to allow air to reach the lungs;
2. Breathing: adequate to allow sufficient oxygen to enter the lungs and pass into the blood;
3. Circulation: sufficient to carry the oxygen-containing blood to the tissues of the body.

Emergency resuscitation is therefore concerned with:

1. The immediate and continued oxygenation of the blood by inflating the lungs;
2. The restarting of the heart to maintain sufficient circulation to ensure that this oxygenated blood reaches the brain and other organs, e.g. heart, kidneys.

The most important single factor in any form of respiratory resuscitation is the speed with which the first few inflations can be given.

When artificial respiration is necessary, the urgency is so great that only obvious obstructions should be removed. i.e. those over the head and face, round the neck, in the mouth (debris—vomit, blood, loose teeth, tongue).

Respiratory resuscitation (artificial respiration)

There are several methods of artificial respiration. The most effective is mouth-to-mouth (or mouth-to-nose) and this method can be used by almost all age groups and in almost all circumstances except when there is severe injury to the face and mouth, when the casualty is pinned in the face down position or if vomiting interferes with respiratory resuscitation.

Vomiting usually occurs when breathing is re-established and consciousness is returning.

A person who is asphyxiated to any significant degree will be in a state of unconsciousness.

In this state, however this has been brought about, the casualty is likely to die—simply because his tongue may have fallen to the back of his throat and blocked his airway. This obstruction may be aggravated by vomit or other matter.

The first thing to do with an unconscious casualty is to check that he is breathing easily. If he is NOT, then the following treatment should be carried out immediately.

Treatment

If the casualty is NOT breathing:

1. Ensure he has a good airway. Support the nape of his neck and press the top of his head so that it is tilted backwards; push the chin upwards.

If the casualty is capable of breathing, this may be all that is necessary; he will gasp and start to breathe. If so, place him in the recovery position.

2. Loosen clothing at neck and waist.

3. To help his breathing, inflate the lungs three or four times.

If the casualty does not begin to breathe when a good airway is ensured, keep the head tilted backwards and begin mouth-to-mouth (mouth-to-nose) resuscitation. This is easier to do when the casualty is lying on his back.

Mouth-to-mouth method of artificial respiration

For an adult:

1. Open your mouth wide and take a deep breath;
2. Pinch the casualty's nostrils together with your fingers;
3. Seal your lips round his mouth;
4. Blow into his lungs until his chest rises;
5. Remove your mouth and watch the chest fall;
6. Repeat, and continue inflations at your natural rate of breathing.

For an infant or young child:

1. Open your mouth wide and take a deep breath;
2. Seal your lips round his mouth and nose;
3. Blow gently into his lungs until the chest rises;
4. Remove your mouth and watch the chest fall;
5. Repeat and continue inflations.

Give the first four inflations as rapidly as possible to saturate the blood with oxygen.

If the casualty's chest fails to rise, there is an obstruction. Ensure that his head is tilted well backwards; turn him on his side and thump his back. Check for, and remove, any foreign matter from the back of the throat.

It may be easier to obtain an airtight seal between your mouth and that of the casualty if his dentures are retained securely in their normal position. If you cannot make a seal round the casualty's mouth, use the mouth-to-nose method. In this case, during inflation, close the casualty's mouth with the thumb of your hand holding his lower jaw.

If the heart is beating normally continue to give artificial respiration until natural breathing is restored.

If the heart is NOT beating:

1. Put the casualty on his back on a firm surface such as the floor.

2. Strike his chest smartly to the left of the lower part of the breastbone with the edge of the hand; this may restart the heart beating.

In cardiac arrest, external heart compression should not be started unless you are satisfied that the heart has stopped beating.

External heart compression

1. Place yourself at the side of the casualty.

2. Feel for the lower half of the sternum and place the heel of your hand on it, keeping the palm and fingers off the chest.

3. Cover this hand with the heel of the other hand.

4. With arms straight, rock forwards, pressing down on the lower half of the breast-

bone (in an unconscious adult it can be pressed towards the vertebral column for about 4 cm).

In adults, repeat the pressure at least sixty times per minute.

In children up to ten years, light pressure of one hand only is sufficient and the rate is 80 to 90 times per minute.

In infants, very light pressure with two fingers is enough and the rate is 100 times per minute.

Pressure in all cases should be firm, but controlled.

Check the effectiveness of the compression of the heart by:

1. Watching for an improvement in the casualty's colour;
2. Noting the size of the pupils, which should become smaller with effective treatment;
3. Feeling the carotid pulse, which will become apparent with each compression.

The rate of lung inflation and heart compression, based on present experience, is as follows:

One person

Fifteen heart compressions followed by two quick lung inflations. Then repeat.

Two persons

Five heart compressions followed by one deep lung inflation. Then repeat.

One person should undertake the external heart compression whilst the other undertakes the inflation and also notes the size of the pupils and feels for carotid pulsation.

Another method is the revised Holger Nielsen, and this is used in certain circumstances, e.g. when the face is damaged and the jaw has been fractured or severely injured so that mouth-to-mouth or mouth-to-nose resuscitation is not practicable.

A further method for use in these circumstances is the Silvester Method:

1. Remove any obvious obstruction from the casualty's mouth.
2. Lay the casualty on his back on a firm surface.
3. Raise his shoulders on a folded jacket (or in some other way).
4. Check that the airway is clear by extending the head backwards.
5. Kneel astride the casualty's head.
6. If necessary turn his head to one side to clear out the mouth.
7. Grasp his wrists, cross them over the lower part of his chest.
8. Rock your body forward and press down on the casualty's chest.
9. Release the pressure and, with a sweeping movement, draw the casualty's arms backwards and outwards as far as possible.
10. Repeat the procedure rhythmically (12 times per minute for an adult).

If no improvement is noticed in the colour and appearance of the casualty, turn him on his side and strike him smartly on the back between the shoulders to clear any obstruction. Re-commence the cycle.

Holger Nielsen method

The casualty should be placed face downwards, arms overhead, elbows flexed, so that one hand rests on the other.

Turn the casualty's head to one side so that the cheek rests on his uppermost hand.

Kneel on one knee at the casualty's head and put the foot of the opposite leg near his elbow.

Place the hands on his back just below the shoulder blades and rock forwards with the elbows straight until the arms are approximately vertical, exerting steady pressure on his chest.

Grasp the casualty's arms just above the elbow and rock backwards, raising his arms until resistance and tension are felt at his shoulders, then drop the casualty's arms.

The phases of expansion and compression should each last 2½ seconds, the complete cycle being repeated 12 times a minute. No time should be lost between the two phases of expansion and compression.

This method is, of course, only practicable when there are no gross injuries to the arm, shoulder-girdle and ribs.

During recovery

On recovery at any stage, outpouring of saliva and of fluid from stomach and nose usually takes place; this may be followed by retching and vomiting.

To prevent inhalation of this fluid or vomit, place the casualty carefully in the recovery position.

Poisoning by carbon monoxide and carbon dioxide

The use of a life-line when entering a gas-filled room or space is a safety precaution which should be used whenever available.

If the casualty is in a room or enclosed space, breathe in and out several times and then take a deep breath and hold it before entering.

Go in and get the casualty out. If you cannot do so at once cut off the source of danger, e.g. turn off the gas, switch off the engine. Obtain a full supply of fresh air, open doors and windows and get out.

Treatment

If breathing is failing or has stopped, start resuscitation immediately. After rescue, ensure absolute rest, placing the casualty in the recovery position.

Suffocation by smoke

Protect yourself by tying a towel or coarse cloth, preferably wet, over your mouth and nose.

The use of a life-line is a safety precaution and should be used whenever available.

Keep low and remove the casualty as quickly as possible.

In smouldering hazards, care must be taken not to increase the fire risk by leaving doors and windows open.

Treatment

As for poisoning by carbon monoxide and carbon dioxide.

Electrical injury

Injury here is caused by the passage of an electrical current through the body. The immediate effect may be extremely severe and cause irregular quivering or tremor of muscles of the heart (fibrillation), or may stop its action altogether.

High voltage injuries

Contacts with electric currents of up to 4 000 000 volts from overhead electric cables, conductor rails of electric railways and some industrial currents may be fatal, or cause serious injury, e.g. severe burns.

Sudden muscle spasm may throw the casualty away from the point of contact with some force and further injuries, such as broken bones, may result. If this occurs, the casualty should be treated in accordance with the priorities of his injuries. When spasm affects the muscles of the chest, asphyxia may result.

Should the casualty remain in contact with, or in close proximity to, high voltage electric current, no attempt at rescue should be made.

Do not allow anyone within twenty yards. Get someone to contact the police. No safe approach to render first aid can be made until you are absolutely sure that the cable or conductor rail is out of service or that it is isolated and earthed near the site of the accident. If this is not done it may, without warning, be re-energised.

Insulating material such as dry wood, clothing, etc. is not proof against high voltages which can jump a considerable gap, also causing flash burns.

NEVER climb an electric pylon or pole in anticipation of rendering first aid.

Cranes and other tall objects sometimes foul overhead electricity cables. If they remain in contact with, or in close proximity to lines, no approach should be made until it has been established that it is perfectly safe to do so.

When you are officially informed that it is safe, then, and then only, can first aid be rendered safely.

Low voltage injuries

These are caused by electricity current of low voltage from the domestic supply.

Moisture and water conduct electricity, and when switches are faulty and there is an electrical current, care must be taken to avoid direct contact with the casualty, thus preventing injury to yourself.

Injury may stop the action of the heart and stop breathing. The local effect is a burn which is deeper than its area suggests.

Action

Break the contact: switch the current off, remove the plug, wrench the cable free. If this is impossible, stand on some dry insulating material and by means of dry wood, folded newspaper or rubber, attempt to break the contact by pushing the casualty's limbs away. Do not touch the casualty with your hands.

Treatment

If necessary give artificial respiration. Treat burns.

Lightning injury

Lightning may produce similar injuries to those of a high voltage electric current.

Instantaneous death may occur. When struck by lightning the person is stunned and falls unconscious to the ground. There may be patches of scorching on the skin, burns being deeper where a metallic object, such as a watch, has been carried close to the skin.

Clothing may be set on fire.

Treatment

If necessary give artificial respiration. Treat burns.

WOUNDS, BLEEDING AND CIRCULATORY FAILURE

Wounds may be classified as follows:

1. Incised or clean cut.
2. Lacerated or torn.
3. Contused or bruised.
4. Punctured or stab.
5. Gunshot.

Bleeding

Bleeding may occur externally or internally and may vary from trivial to severe to fatal.

External bleeding

Treatment

1. Reassure casualty.
2. Place him at rest.
3. Apply a dressing with a pad if necessary and bandage firmly in position. An adhesive dressing may be suitable.
4. Raise the injured part and support it in position, unless an underlying fracture is suspected.
5. If the wound is dirty wash it if possible in running water, wiping from the middle outwards, before applying the dressing. Protect the wound temporarily with a sterile swab and gently clean the surrounding skin. Dry the skin with swabs of cotton wool, wiping away from the wound and using each swab only once.

Wounds with severe bleeding

Treatment

1. Apply direct pressure with the fingers to the bleeding point or points (over a dressing, if immediately available), for 5 to 15 minutes. If the wound area is large, press the sides of the wound firmly but gently together.
2. Lay the casualty down in a suitable and comfortable position, and lower the head if possible.
3. Raise the injured part and support it in position, unless an underlying fracture is suspected.
4. Carefully remove from the wound any foreign bodies which are visible and can easily be picked out or wiped off with a dressing.
5. When a dressing is available:
   a. Apply it directly over the wound and press firmly down;
   b. Cover with a pad of soft material;
   c. Retain the dressing and pad in position with a firm bandage;
   d. See that the dressing and pad extend well above the level and beyond the edges of the wound.

If bleeding continues, apply further dressings and pads on top of the original dressing, and bandage more firmly.

6. Immobilise the injured part by a suitable method, e.g. for an upper limb use a sling; for a lower limb, tie it to its fellow with adequate padding.

Wounds from which foreign bodies cannot be removed

Treatment

If it is not possible to remove the foreign body, or if the ends of a broken bone protrude through the skin:

1. Apply pressure alongside the foreign body or broken bone, or press the sides of the wound firmly but gently together;
2. Apply a dressing over the wound. Place pads of cotton wool or other soft material round the wound to a height sufficient to prevent pressure on the foreign body or projecting broken bone.

Indirect pressure

If bleeding cannot be controlled by the application of direct pressure on the wound, or when it is impossible to apply direct pressure successfully, indirect pressure may be applied at the appropriate pressure point between the heart and the wound. This pressure is not always successful owing to subsidiary bleeding.

A pressure point is where an important artery can be compressed against an underlying bone, thus preventing the flow of blood. Such pressure may be applied while dressing pad and bandage are being prepared for application—which should take no longer than fifteen minutes.

Brachial pressure point

To apply pressure, pass your fingers under the casualty's upper arm and compress the artery against the humerus.

Femoral pressure point

To apply pressure, bend the casualty's knee, grasp his thigh with both hands and press directly and firmly downwards in the centre of the groin with both thumbs, one on top of the other against the brim of the pelvis.

Internal bleeding

Internal bleeding may:

a. Remain concealed;
b. Subsequently become visible.

Concealed

Bleeding may remain concealed in the following instances:

1. Fracture of vault of the skull or cerebral bleeding;
2. Bleeding into the tissues, associated with fractures;
3. Bleeding from the spleen, liver, or other organ into the abdomen.

Concealed bleeding should be suspected when progressive signs and symptoms of bleeding develop following an injury to the abdomen.

Subsequently visible

Internal bleeding may become visible in the following ways:

1. When blood issues from the ear canal, the nose, appears as a bloodshot eye, or is swallowed and afterwards vomited, as in the case of a fractured base of the skull;
2. From the lungs when blood is coughed up;
3. From the stomach when blood is vomited;
4. From the gut;
5. From the genito-urinary tract.

Treatment

1. Place the casualty at complete rest with legs raised. Warn him not to move.
2. Loosen all tight clothing about his neck, chest and waist.
3. Reassure him and explain the necessity to relax mentally and physically.
4. Ensure that no other injuries are present; the casualty's word may be unreliable in severe cases.
5. Protect him from cold.

Do not give anything by mouth.

Bleeding from the scalp

Treatment

Do not press into or probe the wound—there may be an underlying fracture.

1. Apply a dressing much larger than the wound and bandage firmly in position.
2. If an underlying fracture is suspected or there is a foreign body in the wound, a large ring pad should be used to permit pressure around the wound, but not over the fracture or foreign body.

From the ear canal

Bleeding, or the discharge of straw-coloured fluid, from the ear canal may indicate a fracture of the base of the skull.

Treatment

1. Place a dressing or pad over the ear and secure lightly in position.
2. Lay the casualty carefully down with his head slightly raised and inclined to side of injury or if unconscious, in the recovery position.
3. Keep careful watch on his breathing and pulse rate. Do not pack the ear canal.

From the nose

Bleeding may be caused by a blow. A fracture of the base of the skull may cause blood to trickle from the nose.

Treatment

1. Support the casualty in a sitting position with his head slightly forward.
2. Instruct him to breathe through his mouth.
3. Tell him to pinch firmly the soft part of his nose for about ten minutes.

4. Warn him not to blow his nose for some hours.
5. Loosen clothing about neck and chest.
6. Do not disturb the clot.

From the tongue or cheek

Compress the part between the finger and thumb, using a clean handkerchief or a dressing, if available.

From the palm of the hand

Bleeding may be severe as several blood vessels are involved.

Treatment

1. Apply direct pressure.
2. Raise the limb if possible.

When no fracture or irremovable foreign body is present:

1. Cover the wound with a dressing.
2. Place a suitable pad over the dressing.
3. Bend the fingers over the pad so as to make a fist.
4. Bandage the fist firmly with a folded triangular bandage, tying off across the knuckles.
5. Support the limb in a triangular sling.

When there is a fracture or irremovable foreign body present:

1. Treat the wound.
2. Support the limb in a triangular sling.

Chest injuries: Penetrating (stab) wounds

Signs and symptoms

Blueness of lips and extremities may be present.

A wound in the chest wall may allow direct access of air into the chest cavity. If so, during inspiration, the noise of air being sucked in may be heard (sucking wound), on expiration, blood or blood-stained bubbles may be expelled from the wound.

If the lung is injured, the casualty may also cough up bright red frothy blood.

Treatment

The aim of first-aid is to seal the wound immediately and so prevent air entering the chest cavity.

1. Until the dressing can be applied, place the palm of the hand firmly over the wound.
2. Lay the casualty down with head and shoulders raised and the body inclined towards the injured side.
3. Plug the wound lightly with a dressing.
4. Cover the dressing with a thick layer of cotton wool.
5. Retain it firmly in position by strapping or a bandage.
6. Remove urgently to hospital.

Stove-in-chest

Signs and symptoms

The casualty is severely distressed and breathing is difficult. Blueness of lips and extremities may be present. The injured part of the chest wall will be seen to have lost its rigidity. Instead of moving normally with the remainder of the chest, it does the opposite—during inspiration it is sucked in, on expiration it is blown out. Sufficient air does not enter the lungs and, in consequence, the blood cannot obtain enough oxygen.

Treatment

The aim of first-aid is to reduce respiratory activity to the minimum necessary.

1. Loosen any tight clothing—collar, belt, etc.
2. Place the casualty at rest, raise head of stretcher to reduce pressure of abdominal contents on diaphragm.
3. Immobilise the injured part of the chest wall by placing the arm, with the elbow bent, against it as a splint.
4. Secure by strapping or bandaging the arm to the chest.
5. Remove urgently to hospital.

Blast injuries

Caused by an explosion.

Signs and symptoms

The casualty may be apprehensive and in a tremulous state; he will have pain in the chest and be restless. Cyanosis of lips and extremities may be present, and frothy, blood-stained sputum may be coughed up. There will be dyspnoea, but not necessarily any signs of bruising or of fractures. On examination, the casualty may not complain of pain or tenderness.

Treatment

1. Reassure him.
2. Loosen any tight clothing.
3. Lay him down in the semi-recumbent position.
4. Remove urgently to hospital.

Wounds of the abdominal wall

Treatment

Place the casualty so that the wound does not gape—generally on his back with head and shoulders slightly raised and supported, with a pillow under his knees.

If no internal organs are visible, apply a dressing to the wound and bandage firmly in position.

If internal organs are protruding, cover lightly with a soft clean towel or a large gauze dressing and secure without undue pressure. Do not attempt to replace protruding organs.

In all cases, support the abdomen if vomiting or coughing is present.

Remove to hospital urgently. Do not give anything by mouth.

Crush injuries

This is a condition in which it is of great importance to prevent acute kidney failure, which is liable to occur if casualties have been crushed or trapped for more than an hour by some heavy weight, such as fallen masonry or machinery.

Crush injury involves soft tissues and sometimes bones are fractured.

On release, such casualties may show little sign of injury except perhaps redness or swelling of the part. There may be some bruising or blister formation and casualties may complain of numbness and tingling.

Complications occur some hours after release.

Treatment

The aim of first-aid is to prevent a dangerous fall in the blood pressure and kidney failure.

1. On release, keep the casualty on his back with head low and lower limbs raised, if possible. Warn him not to move.

2. Arrange for removal to hospital with the least possible delay, as this is the danger period. It is important to inform the hospital of the possibility of crush injury as initially there may be little evidence to suggest it.

3. If he is conscious and an internal abdominal injury is not suspected give an adult casualty sips of iced water to wash out his mouth but no other fluid.

4. Leave an injured limb uncovered.

Acute heart attacks

Treatment

1. Do not move the casualty unnecessarily but place him in the most comfortable position, which is usually semi-recumbent, with head and shoulders raised on two or more pillows; or supported in a sitting position if this makes his breathing easier.

2. Loosen clothing about neck, chest and waist.

3. If breathing fails, begin artificial respiration immediately and, if necessary, give external heart compression. Both these procedures may have to be continued on the way to hospital.

SHOCK

Treatment

1. Lay casualty down and deal with the injury or underlying cause of the shock.

2. Get the casualty to hospital, if possible.

3. Keep his head low and turned to one side with the lower limbs raised, when possible. If there is an injury to his chest or abdomen, the shoulders should be raised slightly and supported, with head turned to one side. If vomiting seems likely, or if the casualty is unconscious, place him carefully in the recovery position.

4. Loosen clothing at the neck, chest and waist.

5. If the casualty complains of thirst, moisten his lips with water. Do not give him anything to drink.

6. Protect him, when necessary, with a blanket or sheet. Do not heat the casualty or use hot water bottles, as this draws blood away from the vital organs to the skin.

Do not move him unnecessarily. Leaving the casualty in the position found, frequently outweighs the benefits of any other action. The more serious the injury, the more important it is not to move the casualty more than is necessary.

INJURIES TO BONES

Fractures

Types of fracture

Closed—when the skin surface is unbroken.

Open—when there is a wound leading down to the fracture, or when the fractured ends protrude through the skin, thus allowing bacteria to gain access to soft tissues and broken bone.

When there is associated injury to the brain, major blood vessels, nerves, lungs, liver, or when associated with a dislocation of a joint, either type of fracture is said to be 'complicated'.

Signs and symptoms

Pain at or near the site of the fracture, made worse by movement of the injured part.

Tenderness on gentle pressure over the affected part.

Swelling. The result of blood loss into the tissues, may later be accompanied by bruising. Swelling may prevent the recognition of other signs, so when in doubt treat as a fracture.

Loss of control. The casualty is unable to move the injured part normally.

Deformity such as:

1. Irregularity of the bone. If the fracture is near the skin, the irregularity may be seen or felt.
2. Shortening of the limb. Due to contraction of the muscles causing the broken ends of the bone to over-ride each other.
3. Angulation or rotation of a limb. Due to a fracture of some supporting bone, e.g. the neck of the femur—the foot falls outwards.
4. Depression of a flat bone as in the skull.

Unnatural movement at the site of the fracture, unless the broken ends are driven into each other.

Crepitus may be felt or heard during the examination of an injured part if the ends of a broken bone move against each other.

Shock, increased by the loss of blood from the circulation.

In addition to the above, the snap of the bone may have been felt or heard. It must also be clearly understood that all the above signs and symptoms may not be present in every fracture. As many signs as possible should be noted by simple observation and without moving any part unnecessarily, as this may cause pain or further damage. If possible, compare the injured and uninjured limbs.

General rules for treatment

1. Asphyxia, bleeding and severe wounds must be dealt with before dealing with any fracture.

2. Treat the fracture on the site of the incident, unless life is endangered (the casualty's or your own), in which case temporary fixation should be carried out before moving the casualty as short a distance as possible.

3. Steady and, if necessary, support the injured part at once to prevent further damage, and maintain this control until the fracture has been immobilised.

4. Immobilise.

5. If possible, raise the injured part after immobilisation in order to reduce discomfort and swelling.

Use of bandages for fractures

Bandages should be applied sufficiently firmly to prevent movement but not so tightly as to interfere with the circulation of the blood or to cause pain.

Separate skin surfaces with soft padding before bandaging together, in order to prevent discomfort and chafing of the skin.

Always tie knots over a splint or on the uninjured side. If both lower limbs are injured, tie the knots in front between them.

Check at 15 minute intervals to ensure that they are not becoming too tight as a result of swelling of the injured tissues. This is especially important when an elbow has been injured and is supported in a sling.

To pass bandages underneath the casualty if he is lying down, use the natural hollows of the body, e.g. the neck, loins, knees.

Use of splints

If splints are required, they should be (a) sufficiently rigid; (b) long enough to immobilise the joint above and below the fracture; (c) well-padded and wide enough to fit comfortably to the limb; and (d) applied over clothing.

In emergencies, a splint may be improvised from a walking stick, umbrella, broom handle, piece of wood, cardboard, or firmly folded newspaper or magazine.

Fractures of the skull

Treatment

1. Place the casualty in the recovery position with adequate support. Establish, as soon as possible, the level of consciousness and check frequently.

3. If blood or fluid comes from the ear canal, apply a sterile dressing and secure lightly in place.

4. Keep a careful check on the casualty's breathing—ensure a clear airway; start artificial respiration if breathing begins to fail or stops.

5. Maintain the casualty's position during transport and avoid all unnecessary movement.

Jaw and face injuries

Fractures and wounds may be complicated by damage to the brain. The skull or cervical spine may also be injured.

The following serious risks are associated with these injuries:

Asphyxia, caused by:

1. The tongue falling to the back of the throat of an unconscious casualty.
2. Swelling of tissues following the injury.
3. Displaced and lacerated tissues.

Inadequate or absent cough reflex, which allows secretions, blood and foreign material to drain unnoticed into the lungs, causing infection and complications such as collapse of the lungs.

Fracture of spine

Signs and symptoms

The casualty is found collapsed and complains of severe pain in his back.

He sometimes says that he feels cut in half, that his lower limbs are numb, or that he has lost control of them.

There is possible loss of power in the limbs; ask the casualty to move his wrists, ankles, fingers and toes.

Test for possible loss of sensation by gently touching the limbs without his knowledge and asking casualty if he can feel touch or pain.

Even though there is no apparent loss of power of sensation, handle with the utmost care to prevent a spinal fracture from causing damage to the spinal cord.

Position of the casualty

The conscious casualty is best transported in the face-upwards position. This is essential where fractures of the neck are suspected.

The unconscious casualty should be carefully supported with rolled blankets, pillows, etc., in the face-upwards position. The recovery position must not be used because of the risk of further damage to the spinal cord. (This is the only exception to this general rule governing the recovery position.) The breathing must be carefully and continuously watched and if it stops, an airway must be achieved even by tilting the head backwards preparatory to mouth-to-mouth resuscitation if this becomes necessary.

Note: This is an example of a calculated risk because injury may result. Otherwise death is certain.

Preparation of stretcher

The canvas bed of a stretcher should be stiffened by placing short boards across it. If these are not available a narrow shutter, a door or board at least as wide and as long as the casualty may be used.

Cover the boards with a folded blanket, then 'blanket the stretcher'.

Place pads on the stretcher to support the natural curves of the casualty's neck, small of back, knees and ankles.

Placing a blanket under the casualty

When the casualty is not already lying on a blanket or rug and one is available:

1. Roll the blanket or rug lengthwise for half its width. Place the roll in line with, and against, the casualty.
2. While two helpers maintain firm control of the head and lower limbs, the other

helpers slowly and gently turn the casualty as in one piece on to his side without bending the neck or twisting the trunk. The two helpers controlling the head and the lower limbs must maintain an even tension while the casualty is being turned.

3. The rolled portion of the blanket or rug is then moved up to the casualty's back.
4. The casualty is then gently turned back over the roll of the blanket or rug on to his opposite side.
5. The blanket or rug is then unrolled and the casualty gently turned on his back.

Blanket lift

Loading the stretcher:

1. Roll the two edges of the blanket up against the sides of the casualty. If poles of sufficient length and rigidity are available the edges of the blanket should be rolled round them. This will make the lifting of the casualty much easier, and prevent sagging.
2. While the two helpers continue to support the head and the lower limbs, the remaining helpers place themselves on each side of the casualty, facing one another.
3. The helpers, acting together, grasp the rolled edges of the blanket, carefully and evenly lift the casualty to a sufficient height to enable the stretcher to be pushed underneath. It will be necessary for the people supporting the feet to keep their legs apart to allow the stretcher to be pushed between them.

If it is not possible to push the stretcher under the casualty, it should be placed close to the casualty's head or feet, and after carefully lifting the casualty the helpers should move with short, even, side paces until the casualty is directly over the stretcher.

Before lowering him on to the stretcher, ensure that the pads are in the correct position. With neck injuries place firm supports at each side of the head to steady it.

Lifting with slings

In special circumstances slings may be made from broad bandages, roller towels or webbing bands, and passed under the casualty's neck, shoulders, small of the back, knees and ankles.

The ends of the slings are tied to stout poles, one on each side of the casualty.

When the weight is taken up there must be an even tension of all slings.

With one person supporting the casualty's head, he is then loaded on to a stretcher in the same way as for a blanket lift.

Bleeding, which initially may be profuse and alarming, but which is not usually prolonged and should be controlled by direct pressure.

Fracture of the lower jaw

This is always the result of direct force, and there is usually a wound inside the mouth. Normally only one side of the jaw is affected.

Signs and symptoms

Pain increased by jaw movements or by swallowing; difficulty in speaking; excessive flow of saliva, which is frequently blood-stained; irregularity of the teeth; swelling, tenderness and, later, bruising of the face and lower jaw; severe bleeding, if tongue is injured.

Treatment

1. Maintain an open airway. Ensure that the tongue has not fallen to the back of the throat and that the mouth is not obstructed.
2. Control bleeding.
3. Remove any false or detached teeth.
4. Support the jaw with a soft pad held in place by hand or by a suitable bandage.
5. The conscious casualty not severely injured may sit up with his head well forward so that any secretions can drain freely; severely injured, with downward displacement of the chin and associated soft tissues, may require to be kept in the recovery position.

The unconscious casualty must be placed in the recovery position, with the jaw kept well forward.

6. If the casualty seems likely to vomit, turn his head to the uninjured side, supporting the jaw with the palm of your hand.
7. If possible, arrange for urgent removal to hospital.

Lifting with webbing bands

These bands, if available, can facilitate the moving and lifting of a casualty. They are made in two lengths:

1. 2 foot, used for lifting at the head, neck or feet;
2. 3 foot, used for lifting under the chest, small of back and the hips.

Method of use:

1. Grasping the junction of the webbing and the long handle, slide the handle under the casualty. The back can then be gently drawn through until there is a handle on each side of the casualty;
2. If the casualty is lying close to the wall and it is not possible to pass the long handle through without disturbing him, the short handle is tied to, or bent over, the long handle and then slid under the casualty:
3. When the bands are applied and the casualty's head and lower limbs are steadied, he can be raised and lifted on to a stretcher.

Removal to hospital

It is important that spinal injuries be transported in as gentle a way as possible.

The casualty may be lifted on to the stretcher in the position in which he is found. If his neck is injured he must be placed face upwards.

If transported on his side, steady the casualty with rolled blankets, pillows, etc.

Retain in position by bandaging over the casualty and under the stretcher.

Fracture of the ribs

Signs and symptoms

Sharp pain at the site of the fracture is increased by deep breathing or coughing; the casualty usually takes short, shallow breaths in an attempt to limit movements and decrease pain. If internal organs are affected, there may be signs and symptoms of internal bleeding. There may be an open wound in the chest wall over the fracture, causing a 'sucking wound' of the chest which will lead to asphyxia unless treated immediately.

Treatment

When the fracture is uncomplicated:

1. Support the upper limb on the injured side in an arm sling.
2. Transport as a sitting or walking case unless otherwise indicated.

When the fracture is complicated:

1. Any 'sucking wound' must be made airtight immediately.
2. Support the upper limb on the injured side in a triangular sling.
3. Lay the casualty down with head and shoulders raised and the body inclined towards the injured side.
4. Support the casualty in this position by means of a folded blanket applied lengthwise to his back.
5. Transport to hospital as a stretcher case.

The breastbone

Treatment

1. Loosen tight clothing about neck, chest and waist.
2. Place the casualty with his head and shoulders raised in the most comfortable position, with due regard to associated injuries.
3. Transport as a stretcher case.

Collar-bone

Signs and symptoms

Pain and tenderness at the site of the injury.

The arm on the injured side is partly helpless and the casualty supports it at the elbow and keeps his head inclined towards the injured side. This relieves pain by reducing muscle tension. Swelling or deformity can be seen or felt over the site of the fracture.

Treatment

1. Fold two triangular bandages narrow.
2. Pass each narrow bandage through one armpit, encircle the same shoulder and tie behind in a reef knot.
3. Carry the free ends across the back over a pad placed between the shoulder blades; tie opposite ends together, or secure with a third bandage.

As the knots are carefully tightened the shoulders are braced well back, in order to correct the overriding of the broken ends of the clavicle.

4. Support the arm on the injured side in a triangular arm sling.

Shoulder blade

This rare injury is the result of direct force.

Treatment

1. Remove overcoat and braces.
2. Place a pad in the armpit.
3. Support the upper limb in a triangular sling with fingertips to opposite shoulder.

4. Give further support by securing the upper limb to the chest by a broad bandage applied over the sling.

The upper limb

Treatment

If the elbow is not involved:

1. Place the forearm across the chest, finger tips touching the fold of the opposite armpit.
2. Ensure adequate soft padding between the limb and the chest.
3. Support the limb in an arm sling.
4. Give further support by securing the upper limb to the chest by a broad bandage applied over the sling.

If elbow cannot be flexed:

1. Do not attempt to force it.
2. Lay casualty down.
3. Place the limb gently by the casualty's side, palm to thigh.
4. Protect with adequate soft padding between the limb and the body.
5. Secure by three broad bandages, tied on the uninjured side of the body
   a. round upper arm and trunk,
   b. round forearm and trunk,
   c. round the wrist and thighs.
6. Transport as a stretcher case.

The pelvis

Signs and symptoms

Pain in the region of the hips and loins, increased by movement.

Inability to stand, despite the absence of injury to the lower limbs.

There may be a desire to pass water frequently, though with difficulty. If passed, the urine may be darkened by blood.

Treatment

1. Lay the casualty down in the most comfortable position—usually on his back with knees straight.

If he wishes to bend knees slightly, they should be supported on a folded blanket.

2. Tell him not to pass water on any account.

3. If journey to hospital is short and smooth transport as a stretcher case in the same position. If journey to hospital is likely to be rough or there may be some delay in reaching hospital:

   a. Apply two broad bandages round the pelvis, overlapping by half, their centres in line with the hip joints of the affected side. Tie on the uninjured side. The bandages should be sufficiently firm to support the part.

   b. Place adequate soft padding between the knees and the ankles.

   c. Apply a figure-of-eight bandage round the ankles and feet, and a broad bandage round the knees.

Femur

Treatment

1. Steady and support the injured limb.
2. Bring the sound limb gently to the side of the injured one.
3. Should it be necessary to move the injured limb, gentle traction should be applied and maintained until the two limbs have been tied together. This may cause temporary discomfort.

Transport

If the journey is smooth, and the casualty can be comfortably removed to hospital within half an hour of the arrival of the ambulance, place adequate soft padding between the thighs, knees and ankles and secure by tying the ankles and feet together with a figure-of-eight bandage, and the knees with a broad bandage.

If journey is likely to be rough or long and if no splints are available further secure by three broad bandages on the legs, the thighs and below site of fracture ('floater' bandage). When splints are available:

1. For a fractured tibia or fibula, apply well-padded splint between the limbs, extending from the crotch to the foot and immobilise with five bandages, as described above.
2. For a fractured femur, apply a well-padded splint between the limbs, and an additional long padded splint to the side of the fractured limb, extending from the armpit to the foot. Immobilise with two bandages, one round the chest, just below the armpits, the other round the pelvis, in line with the hip joints. These are in addition to the five bandages described above, using a total of seven bandages. One of the bandages may have to be omitted in some instances in order to avoid pressure over the site of the fracture.

Crushed foot

Commonly caused by a heavy weight dropping on or going over the foot. A fracture should be suspected when there is pain, swelling and loss of power.

Treatment

1. Carefully remove shoe or boot and sock or stocking, cutting if necessary.
2. Treat a wound, if present.
3. Apply a well-padded splint to the sole of the foot, reaching from the heel to the toes.
4. Secure the splint with a figure-of-eight bandage as follows: The centre of a broad bandage is placed on the sole of the foot, the ends are crossed over the instep and carried to the back of the ankle. Cross them and bring them to the front of the ankle where they are crossed once more and passed under the sole of the foot. Tie off over the splint.
5. Raise and support the foot in a comfortable position.

Transport

All casualties with fractures of the lower limbs must be transported by stretcher.

BURNS AND SCALDS

The effects of burns or scalds are similar and their seriousness depends upon many factors, the most important being the area and extent, rather than the depth, of the injury.

However, in young children, especially infants, even small burns should be regarded as serious and hospital treatment sought without delay.

The area of most burns and scalds, including the clothing involved, is usually sterile initially and every effort should be made to keep it sterile.

Types of injury

Superficial—a burn or scald where only the outer layers of the skin are damaged.

Deep—when the whole thickness of the skin, including the nerve endings, is destroyed.

An extensive superficial burn or scald is more painful than a small deep burn.

Burns are caused by:

1. Dry heat;
2. Electricity;
3. Friction;
4. Corrosive chemicals: acids such as sulphuric, nitric, hydrochloric; alkalis such as caustic soda, caustic potash, ammonia solution, quicklime;
5. Other chemicals such as phosphorus, phenol (carbolic acid).

Treatment of burns

1. Lessen the spread of heat in the tissues and alleviate pain by placing the burn gently under slowly running water or by immersing the part in cool water, keeping it there for at least ten minutes or until the pain eases. At this early stage reduction of heat is essential, the risk of added infection being of lesser importance.
2. Remove promptly anything of a constrictive nature—rings, bangles, belts and boots—before the parts start to swell.
3. Clothing soaked in boiling water should be carefully removed. Cooled, dry, burned clothing already sterilised by heat need not be removed.
4. Lay the casualty down.
5. Cover the injured part with a dressing, clean sheet, pillow case, etc. With a burn of the face it may be necessary to cut a mask with a hole for breathing.
6. Immobilise a badly burned limb.
7. Give small cold drinks at frequent intervals to a badly burned casualty, if conscious.
8. Arrange for the immediate removal to hospital of all badly burned or scalded casualties as soon as possible, by stretcher if available.
9. Reassure the casualty at all stages.

Clothing on fire

Action

Exclude air immediately to stop combustion.

When a person's clothing catches fire, the immediate need is to remove the heat. Quench the flames and cool the tissues with water or other non-flammable fluid immediately to hand.

If no such fluid is immediately available, approach the person, holding a rug, blanket or coat in front of yourself for protection, wrap it round him, lay him flat, and smother the flames by excluding air. On no account should nylon or other similar material be used.

If a person's clothing catches fire when he is alone, he should roll himself on the floor smothering the flames with the nearest available wrap. On no account should he rush into the open air.

Injuries from corrosive chemicals

In all cases speed is essential to prevent further damage.

Treatment

1. Flood the part thoroughly and continuously with running water if immediately available, to dilute and eliminate the chemical. Avoid further damage to the burned tissues by using slowly running water. Make sure that the water drains away freely and safely.
2. Remove contaminated clothing carefully, if possible while flooding the injured part. Remember to take precautions against contamination yourself.
3. Continue treatment as for a burn.
4. Arrange urgent removal to hospital.

Special corrosives

Phosphorus. Yellow phosphorus ignites on exposure to air, as when drying on the skin.

Treatment

1. Keep the area flooded with water.
2. Apply a dressing soaked in water and ensure that it is kept wet.
3. Arrange urgent removal to hospital.

Electrical contact burns

These burns are normally found at those places where the current entered and left the body.

The effect of the passage of an electric current through the body may be extremely severe and cause stoppage of breathing and heart action. Immediate treatment is required. Muscle spasm may throw the casualty away from the point of contact and cause other injuries, such as broken bones.

The actual depth of the burn is likely to be greater than it appears, with damage to underlying tissues, although its area may be relatively small.

If the casualty is not thrown clear, he may be fixed to the point of contact and receive extremely severe local burns.

Lightning may produce effects similar to those of an electrical injury. Patches of scorching may occur on the skin.

Treatment

1. If necessary give emergency resuscitation.
2. Treat as a burn.

MISCELLANEOUS CONDITIONS

Extremes of temperature

Excessive cold or heat can cause damage to the skin or body in such a way that tissues locally or body function generally may be so seriously affected that death results. Locally, cold may cause frostbite at the extremities (fingers, toes, ears and nose), while heat can cause blistering and ulceration of exposed parts.

If the whole body is affected, the important factors determining the type of treatment to be given and the result are the age of the person affected and the degree of the fatigue or exhaustion. The young adult after exposure to cold can be warmed up quickly, but care should be taken to heat an infant or elderly casualty gradually.

Cold exhaustion

Signs and symptoms

An increasing slowness of physical and mental response; stumbling, cramps and shivering; slurring of speech and difficulty of vision; unreasonable behaviour or irritability; pulse and respiration increased at first, while the body can still respond to cold by shivering.

Warning to travellers. If these symptoms occur, take or improvise shelter, and rest.

It is essential to prevent further loss of body heat, to overcome exhaustion and to obtain help, if possible.

If these precautions are not taken, the excessive cold will overcome the heat-regulating processes, the temperature will fall, and the casualty will fall asleep from cold exhaustion. Temperature falls to about 25°C (77°F), breathing is depressed (slow and shallow) and the pulse rate is very slow. Death will result when the body temperature falls to about 20°C (68°F).

All severely affected cases should be placed in the recovery position and taken by stretcher to medical aid as quickly as possible, protecting them from cold during the journey.

Treatment

At the site:

1. Protect the casualty from wind, rain or sleet, and from cold wet ground under him.
2. If possible, wrap him in dry clothing. Put him in a sleeping bag.
3. Give warm drinks, e.g. warmed condensed milk.

At base:

Rapidly re-warm in a hot bath bringing the temperature up to 42° to 45°C (107° to 113°F).

Note: All cases of prolonged exposure to cold should be considered as serious and in urgent need of medical supervision.

Severe accidental cooling of the body (hypothermia)

This is a dangerous lowering of the body temperature which may occur at any age, but especially in babies and the elderly who lack the ability to regulate their own temperature, even when not fatigued. There is a loss of surface heat followed by cooling of the deep tissues and organs of the body.

Treatment

The aim of first-aid in all cases is to prevent further heat loss, improve body heat and circulation and obtain medical aid or transport the casualty to hospital.

1. Place the casualty between blankets so that the body temperature can recover gradually.
2. If conscious, give tepid or warm sweet drinks.

Do not use hot water bottles or electric blankets as these will cause sudden dilation of the superficial blood vessels taking away blood from the deep tissues and essential organs; this may cause a fatal collapse due to a drop in the casualty's blood pressure and temperature.

Frost bite

Signs and symptoms

The casualty may feel the affected part cold, painful and stiff. Feeling, and power of movement, may be lost; blanching and numbness of the part is evident. In severe cases, if treatment is not urgently carried out gangrene of the affected parts, or death, may occur.

Treatment

1. Take care of the casualty's general condition by sheltering him from the weather and giving warm drinks.
2. Promptly remove anything of a constructive nature—gloves, rings, boots.
3. Thaw the affected part:
   a. face—cover with a dry, gloved hand until normal colour and sensation return;
   b. hands—place in his armpits under the clothing;
   c. feet—wrap in a warm blanket or sleeping bag.

Do not rub the affected part.

Do not apply direct heat in any form.

Effects of excessive heat

In persons who are not accustomed to high temperatures, heat exhaustion or heat stroke can occur.

Heat exhaustion

This is slow in onset and gives rise to a shocked condition due to a salt and water deficiency.

Causes

Exposure to excessive heat, especially moist heat, is commonly found in newcomers to very hot climates. Fluid and salt loss is considerable from excessive sweating and is often aggravated further by a gastro-intestinal upset with diarrhoea and vomiting.

A person who is acclimatised to the tropics may also be affected by water deficiency following a severe attack of malaria or other tropical fever.

Signs and symptoms

Muscular cramp from salt deficiency is an early sign; the casualty is exhausted and may be restless; the face is pale and cold and has a clammy sweat; there may be sudden collapse and loss of consciousness; pulse and breathing are rapid; temperature may be normal, sub-normal, or slightly elevated.

The casualty may complain of headaches, dizziness and nausea and sometimes, of abdominal cramp.

Sudden movement may cause syncope.

Treatment

1. Place and keep the casualty in cool surroundings.
2. If conscious, give cold water to drink. If casualty has had excessive sweating, cramps, diarrhoea and/or vomiting, add half a teaspoonful of common salt to each pint (half litre) of water.

Heat stroke

The onset is more sudden and may be preceded by heat exhaustion.

Signs and symptoms

Unconsciousness may come on quickly. A temperature of 40°C (104°F) or more may occur.

The casualty is restless and, if conscious, complains of headache, dizziness and feeling hot; the face is flushed, the skin hot and dry to the touch; the pulse is full and bounding, the breathing noisy. There may be confusion or stupor, and coma may result.

Treatment

The aim of first-aid is to reduce the casualty's temperature as quickly as possible.

1. Strip the casualty and wrap in a wet, cold sheet. Keep it wet until the casualty's temperature has been lowered to 30°C (101°F).
2. Place him in the recovery position.
3. Direct currents of air on to the casualty from above and below by hand or by electric fans.
4. On recovery the casualty, with a dry sheet over him, should be transported into air-conditioned accommodation to prevent relapse.
5. If his temperature rises again, repeat the treatment.
6. Send to hsopital.

10. Mass inoculation and vaccination programmes

The medical effects of disaster consist mainly of:

1. Traumatic injury,
2. Emotional stress,
3. Epidemics,
4. Indigenous diseases.

The types of infectious diseases likely to occur after a disaster are controlled in advanced countries by a good disease surveillance, the high level of vaccine-induced immunity in the population, and prompt treatment of the diseases when they occur. In many countries some diseases have been successfully eradicated from the community.

Because the incidence of disease is often inadequately documented in poor countries it is sometimes difficult to distinguish between endemic and epidemic diseases. It should be remembered that natural immunity is likely to be present to some degree in the indigenous population and mass vaccination programmes are not necessary after every disaster. The apparent increased incidence of a disease after a disaster may be the result of increased surveillance.

Mass vaccination programmes are logistically difficult to carry out after a disaster because of the inevitable disruption of transport and communications. It is easy to miss those most at risk.

Many vaccines give short-lived protection or require more than one widely spaced injection.

It is becoming increasingly recognised that keeping a watchful eye out for the outbreak of a disease is the best way of controlling an epidemic. An epidemic can then be identified in its early stages and contacts can be vaccinated rapidly, thus stopping spread of the disease.

Indigenous health problems must be recognised and, if possible, previous health programmes continued. Moral difficulties are raised by the provision of a better health service after a disaster than that which existed before it. It sometimes happens that a demand is created which is not met when the relief teams leave.

After floods in the USA in 1958 and 1969 it was reported that no data existed which supported the need for mass typhoid immunisation. Enteric diseases other than typhoid and infectious hepatitis were the chief dangers. Tetanus resulted from injuries and basic immunisation with tetanus toxoid was recommended. (It was also emphasised that strict public and personal hygiene was the best preventive measure.)

To paraphrase Florence Nightingale, it may seem a strange principle to enunciate that, as a first requirement, mass immunisation should do no harm. It is most important to realise the potential danger of such an undertaking. In conditions where mass immunisation is contemplated it may not be possible to give any consideration to the suitability of individuals for vaccination and illness and allergic reactions will result.

There are inherent dangers in all vaccination procedures and the diseases in which vaccination has played a dominant part in the reduction of mortality are those resulting from the action of a bacterial exotoxin, e.g. diphtheria and tetanus, or those resulting from infection by a virus, e.g. poliomyelitis, smallpox and yellow fever. A poor standard of hygiene cannot be chiefly blamed for the transmission of any of these but the same cannot be said for the intestinal infections of cholera and enteric fever. In protection against these diseases immunisation should never be regarded as more than an adjunct to the radical measures of controlling the source more than an adjunct to the radical measures of controlling the source and the means of transmission of infection by strict attention to personal and environmental hygiene in the widest sense. In disaster conditions energetic and ruthless public health measures may well achieve greater and more rapid results in the control of intestinal infection than mass immunisation.

The ideal for any country is for the routine immunisation of its population to be so well organised that mass immunisation should seldom, if ever, be called for.

If large numbers of people are to be vaccinated one of the many devices which use a high speed jet may be used. Syringes and needles have many disadvantages—they may be stolen, they are cumbersome to sterilise, and there is always the danger of serum hepatitis if techniques are poor.

The Heaf Gun

This takes short solid needles which are capable of introducing about 0.002 ml of fluid into the skin. It can be used for tuberculin testing as well as for immunising with vaccinia and BCG.

The Panjet

This was originally designed for anaesthetising the gums in dental surgery. Inside the outer case (which looks rather like a large fountain pen), there is a vaccine container and a piston arrangement driven by a very powerful spring (Fig. 10.1). A fine jet of fluid is injected into the skin, entering the tissues, either approximately 0.05 ml or 0.1 ml depending on size. The Panjet can be sterilised by boiling and, as no vaccine-containing part comes into contact with the patient's tissues, it may be used for many patients and sterilised only at the beginning of each session. It is especially valuable for the administration of measles vaccine.

Porton Injector

This works on the same principle as the Panjet except that foot power has to be used to operate the strong spring. As a volume of 0.5 to 1 ml can be injected, this is suitable for giving triple vaccine and tetanus toxoid.

Ped-O-Jet

This is similar to the Porton Injector, and is capable of injecting from 0.1 to 1.0 ml of fluid. In this instrument the foot pedal remains permanently connected to the gun with hydraulic hoses. It requires skill to operate and service and is expensive. The cost of these devices rises sharply in ratio to the volume of vaccine they are capable of injecting.

Syringes

When large numbers of people are being vaccinated, the provision of a separate syringe

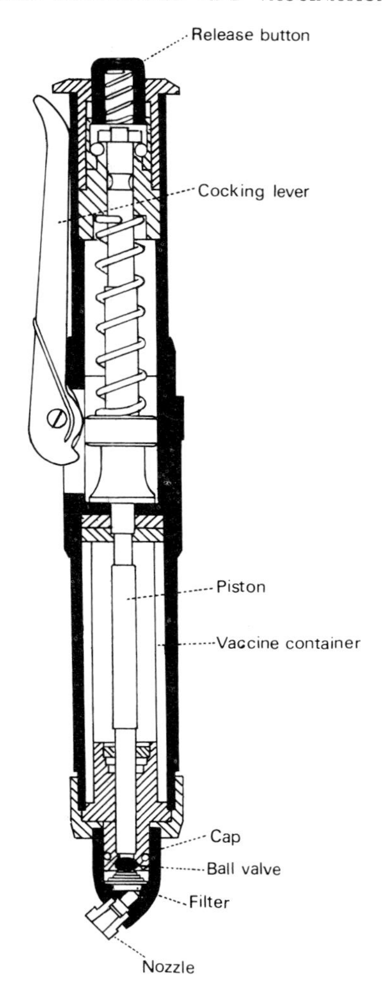

Fig. 10.1 The Panjet, manufactured by Wright Dundee Group, Dundee.

and needle for each individual (which is essential to avoid the risk of transference of infection) may present a special problem in the absence of large numbers of disposable syringes since speed of operation is necessary.

There is a danger in using one syringe and several needles because of the transference of serum hepatitis by the reflux of tissue fluid which occurs on changing the needles. This problem will be overcome when needleless injectors are available for general distribution.

Separate syringes. The ideal solution of this problem is the provision of a disposable sterile syringe for each person. Issuing a separate sterile syringe for each person from a central syringe supply service is feasible when numbers required do not exceed the resources of the centre; numbers should rarely be excessive under normal peacetime conditions.

Rapid sterilisation between injections. Under emergency conditions, however, when large numbers are involved, recourse to re-sterilisation may be necessary between injections.

Since the syringes used will have been supplied sterile, the only organisms requiring destruction should be those derived from a person in the course of vaccination. Of these, the viruses of hepatitis are among the most important and most heat-resistant. For the destruction of such contaminants the temperatures and durations of exposure needed to kill bacterial spores are not essential.

1. *Complete re-sterilisation.* Ideally, the whole syringe should be treated and, for this purpose, should be boiled for not less than ten minutes. To ensure 'sterilisation' within this time, each syringe may be boiled separately, or a number boiled at the same time. Introduction of other syringes into the container once the ten-minute period of boiling has begun may recontaminate those syringes already in it. The sterilising period for all the articles in the boiler must be reckoned from the time the last article is put in.

When more than a few persons are to be vaccinated, the syringes must be sterilised in batches. At least two boilers with lids must be provided.

The syringes are rinsed out with sterile water after use. When a batch has been collected, they are placed, still wet, in the boiler and the lid closed. Using a timer, the period of sterilisation is reckoned from the time the contents of the boiler reach boiling point. Time must be allowed for this and for the syringes to cool after sterilisation.

One doctor with three assistants is, on average, able to vaccinate six persons per minute. Sixty syringes will therefore be used during a sterilising period.

Approximately one-third of the syringes in use must be collected to make up the first batch for re-sterilisation which, therefore, cannot start until about six minutes after the session begins. Thus, to avoid delay, not less than one hundred syringes should be provided sterile for the vaccinator so that he has enough to work with until the first re-sterilised batch is ready for use. Proportionately fewer syringes will be needed if a slower rate of vaccination is accepted or if extra boilers are used.

2. *Re-sterilisation of the needle only—for use in emergency.* Re-sterilisation of the needle only is acceptable provided that reflux of potentially infected tissue fluid into the skin does not take place. Then, only the needle can become contaminated with an infective agent from an individual in the course of giving him an injection and re-sterilisation of the whole syringe becomes unnecessary.

The needle must be re-sterilised, however, while still attached to the syringe, since removing it before sterilisation transfers its possibly infected contents to the tip of the syringe. A method of treating needles based on the above is as follows:

After each injection the vaccinator himself dips the needle half-way up the butt for ten seconds into a bath of oil maintained at 150° to 160°C. The temperature is shown by a thermometer dipping into the oil. Medicinal liquid paraffin is considered suitable for this purpose. The piston must be firmly held against the base of the barrel of the syringe from the time of completion of the injection until the needle is removed from the oil.

Several syringes in rotation should be used in order to allow the needle to cool before recharging with a dose of vaccine.

This method has been used for some time and remains acceptable provided that the technique of sterilisation described above is strictly adhered to and that at no time, from the moment the needle is inserted into the skin before an injection until its completion, is any backward movement of the piston allowed. This second proviso, which is essential to ensure fulfilment of the assumption on which the method is based, is not an easy one with which to comply.

Minor disadvantages of the method are that one operator is unlikely to vaccinate more than three persons a minute if it is properly carried out, and that the piston must not be withdrawn before making an injection. However, though this is a useful way of ensuring that a vein has not been entered, it is not essential before making an intradermal or a subcutaneous injection, when such an accident should be avoidable by exercising reasonable care.

Sterilisation of the needle only should therefore be reserved for circumstances in which resources are not available for providing a sterile syringe for each person in any of the other ways mentioned.

3. *Alternative method.* A domestic pressure cooker will be found useful in many disaster circumstances. Calculating in terms of one syringe and 10 needles for every 10 people, one pressure cooker will sterilise and store enough needles and syringes to immunise 300 to 400 people. It should be operated at its maximum setting (or 15 lb (6.8 kg) per square inch if this is not known) for 15 minutes.

Needle racks should be used in preference to kidney dishes as containers for needles. These may be used in sets of three: one containing sterile needles ready for use, another initially empty and receiving the dirty needles after use, whilst the third, holding needles, is being sterilised. These racks should be rotated. A great advantage is that forceps are not needed as the nozzle of the syringe may be applied directly to the needle adaptor as it stands in the rack. Care should be taken to see that the adaptors of the needles are covered with water whilst they are being boiled. The rack should be lifted out by a simple-attached wire hook when sterilisation is complete.

To wash dirty needles, the whole rack should be held under a tap or running water. As they are in a vertical position, water will run through them easily. It is useful to make the racks (from 20 gauge aluminium) capable of holding 12 needles (Fig. 10.2). This instils into the mind of the user the association of a separate syringe for each rack.

Whilst this technique does not entirely remove the danger of 'syringe-jaundice', it should diminish it.

Oral vaccination

The development of attenuated strain vaccines for oral administration, such as the poliomyelitis vaccine used at present, avoids all the difficulties of sterilisation of syringes described above. This method may also be extended to other diseases in the future as new vaccines become available.

Storage of vaccines. All vaccines should be stored in a temperature of between 2°C and 10°C. They should not be frozen solid, neither should the temperature be allowed to rise above 10°C. Paraffin or kerosene refrigerators are adequate.

Live liquid vaccines may be transported on ice in thermos flasks.

If freeze-dried BCG, vaccinia and triple vaccines are transported, they must be refrigerated as soon as possible after their arrival.

Live vaccines should not be exposed to strong sunlight. This is especially important with BCG.

An ampoule of live vaccine must be used the day it is opened.

Syringes which have been stored in an antiseptic solution should not be used for giving live vaccines—the fluid remaining in the syringe may kill the vaccine.

The maker's instructions with each brand of vaccine should be read and followed.

Records of vaccinia given must be kept at all times.

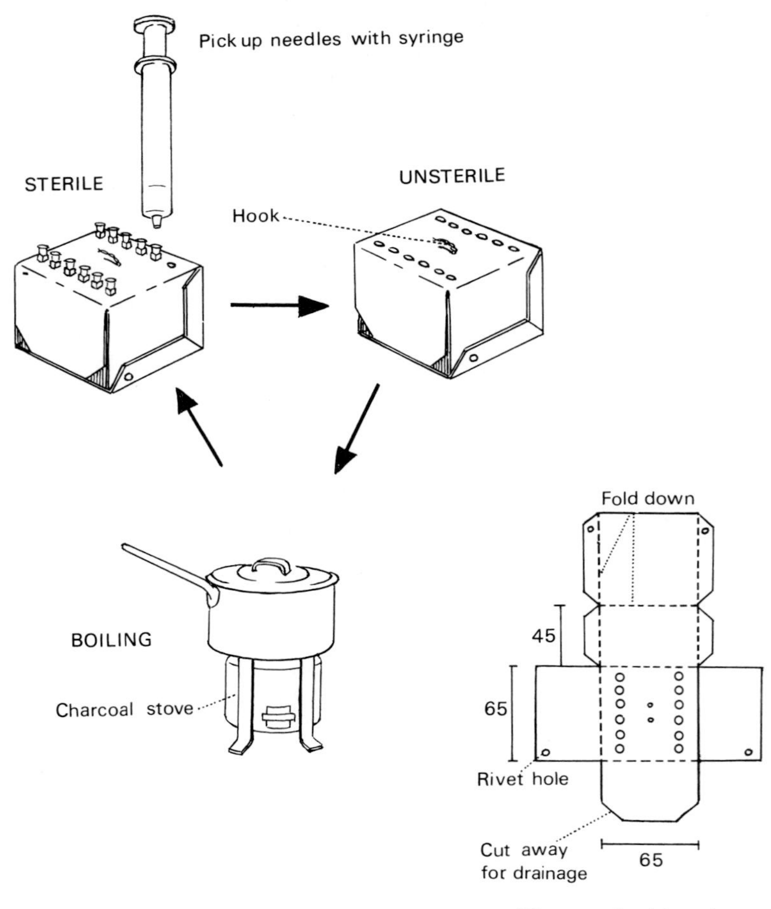

Fig. 10.2 Sterilising needles. When boiling, make sure that the whole of the needles are covered with water. Use a freshly boiled syringe with each new rack of needles.

Techniques

Vaccine containers, filling of syringes

Ampoules. Once an ampoule has been opened the whole of the contents must be used at one session or the unused portion must be discarded. Material in opened ampoules must not be reserved for future use.

Before opening an ampoule of vaccine the label should be checked, the ampoule shaken and any liquid in its neck dislodged. If not already present, a file mark should be made on the neck of the ampoule which should then be swabbed with alcohol and broken off with sterile forceps or with the fingers covered with a sterile gauze swab. The ampoule is then held on a slant, the sterilised needle inserted and the syringe charged with a dose of vaccine.

Rubber capped bottles. The label of the bottle should be checked. If the bottle contains suspended antigen it should be shaken thoroughly to ensure a uniform vaccine. The rubber cap is then treated by a thorough wiping with a sterile swab dipped in 70 to 75 per cent v/v alcohol.

An air inlet in the form of a sterile needle, adequately plugged with sterile cotton-wool to act as a filter, may be inserted through the rubber cap before the vaccine is withdrawn. This allows the easy removal of the vaccine without producing a negative pressure which could be a cause of later contamination.

Vaccine is then taken up into the syringe by passing the needle vertically through the cap, inverting the bottle and withdrawing the quantity required into the syringe.

An alternative method of avoiding a vacuum and assisting removal of the vaccine is to inject a volume of air from the syringe into the bottle before withdrawing the vaccine. To render this procedure safe, however, this air must be sterile. This may be achieved by withdrawing air from the container in which the syringe has been sterilised when removing the syringe. Before making an injection, any air which has entered, or remains in, the syringe should be expelled. Too frequent punctures of the cap may lead to contamination of the contents, and bottles with caps in bad condition should be discarded, as should any container which is nearly empty at the end of a vaccination session. Ideally, the contents of a bottle should be finished in one session, otherwise the bottle should be replaced in its carton and placed in a refrigerator.

Site of injecting vaccine

Intradermal injection. For intradermal TAB, TABT or cholera vaccine the site of election is behind the posterior border of the distal portion of the deltoid muscle.

For BCG the injection must be made over the insertion of the deltoid or up to half-way between the insertion and origin of the muscle. With this vaccine, injection higher up the arm towards the point of the shoulder may involve the cervical glands or lead to unsightly keloid scarring.

For sensitivity tests, intradermal injections are usually given in the middle of the front of the forearm. This site should not be used for injecting vaccines.

Subcutaneous injection. Subcutaneous injections should be made in a location where the skin is loose, the tissues yielding and the veins scarce. The site of election for the subcutaneous injection of most vaccines is the same as that given for the intradermal injection of TAB or TABT.

Intramuscular injection. Intramuscular injections are best made into the deltoid or triceps for small amounts, and into the middle third of the lateral aspect of the thigh if the amounts are large. In using the deltoid, care must be taken to avoid the circumflex nerve. With these injections there is some risk of the needle entering a vein. The piston should therefore be withdrawn before making the injection and sterilisation of the needle only between such injections is not acceptable.

Choice of arm. In left-handed people the right arm should be used.

The injection

The site of injection should be clean and should be treated with acetone, 75 per cent alcohol, or surgical spirit. The skin should be allowed to dry before the puncture is made.

Intradermal injection. The operator stretches the skin by holding the part tightly in one hand and with the other slowly inserting the needle with the bevel upwards for about 2 mm into the superficial layers of the dermis almost parallel with the surface.

The needle should be short with a short bevel which can usually be seen faintly through the epidermis during insertion. A raised blanched bleb showing the pits of the hair follicles is a sign that the injection has not been made too deeply, and its diameter gives a useful indication of the amount which has been injected. A bleb of 7 mm diameter is approximately equivalent to 1 ml of vaccine.

Subcutaneous injection. The subject is instructed to place his hand on his hip. The operator steadies the arm with one hand, picking up a fold of skin between forefinger and thumb or drawing the skin taut with the thumb. Holding the syringe in the other hand he then passes the needle at an acute angle well into the subcutaneous tissue. On completion of the injection the needle is withdrawn and the skin again swabbed.

Vaccination against smallpox

Vaccine is supplied in glass capillary tubes containing 1 to 4 doses, in collapsable initiative tubes, as liquid in multidose ampoules and in the freeze-dried state.

In ordinary circumstances babies may be vaccinated when one month old. If there is much smallpox in the area, they should be vaccinated at birth.

Ideally, vaccinations should not be given to people with eczema, scabies, any scaling disease or malnutrition, but often in disaster areas of developing countries there is no alternative.

Method

1. Wash the right shoulder with soap and water, and dry it.
2. Place a drop of vaccine on the skin. (Use a short glass rod if the vaccine is from a multidose ampoule. If from a glass capillary tube, use one of the special rubber devices made for the purpose. If not available, the vaccine can be delivered from the tube in a controlled way by using an ordinary rubber teat. Prick this with a hot needle and insert the capillary tube into the hole thus made. Close the open end of the teat and gently squeeze the 'bulb' so formed).
3. Pass a straight sharp triangular sectioned needle quickly through the flame of a spirit lamp. Do not let it get red hot as this will blunt it. Let it cool for a moment.
4. Place the needle flat on the skin placing its tip in the drop of vaccine.
5. Lift the needle up and down 30 to 40 times so the tip stays in the area of the vaccine and just marks the skin. Do not draw blood.

The aim is to get the vaccine into contact with the cells of the deeper layers of the epidermis. There the vaccinia virus is able to multiply, but if blood is drawn the dermis has been entered and a good 'take' is less likely.

Do not apply a dressing.

6. Tell the patient (or if a child, the adult responsible) to let the vaccination site dry. The shoulder should not be washed until the next day.

Typical progress of a vaccine lesion

Three days after a successful vaccination, the site becomes raised and red and then passes through the stages of macule, papule, vesicle, postule, crust and scar.

In endemic areas, re-vaccination should take place three-yearly.

Vaccination against cholera

When vaccination is used for mass protection, a single dose of 1.0 ml is employed. (Vaccine is standardised to contain 8000 million organisms per 1.0 ml).

In normal preventive practice, individual injection is given in two doses a week apart, first dose 0.5 ml, the second 1.0 ml. Visitors (including relief workers in disaster areas) should have the double vaccination. Natives of a place where disease is constantly or generally present need only a single injection.

Modern vaccines do not usually produce a febrile reaction.

The vaccines will reduce overt disease in an individual in about half the people vaccinated. Cholera has been reported in individuals who have been vaccinated repeatedly.

Partial protection lasts for approximately three months.

The International Certificate is valid for six months.

Vaccines made from the classical vibrios are effective for a few months against El Tor infection for about six months.

Race, sex and age appear to play little part in incidence. Malnutrition and poor health probably predispose to infection but healthy subjects may become infected.

Vaccination does not reduce the number of people in an infected area who excrete the El Tor vibrio.

In an outbreak, contacts and local populations are usually vaccinated using the single dose technique. Mobile teams equipped for immediate rehydration therapy should be organised. In addition to early rehydration of patients, such teams should deal with contacts, arrange disinfection, the control of faeces and water supplies, as well as carrying out vaccinations. They should also look out for people showing early symptoms of the infection.

Protection from light is less important here and partly used ampoules may be kept for up to three days in a refrigerator. They should not be used if they have been open for more than 72 hours.

There is little or no immune response to a single injection of the 'mineral carrier vaccine'—the type made with alum. Every attempt should be made to give the second and third injections at monthly intervals.

Method

1. Sterilise the skin with spirit.
2. Give 0.5 ml or 1.0 ml (according to the maker's instructions) by deep subcutaneous injection into the lateral or anterior part of the thigh. (This leaves the shoulders free for BCG and smallpox immunisation sites.)

Give half the standard dose if the patient is under 6 months old.

Sometimes there is slight fever after 24 hours. Other complications are rare.

Immunisation against poliomyelitis

The Sabin type of live vaccine is unstable and has a short storage life. This makes it difficult to stock regularly in remote hospitals and health clinics.

Do not give it if the patient is suffering from diarrhoea or vomiting.

Method

Place three drops of the live virus vaccine on the tongue and ensure that the patient swallows it.

Two further doses should be given at four to six week intervals.

Immunisation against measles

Measles is a lethal disease in many tropical countries.

The vaccine is very sensitive to traces of metal and must be stored carefully.

Use the special diluent supplied by the makers, or commercially prepared ampoules of 'water for injection'.

Use a disposable or glass syringe as the metal piston may be deleterious.

Method

1. Reconstitute the vaccine with metal-free distilled water.
2. Inject it intramuscularly into the thigh in the dose stated by the makers (usually 0.5 or 1.0 ml).

Immunisation against tuberculosis

Two forms of freeze-dried vaccine are available. One is given intradermally with a 1 ml tuberculin syringe, whilst the other is given by multiple puncture with a modified Heaf Gun.

The multiple puncture technique is to be preferred if many patients are to be immunised. Technically, it is much simpler—an intradermal injection requires some skill whilst the way to 'fire a gun' can be taught to intelligent indigenous people very quickly.

The modified Heaf Gun may have 20 needle points instead of only six and is 'fired' into the skin twice.

It is possible—and economical—to use the standard six needle gun for both Heaf testing and BCG giving. Six 'firings' at 2 mm is the usual method.

With both types of gun about 40 punctures are required, either 2 × 20 or 6 × 6.

Neither method is painful, and both are equally effective.

Once a Heaf Gun has been used for tuberculin testing it is almost impossible to render it free from the tuberculin. As it would complicate other procedures for which it might be used, either use separate guns for testing and BCG, or use the same gun with different magnetic heads.

BCG is the most light-sensitive of vaccines. Even one to two minutes' exposure to sunlight will cause a significant decrease in its potency, so the following points should be observed:

Do not vaccinate out of doors.

Keep ampoules and vaccine-filled syringes covered.

Ensure that the BCG vaccine is freshly made up.

Discard any unused vaccine after a few hours.

Methods

A. Intradermal BCG

1. Using a sterile syringe, add normal saline or 'water for injection' to the contents of the ampoule.
2. Allow it to stand for a minute. Do not shake it.
3. Using a short intramuscular needle draw the mixture into the syringe.
4. Replace this needle with a fine hypodermic, fitting the needle on the syringe so that its bevel faces the graduations on the syringe barrel thus making it easier to read the amount of vaccine given.
5. Pass the needle through a spirit lamp flame. Do not make it red hot.
6. Select a clear site on the arm (for adults, the dorsum of the right forearm at the junction of the upper and middle thirds; for babies and children, the left deltoid region).
7. Stretch the skin between the thumb and index finger of the left hand.
8. Discard a few drops of vaccine from the needle (this will cool it and also removes heated vaccine).
9. Push the needle, bevel uppermost, into the skin. Do not enter the subcutaneous tissues.
10. Keeping the needle as flat as possible, inject slowly about 0.1 ml of vaccine to produce a weal in the skin of about 5 mm in diameter.

It may be wiser to judge the size of the weal than to measure the volume of the vaccine delivered by the syringe.

If no weal appears (and no leak has occurred), the vaccine is probably being given too deep—subcutaneously rather than intradermally. If this happens, pull the needle out and repeat the procedure.

B. Multi-puncture BCG

1. Apply a thin film of the special vaccine to the skin of the arm with a short glass rod or wire loop dipped into the reconstituted vaccine.
2. Sterilise the apparatus by holding the needles against a cotton wool pad soaked in spirit and flaming them rapidly.
3. Set the gun at 2 mm (for both adults and children) and allow its plate to cool.
4. Apply it to the vaccine-covered area of the patient's arm.
5. Press the trigger—twice if the 20 needle device is being used, six times if the ordinary Heaf Gun is being used.

No dressing is necessary.

C. Dermojet BCG

1. Sterilise (by boiling the body and the vaccine container of the Dermojet).
2. Reconstitute the vaccine to twice the concentration advised for intradermal use with the usual large-bore needle.
3. Shake the vaccine container dry.
4. When cool, fill it with the volume of vaccine required taking care not to exceed the volume indicated by the red line.
5. Assemble the Dermojet and, holding it vertically, load it by depressing the cocking lever.
6. Press the release button.

7. Load and fire again.

Do this three times in order to clear water from the compression chamber.

8. Place the left forefinger and thumb about 3.8 cm apart on the patient's left deltoid region. Draw them together slightly to take tension off the skin. Do not 'bunch' the skin.

9. With the rubber nozzle over the jet apply the Dermojet to the skin and fire.

A small weal will be raised.

No dressing is required.

Inoculation against the typhoid fevers

Prophylactic inoculation with TAB vaccine of those entering a typhoid endemic area is an established practice.

The vaccine contains 1000 million of *Salmonella typhi* and 500 million each of *S. paratyphi* A and B organisms.

Acetone-inactivated vaccines are reported to be superior to those killed by heat or phenol.

TAB inoculations should be repeated yearly for a number of years.

Although vaccination reduces the incidence of infection it does not provide complete immunity.

TABT is a TAB vaccine containing tetanus toxoid concentrated into a smaller bulk for intradermal injection (0.2 ml). The antibody response to intradermal injection is comparable to that obtained by the subcutaneous route.

Both local and systemic reactions are minimal.

It must be emphasised that infection can be best avoided by personal cleanliness, protected water supplies, proper sewerage, caution in the consumption of fluids and foods, attacks on places where flies breed, the detection of carriers and their debarment from handling food.

All patients with the disease must be strictly segregated and linen and utensils used by them must be placed in disinfectant before destruction. All discharges must be disinfected before disposal. All attendants and visitors must wear protective clothing.

The typhus fevers and prophylaxis

Epidemic louse-borne typhus

Personal prophylaxis for those at risk is vitally important. This includes precautions against louse-infestation by employing insect repellents such as dimethyl phthalate, and the wearing of protective clothing.

For some years vaccines prepared from cultures of *Rickettsia prowazeki* and *R. mooseri* and from the hyper-infected tissues of animals have been used. Cox's vaccine is made from killed cultures of strains of the two organisms grown on the yolk-sacs of developing chick embryos.

The vaccine should be given subcutaneously in doses of 1.0 ml on two or three occasions at ten-day intervals. Reinforcing doses should be given at six-monthly intervals during the period of risk.

This is not an absolute protection but if an attack of either louse-borne or flea-borne typhus develops its severity is much modified.

Mite-borne typhus

Vaccines have been produced from *Rickettsia orientalis* but none affords adequate protection to man.

Again personal prophylaxis is most important. Protective clothing drenched in dimethyl phthalate should be worn.

Chloramphenicol in dosages of 3.0 g once weekly will abort an attack.

Tick-borne typhus

Vaccines prepared from tissues of infected ticks are available and these offer a substantial protection.

Again, vaccines prepared from growth of the organism on the yolk-sac tissues of chick embryos are available. These should be given subcutaneously or intramuscularly on three occasions at weekly intervals.

Vaccination against plague

Some protection may be given by vaccination with dead or attenuated living vaccines of *Pasteurella pestis*.

Dead vaccines are usually preferred because of difficulties in handling and transporting attenuated vaccines.

Single dose mass vaccinations during epidemics may lower the attack rate and vaccinated victims appear to respond to chemotherapy better than patients who have not been vaccinated.

Vaccination against rabies

Vaccines most commonly used are:

1. Suspensions of infected animal (usually rabbit) brain inactivated by phenol (Semple type).

2. Suspensions of duck embryo on which the virus has been grown, inactivated by β-propiolactone (DEV).

The DEV vaccine is usually preferred as neurological complications after its administration are rarer than with Semple vaccine and the amount injected is smaller.

Both vaccines are given subcutaneously in daily doses, usually into alternate sides of the abdominal wall, for periods of 14 to 21 days. The maker's instructions should be followed carefully.

Immune serum prepared from rabbits may be given intramuscularly wthout risk of sensitivity reaction. If serum prepared from horses is used the usual test for sensitivity must be undertaken. Adrenaline 1 : 1000 should be immediately available for use in the event of an anaphylactic reaction.

Some patients suffer erythema, pruritis and pain at the site of the vaccination. Others may develop fever and glandular swellings. This can lead to encephalitis and paralysis if treatment is not stopped immediately.

These complications are due to sensitisation to the animal tissue from which the vaccine is prepared, rather than to the vaccine itself.

Immune serum

The most effective means of preventing rabies after severe exposure to infection is provided by serum followed by a vaccine. It is given intramuscularly in a single dose of not less than 40 IU per kg body weight. Part of the dose can be given as local infiltration of the bite.

Antihistamine drugs given at the time of injection, and for a week afterwards, reduce the risk of serum sickness.

Summary of general precautions

1. Before performing a vaccination the vaccinator should satisfy himself that the individual is in good health; that there is no history of recent exposure to infectious disease or previous severe reactions to vaccination; that the individual is not undergoing radiotherapy or treatment with corticosteroids; and that the appropriate time interval after any previous immunisation has elapsed. It is also important to ascertain whether a woman is pregnant or not. When vaccinating with a live vaccine further precautions may have to be taken.
2. The vaccinator and all assistants must wash their hands thoroughly before commencing work and at intervals during prolonged sessions. All the staff should wear clean gowns or coats.
3. Syringes should only be handled with dry, washed hands, care being taken only to touch the outside of the barrel and the handle of the piston. When not in actual use they should be replaced in the sterile containers in which they were sterilised, or in a sterile test tube placed in a horizontal or slightly inclined position.
4. There must be no talking, coughing or sneezing over a sterile syringe. Needles, if not already attached to the syringe, must be handled only with sterile forceps.
5. In order to avoid nausea and fainting, persons to be vaccinated must not be kept waiting for long periods in extremes of temperature, and queues in the actual room where the vaccinations are taking place should be avoided. A solution of 1 : 1000 adrenaline, which on rare occasions may be needed urgently, should be kept available.
6. Only one dose of vaccine should be taken into each syringe at a time. Multiple doses in a syringe are not permissible.

Types of reaction

The more serious types of reaction which may follow the administration of vaccines are:

Local reactions. Some local discomfort, swelling and redness may be expected, but occasionally this may be more severe and progress to local necrosis, ulceration and scarring.

Pyrexial reaction. A pyrexia may occur which lasts, in the majority of cases, 24 to 48 hours. This may be associated with malaise, headache, vomiting and rigor. A temperature above 38.5°C (101°F) is unusual.

Neurological reaction. This may consist of the very occasional occurrence of blindness due to optic neuritis which may be transient or permanent.

Encephalopathy is more common. It may be transient with convulsions, or permanent due to encephalitis. Ascending myelitis, transverse myelitis and peripheral neuritis have all been reported. It is not known whether these neurological reactions result from undue sensitivity of the patient or from some material in the vaccine, but they are generally regarded as allergic manifestations.

Dermatological reaction. This may consist of local or generalised urticaria, non-specific rashes, eczema or a generalised infection such as vaccinia.

Anaphylaxis. Although severe anaphylactic shock is rare following vaccination, minor degrees are relatively common. Delayed allergic reactions are not uncommon following certain immunisations, e.g. tetanus toxoid and diphtheria toxoid. Severe generalised reaction. Vaccination may be associated with a local or generalised lymphadenopathy and with splenic and/or hepatic enlargement. Generalised arthropathy has also been reported. Very occasionally, collapse and death a few hours after vaccination has been reported, especially with TAB vaccine. This is presumably due to a direct cardiovascular reaction.

Provocation disease. In certain cases a vaccination may precipitate an attack of the specific disease or of unrelated disease. Owing to the risk of provocation, vaccination of those not immunised by injection should be avoided in an explosive epidemic.

11. Public health programmes

Introduction

Emergency public health procedures are top priority following any disaster in which housing, sewerage and water systems are damaged and large numbers of people displaced.

Provision of potable water is always more important than the provision of food. Equipment for water purification and for sinking wells is vital. Generally speaking, ground water is safer than surface water.

Shelter is important and may be the first priority as even short periods of exposure are dangerous in some climates.

The applicability of any system of emergency sanitation to a disaster situation depends on soil conditions, availability of equipment, cultural factors and the number of people for whom provision must be made. An important component of any emergency public health service is education in hygiene and sanitation and every opportunity to teach should be taken. In an industrial society this may be carried out via the mass media. In developing countries, it is most easily carried out when the affected population is grouped together—as in a refugee camp. Simple, clearly illustrated posters should be provided.

Food hygiene, especially at mass feeding centres, and disposal of contaminated food and drink is important. The latter is particularly necessary after floods. Again, every opportunity for education—in nutrition and food hygiene—should be taken.

Drainage, disposal of waste and pest control are important factors to be considered when siting refugee/evacuee camps.

In tropical climates the disposal of dead bodies and animal carcasses should be dealt with promptly.

WATER SUPPLY

Provision of a safe and adequate supply of water is essential, and it is the responsibility of the sanitary engineer or the sanitarian involved in emergency relief work to make certain that such a supply is available and readily accessible. The bacteriological, chemical, and physical condition of water for human consumption should comply with established standards.

Requirements

The following figures regarding water needs are intended as a guide in calculating minimum water requirements for drinking, cooking, and basic cleanliness.

1. Field hospitals and first aid stations: 40 to 60 litres per person per day.
2. Mass feeding centres: 20 to 30 litres per person per day.
3. Temporary shelters and camps: 15 to 20 litres per person per day.

Unless there are severe limitations on the supply of safe water, no restrictions should be placed on its use. If there is a shortage of water, rationing, close supervision of consumption and other water conservation measures should be practised. As soon as the early days of emergency have passed and the water supply has been increased restrictions should be lifted, since there is a correlation between water consumption and cleanliness on the one hand, and between cleanliness and the incidence of diseases on the other. With no restrictions the use of water may approach 100 litres per person per day.

Investigation and selection of source

A thorough search should be made for all the possible sources of water within reasonable distance of the camp. The importance of an investigation and sanitary survey of the available sources cannot be over emphasised; treatment operations adopted under emergency situations are at best only improvisations of the conventional methods of water purification, and it is clearly of the utmost importance to select the sources that are least exposed to the contamination.

The possible sources of water are:

1. Municipal system

If the disaster has affected the water supply system of a city or town, top priority should be given to putting the system back into operation. Damaged mains and feeders should be repaired as fast as is practicable. It is often possible to by-pass a damaged section by closing certain valves and to restore the water service in the major part of the distribution system. New methods for the quick coupling and plastic patching of pipes have been developed so that repairs can be made in the shortest possible time. This work, however, requires advance planning by the water authorities, the procurement of the necessary equipment and supplies and the training of techniques for emergency operations. The maintenance of good records and maps, proper operation of the system, and the stocking of spare parts are essential preparatory measures.

After a disaster has occurred the water pressure should be raised and the chlorine concentration should be increased to protect the distribution system from polluted water that may enter the pipes, especially after floods. If the water treatment plant or pumping stations are flooded, the flood water should be pumped out and floors and equipment cleaned and disinfected. After any repair on the distribution system the repaired main should be flushed and disinfected with a chlorine solution of 50 mg/litre for a contact period of 24 hours, after which the main is emptied and flushed again with potable water. If the demand for water is urgent, or the repaired main cannot be isolated, the concentration of the disinfecting solution may be increased to 100 mg/litre and the contact period reduced to one hour. At the end of disinfection operations, but before the main is put back into service, samples should be taken for bacteriological analysis and determination of chlorine residue.

When a water treatment plant, pumping station or distribution system is so badly damaged that operation cannot be restored for some time, other methods described in the following paragraphs must be used.

2. Private systems

There are often some private water supply systems in the vicinity of a disaster-stricken

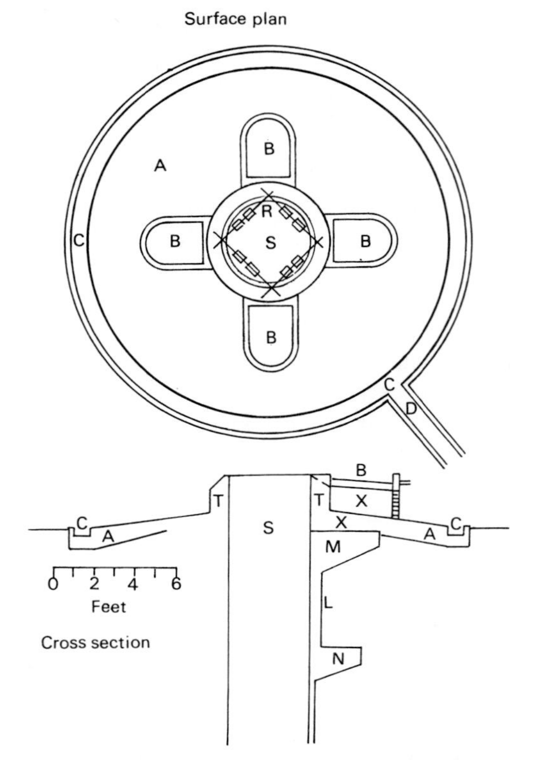

Fig. 11.1 A village well in Nigeria, a good example of sound and permanent construction. The principal features are a concrete lining extended well above a surrounding concrete apron with a perimeter drainage channel, basins into which the raised water is emptied and from which a delivery pipe can fill a household container, and rollers over which the bucket ropes run.

A. Apron, 6 foot width, 1 foot depth (10 inches of rock filling, 2 inches of concrete)
B. Well-top basins, 3 ft × 2¼ ft fall to outlet; curb and bottom 3 inches of concrete supported by rock filling and wall of cast concrete bricks
C. Channel 9 inches wide, 6 inches deep with 3 inches of concrete outer curb
D. Drainage from C, 15 feet long
L. Six inches reinforced lining
M. Main collar
N. Secondary curb
R. Eight grooved rollers mounted on four metal bars fastened by metal plates bolted into concrete
S. Shaft, four feet in diameter
T. Well-top wall 12 inches thick
X. Rock filling
(Nash, T.A.M., 1948, *The Anchau Rural Development and Settlement Scheme.* HMSO.)

community. These systems may belong to dairies, breweries, food and beverage plants, or other industrial or agricultural establishments. The source of supply is often a deep well or a private treatment plant. Water from these sources, with adequate chlorination as necessary, can be connected to a distribution system or hauled to the points of consumption. Owners are usually ready to co-operate and the possibility of using such supplies should never be overlooked in investigating the sources of water in an area.

3. Springs and wells

Ground water can often be found in the vicinity of a disaster area. It is not as subject to gross contamination as surface water. Ground water originating from deep aquifers (such as is obtained from deep wells and certain springs) will be free from contamination if certain simple protective measures are taken. Another great advantage of ground water is that it is clear and needs no treatment other than disinfection. Springs are simpler to exploit, as no pumping is needed to bring the water to the surface.

When springs are used as a source of water supply for a disaster area, careful attention must be paid to geological formations. Limestone and certain rocks are liable to have holes and cracks, especially after an earthquake, that may lead to the contamination of ground water. Springs are also exposed to contamination from flood waters. Proper location and well-built protective structures are therefore necessary to safeguard the quality of ground water.

The development and protection of springs and wells can be effected within a short time, provided that construction materials, tools and skilled workers are available. It is possible, depending on the geological conditions of the area, to sink different types of wells—dug, bored, driven, jetted or drilled—and so provide a dependable source of water that can also be used in the rehabilitation process.

A sanitary survey of the area surrounding a well site or spring is of the utmost importance. This survey, which should be carried out by a qualified professional environmental health worker, should provide information on sources of contamination, geological structures (with particular reference to overlying soil and rock formations), quality and quantity of ground water, direction of flow, and so on.

The well should be at least 30 metres from any potential source of contamination, and should be located higher than all such sources. The upper portion of the well must be protected by an external impervious casing extending at least 3 metres below and 30 cm above ground level. The casing should be surrounded by a concrete platform, at least 1 metre wide, that slopes to allow drainage away from the well. It should connect to a drain that will carry the spilled water away. The opening for drop pipes should be sealed to prevent outside water from entering the well. The rim of manholes should project at least 8 cm above the surrounding surface, and the manhole cover must overlap this rim.

Immediately after construction (or repair) the well should be disinfected. First, the casing or lining should be washed and scrubbed with strong chlorine solution containing 100 mg of available chlorine per litre. A stronger solution is then added to produce a concentration of 50 to 100 mg/litre in the water stored in the well. After adequate agitation, the well water is left to stand for at least 12 hours, then pumped out. The well is then allowed to refill. When residual chlorine of the water drops below 1 mg/litre the water may be used.

The foregoing applies also to the location and protection of springs. The following points may be added:

1. The collection installation should be built to prevent the entrance of light.
2. The overflow should be located to prevent the entrance of surface water at times of heavy rainfall.
3. The manhole cover and gates should be locked.
4. Before using the water, the collection chamber should be disinfected with a chlorine solution.
5. An area within a radius of 50 metres around the spring should be fenced off to prevent ground surface contamination.

Detailed information on the development and protection of water supplies is given in a monograph published by WHO in 1959.

4. *Surface water*

Surface water should be used as a source of water supply only as a last resort. Malodorous, highly-coloured, or highly polluted waters should be avoided. Water from surface sources should be disinfected and, if possible, treated to remove turbidity, colour and impurities. If the usual purification equipment is not available, improvisation is necessary. Prior to treatment, an infiltration gallery or several well-points connected to a manifold, located on the bank of a stream, could reduce turbidity and the number of bacteria in the water. Measures should be taken to protect the watershed from pollution by animals and people. As it is usually difficult to enforce control regulations, the point of intake for water supply should be located above any tributary carrying grossly contaminated water. The pump intake should be screened and placed so that it will not take in mud from the stream bed or floating debris. The device can be something extremely simple, such as a perforated drum fixed in the middle of the stream.

Treatment

Treatment should be improvised according to the degree of impurity of the water and the materials and equipment available. It may take various forms.

A. *Disinfection*

Disinfection kills pathogenic organisms and thereby prevents water-borne diseases. Water can be disinfected by boiling or by chemical treatment. Chlorine and chlorine-liberating compounds are the most common disinfectants. Chlorine compounds for water disinfection are usually available in three forms:

1. Chlorinated lime or bleaching powder, which has 25 per cent by weight of available chlorine when fresh. This is an unstable compound that loses its chlorine rather quickly, especially when stored in humid and warm places. Its strength should always be checked before use.
2. Calcium hypochlorite a more stable compound sold under various proprietary names. This compound contains 70 per cent by weight of available chlorine. If properly stored in tight containers and in a dark cool place, it preserves its chlorine content for a considerable period.
3. Sodium hypochlorite, usually sold as a solution of approximately 5 per cent strength under a variety of proprietary names. Its use in water disinfection is limited to small quantities under special circumstances. Chlorine and iodine tablets are also available, or the water can be boiled, but the use of these methods is limited to small quantities of water intended exclusively for drinking. Other commonly available materials suitable for emergency disinfection of water include Lugol's solution (5 per cent available I_2) and various iodophor compounds.

Factors affecting chlorination include:

Chlorine demand. Some of the chlorine added to the water reacts with organic matter and other reducing substances and is lost for disinfection. This 'chlorine demand' can be determined experimentally. A 'chlorine residual' for disinfection should be added in excess of the demand to ensure that the specified concentration is available. Thus the chlorine required for disinfection is the sum of the 'chlorine demand' and the 'chlorine residual'.

Contact time and concentration. Adequate mixing and contact time is needed to produce maximum disinfection. Generally speaking, the higher the concentration the shorter the time required for disinfection. With ordinary doses of chlorine a minimum contact time of 30 minutes should be maintained.

Temperature. The effectiveness of chlorine is reduced as the temperature of water is decreased.

Hydrogen ion concentration. The disinfecting power of chlorine is reduced as the pH value of the water increases.

Free chlorine residual. At the same concentration, the free chlorine residual is a more effective disinfectant than the combined chlorine residual.

Gas chlorinators. These machines draw chlorine gas from a cylinder containing liquid chlorine. Mix it in water and inject it into the supply pipe. Mobile gas chlorinators are made for field use.

Hypochlorinators. These are lighter than gas chlorinators and more adaptable to emergency disinfection. Generally, they use a solution of calcium hypochlorite or chlorinated lime in water and discharge it into a water pipe or reservoir. They can be driven by electric motors or petrol engines and their output can be adjusted.

Hypochlorinators are small and easy to install. They consist usually of a diaphragm pump and standard accessories, including one or more rubber-laid solution tanks, and a chlorine residual testing set. The usual strength of the solution is 0.1 per cent and it seldom rises above 0.5 per cent.

Improvisation is an unavoidable necessity during post-disaster operations. The following description is of an improvised device used in Yugoslavia:

'In essence, the chlorinator consists of a balance fixed to a wooden frame. From the long arm of the balance hangs a vessel for the chlorine solution, and on the short arm a regulator controls the inflow of the solution by pressing against the feed tube; a bag of sand hangs from the short arm to counterbalance the vessel on the long arm. The balance is fitted with two rubber tubes, one that feeds the chlorine solution into the vessels and another that siphons it from the vessel to the delivery point. The outflow is controlled by adjusting the height of the delivery tube, which is fixed to a sliding support outside the frame. It can be set by hand to the required dose of chlorine.

The wooden frame is 55 to 60 cm long and 35 cm high. To ensure stability, the baseboard is 20 cm wide. The rest of the frame can be made of boards 10 cm wide. The short arm for the inflow regulator and the counter-weight is 15 cm long, while the long arm that holds the vessel is 24 cm long. A sharp-edged piece of wood acts as inflow regulator when pressing against the rubber tube.'

The chlorine solution is kept in various types of container, usually in barrels. To complete the improvised device, a float (e.g. a spent electric light bulb or a piece of wood) is fixed to the immersed end of the rubber tube to ensure that the solution of chlorine drawn off is clear and does not contain bleaching powder sediment.

The chlorinator operates by balancing the outflow and inflow of the solution. The apparatus is so adjusted that the outflow regulator only lets pass a certain number of drops.

When the number of drops delivered to the water supply is equal to the number fed into the vessel, equilibrium is established. Once the vessel is full any additional supply of solution increases its weight and breaks the equilibrium; the regulator presses the feeding tube, and the supply is interrupted until the balance is restored. The chlorinator is started by lowering the support of the delivery tube until the flow is established, when it is adjusted to the proper height to deliver the required amount of solution. The apparatus stops when there is any blockage. The use of this type of chlorinator has proved to have the following advantages:

1. Cheapness and speed of construction (two to three hours of work for a semi-skilled worker, four short boards, a piece of plywood, 1.5 to 2 metres of rubber tube, a corrosion-proof vessel, and a few nails.
2. The apparatus is easy and simple to handle and instal anywhere.
3. The use of the most easily obtainable disinfectant—bleaching powder—reduces running costs.
4. The apparatus is suitable for use in small gravity water supplies, yielding 3 to 10 litres per second (in circumstances where expensive chlorinators are not suitable).
5. The apparatus is not big and does not take up much space.
6. The apparatus is corrosion-proof.
7. No blockages occur.

The batch method. In the absence of chlorinators, water is disinfected by the batch method. This method is more likely to be used in emergencies. It involves applying a predetermined volume of chlorine solution of known strength to a fixed volume of water by means of some gravity arrangement. The strength of the batch solution should not be more than 0.65 per cent of chlorine by weight, as this is about the limit of solubility of chlorine at ordinary temperatures. For example, 10 grams of ordinary bleaching powder (25 per cent strength) dissolved in 5 litres of water gives a stock solution of 500 mg/litre. For disinfection of drinking water, one volume of the stock solution added to 100 volumes of water gives a concentration of 5 mg/litre. If after 30 minutes' contact the chlorine residual is more than 0.5 mg/litre, this dosage could be reduced.

After the necessary contact period has elapsed, excess chlorine can be removed to improve the taste by such chemicals as sulphur dioxide, activated carbon, or sodium thiosulphate. The first two are suitable for permanent installations whereas sodium thiosulphate is more suitable for use in emergency chlorination. One tablet containing 0.5 grams of anhydrous sodium thiosulphate will remove 1 mg/litre of chlorine from 500 litres of water.

There are two types of device that can be used for applying stock solutions. The first is a simple but reliable device for discharging a batch-mixed chlorine solution into a tank, open conduit or well. When the device is used in conjunction with a water-seal tank and float valve, the solution can be discharged into the suction side of a pump. When the liquid level in the water-seal tank is above the hydraulic gradient, stock solution can be fed into a closed conduit. The wooden float maintains a constant head at the opening which can be made large enough to prevent clogging. A similar device can be carefully constructed with tanks and barrels lined with asphalt or some other corrosion-resistant material: this can be a semi-permanent method of applying stock chlorine solution.

Another simple apparatus for applying chlorine solution to water has been developed in Sudan. It consists of an inverted plastic jerrycan with a hole cut in the base.

The float is made of light packing material. A glass tee is used for drawing the solution out of the jerrycan, and the stem of the tee is tapered off when hot to reduce the diameter of the open end. Several tees of different sized openings are made and tested to determine the discharge flow. The strength of the solution is adjusted to deliver the required amount of chlorine.

The materials required for this device are as follows:

Chlorinator

1 Plastic 25-litre jerrycan
1 Float of plastic foam (28 × 12 × 1.2 cm)
3 Glass tees, external diameter 7 mm, stems tapered to give various intake openings
3 Rubber stoppers, 25 to 29 mm diameter
1 Rubber tube, external diameter 9 mm, internal diameter 6 mm, length 120 cm, extremely flexible

Auxiliary materials

1 Plastic funnel
1 Measuring cup
1 Plastic tube, external diameter 12 mm, internal diameter 9 mm, length as required (about 10 metres)
2 Plastic 5-litre buckets for preparing chlorine solution

Continous chlorination. This method, in which porous containers of calcium hypochlorite or bleaching powder are immersed in water, is used mainly for wells and springs but is also applicable to other types of water supply. It has been developed in Bulgaria and some other countries with good practical results. A description of its application in Bulgaria is here summarised.

The device for controlling the dosage of active chlorine is a cylindrical, hollow earthenware vessel known as a 'dosing cartridge'. This cartridge is made of infusorial earth or ordinary potter's clay, which ensures sufficient permeability for active chlorine to percolate through it.

The cartridge is packed with moistened bleaching powder or hypochlorite, and tightly closed with a rubber stopper. It is immersed in water until the active chlorine begins to percolate. This takes from 12 to 24 hours.

The quantity of active chlorine that passes through the cartridge depends on the strength of the compound, the porosity of the walls, and the surface area of the cartridge in contact with the water.

The size and number of cartridges used should be selected according to requirements; their adequacy can be checked by determining the amount of chlorine residue. As percolation depends on the surface area of the cartridge immersed in the water, it is possible to regulate the amount of chlorine delivered by raising or lowering the cartridge.

Most frequently, emergency chlorination is carried out in reservoirs. One or more cartridges must be placed so as to ensure the free discharge and even distribution of the chlorine throughout the water entering the reservoir. This may be achieved in two ways:

1. A small quantity of water is diverted from the inlet pipe to a small vessel in which the cartridges stand upright. As the quantity of water diverted is proportional to the amount

flowing through the inlet pipe, the water level in the vessel rises or falls according to the amount of water entering the reservoir, and by covering the cartridges to a greater or lesser extent automatically regulates the percolation of chlorine.

2. Cartridges may be immersed at the discharge challen or flume of the reservoir through which the whole quantity of water passes. This method is also applicable to storage tanks and water towers of small water systems with a flow of up to 5 litres per second.

In the case of pumped water, the delivery pipe from the vessel containing the cartridges is connected to the suction pipe of the pump. The operator must immerse or remove the cartridges when he starts or stops the pump. In automatically operated pumps, the lowering and raising of the cartridges can also be made automatic by using the change in water pressure in the discharge pipe of the pump to move a lever arm from which the cartridges are suspended.

Continuous disinfection of protected wells and springs is especially important in areas where ground water is less than 3 metres below the surface. Dosing cartridges should be immersed in a suitable place to ensure complete disinfection of all the water drawn from a well or spring.

In the case of open wells, cartridges may be lowered into the water. The number and size of cartridges selected, which determine the amount of chlorine released, should be varied according to the volume of water in the well and the rate at which it is drawn off. To ensure even chlorination of water obtained from springs, the cartridges may be placed in a water chamber at the point of abstraction, in such a way that they are completely covered with water at the maximum rate of flow. If the flow decreases, the level in the waterchamber falls and the area of the cartridge immersed is reduced. As a result, the amount of active chlorine released decreases proportionately.

In using dosing cartridges the following precautions must be taken:

1. Before charging, the condition of the cartridge must be checked to ensure that it is not cracked and that the rubber cork fits firmly.
2. The cartridge must be charged with a compound of known active chlorine content.
3. The water in a well should not be used for 24 hours after immersion of a newly charged cartridge.
4. Chlorine residual tests should be carried out regularly and supplemented, if possible, by bacteriological examination.
5. Cartridges should be replaced before they are empty.
6. Spare cartridges should be kept to hand.

A free residual chlorine level of 0.7 mg/litre should be maintained in water treated for emergency distribution. A slight taste and odour of chlorine after half an hour gives an indication that chlorination is adequate. In flooded areas where the water distribution system is still operating, higher chlorine residuals should be maintained. Occasionally, an unpleasant taste develops from the reaction of chlorine with phenolic or other organic compounds. This taste should be accepted, as it is an indication of safe disinfection.

B. Coagulation—Disinfection

Part of the suspended matter in turbid water will settle if left undisturbed for several hours. The addition of chemicals such as alum, ferric chloride and ferrous sulphate hastens the settling process since these compounds help to form a 'floc' of larger particles by reacting with, and adhering to, the suspended matter. This process is known as coagulation, and the chemicals used are called coagulants. The 'floc' becomes heavier and settles readily. Removal of the organic matter greatly lessens the amount of chlorine needed for disinfection.

There are many factors that govern the coagulation process. These include:

1. Hydrogen ion concentration. The optimum pH value for coagulation is the value that provides the best 'floc' formation and settling. The pH value of the water changes when coagulants are used, and has to be adjusted to its optimum value by the addition of alkalis or acids.

2. Mixing. Coagulants must be thoroughly mixed with the water to give satisfactory results. This may be accomplished by (a) pump action, whereby the coagulant solution is added to the suction pipe of the pump and the pump does the mixing; (b) the drip-bottle method, i.e. hanging a drip bottle over the discharge pipe or hose of raw water that feeds the tank and letting the coagulant solution drip on the water jet; or (c) dis-solution, allowing the discharge of raw water to splash on to a basket containing solid coagulant.

3. Coagulant dosage. The amount of coagulant and chemicals required to adjust the pH value of the water may be calculated when the pH and the type of alkalinity are known. However, optimum dosage for a given water may be determined approximately using the jar test.

C. Coagulation—Filtration—Disinfection

In this method, filtration is added to the procedures described above. If temporary reservoirs can be arranged, it is preferable to let the water settle before filtering. In mobile purification units, however, the water is filtered through a pressure filter without settling. They usually have a capacity of 4000 to 7000 litres per hour, and consist essentially of: (a) a centrifugal pump directly coupled to a gasoline engine; (b) a filter pressure, rapid sand filter; (c) a hypochlorinator; (d) chemical solution tanks (one for alum and one for soda ash); (e) a chlorine solution tank; (f) hose adapters; (g) valves (pump suction, inlet, drain, air release, outlet, flow control, etc); and (h) a tool box. Instructions in the manuals supplied with such units must be followed.

D. Filtration—Disinfection

In this method water is mixed with diatomaceous earth, then passed through the filter unit in which filtering partitions (septa) are installed. Mobile purification units using this process have been produced with capacities up to 50 000 litres per hour. They consist essentially of: (a) a centrifugal pump driven by a rope-started gasoline engine; (b) a filter (diatomite); (c) a hypochlorinator; (d) a slurry feeder and an air compressor; (e) a precoat and recirculating tank; (f) a chlorine solution tank; (g) hose adaptors; (h) valves (pump suction, inlet, drain, outlet, flow control, air release, etc.); and (i) a tool box. Instructions in the manuals supplied with such units must be followed.

Storage

Emergency storage of water can be improvised in canvas, rubber-coated nylon and plastic containers with a capacity up to 10 cubic metres. Polyethylene containers erected in pits dug to size can provide up to 50 cubic metres storage capacity. If the purpose of storage is only to provide contact time after chlorination, the minimum capacity should be such as to secure contact of at least 30 minutes. The total storage capacity for water distribution should be equal to the amount required for 12 to 24 hours. Elevated tanks can be set up within a short time by using drums, iron sheeting or asbestos cement tanks. Wooden poles, timber or iron tubing can be used for the supports. In many countries, elevated storage tanks are manufactured in standard sizes with all parts prefabricated. They can be transported and erected rapidly.

In long-term emergency camps all reservoirs should be covered, primarily for protection from sunlight and consequent growth of algae that produces an unpleasant taste in the water, and secondarily for protection from birds, insects and dust. The roof may be made of asbestos-cement sheets or corrugated iron sheets. An overflow pipe should be provided, care being taken that the overflow water will not endanger the foundations. The inlet pipe will normally discharge at the top of the reservoir and be fitted with a float valve. The outlet pipe should be about 5 cm above the bottom of the tank. A small drain pipe should be installed flush with the bottom of the tank, and a manhole on the roof is necessary to permit cleaning, inspection and repair. The openings of vent pipes should be screened to keep out insects and small birds.

Tests

Until the laboratory facilities of urban water supply system can be restored to normal operation, complete tests of water samples should be made at laboratories in the vicinity of the disaster area.

The most important tests to be carried out under emergency and field conditions are:

1. Determination of residual chlorine (free and combined);
2. Bacteriological examination for coliform bacteria;
3. Determination of hydrogen ion concentration;
4. Determination of type of alkalinity.

Techniques, media and equipment have been developed for the application of membrane filters in the bacteriological examination of water under field conditions. Residual chlorine, hydrogen ion concentration and type of alkalinity can be determined by the use of appropriate colour indicators.

WATER SUPPLIES IN A DEVELOPING COUNTRY

When considering the provision of a water supply in a developing country (especially in rural areas) schemes must be designed in the light of prevailing local conditions. This usually means a simpler form of supply which may not attain all the requirements advised by WHO. It is, therefore, all the more important to obtain water from the purest possible source in the first instance and to protect from pollution.

A. Preliminary information

When planning a new supply first ascertain (a) the population to be catered for (with some estimate of future population expansion); (b) the likelihood of major industrial or agricultural use of water; (c) available funds; (d) the availability of expertise amongst local population; and (e) the local water resources (a survey is required).

B. Selection of source of supply

Rain water
This is basically pure but urban areas collect impurities in the atmosphere and during collection and storage. It is often used in rural areas, being obtained from roofs of houses and run into tanks.

Surface water
This is water from streams, rivers, ponds and lakes. The quality depends on the location. Such sources must be surveyed for potential causes of pollution such as latrines, rubbish dumps and washing places. These must be removed. Survey upstream as far as is practicable and immediately downstream. Pollution by animals must also be considered and attempts be made to prevent it by use of catchment areas. Surface water is commonly used for water supplies, as it is most convenient, but it is highly liable to pollution and thorough purification treatment is required.

Ground water
This is water which soaks into the ground and seeps downward till it meets an impermeable layer. From here it may track laterally to appear as seepages or springs (springs are often good supplies but are liable to dry up in the dry season); accumulate above the impermeable layer, where it is tapped by shallow wells; or percolate through faults in the impermeable layer to form accumulations of 'deep ground water' which may be under pressure and, if tapped, will form an artesian well.

Care must be taken to ensure that all possible sources of contamination (latrines, cesspits, etc.) are at least 30 metres from shallow wells.

Ground water is much used for water supplies. Its main disadvantages are the high mineral content and hardness, and the fact that it usually requires pumping.

Other sources

Solar stills. There have been extensive trials of this method in the S.W. Pacific Islands but only small quantities have been produced.

The sea. Distillation of sea water is not yet economically practicable except where there is a very cheap source of fuel available in quantity locally. This method is used in Bahrein, Kuwait and Cyprus.

Selection tests
1. Ground survey, e.g. check catchment area for pollution;
2. Quality:
    a. Chemical: poisons, hardness, evidence of pollution;
    b. Bacteriological: presumptive coli count or 'Millipore' colony count;
3. Quantity.

C. Sanitary collection

Having decided on the source, it is necessary to have a sanitary method of collection to avoid contamination.

Rain water

To use rain water one requires clean roofs and gutters and clean storage tanks. (Bird droppings may be a problem.) A device is required to ensure that the first water from the roof runs to waste to avoid contaminating the storage tank. The risk of mosquitoes breeding in storage tanks or other water storage containers must be borne in mind (e.g. *Aedes aegypti* and yellow fever in Eastern Nigeria, and filariasis in SE Asia).

Surface water

In streams, river and lakes, water intake should be from the centre or as far away as possible from the bank. It should also be below the lowest annual surface level. As an alternative, infiltration channels may be dug, providing a certain amount of filtration. Less ambitious schemes include damming a stream or cutting a channel from a river into a concrete pool. It is important that people are able to fill containers without having to step into the water.

Ground water

Protection of springs. The spring head must be thoroughly cleaned and then enclosed with a concrete chamber provided with a lid. From the lower part of the chamber a pipe is led to a storage tank, and from the highest point an overflow pipe is led to waste. A drainage channel is cut across uphill of the spring to divert all surface water away from it.

Protection of wells. The two recognised forms are: Deep wells which draw water from below the first impermeable layer and shallow wells draw water from above the the first impermeable layer. The latter are more liable to pollution.

They should be protected by:

1. Fencing around well to prevent animal contamination, at a radius of 30 metres;
2. Steining (an impervious layer) extending downwards to below the surface of the water in shallow wells, or to the first impermeable stratum in deep wells;
3. A parapet, with a lid, around the top of the well;
4. A concrete surface extending for two metres around the well, and sloping away from it;
5. A fixed system of drawing water, ideally a pump, or a bucket and chain system attached to the well.

Water should be discharged from this system into storage containers, from which drums, etc., may be filled.

D. Water storage

Water should be stored in containers or tanks with covers that are dust-proof and that prevent the entry of light and animals. Overflow pipes should be screened against the access of mosquitoes and other insects. The outlet pipes should be 5 mm above the bottom of the tanks and the clean-out pipes flush with the bottom. There should be no connection between drains from water tanks and sewage drains. Metal tanks are commonly used for above-ground storage and should, if possible, be shaded from the sun. Masonry or concrete tanks are frequently used and should be built underground to keep the water cool.

E. Distribution

If a piped system is used, pressure should be sufficient to fill the pipe at all times to ensure that contamination is not sucked into the system from cracks in the pipe work. Pipe work should not be laid through or near foul drains (this practice is believed to be the route of contamination of water supplies with cholera vibrios in Calcutta). In order to prevent waste, spring loaded taps may be needed where communal stand pipes are used.

PURIFICATION

Clarification

Storage permits passive sedimentation of suspended matter, and if continued for more than 48 hours results in the death of *schistosoma cercariae.* It is a cheap and practicable method.

Coagulation and sedimentation involves the use of a coagulant such as alumino-ferric to produce a 'floc' (3 to 5 grams per litre with 0.5 g of lime added if water is acid). It is often employed as an aid to rapid filtration.

Filtration has long been established as an effective purification method. Apart from removal of particulate matter it may remove as much as 99 per cent of bacteria. It is often the only purification measure employed in rural areas.

1. *Slow sand filtration* is carried out in concrete or similar impervious tanks, usually rectangular in shape, of varying sizes. From the base of the tank collecting channels designed to give uniform drainage pass to a collecting main. The filter bed is formed from 30 to 50 cm of gravel supporting one metre of sand.

This sand should be of suitable uniformity and size. Raw water is pumped in, distributed as evenly as possible, to a depth of 1 or 2 metres. A biologically active layer forms in the top 1 or 2 cm of sand (the 'mat') and this reduces the interstices between the grains of sand forming an effective filter. This layer takes some time to form, up to three days according to climate and thus the first imperfectly filtered runnings are allowed to flow to waste. The effective filtering rate for this type of filter is about 1 litre/m_2/hour. The mat will gradually clog and reduce the rate until it is useless, the period varying from days to weeks according to temperatures, etc. When this happens the filter is drained, the top 2 cm of mat removed and the tank refiltered, after which the mat is allowed to reform. This process can continue until the depth of sand is reduced to about 0.3 metres. The mat which has been removed can be washed and re-used. This type of filter is simple to construct and maintain and gives good results, but takes up much space.

2. *Rapid sand filtration.* This may be carried out by gravity in concrete tanks or under pressure in steel containers. The yield is anything from 30 to 70 litres/m_2/hour and it may be employed in various ways, e.g. before slow sand filtration to spend up the latter process, or after preliminary coagulation, the resultant 'floc' being precipitated on the surface of the sand replacing the biological filter of the slow method. The bed of these filters may require cleansing daily and this is accomplished by flushing with pure water aided by compressed air or by raking and drawing off the contaminated 'floc' from the surface whilst retaining the sand. These filters cannot readily be improvised or built from locally available materials and, although efficient, flexible in operation and less space-consuming than slow filters, they are less applicable to rural tropical supplies.

3. *Mechanical filtration.* The principle of filter candles backed up by kieselguhr as used in army water trucks may be employed on a larger scale in permanent installations. Meta

and stellar filters are used, or, alternatively, the katadyn filter. This consists of one or more ceramic filter candles, the hollow cores of which have been filled with sand that has been impregnated with activated silver (known as 'katadyn'). In filtration the water takes up minute quantities of silver which have bactericidal properties. This method is effective provided the water contains no sulphides, no iodine in excess of 0.05 parts per million, no chlorides in excess of 40 parts per million, is not hard, and is stored for 20 minutes. The water is thus filtered and sterilised in one process.

Sterilisation

This is rarely carried out for small rural supplies. If the source is pure and not accessible to pollution it may not be important: but in many instances this is not so and sterilisation should be undertaken.

Chlorination

Either chlorination or super-chlorination is probably the method of choice, being effective, easy and cheap. Stabilised bleach powder can be applied by hand dosage or drip feed into storage tanks or by injection by mechanical chlorinator. In larger plants a chlorine gas injector may be used. Whatever method is used at least two trained operatives will be required.

Purification of water on a domestic or individual scale

Methods

Disinfection: boiling, chlorine, iodine.
Filtration, with or without sterilisation.

Disinfection

Boiling. This is effective but expensive except for small quantities of water.

Chlorine. This is effective either as solution (e.g. Milton) or tablets (e.g. Sterotabs). It is not effective against cysts, cercariae or helminth ova, or organisms embedded in organic material.

Iodine is very effective provided the water is clear. If water is muddy or translucent clarify first, using either tincture of iodine or 'Portable Aqua' tablets. Iodine is effective against cysts, cercariae, leptospira, and some viruses.

Domestic filters

Sand filters. These are easy to improvise, but slow. They are also liable to clog up easily; they then become water-infectors rather than purifiers.

Household pressure filters. These are effective but require a plant and maintenance.

Candle filters

1. Fine ceramic. These are delicate and require weekly cleaning, boiling, and inspection for cracks.

2. Meta or stellar filters. These are metal filters backed up by kieselguhr.

3. Metal filter incorporating silver in the candle (Katadyn, Sterasyl, Meta Filter) combines both filtration and sterilisation, provided the treated water is retained for 20 minutes in a non-metal container.

Long-range and immediate goals

Taken from *WHO Public Health Paper No. 23* (1963).

The human suffering and economic loss resulting from inadequate water supplies are so great that bold measures are needed. No compromise should be permitted in planning these measures, which are essential to economic development and higher living standards in the nations concerned. They must, however, be chosen realistically. The targets set must be generally attainable in most developing countries and have sufficiently wide appeal to win public support. *The following standards are proposed:*

a. Piped water should be available in all premises of a community;

b. Adequate service (i.e. a water pressure that does not fall below an established minimum should be maintained at all times);

c. Water for drinking, household and other purposes should be provided in adequate volume;

d. Standards of drinking water quality should be adopted and enforced that would be no less rigid than those set by WHO;

e. Water sources should be protected against pollution or contamination;

f. Water supply schemes should be administered independently and according to sound management practices;

g. Regular revenues should be established, sufficient to cover all costs of operation, maintenance, capital charges and depreciation;

h. The operation of all treatment works and the quality of water as supplied to consumers should be adequately supervised.

The time required for the attainment of these standards will obviously vary from country to country and region to region, depending on rates of economic development, availability of loans, and many other factors. Meanwhile, it is proposed that an intermediate goal be aimed at, i.e. the provision of minimum quantities of piped water to everybody within a reasonably short time, mainly through inexpensive systems with public outlets. These systems should be designed so as to facilitate eventual expansion and improvement. The proposed intermediate goal is as follows:

a. Piped water should be supplied within fifteen years to all people living in urban communities, either through house connections or by public outlets within a reasonable distance from each home;

b. During this period of fifteen years, the percentage of people served from house connections should be increased at a rate appropriate to local conditions;

c. Adequate volumes of water should be provided through a non-intermittent service maintaining at least a suitable minimum pressure at all times;

d. Drinking-water quality should reach suitably established standards which should be adapted to WHO International Standards for Drinking-Water;

e. Administration of water supply schemes should be independent and in accordance with sound management practices;

f. Regular revenues should be provided for operation, maintenance, capital charges and depreciation;

g. Operation of treatment works and water quality should be adequately supervised.

(This presupposes progress from a disaster relief to a development programme and a fifteen year period is proposed for the attainment of this intermediate goal. It is believed that countries can afford this rate of improvement, and the capacity of the construction and supply industry would not be overloaded.)

EMERGENCY SANITATION

An emergency sanitation system must be culturally acceptable, conveniently situated, easy to clean, well lit at night, quick, easy and cheap to set up and operate, and suited to climate and soil conditions.

The main disadvantages of trench and dug well latrines are the practical difficulties of construction and use. The septic tank built of bricks and mortar is expensive and is only possible in places where the necessary materials and labour are available. The butyl septic tank has limited capabilities, whilst bleaching powder provides only very short term protection. Open spaces, bulldozed from time to time, provide inadequate privacy and no protection from flies. In addition, bulldozers are very expensive.

Bore-hole latrine

This is often found to be the best method. It requires an efficient means of drilling the hole. Earth augers are probably the best as they are cheap and are operated manually. They should be specially designed to suit the conditions of the area. A plate which is easy to clean must be provided for the top of the latrine to support the weight of users and keep out flies. Reinforced concrete plates using steel moulds are recommended. Plastic (PVC) plates, injection moulded, can also be used if modified to withstand high temperatures. Wooden plates should only be used as a temporary measure.

The bore-hole latrine is a vertical boring usually 40 cm in diameter and anything up to 6 m deep. A fly-proof seat superstructure should be provided. The boring is made by a special hand-operated auger, the shaft of which is made in sections for easy transport and lengths can be added as the work proceeds. Shears are erected over the site of the boring to act as a guide for the upper end of the shaft and to provide a support for the pulley block used in withdrawing the auger from the ground. The auger is rotated by hand by means of a detachable cross-T handle which can be adjusted in the shaft as the boring deepens. If the bore reaches water, it will greatly assist in the digestion of the sewage. When ground water is not reached, a concrete skin covering the base of the bore and extending for 60 cm up the sides will hold water poured in from the top for some time. This type of latrine should be provided with adequate hard standings and drainage around it and a centrally placed seat over the bore to ensure that the edges are not fouled. Such latrines will last for years and are a most satisfactory form of sewage disposal in the field.

In estuaries and places where the subsoil does not contain rock, this type of latrine offers a fast solution for excreta disposal in emergencies. With the use of earth augers, family latrines can be set up. Mass production of concrete slabs for the latrine floor can be undertaken on the site. If the number of available augers is limited, shallow trenches may be used while bore-holes are being made.

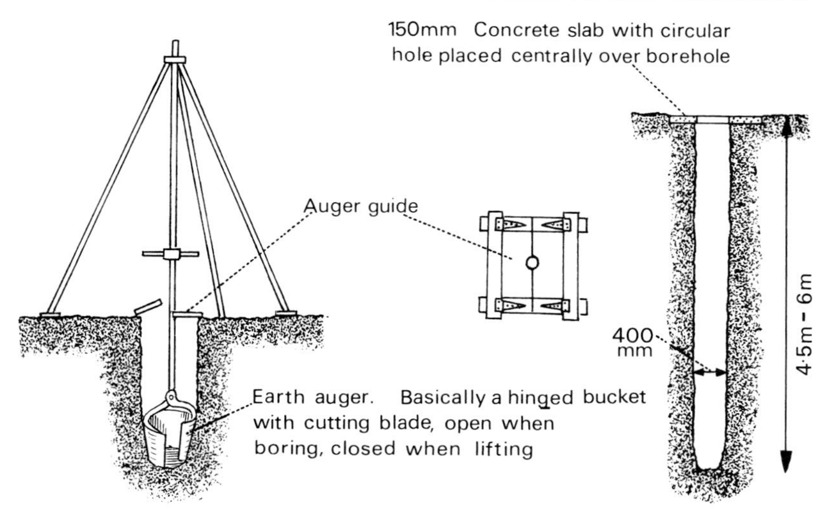

Fig. 11.2 Bore-hole latrine. A circular hole 400 mm in diameter bored into the earth down to subsoil water. A simple auger worked on a tripod is the standard boring implement. In loose soil the sides may require rivetting. A latrine seat is placed over the hole. These should not be used in proximity of shallow wells. One hole will serve 12 men indefinitely.

Shallow trench latrine

This is simply a trench dug with picks and shovels. It should be 30 cm wide and 90 to 150 cm deep. Its length depends on the number of users: 3 to 3.5 m is necessary for every hundred people. Separate trenches should be provided for men and women. The earth from the trench should be piled up at the side. Shovels should be left at the site, and people should be instructed to cover faeces with earth each time they use the latrine. However, these instructions may not be carried out and it will be necessary for the sanitation squad to complete the work twice a day to keep flies and odours under control. It may be necessary to place lumber or boards along the sides of the trench to provide a footing and to prevent the walls from caving in. Privacy may be secured by the use of brush, canvas,

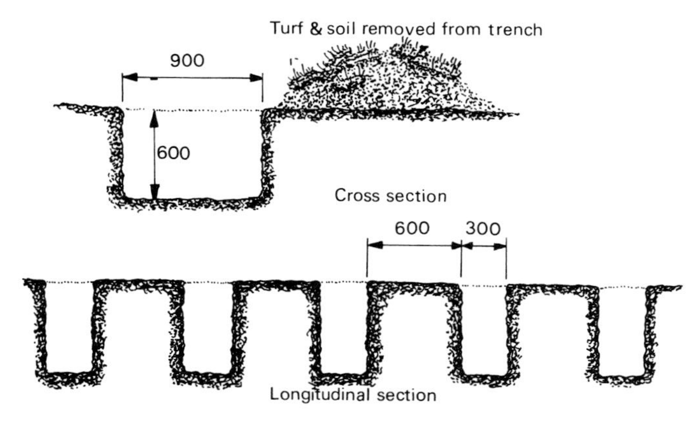

Fig. 11.3 Shallow trench latrine (5 for every hundred men, 3 for each extra hundred). Soil is placed at the head of the trench and a scoop provided. It is used for 24 hours and filled, and the next set of trenches dug nearer the camp to prevent stepping over soiled ground.

wood, or sheet-metal fencing. Toilet paper or ablution water (depending on local custom) should be provided.

The shallow trench is a rudimentary arrangement suitable for a short period (up to one week). When the trench is filled to 30 cm below ground level, it must be covered with earth, heaped above ground level and compacted. If necessary, a new trench must be dug. Before a trench is abandoned, sanitation personnel should ascertain that it is properly filled in.

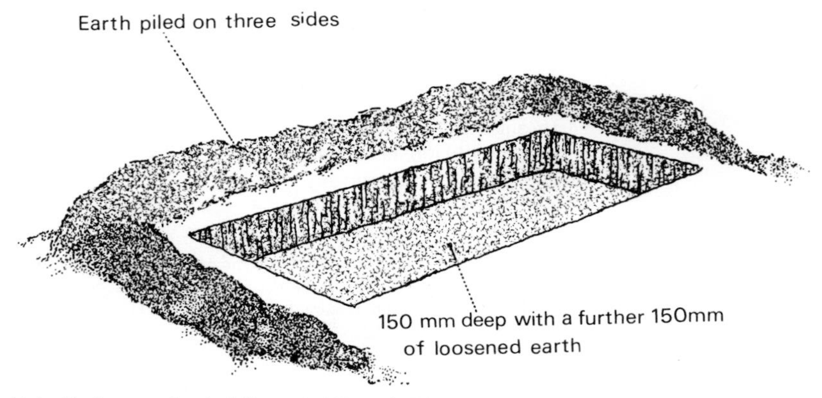

Fig. 11.4 Shallow trench urinal (for each 250 men). Dig a trench 3 m × 1 m × 150 mm, and loosen a further 150 mm to ease soakage. Heap soil on three sides to encourage use from the front only. It is used for 24 hours and filled in.

Deep trench latrine

This type of latrine is intended for camps of longer duration, from a few weeks to a few months. The trench is 1.8 to 2.5 m deep and 75 to 90 cm wide. The top of the trench is covered with a fly-proof floor. A seat or a squatting hole is provided, depending on local custom. A good super structure is built for privacy and protection. Other requirements are the same as for shallow trenches.

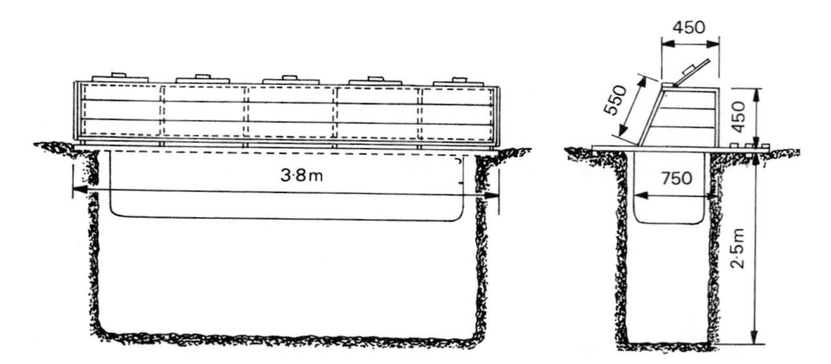

Fig. 11.5 Deep trench latrine (5 seats for 100 men, 3 for each extra 100). 150 mm earth is removed for one metre around trench. Oiled sacking is laid and covered with packed earth, flaps hanging into trench. A fly-proof superstructure is then placed on top and banked around with earth. Used until 600 mm from top, then filled with rammed oiled earth.

Pit privy

Where the subsoil is loose and easy to dig up, a pit privy may be built for each family or for each tent sheltering a few families. If tools are provided, the refugees/evacuees may do the work themselves.

In long-term camps, and where the local custom is to use water for cleansing, a water-seal can be incorporated in each slab.

Aqua privy (or septic privy)

This type consists essentially of a water tight tank (filled with water) into which excreta are discharged, stored and digested. It has been used with success as a communal latrine in some long-term refugee camps. Aqua privies take a long time to construct and are not recommended during emergencies except, perhaps, for field hospitals, first aid stations and mass feeding centres.

Urinals

These may be provided in communal blocks of latrines for men, to reduce the number of seats required. One urinal space for 25 males is recommended.

Odours can be controlled by applying chlorine solution.

Mobile latrines

These are tanks mounted on a truck or rail wagon. They are used in post disaster situations and even in 'unsewered' areas adjacent to urban centres in normal times.

They are necessary in disaster areas where the ground-water table is high. The proper disposal of the tank contents and the washing and disinfection of tanks after each emptying must be supervised by knowledgeable field workers.

Communal latrines are difficult to keep clean and should be used only when the emergency is expected to be of short duration.

Strict measures are needed for control and cleanliness. Every attempt should be made to provide communal latrines with water so that cleaning is practicable. Five seats are needed for every 100 persons, in separate blocks for men and women.

Latrines should be situated downhill from any water source and at least 15 metres away from it.

When the ground water is used for drinking or other purposes, the bottom of the latrine should be at least 1.5 metres above the ground-water table; in the presence of limestone formations and fissured rocks, additional precautions are necessary to protect sources of water supply.

The site must be dry, well-drained and above flood level. The immediate surroundings of latrines should be cleared of all vegetation, wastes and debris.

Solid wastes disposal

Solid wastes to be disposed of may include: (*a*) refuse; (*b*) manure; and (*c*) animal carcasses.

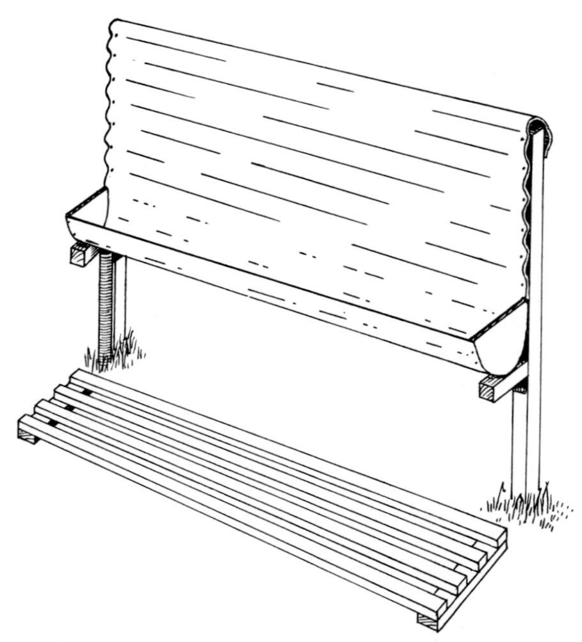

Fig. 11.6 Trough urinal (per 100 men). A sheet of corrugated iron is fixed to two legs. The bottom of the sheet is turned up to form a trough and the ends are blocked. Legs are placed in the ground to give a trough height of 750 mm sloping to 70 mm. A pipe is fixed at the lower end and run into a soakage pit.

There is a correlation between the improper disposal of solid wastes and the incidence of vector-borne diseases. Provisions should therefore be made for the effective storage, collection, and disposal of refuse and manure. Carcasses should be disposed of as quickly as possible. If the disaster area is urban and is provided with a proper collection and disposal service, or if the area is close to a municipal system, all efforts should be made to restore or extend the existing organisation.

Storage of refuse

To expedite the disposal of refuse, it is advisable to provide separate containers for storing organic and inorganic wastes. The containers for organic wastes should be made of

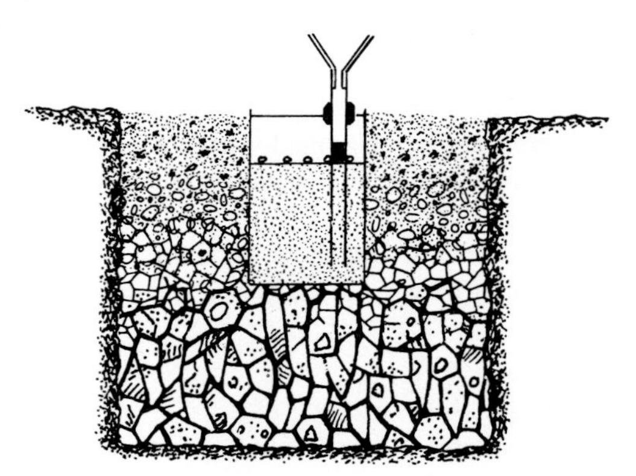

Fig. 11.7 Urinal.

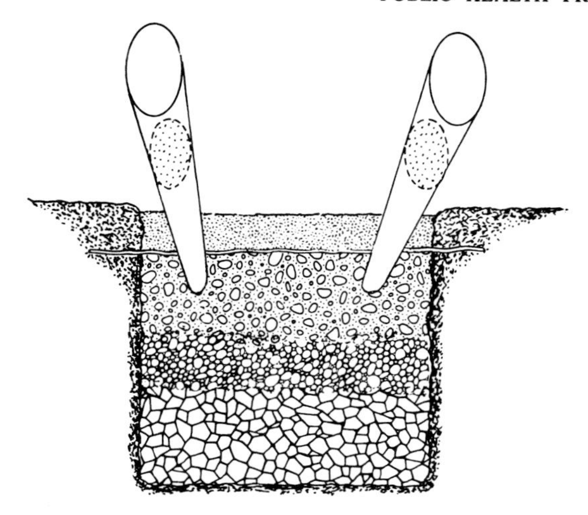

Fig. 11.8 Funnel urinal (4 funnels for 100 men). A soakage pit is dug (1 m^3) with large stones at the bottom graduating to small ones at the top. Cover with oiled sacking from top and filled with soil soaked in waste oil. Ram down hard. At each corner place an improvised funnel.

heavier material than those for inorganic wastes, and should be washable, watertight, and provided with tight-fitting, overlapping covers. In emergencies, however, empty foodstuff containers and disposable water-resistant paper bags may be used for short periods. The capacity of containers should not exceed 100 litres. It is recommended that three or four containers be provided for every 100 persons. They should be so distributed that each family has a container within easy reach. The containers should stand off the ground, on wooden racks. In large emergency feeding centres, garbage stores may be practicable. They should have concrete floors and walls, floor drains, and a water supply. They should be emptied and washed every day.

Collection of refuse

An estimate should be made of the quantity of refuse, frequency of collection, number and size of collection vehicles, personnel required, method of final disposal, and disposal sites. In emergencies, all types of trucks may be used. However, the compacting type of refuse truck will reduce the number of trips and the hazards associated with the scattering of refuse. A truck with a capacity of 10 m^3 and manned by a driver and two helpers can serve 5000 to 8000 people making three journeys per day to the disposal area.

Disposal of refuse

Refuse may be disposed of by sanitary landfill, burial, incineration, or open dumping.

Sanitary landfill. For most situations sanitary landfill is the preferred method of final disposal. Heavy earth-moving equipment may be available from the army or the public works department. Refuse is compacted and promptly covered with earth, which in turn is compacted. Three methods are used in this operation:

1. The trench method: a long trench is dug out and the excavated earth is used to cover the compacted refuse.

2. The ramp method: the covering material is obtained from the working face of the fill.

3. The area method: this method is used for filling land depressions and in swampy areas where soil conditions do not allow the use of heavy equipment.

Burial. This method is suitable for small camps where earth-moving equipment is not available. A trench 1.5 m wide and 2 m deep is excavated, and at the end of each day the refuse is covered with 20 to 30 cm of earth. When the level in the trench is 40 cm from ground level, the trench is filled with earth and compacted, and a new trench is dug out. The contents may be taken out after four to six months and used on the fields. If the trench is 1 metre in length for every 200 persons, it will be filled in about a week.

Incineration. Where burial is not practicable, refuse should be incinerated. If the refuse is very wet, fuel will need to be added. Refuse from first-aid stations and hospitals that contains pathogenic material should be incinerated, regardless of the method adopted for disposal of garbage and rubbish. A basket incinerator, which is simply a wire basket standing on an iron drum or stone supports, may be used for this purpose. Incinerators made of corrugated iron sheets and empty oil drums are illustrated in Figures 11.9 and 11.10. The incinerator shown in Figure 11.11 is more suitable for long-term use. A little kerosene or fuel oil may be added to ensure complete combustion.

In the construction of incinerators used for the final disposal of any kind of refuse, it is essential to observe the following points:

1. The incinerator should be located away and downwind from the camp or temporary shelters;

2. The incinerator should be built on an impervious base of concrete or hardened earth;

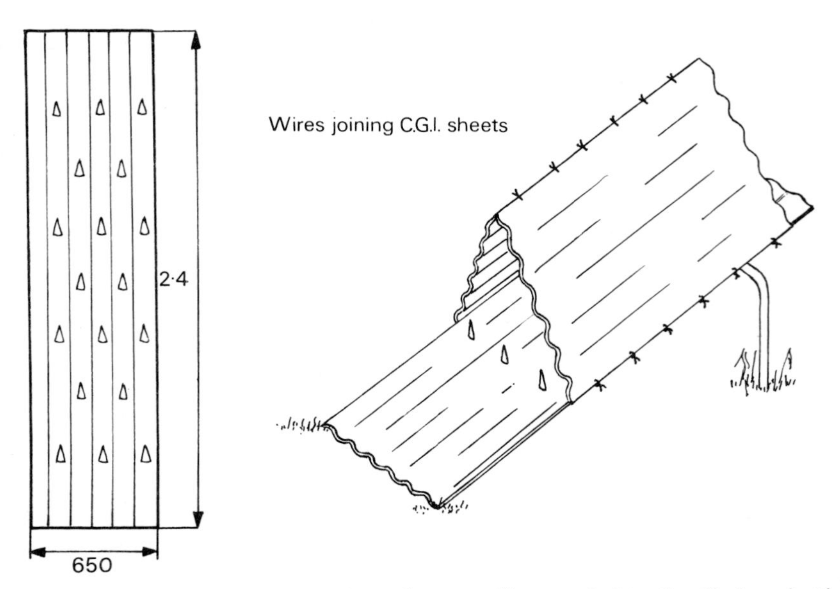

Fig. 11.9 Inclined plane incinerator. Three sheets of corrugated iron are wired together. The base sheet is perforated with triangular notches which are turned up to provide catches for the refuse and extra draught. One end of the structure is raised 750 mm from the ground. Refuse is placed into the higher end and burnt at the lower end. Wet refuse may be dealt with as it is dried by the rising smoke through the length of the incinerator.

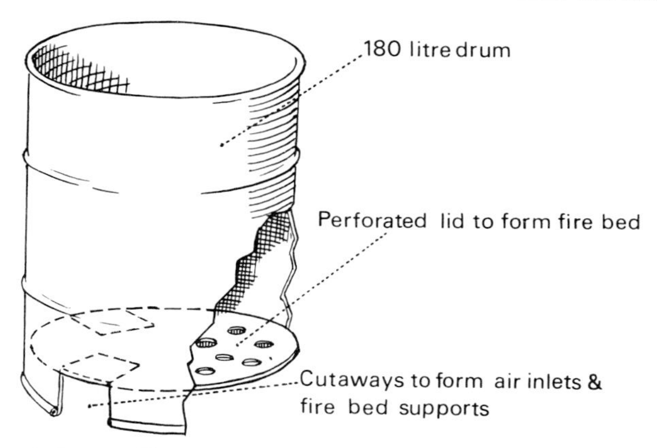

Fig. 11.10 Oil drum incinerator. The top is cut out of a 180 litre oil drum and perforated with 20 mm holes. Four 150 mm squares are cut in the sides of the drum at the base and turned inwards. The lid is dropped into the drum to rest on the turned-in flaps, forming a fire bed. This incinerator is very quickly constructed and very efficient.

3. The air inlet must be sufficiently large; it should be funnel-shaped, narrow end inwards, to produce a blower effect;
4. The fire bars should be placed loosely on their support to allow for expansion;
5. The stoking gates should be suitably situated so that fresh material can be added from above;

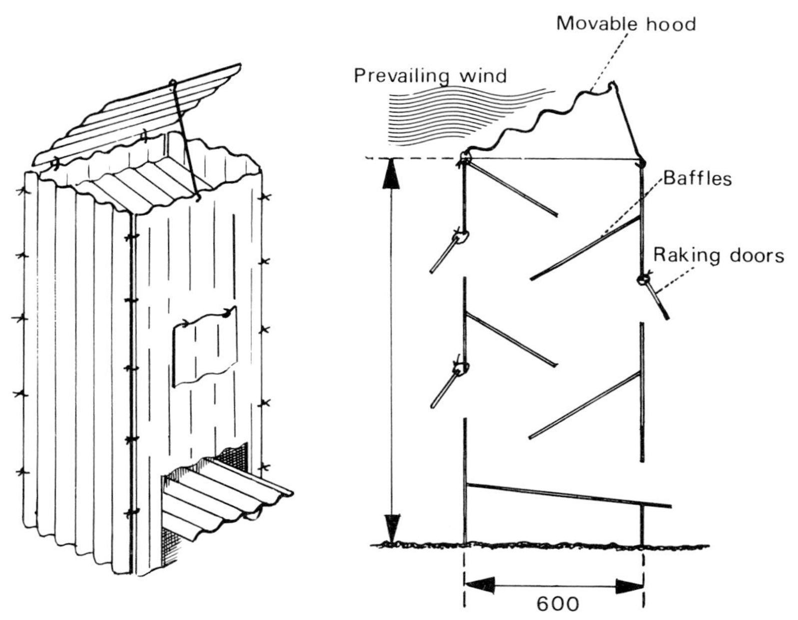

Fig. 11.11 Semi-closed incinerator. This is formed from four sheets of corrugated iron fastened at the edges with baling wire. Angled baffle plates are fitted to form a graduated feed. This ensures drying of the refuse before incineration. The movable hood should always back on to the prevailing wind. This incinerator may be used with an oil-and-water flash fire.

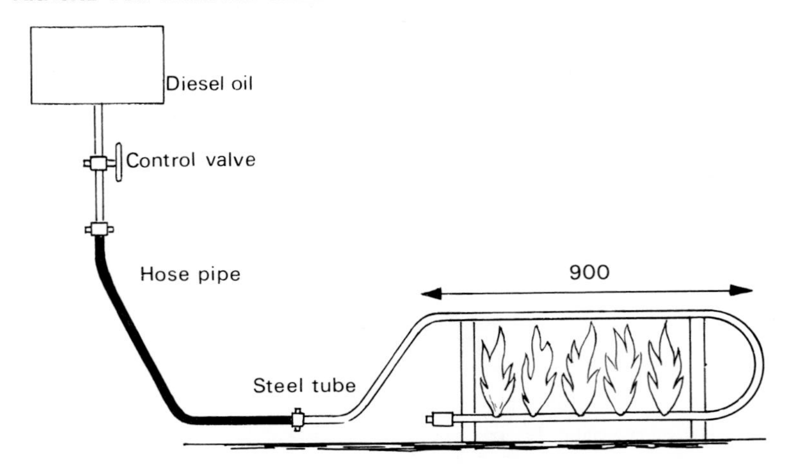

Fig. 11.12 Trombone burner. The shape of the pipes in this heater give it its name. The lower pipe run has a stopped end and five 0.4 mm holes bored in the upper wall. It is necessary to preheat by burning oily rags beneath the pipe before the fuel is lit. Waste sump or diesel oil is placed in the reservoir, usually 2.5 to 3 m above ground level and, when the pipe is hot, is turned on by means of a stop-cock. As the oil passes along the heated pipe it vaporizes and burns as a gas on leaving the small holes.

6. The raking openings must allow sufficient room for efficient raking and for cleaning out the interior;
7. A long chimney is necessary for a closed incinerator, to ensure a good draught.

Open dumping. This must be avoided. In extreme emergencies only, refuse may be hauled to a suitable site for dumping and burning, provided that sanitation personnel supervise the operation. Cans should be crushed flat to prevent mosquitoes breeding, and burned refuse should be covered to deter flies and rodents.

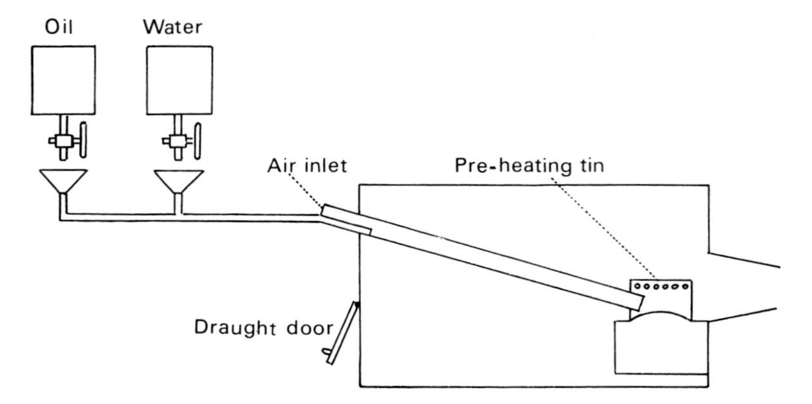

Fig. 11.13 The oil-and-water flash fire is an effective heater using waste sump oil. The flash plate is preheated by burning oily rages on it. Fuel and water is then allowed to run from the fuel tanks, in the proportion of 3 drops of oil to one of water; 60 to 90 drops of oil pass through to the flash plate per minute. The oil and water are conveyed via a small gutter to the flash plate, where water drops explode, breaking up the oil into minute droplets which burn freely.

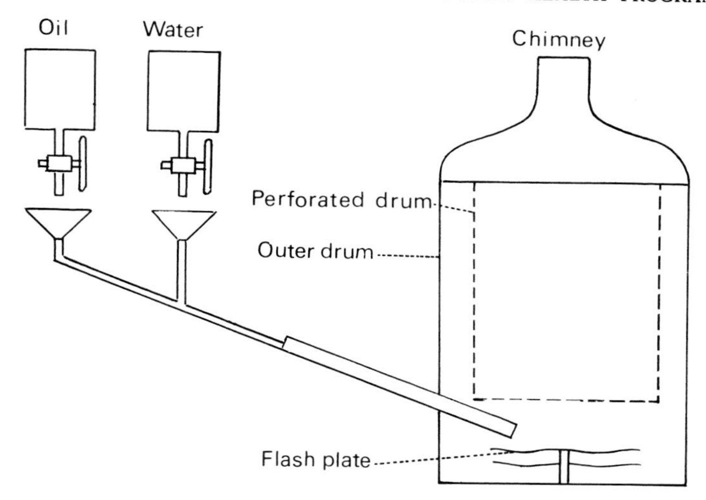

Fig. 11.14 Dressing destructor. This shows one practical application of the oil-and-water flash fire (see Fig. 11.13). The flash plate is inside a 180 litre drum. An inner drum with sides and bottom is fitted directly above, and a cone-shaped top is placed over the outer drum to form a chimney. An access door is cut in the outer drum. This appliance is invaluable in field hospitals.

Manure

In rural areas where disaster has hit attention should be paid to the collection and disposal of manure because, if left in the open, it will attract flies and provide them with a good breeding-place. Pits with concrete floors and cement-lined walls may be built for manure collection. Each pit should be sufficiently large to hold one day's manure; two pits must be provided so that one can be cleaned and washed while the other is in use. The floor should slope towards a drain connected to a soakage pit. The owners of animals should be responsible for hauling the manure to these collection points. Daily removal for final disposal should be carried out by the camp's sanitation team.

Manure may be disposed of with other refuse by burying, composting or incineration. In emergencies, the most practicable method is to bury it in trenches similar to those described for refuse. The contents of these trenches may be taken and used as soil conditioner after four to six months of anaerobic decay.

Animal carcasses

The problem of disposing of dead animals may assume serious proportions in certain natural disasters, particularly in floods. Burial is slow and laborious. For instance, a pit three metres deep is needed for a dead horse. When there are many carcasses it is difficult to bury them all unless heavy excavation machinery is available. The burning of small animals like cats and dogs, is feasible, but the burning of larger carcasses is difficult unless special incinerators are built. Efforts should therefore be made to obtain heavy equipment for burial. If this is not available, a combination of burial and burning should be used, i.e. burial of the internal organs and burning of the carcass with the aid of fuel. For better supervision, it is advisable to centralise operations in suitably located animal cemeteries. Carcasses awaiting burial should be sprinkled with kerosene or crude oil to protect them from predatory animals.

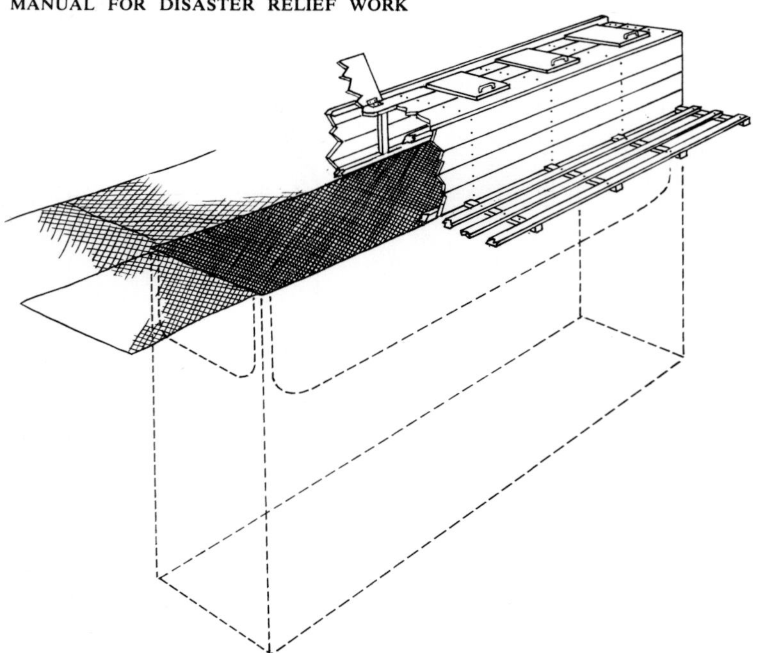

Fig. 11.15a Improvised strainer. A drum or tin is filled with bracken and is placed on top of a soakage pit. Grease and fat filled bracken is burnt or buried daily.

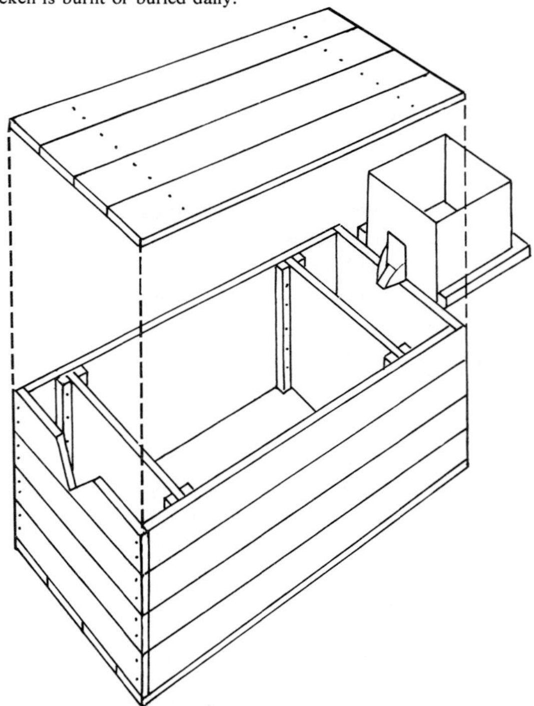

Fig. 11.15b Standard grease trap. This is a box constructed of tongued and grooved board 1.20 m long × 400 mm wide × 750 mm deep. Baffles are inserted 150 mm from each end with a space of 100 mm at the base. The box is sunk into the ground and discharges into a soakage pit. A strainer is placed at the head of the box. Grease is trapped by the baffles. Scum is removed and burnt daily, completely emptied and cleaned weekly.

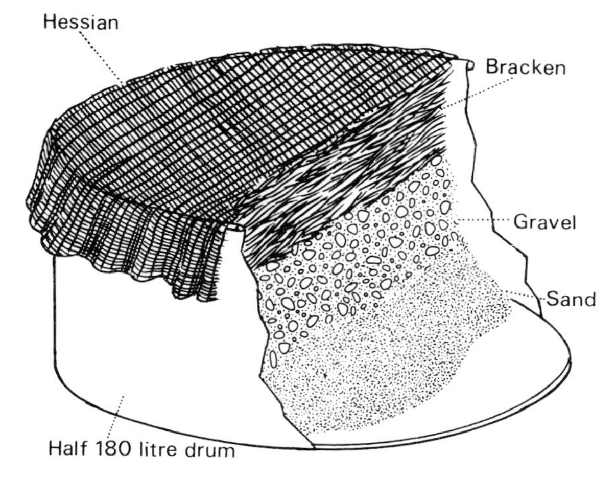

Fig. 11.16 Although called a grease trap, this appliance is in effect a grease strainer. Grease is extracted by filtration and the contents of the drum should be removed when it becomes clogged.

Waste water disposal

Waste water from field hospitals, mass feeding centres, milk distribution centres and water points requires proper disposal. The usual way is to discharge it into a seepage pit. To prevent rapid clogging of such a pit, a French drain or absorption trench may be constructed in advance of it. Liquid wastes from feeding centres and bath-houses contain grease and soap, and even where the soil is very porous seepage pits get clogged in time. It is therefore necessary to install a grease trap to the drain and pit at the upper end of the inlet pipe. Dry water-courses may also be used if precautions are taken to prevent the breeding of mosquitoes. Subsurface drainage can be recommended only for permanent camps. In areas where the soil is impermeable and the climate is hot and relatively dry, the waste water may be disposed of by evaporation. Shallow pans should be used for this purpose; they should be provided in pairs and used alternately to prevent mosquitoes breeding.

Other installations

Communal facilities for maintaining personal cleanliness should be provided in temporary shelters and camps. These may include showers, washrooms, laundries and disinfestation and disinfection rooms. They will help to prevent skin diseases and infestations that lead to vector-borne diseases. Disinfection rooms are necessary to halt the spread of infectious disease transmitted through fomites. The proper operation and maintenance of these services depends on constant supervision by sanitation personnel.

Baths and showers

Showers are preferable to baths for reasons of hygiene and because they save water. One shower head should be provided for every 100 people. Bath registers or bath tickets can be used for making sure that everyone in the camp bathes at least once a week. In hot climates, cold water should be adequate. If hot water is provided, 20 litres should be supplied for each bath. Overall consumption of water for bathing should be calculated on the basis of 30 to 35 litres per person per week. The communal use of towels should not be

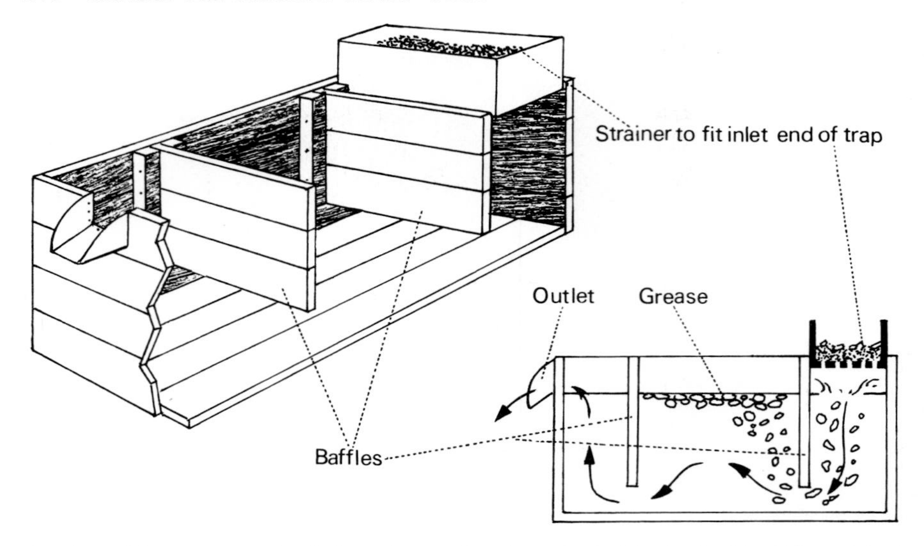

Fig. 11.17 If hot water containing fat is run into an adequate supply of cold water, the fat solidifies and rises to the surface, where it can be skimmed off. A strainer is fitted to the inlet to extract any large particles which might pass through the trap and choke the inlet to the soakage pit. The first baffle prevents the entering water from disturbing the layer of grease, the second keeps the effluent from carrying it off.

permitted unless arrangements are made for washing and disinfecting them after each use. For hygienic and economic reasons, communal baths should be located near the disinfestation and disinfection rooms. Proper arrangements should be made for the disposal of waste water from baths. Temporary shower baths can be set up within a reasonably short time. Figures 11.19, 11.20 and 11.21 show quick methods of providing temporary water heaters and showers on a small scale. More permanent and larger installations should be established at long-term camps. Bath rail wagons and trucks are eminently suitable for use in disaster situations.

Laundries

In temporary encampments people must expect to wash their clothes in plastic or iron tubs. In long-term camps, however, it is necessary to provide communal laundries. Where

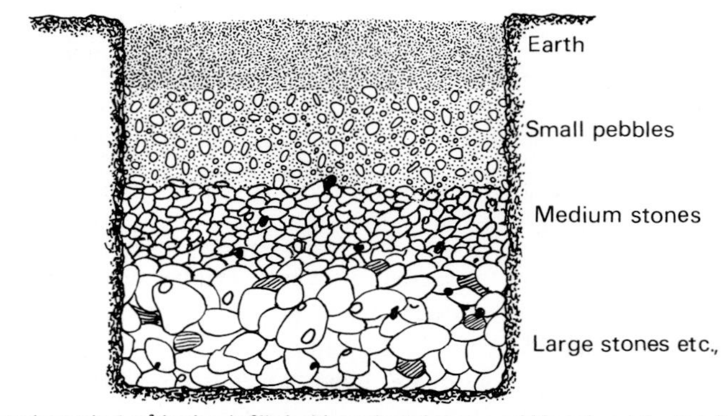

Fig. 11.18 A soackage pit, 1 m^3 in size, is filled with graduated stones, rubble or burnt tins to within 150 mm of the top. A layer of brushwood or sacking is added and the pit filled in with earth.

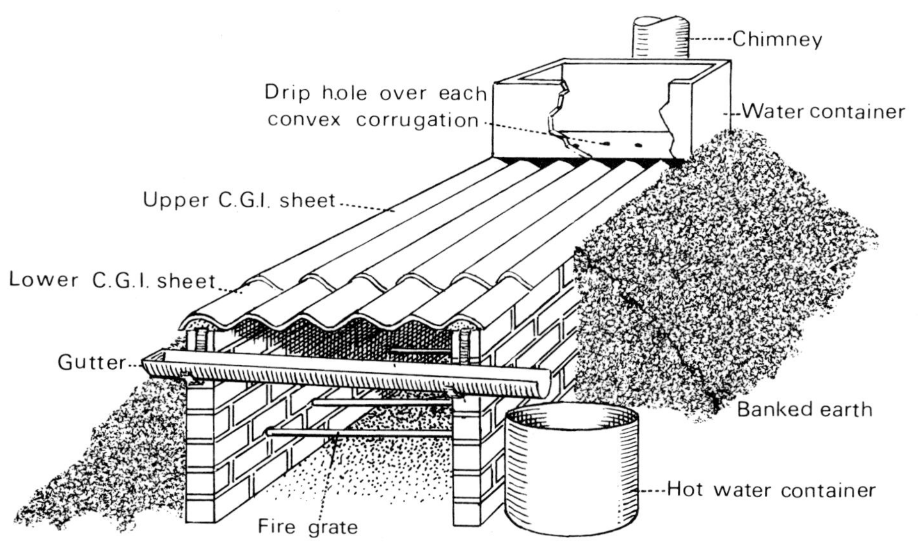

Fig. 11.19 The simplest and most efficient hot water heater in the field. Cold water is poured into the perforated receptacle at one end, passes between two corrugated metal sheets, and is collected in a receptacle at the other end via a small gutter. Any form of heating is placed under the sheets. The water is heated immediately. Turf may be placed over the upper sheet to give insulation.

disinfection rooms are needed, these and the laundries should be housed together and, whenever possible, hot water should be provided. One washing stand for every 100 people is recommended. A schedule must be established for the use of laundries on a family basis, otherwise they will be crowded at times and empty at others. Proper drainage and grease and soap traps should be provided for waste water.

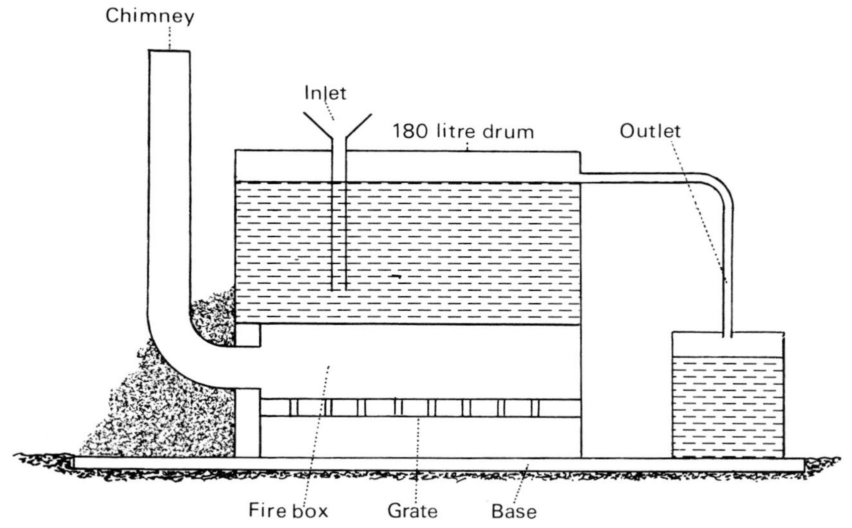

Fig. 11.20 'Put and take boiler'. Commonly known as the lazy man's boiler, this appliance works on the principle of water finding its own level. The water in the boiler is heated and thereafter cold water poured in will displace the same quantity of hot water through the outlet. The inlet pipe extends to 50 mm from the bottom of the boiler and acts as a safety valve. If no water has been drawn off, the contents of the boiler will eventually evaporate. When steam emerges from the inlet pipe, it gives warning that the water level is low.

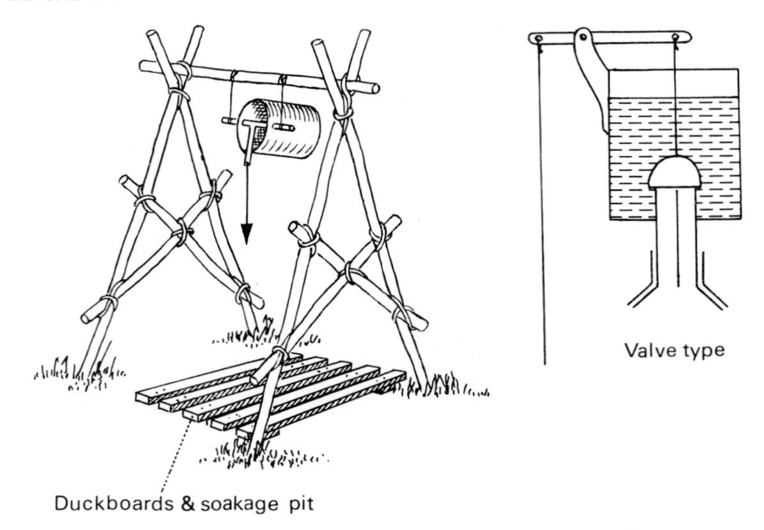

Fig. 11.21 A shower can be improvised by mounting a 25 litre drum on a pivot. Perforations are made in the drum above the pivot and a filler inlet made on the top. The drum is filled to the lowest perforation. Several fillings are required to give a satisfactory shower.

Disinfection and disinfestation rooms

Disease germs are destroyed during disinfection. Disinfestation is the process by which insects, their eggs, and other vermin that transmit disease or cause annoyance are removed or killed. Disinfection methods will be effective for disinfestation, but the reverse does not hold true. In practice, disinfestation is used more often than disinfection. The methods employed in disinfestation will destroy vermin but will not necessarily kill the disease germs carried by them such as lice. Therefore, when there is any risk that vermin may cause an epidemic it is safer to employ disinfection.

Effective disinfection calls for trained personnel, since if any of the various steps of the disinfection process are not carried out properly the purpose will be defeated. Well-trained

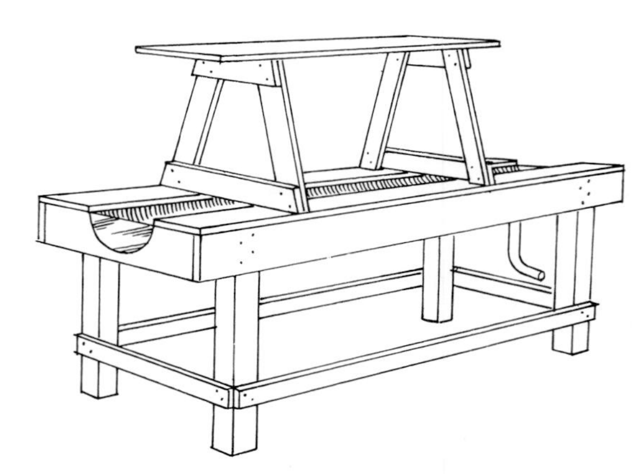

Fig. 11.22 An ablution bench for use in semi-permanent camps. It consists of a double-sided bench with a central drainage channel, which is conducted via a grease-trap into a standard soakage pit. Basins may be made by cutting 25 litre drums in half.

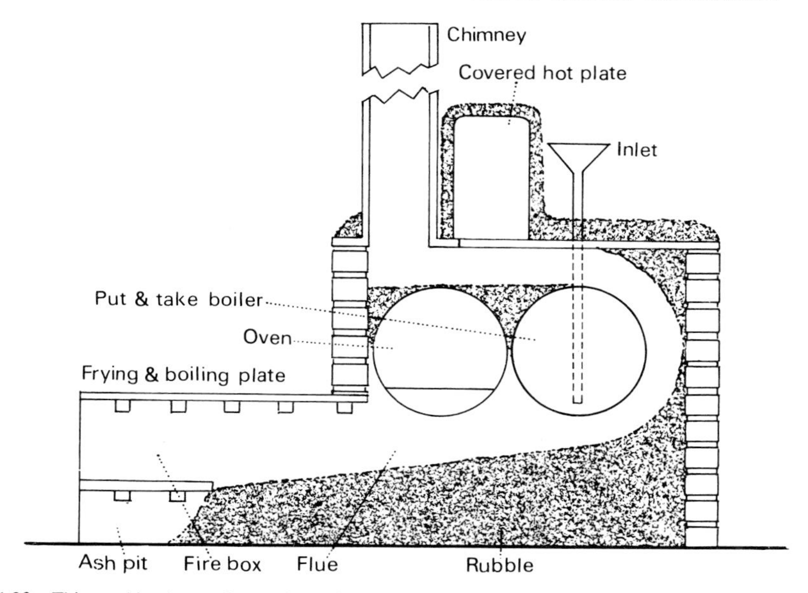

Fig. 11.23 This combination cooker performs five tasks. The direct heat from the fire heats a frying and boiling plate, the hot air currents circulate around an oven and a hot water boiler, under a covered hot plate and are discharged via the chimney.

and experienced sanitarians should therefore be in charge of disinfection and disinfestation operations.

Methods used in disinfection and disinfestation involve the use of physical agents such as ultra-violet light, dry heat, boiling water, and steam or chemical agents such as sulphur dioxide, ethylene oxide, formaldehyde, formol, cresol, phenol, and carbolic acid. Some of these agents are dangerous, and should only be used under expert supervision.

The area or building used for disinfection should be divided into a 'dirty' side for the receipt of infected articles and a 'clean' side for their distribution. The only communication between these two sides should be through a disinfection and laundering room (for clothing, etc.) or through a bathroom (for people).

Arrangements should be made on the 'dirty' side for disinfecting the vehicles used for the transport of infected materials. Personnel employed in handling infected materials must be suitably protected against infection. On the 'clean' side, storage space should be available for disinfected articles.

All articles not likely to be damaged are disinfected by steam; the steam flow can be either downwards or upwards. Leather goods, clothing with leather facings or strappings, furs, rubber and other materials that may be spoilt by steam are sprayed with a 5 per cent formol solution.

The layout of a disinfestation unit is the same as that of a disinfection unit. Disinfestation will not be effective unless infested individuals have previously been segregated. If this has not been done, the entire camp population will have to be disinfested.

Abattoir

If there is an absence or shortage of refrigeration equipment, it is often necessary to make simple slaughtering arrangements in camps. The site should be secluded, but kept under close supervision. The floor should be of concrete or asphalt, sloping towards a central drain covered with a trap or strainer to collect solids. The liquid waste may be discharged into a seepage pit. Ample water should be provided for washing. Hooks hung on a horizontal beam at a height of about two metres, supported by two vertical poles, position the carcasses conveniently for skinning.

Offal, bones, and other solid waste should be buried, or burnt in a closed incinerator. In the case of burial, a series of pits should be dug and the offal covered with at least 90 cm of earth thoroughly treated with heavy oil, and well compacted.

Education in sanitation of disaster victims

Experience has shown that sanitary installations provided as part of the relief work after disasters do not always fulfil their purpose because they are either misused or not used sufficiently. Among the most important reasons for this lack of appreciation among disaster victims are: (*a*) the psychological effect of the disaster, manifested mainly in an apathetic attitude, (*b*) the victims' low standard of living prior to the disaster, and (*c*) their ignorance as to the use and maintenance of the installations provided.

In itself, therefore, the provision of sanitary installations is not enough to solve the problem; the people must use them properly and frequently so that an adequate level of personal cleanliness and of environmental hygiene is attained. It is, therefore, the responsibility of all environmental health workers to participate actively in educating disaster-stricken people to use sanitary installations properly, to comply with the rules of personal hygiene, and to safeguard the health of the community.

A number of points concerning education should be borne in mind:

1. To be successful, education should be based on the trust and collaboration of the people. To gain their confidence, it is extremely important that the health worker should have a sympathetic disposition. An authoritative attitude is detrimental.

2. The sanitary installations used should be of a type easily understood by the people. Simple and accessible solutions can generally be devised without sacrificing the basic principles of sanitation. If a complex installation is unavoidable, patient and constant instruction is necessary to make it understood and ensure that it is used properly.

3. On-the-spot education is most effective.

4. In relief situations of short duration there is not enough time to start educational processes, and the proper operation of sanitary installations will depend on effective inspection. Young people from the afflicted area and from welfare agencies, such as the Red Cross, should be used to help professional inspectors. Systematic and regular inspections must be carried out.

5. As a means of mass education the media have proved their value in emergency situations. Sanitation education is needed in the following areas:

a. The avoidance of using contaminated water;

b. The avoidance of wasting water;

c. Co-operation in protecting the water supply system;

d. Co-operation in distributing water;

e. Co-operation in using the excreta disposal installations properly and in keeping them clean;

f. The avoidance of scattering refuse, and observance of rules for proper collection of refuse;

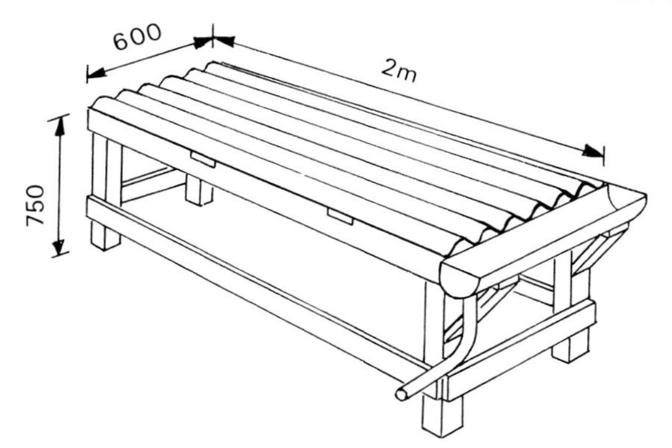

Fig. 11.24 A wash-up bench, consisting of a corrugated sheet forming a draining board, mounted on a wooden platform. A gutter, located at the lower end, drains into a soakage pit via a grease trap. An improvised wash-up basin can be made by cutting a 180 litre drum in half.

g. Co-operation in reducing insect populations;
h. Cleanliness of the shelters and camp;
i. Cleanliness of food containers, dishes, utensils, etc.;
j. Observance of personal hygiene rules (body and clothing);
k. Proper collection of manure;
l. Participation in community clean-up work.

Mortuary services and burial of the dead

Supervision of the emergency mortuary service is the responsibility of the public health service. It is likely that, apart from the medical examination of the dead, the supervisory work will be carried out by sanitation personnel. In any case, this supervision is necessary, especially in outbreaks of epidemics. The work to be carried out consists of:

Removal. The removal of dead bodies from the scene of disaster is not the responsibility of sanitation personnel, but they often co-operate with other workers as the situation demands. Quick and quiet removal of bodies from public view plays an important role in maintaining morale.

Morgue. This should have four sections: a reception room, a viewing chamber, a storage chamber for bodies not suitable for viewing and a room for records and for storage of personal effects. In some severe emergencies it may be necessary to by-pass the morgue.

Establishment of legal proof of death. This is the responsibility of the medical examiner who issues the death certificate.

Identification of the dead. Efforts should be made to identify bodies or, at least, to obtain all possible information.

Preparation of an official record of death. An identity tag should be affixed to the body and all available information recorded in a special book.

Final disposal of the body. Mass burials in a common grave should be avoided. The location of graves should be charted on maps and identified by tag numbers.

Return of valuable personal effects. The next of kin should receive the valuable personal effects of the dead. In the event of epidemics, personal belongings should be disinfected before they are returned.

The following items are needed for the mortuary service: stretchers, leather gloves, rubber gloves, overalls, boots, caps, soap and disinfectants, cotton cloth, picks and shovels. Heavy earth-moving machines and trucks may also be required.

Precautions should be taken always in handling dead bodies, but more particularly in cases of death from a contagious disease. In epidemics, strict sanitary supervision should be maintained at all stages of handling the dead; the mortuary personnel should have special working clothes and at the end of a day's work they should wash themselves thoroughly with a disinfectant soap.

VERMIN CONTROL

Conditions subsequent to a disaster usually favour a rapid increase in the insect and rodent population. The immediate cause may be the breakdown of sanitary arrangements, such as the collection and disposal of refuse, and the subsequent production of sites suitable for extensive breeding and harbouring of vermin. The accommodation of large numbers of people in temporary shelters under such conditions will expose them to diseases carried by insects and rodents.

Opportunities and facilities for personal cleanliness to be maintained may be extremely limited in temporary shelters. Carriers of infectious diseases and people infested with vermin may be in close contact with others free from infection. A situation such as this, more often than not already complicated by somewhat primitive sanitary installations and services, creates potential hazards calling for immediate attention and action.

The movement of people to a new place often exposes them to insects and to such diseases as typhus, malaria and plague. Flies, fleas, lice, mites, mosquitoes, ticks and rodents are disease vectors that develop rapidly in an uncontrolled environment.

The insects likely to cause trouble, annoyance, or localised infection include chiggers, gnats, bedbugs, mosquitoes and cockroaches. In some areas, disaster victims will be exposed to poisonous reptiles, spiders and other creatures. While these endanger only the specific individual who comes into contact with them, an attack may have a demoralising effect on other people who, because of the circumstances, are prone to hysteria.

The vectors most likely to be present in encampments and temporary shelters and the main diseases they may transmit through biting, skin infection, and pollution of food and water are listed below:

Vector	*Main diseases*
Mosquitoes	Malaria, yellow fever, dengue, viral encephalitis, filariasis
Houseflies	Diarrhoea, dysentery, conjunctivitis, typhoid fever
Cockroaches	Diarrhoea, dysentery, salmonellosis

Lice	Endemic typhus, pediculosis, relapsing fever, trench fever, skin irritation
Bedbugs	Severe skin inflammation
Cone-nosed bugs	Chagas' disease
Ticks	Rickettsial fever, tularaemia, relapsing fever, viral encephalitis
Rodent mites	Rickettsialpox, scrub typhus
Rodent fleas	Bubonic plague, endemic typhus
Rodents	Rat-bite fever, leptospirosis, salmonellosis, melioidosis

Vector control programmes should be planned in order to cope with two distinct situations:

1. The initial or emergency phase immediately following the disaster. Control work should concentrate on the destruction, by a physical or chemical process, of vermin on persons, their clothing, bedding and other belongings and on domestic animals. An emergency sanitation team should be available from the beginning for carrying out this disinfestation.

2. The period after the emergency has subsided. Control work should be directed towards proper food hygiene, safe disposal of wastes (including drainage) and general and personal cleanliness.

A direct attack on insects and their breeding and harbouring places should be carried out throughout the post-disaster period.

Insects

Great attention should be paid to the cleanliness of victims and their belongings in order to reduce the incipient hazards of infestation, infection, dermatitis and other personal afflictions. Arrangements for washing are discussed in the section entitled 'Other installations'.

Louse proliferation must be expected in overcrowded, temporary shelters and encampments. Under such conditions, dusting with an insecticidal powder should be an established routine for all refugees arriving at the reception centre or camp. Voluntary helpers should, if needed, be trained in dusting operations. The efficacy of the insecticide should be tested in advance. At encampments of 500 persons or more, the disinfestation station should be a compactly planned unit, with suitable quarters for quick and efficient treatment. This unit should also be equipped for emergency disinfestation of clothing, bedding and other articles, tents and living quarters. The teams operating from a disinfestation unit should be able to cover several neighbouring camps.

Preliminary surveys should be made in camping areas to determine the number and extent of sites where insects and rodents may breed or harbour. These sites should be mapped to indicate the places where control measures are required. There are three types of area on which it is particularly important to obtain information:

Mosquito-breeding areas. Breeding sites may be detected from larval collection and inspection. Suitable data sheets and maps should be used to record pertinent information. The trapping of adult mosquitoes will give quantitative information on their number and distribution and on the effectiveness of control measures.

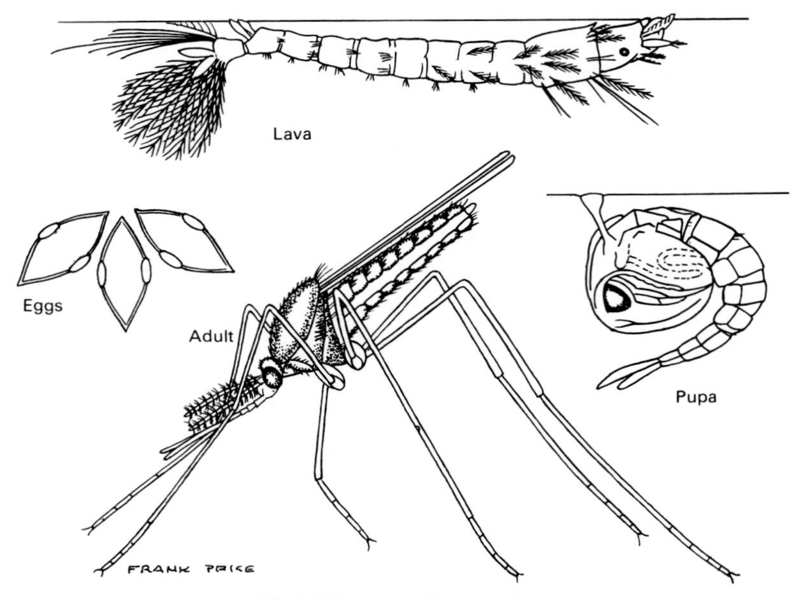

Fig. 11.25 Anopheline mosquito.

Fly-breeding areas. Inspection for fly breeding areas should include all refuse disposal sites, animal yards and shelters, surface toilets, heaps of uncovered garbage, and places where abattoir wastes or any other decaying organic material may accumulate. Climate and season of the year are important factors in evaluating the fly-breeding potential. Temperatures above 20°C are conducive to the rapid increase of the fly population. Where experienced personnel are available, routine determination of fly densities may serve to assess the effectiveness of control measures.

Rodent harbourages. A rodent control programme should be preceded by a preliminary survey to determine the extent and location of rodent infestation, the probability of the occurrence of rat- and flea-borne or mice- and mite-borne disease, the possibility of food and property being spoilt and of people in temporary shelters being bitten. An effective programme requires recognition of the prevailing species.

Vermin control should follow a definite plan and programme. Special teams should be organised for this purpose. The team leader should be a sanitarian with adequate knowledge and experience in the field of vector control. The Malaria Control Organisation, The National Institute of Health, and other bodies concerned with vector control and research, must be consulted as to the presence in the disaster area of vectors resistant to pesticides. In its seventeenth report, the WHO Expert Committee on Insecticides made a number of important recommendations:

'To obtain maximum control of an insect or rodent, the operator should have some knowledge of the biology and ecology of the species with which he is concerned and experience with the various procedures and pesticides available. Non-selective application of pesticides by routine methods based on a single technique or chemical may lead to unsatisfactory results. For example, the application of insecticidal fogs before dusk is often unsuccessful in controlling certain species of mosquitoes, whereas the same treatment at

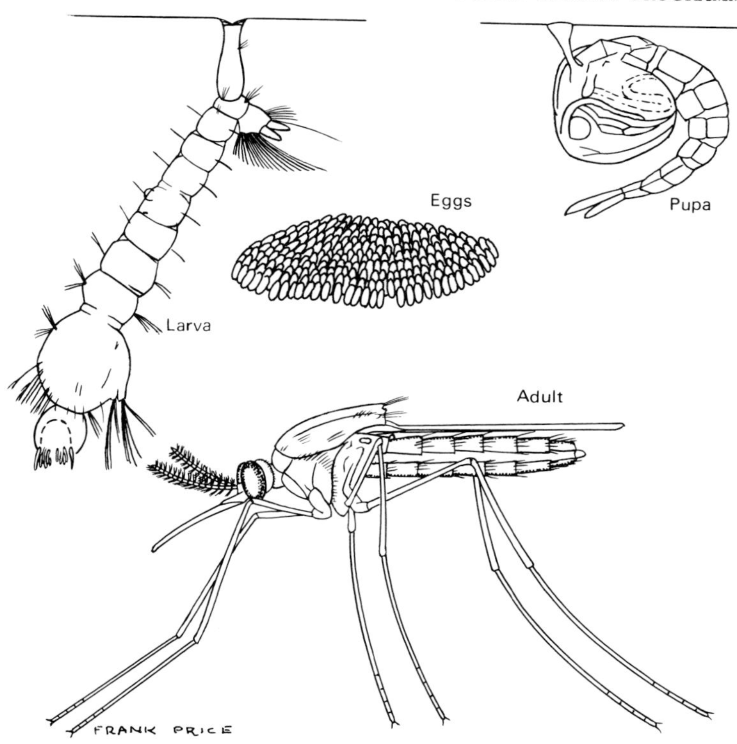

Fig. 11.26 Culicine mosquito.

dusk or shortly thereafter gives excellent results. Likewise fogging under unfavourable weather conditions can be valueless. In some countries the species of anopheline are semi-domestic in their habits (for example, *Anopheles sergenti* in Israel and Jordan) and residual treatment of homes is only partially effective in interrupting malaria transmission. However, in the same countries a domestic species (*An. sacharovi*) has been almost completely eliminated by the same operations. A similar situation prevails in Africa where *An. funestus* has disappeared in areas subject to residual applications. In other areas, where the outdoor biting habits of the anopheline mosquito decrease the efficiency of residual treatment in dwellings, such approaches as larviciding may be of importance, particularly where the mosquito breeding is reduced or confined to limited habitats during certain seasons of the year (for example, *An. albimanus* in stream beds in Central America during the dry season). Where measures are to be directed against both larvae and adults, it is advisable to use different chemicals for each type of treatment to reduce the possibility of the species developing resistance to the insecticide.

The efficacy of the chemical control measures is markedly influenced by a number of other factors: (*a*) the species involved; (*b*) the efficiency of the application; (*c*) the type of formulation and application; (*d*) the nature of the surface to which the formulation is applied; (*e*) the stability and potency of the pesticide; (*f*) the biotic potential of the species, and (*g*) the management of the control programme.'

It is emphasised that all control procedures, if they are to be successful, must be adequately supervised by competent personnel.

Mosquitoes

In areas where mosquito-borne diseases are endemic, initial control should be directed against adult mosquitoes and their breeding places.

Adult control. The interior surfaces of occupied dwellings, outbuildings, culverts and other resting places should be sprayed with a liquid mixture containing DDT, chlordane, or some other suitable insecticide. Tent encampments may be treated at dusk with insecticidal fogs produced by power space-sprayers.

Larviciding. Treatment used will depend on the location, size, and accessibility of the mosquito-breeding area. Where breeding areas are accessible and of less than five hectares, larviciding operations from the shore using either hand-operated or power sprayers will prove effective. For areas of over 10 hectares, motor vehicles or boats with power-spraying equipment will prove more efficient. For extensive breeding areas, where control measures are urgent, the use of aircraft with spray equipment may be required.

Flies

Control by sanitation. The most effective method of fly control is to observe good sanitation in the disaster area. This includes the sanitary storage, collection and disposal of organic wastes. If sanitary landfill or incineration is not possible, wastes should be dumped at suitable sites located at least five kilometres from any densely-populated area. Stockyards and cattle shelters should be inspected frequently, at least once a week, to ensure proper disposal of wastes. Manure may be held in fly-proof bins, spread in thin layers over a field, or buried under 30 cm of compacted earth. Only sanitary latrines or privies should be permitted in areas not served by sewerage systems. In all other potential fly-breeding places, such as kitchens, eating places, abattoirs and dairies, cleanliness should be insisted upon to discourage flies and other vermin.

Control by chemical treatment. Flies may be controlled by residual spraying of the areas where they breed and rest. Where vehicles are available, the use of power spraying equipment is desirable. Space spraying machines are very effective in emergency fly control. Some hand-sprayers may be required to reach areas inaccessible to the machine—the inside of house, privies and other buildings. Insecticides, particularly dieldrin, should not be used in privy pits, since such use may result in an increase of flies.

Screening. Hospitals, foodstores, mass feeding centres, kitchens, milk distribution centres and similar places should be adequately screened with wire or plastic mesh to prevent the entrance of flies not eliminated by chemical control.

Other insects

Cockroaches and ants may infest kitchens, mess halls and toilets. Their control is primarily a matter of cleanliness. A 5 per cent chlordane dust or spray, used behind shelves and skirting boards, in crevices, under the tops of tables, sinks and stoves, around garbage cans, on latrine floors and in similar places will also prove effective in holding these insects in check. Lice, fleas and mites may be controlled by applying 10 per cent DDT powder to the hair and inner and outer clothing of individuals. Several applications should be made

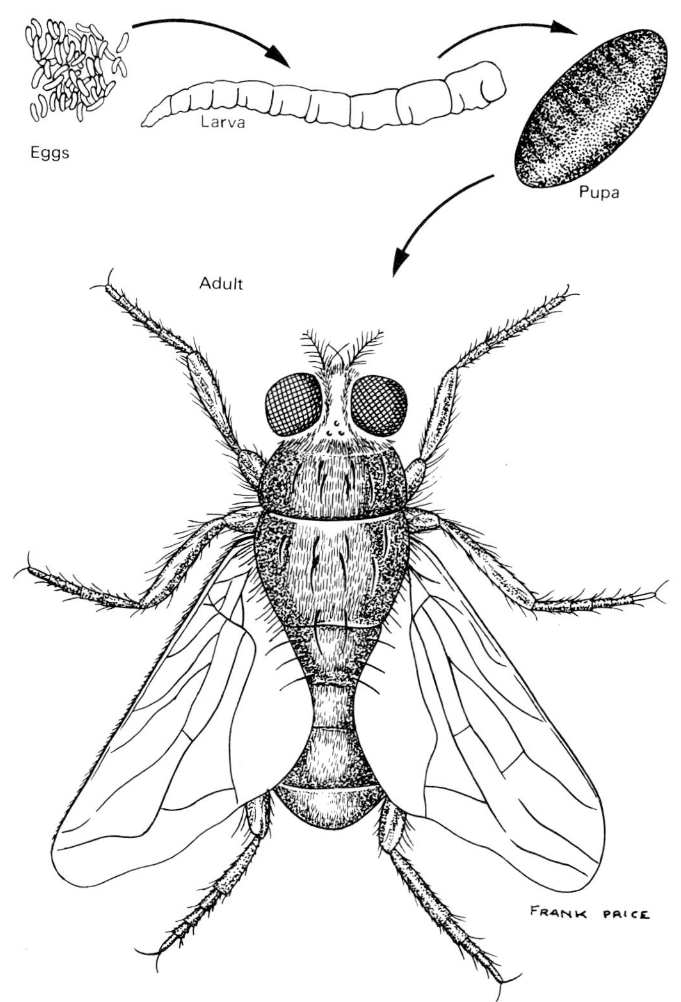

Fig. 11.27 The housefly.

at weekly intervals. Living quarters in camps and temporary shelters may be fumigated under competent supervision.

Rodents

When there is imminent danger of an outbreak of rodent-borne disease emergency action should be taken immediately. The following measures of control are recommended:

1. Dust rat-runs with 10 per cent DDT or some other tested insecticidal powder to eliminate first the ectoparasite in the rat. This is extremely important if there is a plague outbreak or where plague is endemic.
2. Extend dusting to other areas in the community where rats and fleas are found.
3. Conduct mass poisoning of rats at dumps and harbourages in the proximity of the populated area.

Where there is no imminent danger of outbreaks of rodent-borne disease, the following programme is suggested:

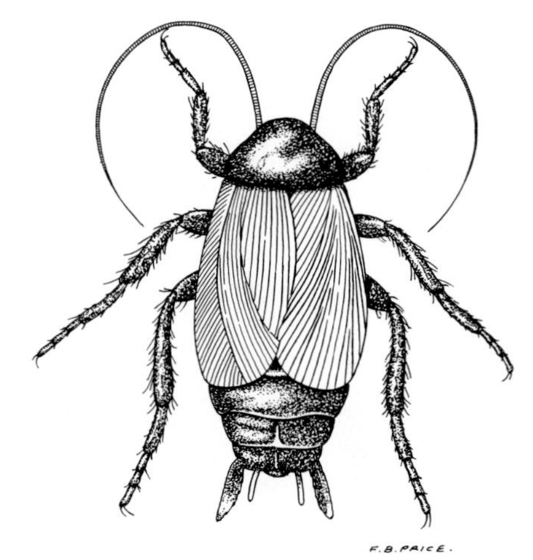

Fig. 11.28 Cockroach.

1. A master map should be prepared, indicating the sections where rat control is required. A well-trained sanitarian should be placed in charge and be provided with sufficient personnel and equipment to meet the requirements. The area should be divided into sections, each covered by a crew for dusting and poisoning.
2. Reduce rat populations with poison.
3. Extend and intensify the collection and removal of refuse within 2 km of the populated area. Enforce proper storage and sanitary disposal methods to deprive rats of food.
4. If the area is close to a port, enforce port regulations on rat control.

Health hazards and precautions

All pesticides in current use are to some degree toxic to man. Persons preparing pesticides, or applying spray or powder, should take care to avoid inhaling the dust, sprays or fumes, and should, as far as possible, prevent skin contact. Spray operators should wear protective clothing, such as rubber gloves, broad-brimmed hats and overalls. Insecticides spilled on the body or hands should be removed immediately with soap and water. Unusual signs of nervousness, dermatitis, and loss of appetite should be reported immediately; a medical examination should follow the appearance of these symptoms. Precautions that should be taken when applying pesticides are described in the seventeeth report of the WHO Expert Committee on Insecticides.

THE CONTROL OF INSECTS AND PESTS

Mites, fleas, ticks, lice and bedbugs of medical importance

Mites are minute creatures which may or may not have a waistlike constriction. The adults are eight-legged. Mites are related to ticks.

There are many different species of mites, but only a few are of medical significance. Forage mites can cause a form of dermatitis in people employed in handling stored food. Straw itch mites can also cause a form of dermatitis in people working with grain and cotton. In America, the red poultry mites can be implicated in the transmission of St. Louis encephalitis from man to man. The poultry mites are reservoirs of infection and pass the infection to chickens. The female mosquito feeds upon the chicken and then upon man.

The most common mites of any great medical importance are the trombiculae and *Sarcoptes scabiei* var *hominis.*

Sarcoptes scabiei var hominis (The human itch mite)

The *Sarcoptes scabiei* will breed only in cutaneous burrows in the skin of man. It is similar in appearance to the mange mite, but since the latter does not breed in the skin of man or remain on his skin for a long period, it is unlikely to be confused with the scabies mite.

Disease relationship

'Scabies' is a condition caused mainly by the female mites defaecating, eating, scraping burrows in the skin and producing acrid secretions. In addition to the damage done by the females, the males and young make secondary burrows and cause further irritation.

People not previously infested with scabies take about one month to develop a sensitivity which induces itching and may give rise to secondary infection. Others who have previously suffered an attack will develop a sensitivity in about 24 hours.

Parts of the body most commonly affected with an infestation are the breast of females, the scrotum of males, the buttocks, the wrist, between the fingers, the small of the back, the axillae, the knees and the shoulder blades. In infants, the infestation is likely to develop in any part of the body.

Recognition

The male mite is smaller than the female, but both are just visible to the naked eye. They are yellowish white, and almost spherical.

The anterior and posterior pair of legs are stumpy and widely separate. The anterior two pairs of legs have terminal suckers. In the female the posterior two pairs of legs end in long bristles, whereas the male presents terminal suckers on the fourth pair of legs. The dorsal surface bears a number of short spines.

Life history

The female develops one or two eggs at a time. She will lay about 40 large ovoid eggs during her life. The eggs, which are laid as she travels along the burrows, will mature in three to five days. From the transparent eggs six-legged larvae emerge, moulting within two or three days to become eight-legged nymphs. There are two nymphal stages before the adult stage is reached. The complete life cycle takes about eight to fifteen days and the average life span is about one month. In some cases the egg-carrying female may deposit her eggs in soiled underclothing and remain alive for up to 10 days.

Habits

The male mites find the females on the surface of the skin and this is where mating occurs. The young females often remain on the surface of the skin for long periods, or until mating occurs. Some pregnant females may lay their eggs away from the host and thus allow the eggs to develop into mites.

Trombicula (Harvest mites)

Mites of the genus *Trombicula* are sometimes referred to as 'harvest mites', 'red bugs', 'bete rouge' and in some Far Eastern countries as 'Kedani mites'.

Distribution

They are found in temperate, sub-tropical and tropical areas.

Disease relationship

When the larvae of trombiculae attack man, they cause a great deal of itching which is often accompanied by dermatitis. In some instances the dermatitis may be accompanied by a fever. Species of trombiculae, such as *Trombicula akamuski* and *Trombicula delienis* (Malaya) can transmit scrub typhus from man to man. The causative organism, *Rickettsia orientalis,* is communicated by the six-legged larval stage of the mite.

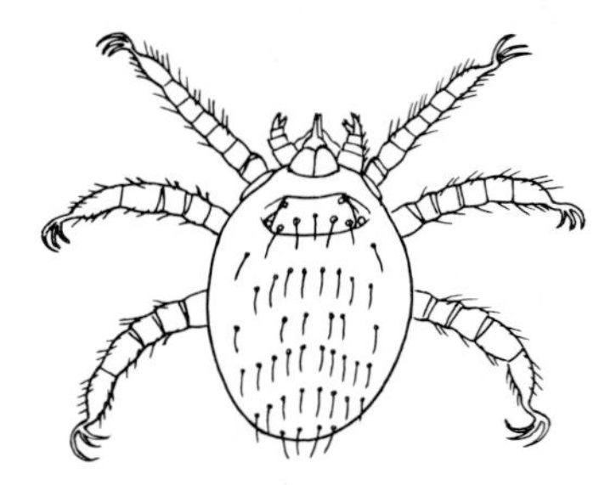

Fig. 11.29 Trombiculid mite.

Recognition of adult trombiculae

The adults are small, but easily seen with the naked eye. They are velvety, reddish and hairy in appearance. There is a noticeable waist constriction and the terminal segment of the first pair of legs is always longer and larger than other segments.

Recognition of the larva

Taken singly, the larva is almost invisible to the naked eye. Several larvae may, however, be seen in rodents' ears as an orange patch.

Microscopic examination of larvae

No visible waist constriction. The six legs end in claws. On the dorsal surface there is a rectangular shield bearing seven hair-like processes.

Life history

The female usually lays her eggs on the ground. From the eggs emerge six-legged larvae. These attach themselves to the hosts (rodents, birds, man, etc.) for a blood meal which may last several days. After this, they drop off and moult to become eight-legged nymphs. Another moult follows and then the nymphs become adults. There is one generation each year.

Habits

The adult mites are harmless to man as they do not suck blood although they are capable of passing on a hereditary strain of typhus in the eggs. The larvae may occur singly or in great numbers. They commonly attack people working in scrub or secondary jungle.

Fleas

Fleas are found all the world over as blood sucking ectoparasites of birds and mammals. They have no wings, are laterally flat and have well modified mouthparts for piercing and sucking. Fleas are of the order *Siphonaptera* (*siphone* = tube, *apteros* = without wings). More than 1000 species have been described, but only about 51 different species are known to occur in the British Isles.

Free running fleas

This is a very active group of insects with worldwide distribution. Included in this group is the vector of plague, the tropical rat flea or *Xenopsylla cheopis,* the human flea *Pulex irritans*, and the cat and dog flea, *Ctenocephalides felis* and *canis*.

Disease relationship

Bubonic plague is caused by a bacilli which is transmitted by the tropical rat flea. This disease has a high mortality rate.

Murine typhus is caused by rickettsiae which are transmitted by the tropical rat flea. This disease is usually referred to as endemic typhus and has a low mortality rate.

Cestodiasis. Infestations of the dog, cat and rat tapeworm may be transmitted to man by some fleas.

Accidental conditions. These may include damage done to the skin by constant biting of the flea and the secondary effects of biting. In households where there are heavy infestations of fleas, there is also likely to be loss of sleep, which may render the inhabitants accident prone.

Pneumonic plague. This may occur as a result of the individual contracting bubonic plague.

Recognition of free running fleas
Free running fleas are brown and present a series of hardened smooth chitinous plates, which are easily seen with a hand lens. In addition to the plates there are spines and bristles which incline backwards. The head is closely attached to the thorax with lateral, small sclerites. The two occelli, when present, are laterally displaced. In *Ctenocephalides canis* and *felis* there are rows of short, powerful spines at the lateral ventral border of the head, which are known as combs. The antennae in free running fleas are short and stout and have three evident segments. There is a four-segmented palpus on each side of the mouth. The thorax is made up of three distinct segments and carries the legs which are well adapted for leaping and clinging. The coxa above each of the third pair of legs is large and flattened. The abdomen consists of ten segments, the last three segments being modified for sexual purposes.

Xenopsylla cheopis
This flea is sometimes referred to as the tropical rat flea. It is light chestnut in colour before feeding and dark brown after feeding.

Microscopic examination of *Xenopsylla cheopis* will show that this flea presents a pair of occelli, together with a pair of brown structural vertical bars which are situated within the sternite of the midthoracic segment (mesothoracic bars). The *Xenopsylla cheopis* can be differentiated from other fleas by the absence of combs. The females are lighter in colour and show a curious comma-shaped organ (spermatheca) within the posterior of the abdomen.

Pulex irritans
This flea is often referred to as the human flea, though it is now more commonly found on pig farms. *Pulex irritans* has the characteristics of a free running flea but has no mesothoracic bars.

Life history of free running fleas
The life history of all fleas is basically the same, though the time taken to develop and the habitats vary considerably. The gravid female flea deposits several eggs at a time. These are ovid and pearly white in colour when laid on the host. The eggs are not attached to hairs or feathers as in the case of lice, so they fall to the ground. In about 48 hours or more (depending on climatic conditions), active legless larvae will emerge. The larvae move away from the light by means of head movements and the concentric rows of bristles covering their bodies. They bury themselves in cracks and crevices where organic substances can be found. At the posterior end of each larva there is a pair of blunt, ventrally pointing anal struts. There are three larval stages which take a minimum of seven days to complete. After feeding and developing, the third stage larva finally reaches a resting period and spins a cocoon around its body to pupate. The silken cocoon adheres to dust which readily acts as a camouflage. The pupal stage lasts about a week and then the adult flea emerges. In some instances, the adult will, however, remain in the protective covering and wait for a passing host to vibrate the cocoon. It will then push the silken threads away and leap upon the intruder.

A female *Xenopsylla cheopis* will lay between 300 to 400 eggs under suitable conditions. Her life cycle may take about three weeks under good conditions and her life span may vary from one to three months. The times taken between the various stages and the life span will depend entirely upon environmental conditions.

Stick tight fleas

These fleas are more often found in drier regions. *Tunga penetrans* (jigger fleas) are found in dry sandy soil around native dwellings in parts of the south American continent and in parts of India.

Disease relationship
Tungiasis, referred to in Guyana and other parts of the Carribean as 'chigger foot', is caused by the fertilised female burrowing into the skin of her host. In human beings the female burrows beneath the toenails of the foot and into the skin between the toes. Here the abdomen of the flea distends with blood and developing eggs until it is the size of a

small pea. Intense itching is caused, which may result in inflammation and secondary infection. In some cases amputation of the toes may have to be carried out and in severe cases with heavy infestation death may result from complications of gas gangrene.

Recognition of Tunga penetrans

These are very small fleas about 1 mm long. The legs are not as well developed as in free running fleas and their frons (forehead) is characteristically pointed. The thoracic segments are pressed together to give a somewhat telescopic shape. The male flea always remains tiny and weak in appearance. The female, however, swells to such a large size after fertilisation has occurred that the membrane between the second and third abdominal segments becomes highly noticeable.

Life history

The fertilised female burrows into the skin, develops rapidly, and soon fixes herself firmly into position in the lesion she creates. When fully gravid, the eggs are forcibly expelled and tend to stick to whatever material they touch.

About 100 eggs are laid and from these emerge larvae very similar to that of other fleas. The larvae develop into pupae and then emerge as adults. The time taken for development will depend on food available and environmental conditions.

Soft ticks

Ticks (*Argasidae*) are primarily found in sub-tropical and tropical areas, but can also be found in other regions suitable to their adaptability. Some species show preference for very dry areas.

Disease relationship

The bites of some species are very painful. Some ticks enter the ears of humans and may inflict severe damage. The most important disease associated with soft ticks is tick-borne relapsing fever (ornithodorous moabata) common in Africa. The disease is passed to man by the biting tick, or when coxal fluid excreted by the tick enters the punctured skin.

Recognition

Soft ticks appear rather 'raisin-like'. The mouth parts and false head lie ventrally and the usual difference in sex is slight. The size varies from 3 to 30 millimetres.

Life history

When not feeding, soft ticks are found in dust, sand, cracks and crevices. The eggs are laid away from the host. They are dark brown, globular and shiny in appearance. From the eggs emerge six-legged larvae which do not have spiracles. The mouth parts at this stage are more terminal than ventral. From the larval stage, development occurs and an eight-legged nymphal stage is reached. The nymphs moult and feed before becoming adults. The time taken to complete a cycle varies from species and is dependent on conditions. Under good conditions it may take about 12 weeks and the life span may last for several years.

Habits

Both sexes feed upon blood and in the act of feeding anticoagulin and toxins may be liberated. Soft ticks are 'ticks of the habitat', because they will only stay with the host to feed and then quickly retreat to a habitat. Some species can last for more than a year without a blood meal.

Hard ticks

Hard ticks are found in areas where the land is not well cultivated and there is some humidity. They are so named because they do not present the crinkled-like appearance of the soft tick and have a much harder chitinous exoskeleton.

Disease relationship

Bleeding caused by bites from these ticks does not easily stop because of the anticoagulin injected with the bite. The bite is, however, less painful than that of the soft tick. The female hard tick may acquire as much as 100 times her weight in one blood meal and, if tugged off whilst feeding, may leave the false head behind to give rise to secondary infection. Other classic examples of diseases associated with the hard tick are:

Tick-bite fever. Symptoms are caused by the bites inflicted.

'Tick paralysis' mainly occurs in children (S. Ethiopian regions).

Tick-borne typhus is an infection by bites from certain species, transovarially passed on by tick.

Q fever. This disease occurs in Australia, Spain, Italy and America. Infective faeces enter a puncture to cause disease.

Tularaemia is passed from rodents to man by the tick and is found in the Japanese Orient.

Recognition of hard ticks

The false head and mouth parts are visible from above. The legs terminate in 'sticky pads' (pulvilli). There is a large spiracle posterior to the base of the fourth leg on each side of the body. The males have a chitinous shield covering the entire dorsal surface, whereas the females have a shield covering the anterior part of the dorsal surface.

Life history

Unlike 'ticks of the habitat' (soft ticks), hard ticks spend the greater part of their life attached to the host. Several thousand shiny, light-brown eggs are laid away from the host by the female, usually in some sheltered place and over a period of days. After laying the globular shaped eggs, the female dies beneath her egg-mass. From the mass emerge many active six-legged larvae which do not have a breathing spiracle. After a series of moults, the nymphs become fully developed adults. The life span varies according to species and general conditions, but some species have been known to exist for more than two years without a blood meal.

Habits of hard ticks

The male hard tick does not engorge blood, but both sexes are blood-sucking. Such ticks are sometimes referred to as 'ticks of the host', as some species opt to spend their development from larva to adult on one host. In addition, they do not retreat from the host hastily as do soft ticks. Individuals usually become infested with hard ticks by sleeping on the ground in tick infested areas, or by coming into contact with animals harbouring them.

Lice

Lice are wingless insects of the order *Siphunculata* (or *Anoplura*). They are found throughout the world as ectoparasites of mammals. Lice are minute but visible to the naked eye. When viewed under a hand lens, they are seen to present tarsi which terminate in a 'claw-like' ending. The eyes in some cases are reduced or absent altogether. The mouth parts are well adapted for piercing and sucking and are retractable. Lice do not have cerci and their thoracic spiracles lie dorsally. There are more than 200 species in the order *Siphunculata*, but only two species is known to infest man. Lice are widely distributed throughout the world and in certain theatres, under suitable conditions, are responsible for the spread of a number of diseases. The most common is *Pediculus humanus* var *capitis* and *corporis* (the human head and body louse).

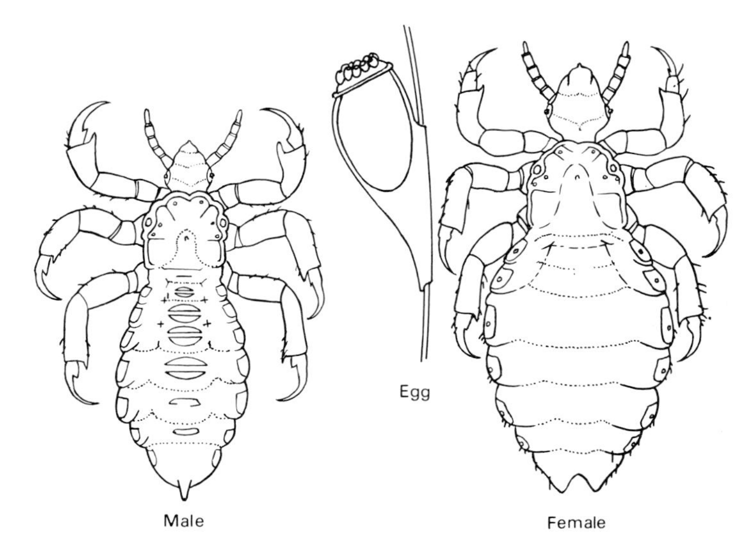

Fig. 11.30 Human body louse.

Disease relationship

Louse-borne relapsing fever. The louse becomes infected and remains infective for the rest of its life. It is a spirochaetal disease which is transmitted in the faeces or saliva of lice.

Louse-borne epidemic typhus. Contact in any way with infected lice may result in this rickettsial disease being contracted. Man is the reservoir of infection and the disease usually occurs in epidemic proportions.

Trench fever. This disease occurred during the First World War amongst men fighting in the trenches and has not been known to recur.

Murine typhus. Normally a flea-borne disease, but there is evidence to suggest that it may become louse-borne.

Dermatitis is due to persistent biting and itching.

Pediculosis is mainly confined to pubic regions and due to individuals being extremely lax in personal hygiene. The first stage in this condition is dermatitis, which is followed by the skin becoming rough, hard and itchy. Secondary infection is likely to occur if action is not taken quickly.

Recognition of lice

The human louse is small, less than 3 mm long, grey, with dark markings. The head and body louse is relatively elongated, whereas the *Phthirus pubis* (crab louse) is 'crab-like' in appearance. The louse is a very tough insect because of its elasticity of structure. The head bears a pair of five segmented antennae, simple, pigmented eyes and retractable mouthparts. The head is longer than it is broad. The thoracic segments are fused and bear six characteristic hair-gripping claws. The abdomen appears heavy and long. In the male the posterior of the abdomen is rounded and in the female it is forked. The difference between the head and body louse is slight, but the body louse is usually larger.

Life history

The fertilised females lay their eggs, which are oval and about the size of a pin-head, on clothing fibres or on hair, and deposit a gum-like cement to keep them from falling off easily. Under a microscope the eggs, or 'nits' as they are often called, present a 'lid-like' structure (operculum) with a series of nodules. These nodules serve as entry for air to the developing larvae. In about 5 to 10 days the larvae emerge from the egg-case by pushing the operculum away. After emerging the larvae become nymphs and must have a blood meal within 24 hours. After the first nymphal stage they moult and become second stage nymphs before maturing into adults. The larvae and nymphs show a resemblance to the adult forms.

The female louse lives about 30 days and lays about 250 eggs during that period. The eggs may remain viable for up to one month when separated from a host, and the time taken from the laying of the eggs to adult stage is usually two to three weeks. In the case of *Phthirus pubis*, only about 30 eggs are laid and are attached to the hair.

Habits

Pediculus humanus and *Phthirus pubis* are blood sucking. Body lice are apt to wander over the body and clothing whereas head lice tend to remain on the head. Lice are slow movers and it has been estimated that they can exist for about 10 days when detached from a host. When a host has a very high temperature or dies the lice will leave the body and try to find another host. When colonies present numerous males and only a few females, the colonies will die out because of the actions of the males. To ensure that total destruction is brought about by separation, infested clothing must be stored for not less than 40 days.

Bedbugs

Bedbugs—blood sucking ectoparasites—are found infesting the habitation of man the world over. In temperate zones they appear in abundant proportions, particularly in unclean homes.

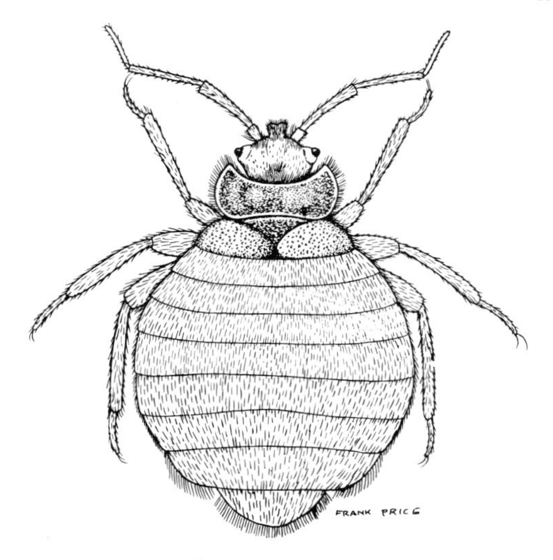

Fig. 11.31 Bedbug.

Disease association
The bites of bedbugs are painful and constant biting can result in individuals contracting a form of dermatitis. In addition to damage done to the skin, their nocturnal feeding habits can deprive the host of sleep which in turn renders him accident prone.

Recognition of bedbugs
Bedbugs are about 6 mm long, brown and oval. Unfed adults are flat and of a lighter brown than fed adults. They have a piercing and sucking mouthpart which, when not feeding, is hinged into a groove on the underside of the head. Bedbugs have prominent black compound eyes and are wingless at all stages. There are traces of wing cases which suggest that they once had the power to fly. Bedbugs in the adult and nymphal stages have 'stink glands'.

Life history
Several eggs are laid singly and intermittently by the female in crevices of furniture, in bedding and behind wallpaper. About 200 eggs are laid and these are glued to the surface on which they are laid.

The eggs are visible to the naked eye. They are approximately 1 mm in length, whitish in colour and present an operculum through which the larva emerges. The eggs hatch into larvae in seven days.

The larval stage is contrastingly small but bears a resemblance to the adult. Nymphal stages follow, which are similar in appearance to the adult, but smaller. There are five moults during the nymphal stages which take about seven weeks, before they become adults. The time taken will depend upon conditions; the cycle (egg to adult) may be completed in a month in good conditions.

The adult's normal life span is about 6 to 8 months, though some are known to exist in the adult form for more than nine months without food. There are about 14 generations in a year.

Habits

Bedbugs tend to hide in cracks and crevices where their habitats are not darkened. At night they come out from hiding and go in search of a blood meal. The feeding habits of adult bedbugs are short—the adult feeds for about 10 minutes and the nymph for an even shorter time. They are less active in cold weather but will feed on birds, bats, rats and any other hosts which may be available. Bedbugs are rarely known to defaecate whilst feeding on their hosts, though their 'stink glands' give off a highly noticeable odour.

Mosquitoes

The mosquito and disease

There are two main types of mosquito, the anopheline, which is responsible for the spread of malaria, and the culicine. The latter spreads the following diseases:

1. *Filariasis.* The later stages of this disease often produce the condition of elephantiasis, a gross swelling of the lower limbs.
2. *Dengue fever,* which is a painful but short-lived illness, not often serious.
3. *Yellow fever.* Once the scourge of the tropics, it is still a serious menace to international health.
4. *Encephalitis* is a serious disease caused by a virus.

By far the most important is malaria. This disease still accounts for 1½ million deaths annually. It is caused by an invasion of the body of the parasite *Plasmodium* which sets up a fever in the blood.

The life cycle of the malaria parasite

When the parasite first enters the body, it lives for about 10 days in the liver where it develops and multiplies. Once the parasites have developed they leave the liver and enter the blood stream. Each new parasite attacks and lives in a red blood cell and again multiplies. During this time the affected person suffers from the fever associated with the disease.

Transmission of the parasite by the mosquito

The parasite is spread from man to man by the bite of the female anopheline mosquito. When a mosquito feeds on an infected person, she sucks up (with the blood) the disease parasites. Once inside the mosquito the parasites again develop and multiply. When the mosquito takes a further blood feed in 10 or 12 days, she injects the new parasites into the blood of the healthy man. They make their way to his liver and the cycle begins again.

Breeding habits

Each particular type of mosquito has its own choice of breeding ground. All mosquitoes breed in water and may be found in any water collection—from tin cans to swamps.

The life cycle of the mosquito

After mating, the female mosquito requires a blood meal to mature her eggs. She then rests in a cool dark place for three to six days. The eggs are laid on water at a rate of 100 or 120 at a time. One female mosquito may lay up to four batches of eggs, but she requires a blood feed prior to laying each batch.

The eggs float on the surface for two or three days, then a small larva emerges from each egg. These larvae are very active and must come to the surface to breathe. The larvae feed on minute particles in the water and gradually increase in size. This stage lasts for four to five days.

Once the larva is fully developed, it changes its form and becomes a pupa. During this stage, the adult mosquito develops within the pupa case. The pupa does not feed but must still breathe at the surface. It remains in pupal form for one or two days after which time the adult mosquito emerges and the aquatic part of the mosquito life cycle is completed. On average, the time taken from egg to adult is 8 to 10 days.

THE APPLICATION OF INSECTICIDES

Residual insecticides are applied using a compression sprayer. The sprayer has a capacity of 8 litres and is fitted with a hand pump. The working pressure is 517 kPa (75 lb per square inch) and, when pumped to this pressure, the air compressed in the chamber will eject the full contents.

The sprayer is fitted with a hose and lance upon which is a trigger control. The nozzle is designed to spray at a rate of 5 litres/100 m^2. Detailed instructions for use are supplied with each outfit.

Safety precautions

BHC is a chlorinated hydrocarbon derivative. Malathion is an organo-phosphorous compound. These are highly dangerous to humans after prolonged contact or ingestion. It is vital, therefore, that only trained personnel should be allowed to handle and use insecticides. Certain regulations should be laid down regarding safety precautions and followed at all times.

1. Protective clothing

All persons engaged in the regular spraying of residual insecticides must wear protective clothing. The main requirements are slacks, long-sleeved shirts and a head covering. It is also wise to wear goggles, a face mask and gloves to give protection to the eyes, mouth and hands. Protective clothing must be laundered weekly and kept in good condition.

2. Washing facilities

Facilities for washing the hands must be available to persons using insecticides. Operators should bathe thoroughly at the end of each day's work and change into clean clothes.

3. Personal hygiene

Persons using insecticides should not eat, drink or smoke without first thoroughly washing the hands.

4. Maximum working day

No person should be employed in spraying operations using residual insecticides for more than five hours in one working day.

5. Skin diseases

No person having cuts, scratches, or any disease of the skin on areas likely to be exposed to insecticides should be employed on spraying duties.

6. Fire hazards
Insecticides should not be used near naked flames. Smoking is strictly prohibited during their use.

7. Power supplies
All power supplies should be switched off before spraying surfaces containing electric switches, junction boxes, electric points, etc.

8. Transfer and mixing of concentrates
Rubber gloves must be worn when handling, transferring, or mixing concentrates. Mixing must be carried out in tall containers using a long-handled mixer. Spillage on to clothing or skin must be removed immediately by dilution with water.

9. Decontamination of containers
Containers and insecticide spraying parts must be decontaminated when empty. Containers which have held insecticidal preparations should be rinsed three or four times in water and then thoroughly scrubbed. For malathion or other organo-phosphorous containers, the rinse should be 5 per cent washing soda. After rinsing, the container must be filled with the solution and allowed to remain overnight. Rubber gloves must be worn during decontamination procedures and a soakage pit should be provided for rinsing.

10. Protection of food
All cooking utensils, tables, working surfaces in kitchens should, if possible, be removed before spraying. Where this is impracticable, cooking utensils and surfaces must be thoroughly cleansed after spraying and before further use.

11. Security
Residual insecticides must be stored in a secure place.

DISINFECTION

Introduction

The purpose of disinfection is the destruction of pathogenic organisms as a means of limiting the spread of infectious disease. The theory of disinfection has changed drastically during the last 50 years, moving from the widely used carbolic compounds to the modern quaternary ammonium compounds (QACs). The emphasis has changed to current rather than terminal disinfection, the former playing a more important part in limiting the spread of infection.

This precis is aimed at assisting the relief worker in the uses of the various disinfection techniques that he may find are being used by other appropriately trained field workers.

Terminology in disinfection and sterilisation

In the past there has been considerable confusion concerning the meaning of the terms used widely in the field. The British Disinfectant Manufacturers Association published the following agreed definitions in July 1970 to avoid this in the future. The terms are classified below according to the following scheme:

Group 1. Absolute definite terms which are not equivocal and which embrace all the other terms in Groups 2 and 3.

Group 2. Classified definite terms which have restrictive meanings.

Group 3. Terms in common use which embrace one or more of those terms in Group 2. They are used in a more generalised sense.

Group 1. Absolute definite terms

Sterilisation. The process of destroying or removing all microbial life.

Sterilant (steriliser). An agent used in sterilisation which destroys microbial life including bacterial spores, therefore not to be confused with a disinfectant.

Sporicide. A *sterilant* but usually confined to the chemical agents.

Group 2. Classified definite terms

Bactericide. A chemical agent capable of preventing the growth of bacteria but not killing them.

Bacteriostasis. A state brought about by a *bacteriostat* in which bacteria are neither growing nor dying. This is a theoretical concept in terms of chemical treatment because the natural spread of resistance in any bacterial population is such that under any form of adverse treatment the weaker cells will die and the stronger ones survive, and even multiply. The net result over a prolonged period is, therefore, death or adaptation and growth.

Fungicide. A chemical agent capable of killing fungi, including their spores (also *fungistat, fungistasis*).

Tuberculocide. A chemical agent capable of killing tubercle bacilli (also *tuberculostat, tuberculostasis*).

Virucide. A chemical agent capable of destroying viruses.

Protozoacide. A chemical agent capable of destroying protozoa.

Amoebicide. A chemical agent capable of destroying amoebae.

Group 3. Terms in common use

Germicide. A chemical agent capable of killing 'germs' usually associated with disease.

Disinfectant. An agent used in disinfection.

Disinfection. The destruction of micro-organisms, but not usually bacterial spores: not necessarily killing all micro-organisms but reducing them to a level not normally harmful to health.

Antiseptic. A chemical agent used in antisepsis.

Antisepsis. The destruction of micro-organisms, but not bacterial spores, on living tissues: not necessarily killing all micro-organisms, but reducing them to a level not normally harmful to health. The term is analogous to *disinfection* (with which it is etymologically synonymous). It implies, therefore, lethal activity, but it is sometimes (and misguidedly) used in the static sense (but see *bacteriostasis).*

Sanitiser. A disinfectant with the connotation also of cleansing: used mainly in the food and catering industries.

Deodorant. An agent that masks or dilutes odours.

Disinfestation. The destruction of bodily ectoparasites and their ova. This term may be stretched to include the destruction of other parasites and vermin such as bugs and rats.

Methods of disinfection

Current disinfection

Indicates the application of disinfectants as soon as possible after the discharges of infectious material from the body of an infected person or after the soiling of articles with such infective discharge. All personal contact with such discharge or articles should be prevented before disinfection.

Terminal disinfection

Indicates the process of rendering the personal clothing and immediate physical environment of the patient free from the possibility of conveying the infection to others at a time when the patient is no longer a source of infection.

Routine disinfection

Indicates the disinfection from time to time of articles in communal use which can be regarded as possible vehicles of infection.

Disinfection may be effective by physical or chemical agents. Physical disinfection is carried out by employing sunlight, fire, dry or moist heat. Chemical disinfection is achieved by gas, liquid, or solid disinfecting agents.

Physical disinfection

Burning

It is best to burn infective articles of little or no value. Sputum and faeces may also be incinerated if the necessary facilities are available but the addition of combustible material such as oil, sawdust or shavings may be required to ensure that combustion is complete.

Radiation

All disinfectants act by destroying the bacterial protoplasm or by inhibiting growth. Physical agents, such as sunlight, ultraviolet light, electricity and ultrasonic waves, have a limited field of usefulness in this connection. Gamma radiation offers prospects of future advances in this field.

Dry heat

Baking at a temperature of 150°C to 160°C applied for one hour will kill all organisms and their spores. This is the method used essentially in laboratories for the disinfection of glassware and similar articles. It is of no use in treating fabrics, as textiles cannot withstand a temperature above 110°C without damage, and leather and fur should not be exposed to more than 70°C other than very briefly.

Boiling

Many articles, including feeding utensils, crockery, glass, towels and linen, can be disinfected by boiling, which destroys all except a few spore-bearing organisms in five minutes. The addition to the water of an alkali (for example 1 per cent sodium carbonate) will effect the destruction of the spores. Boiling the water will also kill spores quickly. Stains should be removed from fabrics by soaking in cold water or by other means, before these are boiled, otherwise they become fixed in the materials.

Steam

It is now definitely established, both experimentally and in practice, that the most efficient means of disinfecting bedding, and other articles capable of retaining and conveying infection, is by the application of heat. The best and quickest means of applying this is by steam. For the purpose of disinfection, it may be used either as current steam or saturated steam.

Current steam

Current steam is at atmospheric pressure and disinfects by passing freely at 100°C through the articles of the chamber. It should always be applied by downward displacement to ensure an even distribution of steam and temperature and to disinfect pockets of cool air. An apparatus using current steam is shown in Figure 11.32.

Saturated steam

Saturated steam is steam under pressure (i.e. above one atmosphere in contact with the water it is generated and at a temperature corresponding with its pressure). The temperature attained under the pressure used in disinfection is shown in Table 11.1.

Figures 11.33 and 11.34 show a large capacity steam disinfector using steam at a pressure of 103 to 138 kPa (15 lb/sq in). This type of pressure disinfector works on pressure steam with a contact period of 15 to 20 minutes. After steaming, hot air is passed through the articles to exclude any remaining dampness.

Tests for steam disinfection

Equipment available for testing apparatus used for disinfection and disinfestation is as follows:

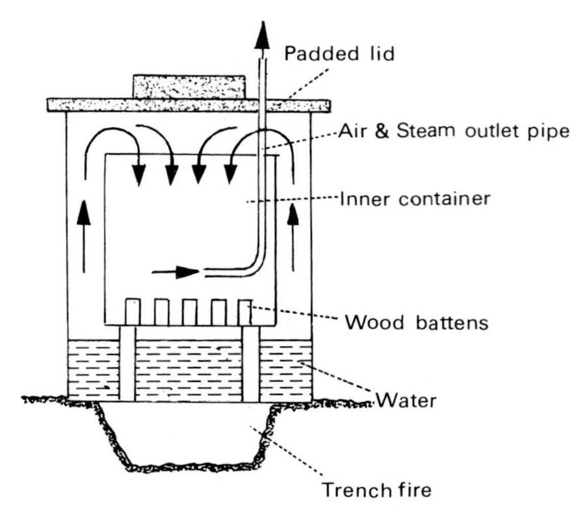

Fig. 11.32 An improvised current steam disinfector. Steam generated from the water in the outer drum passes over and into the inner drum, displacing the air therein downwards, to be expelled through the outlet pipe. The steam temperature is 100°C.

Brown's tubes are in two grades, each grade being identified by a coloured spot at the end of the tube. The tubes are made of glass, completely scaled, and contain a red dye. When subjected to a certain amount of heat the dye changes from red to green. The colour spot on each tube indicates for which apparatus the tube may be used and the temperature required to obtain the colour change. Tubes are placed indiscriminately in a bundle of blankets, clothing or other articles being treated. When the operation has been completed the tubes are checked for a colour change. If none has taken place then the articles must be re-treated until a satisfactory colour result (i.e. green) is obtained.

Spot identification involves using the black spot tube employed for equipment relying on the downward displacement of steam. Steam disinfectors Mk I and II and improvised steam disinfectors fall into this class. The temperature required for a colour change is 115°C.

The yellow spot tube is used for steam disinfectors of high vacuum type, such as the autoclave. The temperature required for a colour change is 134°C.

Table 11.1 Temperatures attained under pressure used in disinfection

Pressure kPa	lbf/in²	Corresponding steam temperature °C
0	0	100
34	5	109
69	10	116
103	15	122
138	20	127
207	30	134
276	40	142
310	45	144

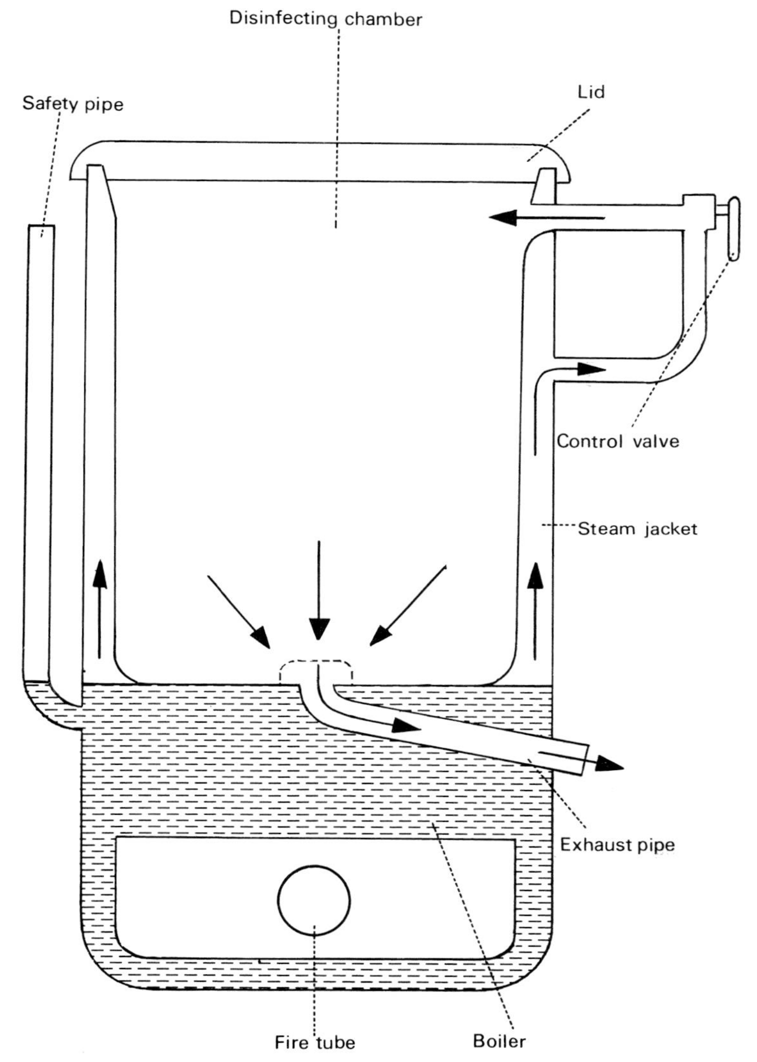

Fig. 11.33 A portable field disinfector.

Sterilisation test envelopes contain a small tablet of *Bacilli stearothermophilus*. These are destroyed at a temperature of 121°C when maintained for 12 minutes. The bacilli can survive 121°C for five minutes. The envelope is completely sterilised and the tablet placed inside. The envelope is sealed and not opened again until it is returned to the pathology department. The tablet is then cultured and any bacterial growth indicates that sufficient heat has not been obtained to destroy the organism. This test is usually carried out on autoclaves once a week to ensure that the apparatus is working properly. The envelope is placed inside a bundle of articles to be treated.

Sensitive tape is one inch wide and has faint lines running across it. When subjected to the correct air pressure a black dye is forced into the lines and these show up plainly. On examination of the tape any lines not dyed black indicate lack of air pressure in that area. Negative results indicate that air locks have formed in the articles being treated.

The Bowie-Dick autoclave efficiency test consists of two or more trips of sensitive tape placed on a thin sheet of paper. The tape is placed to form an X going from corner to corner of the paper sheet. The sensitive test sheet is placed in the centre of eight huckaback towels which have been folded into quarters, giving 32 thicknesses. These are then placed in a metal box with a top and base consisting of two sheets of perforated tin with a sheet of asbestos placed in between the sheets. The steam penetrates the perforated tin and asbestos sheet into the towels. After being subjected to the correct temperature for the minimum time, the box is removed and the test sheet examined. If the lines are all evenly dyed the test is satisfactory. If not, the test is repeated, and if it fails again the machine should be examined for fault.

Holding time $3\frac{1}{2}$ minutes at 134°C
12 minutes at 126°C

The test must be supported by a satisfactory time relationship in the chamber.

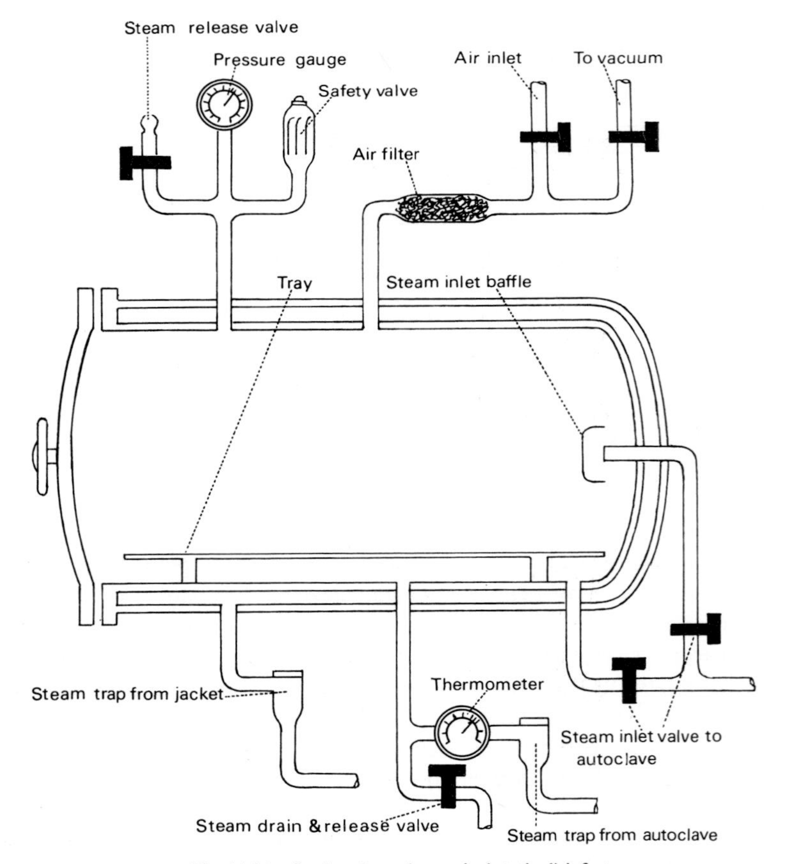

Fig. 11.34 Section through a typical static disinfector.

Chemical disinfection

The mode of action of chemical disinfectants is barely understood. The bacteria are killed in various ways: by oxidation, by coagulation or precipitation of protein, or by the formation of organic protein compounds and this is emphasised by the diverse nature of the chemicals which are effective. The ideal disinfectant has not yet been found, but the desirable properties in any chemical used are high germicidal power, efficiency in the face of organic matter, stability, ease of solution or emulsification with water, penetration, non-toxicity to man or animals and harmlessness to materials, cheapness and ability to be packed and transported in concentrated form.

Contact period

Most chemical disinfectants penetrate slowly even when used in strong concentration so they must be allowed time to act. Bacteria are commonly embedded in lumps of faeces or in masses of thick sputum and such matter should be disintegrated sufficiently to allow reasonable penetration. Most agents work more efficiently in a warm solution.

The efficiency of a chemical disinfectant

The germicidal power of a disinfectant is assessed either by the Rideal Walker coefficient or the Chick Martin coefficient, the latter having superseded the former in the laboratory although the R W coefficient is still quoted on commercial products.

The Rideal Walker test

This is the method of grading the germicidal efficiency of a disinfectant by comparing it with phenol and stating it in terms of its carbolic coefficient. If the coefficient is 10, it means that the disinfectant will kill the organisms of *Salmonella typhi* in the same time as a certain strength of carbolic but in a solution 10 times more dilute. This test is only of value when carried out under special laboratory conditions.

The Chick Martin test

This is a modification of the Rideal Walker method where allowance is made for the presence of organic matter which normally would deviate the disinfectant. It is now more commonly referred to than the previous test.

Chemical disinfectants

Cresol (black fluid disinfectants). Cresol disinfectants are the most useful for general purposes. Previously known as 'Cresolis', cresol is used in current, terminal and routine disinfection and has a R W coefficient of between 10 and 12. Occasionally, double strength cresol is issued with a R W coefficient of 18 to 20. In such cases, the cans are always marked 'double strength'. When used for routine disinfection, cresol should be diluted to 0.5 per cent solution. This may then be used for scrubbing latrine seats and shower floors, but should never be used for soaking clothing as it will stain. When used for current disinfection cresol is diluted to a 10 per cent solution, and faeces, urine, vomit and sputum must be immersed in this solution for not less than four hours.

White fluid disinfectant. This disinfectant was formerly termed White Cyllin. It should have a R W coefficient of not less than 18. White fluid is a fine derivative of cresol and in

Table 11.2 Recommended methods of disinfection

Item	Method	Dilution (%)	Contact	Remarks
Current disinfection (RAMC)				
Linen	White fluid	1	Overnight	To laundry steam disinfector
Napkins	White fluid	1	As long as possible	Straight to laundry. Remember bin.
Face masks	White fluid	1	Until evening	Then boil, rinse, iron. Remember bin.
Handkerchiefs	White fluid	1	Until evening	Boil. Remember bowls.
Baths	Cresol	1	As long as possible	Rinse before reuse.
Surgical bowls, dishes, etc.	Boil	—	5 minutes	—
Soiled dressings	White fluid	1	1 hour	Follow by boiling in soapy water for 5 min. Bins to be washed in 1% cresol.
Non-recoverable	Incinerator	—	—	—
Spatula	Boil	—	5 minutes	Keep in liquor boracis et formaldehyde
Nose and ear specula	Boil	—	5 minutes	Store dry
Stethoscope chestpiece	Antiseptic fluid undiluted	—	Swab	Between each infectious patient
Faeces, vomit, urine	Cresol	10	4 hours	Cover completely
Bedpans, chambers, urinals	Cresol	1	as long as possible	Rinse before reuse. Bedpans, urinals, etc. used for collecting specimens for pathological examination must be boiled after chemical sterilisation
Sputum and sputum mugs	Cresol	10	2 hours	Expendable, burn
	Boil		5 minutes	
Refuse	If for swill, boil	—	—	—
Refuse bins	Swill with hot water and slaked lime	—	Sprinkle	—
Articles falling to floor	Hot soapy water and cresol	1	—	Wash well
Dusters	Boil	—	5 minutes	—
Brooms	Cresol	½	—	—
Sinks and drains	Slaked lime	28g/l (1 oz/l qt)	—	—

Item	Method	Dilution (%)	Contact	Remarks
WC seats	Cresol	½	Swab	—
Band instruments (metal)	White fluid	1	Wash thoroughly with soap, disinfectant and water	Remove all traces with water before further use
Band instruments (woodwind)	White fluid	½	Wash thoroughly with soap, disinfectant and water	Bagpipes should be taken to pieces; leather valves, reeds and bag should be burnt
Uniform:				
Battle dress	Steam 34 kPa (5 lbf/in²)	—	30 minutes	Then iron and press
Denims or drill	Steam disinfection at 34 kPa for cases of typhus, smallpox, cholera, plague, glanders	—	30 minutes	Then iron and press
Head-dress	White fluid	1	Wash and swab	Dry in sunlight and iron
Footwear	Cresol	1	Wash with soap	Dry in air and sun
Bed, locker, drawer, chairs, bed table, walls, floors	Hot soapy water and cresol	½	—	—
Hot water bottle, mackintosh, sheets, air cushions, Dunlopillo mattress, chart board	Hot soapy water Lysol	1	—	Rinse well
Tooth mug, metal comb, bowls, instruments, thermometer, phial, metal toys, medicinal glasses, face flannel	Boil	—	5 minutes	—
Mattress, pillows, blankets, stretcher pillow	Steam disinfector, 34 kPa	—	30 minutes	Carry in sheets soaked in 1% cresol.
Sheets, pillow slips, bed jackets, counterpane, hot-water-bottle cover, towels	White fluid	1	—	Overnight to laundry
	Steam 34 kPa, for typhus, relapsing fever, cholera, smallpox, streptococcal infections, plague, diphtheria, enteric dysentery, glanders, tuberculosis	—	30 minutes	—
Thermometer, non-metal combs	Lysol	1	1 hour	Wash in soapy water first
Toothbrush powder, oil, ointment, magazines, papers, parcels	Incinerator	—	—	Care in transport; protect carrier
Ambulance interior	Cresol	1	Swab thoroughly	

all cases, except one, is used as a 1 per cent solution. At this strength fabrics may be immersed and will not be stained. The exception is that when used for current disinfection of woodwind instruments the concentration is lessened to 0.5 per cent. White fluid disinfectants should be more widely used than at present.

Lysol. This is a general purpose disinfectant used in hospitals as a 1 per cent solution. Lysol is a soapy solution of 50 to 60 per cent cresol and has a R W coefficient of between 5 and 10. Its uses are limited.

Antiseptic fluids (chloroxylenol). Chlorinated phenol is the active principle in such disinfectants as Dettol Strept and Zant. Liquor chloroxylenol (BP) contains 5 per cent of the active principle, Dettol 3 per cent, and Instrument Dettol 6 per cent. These disinfectants are now more suitable for wards and medical centres use than for general purposes. They are particularly effective against Streptococci but the germicidal power dwindles rapidly if the concentration of chloroxylenol is less than 1 per cent. They should not, in general, be diluted more than 1 : 3 or 1 : 4. Their activity is also reduced in the presence of organic matter.

Chlorinated lime (WSP). In the Services, this is usually termed *Water Sterilising Powder.* It is unstable and deteriorates in storage, although specially stabilised preparations can be obtained. Its chief use is in water sterilisation and the disinfection of vegetables. Its application as a solid around refuse bins and other foul sites is quite ineffective except perhaps as a temporary deodorant.

Lime may sometimes be used as a solid—for example, in the disposal of infected animal carcasses or infective faeces. A 1 per cent solution will kill all organisms other than spores in a few hours. It is a useful disinfectant applied as a lime wash for the walls of stables and byres, stands for refuse bins and other places liable to fouling. The wash is prepared from one part slaked lime to four parts water.

Formalin. This is a 40 per cent solution of formaldehyde in water. It is an efficient germicide and has the advantage of being harmless to leather, fur, rubber and fabrics which are affected by heat. Unfortunately, it has little penetrating power. The gas is usually stored in liquid form as formalin, or as paraform tablets.

Formaldehyde gas may be liberated from formalin by mixing 1 kg (2 lb) of WSP to 1 litre (2 pints) of the liquid for 273 m^3 (1000 cu ft). If paraform tablets are used, 26 to 30 tablets should be heated for 273 m.

Formalin liquid may be used for disinfecting footwear, by first diluting the liquid 1 : 8 with water, placing a cotton wool pad in each article and adding one tablespoon of the solution to each pad. The footwear should be placed in an airtight box for four to six hours and then aired for 24 hours.

Stabilised hypochlorite solutions. These are liquid disinfectants with an active ingredient of chlorine. They are more stable than a WSP solution. The most commonly used of this group is ‘Milton’ which is used for disinfecting articles such as feeding bottles.

Quarternary ammonium compounds. These compounds are cationic detergents. Examples with trade names are Cetrimide (Cetavlon CTAB), Benzalkonium Chloride (Roccal Zephiran) and Domiphen Bromide (Bradasol). Their germicidal property is due to interference with the mechanism of synthesis and cell division of organisms, which are killed by disruption of the cell membrane, inactivation of enzymes and precipitation of essential proteins. Their cleansing properties also augment their disinfecting powers which are, however, inhibited by soaps, phospholipids and proteins. They are particularly useful for cleaning and disinfecting glasses and crockery in bars and canteens. They are also of use in medical centres for disinfecting instruments, small items of ward equipment and baths. For these purposes Cetrimide and Benzalkonium Chloride should be used at 1 per cent strength.

Conclusion

Table 11.2 shows the methods used in current and terminal disinfection of some common articles. Used wisely it is a valuable weapon in the fight against communicable disease. Used unwisely it is both wasteful and valueless. Hygiene assistants working in the field must know and understand the benefits of good, and the pitfalls of bad, disinfection policy.

12. Shelter programmes

Following any disaster in which housing, sewerage and water systems are damaged, and large numbers of people are displaced, shelter may be of top priority. Even short periods of exposure can be dangerous.

Design of shelter for disaster victims is a popular project assigned to students of architecture, but the results are seldom field tested and assessed for suitability to any particular climate or cultural group.

The considerations listed below apply specifically to emergency shelter, but are typical of the type of assessment which must be made for any supplies before they can be considered suitable for use in a relief operation:

1. Expense and ease of transport
Local materials and labour should be used whenever possible and any imported materials should be cheap, lightweight and compact.

2. Ease of construction
Shelters should be cheap and easy to assemble. They should require the minimum of trained personnel to erect and no equipment not available locally.

3. Cultural acceptability
The structure should be as similar as possible to traditional housing design. The use of local materials is desirable.

Size must be appropriate to the society. It may be necessary to house together groups of families, large extended families, or a small nuclear family. So the unit should preferably be of variable size.

In a Muslim country a separate area should be provided for women. In many countries space for domestic animals should be included.

4. Suitability to climate
Insulation against the climate must be adequate. The degree of insulation provided may influence energy requirements of the population and in times of disaster may need to be considered in relation to food availability.

Wind resistance must be adequate. The population should be taught to adapt the shelter to changes in the weather.

5. Location and arrangement of shelters
It is important that an appropriate site be selected for an evacuation camp. This site should offer adequate drainage, water supply and space; it should not occupy cultivated land; it should be suitable for all seasons and isolated from likely insect and vermin breeding grounds.

Fig. 12.1 Using local materials for building temporary shelter (Bangladesh, 1972).

If the camp is likely to be inhabited for a long period the shelters should be arranged in such a way that they provide 'communities' within the camp with adequate space for agriculture and even light industry.

Services must be provided—particularly sanitation facilities, a portable water supply and waste disposal.

Access routes and administrative buildings will be required.

Fig. 12.2 Using local materials for building temporary shelter (Bangladesh, 1972).

Fig. 12.3 Using local materials for building temporary shelter (Bangledesh, 1972).

6. Long term effects

It is important that emergency shelters should not be sufficiently permanent that there is a danger of them becoming slums. They must be easily convertible, at a later date, into warehouses, godowns, animal housing, and so on.

7. Assessing the need

It should be remembered that many people in developing countries can rapidly rebuild shelters which are culturally acceptable. It is as well to establish at the beginning of the programme whether the need is for shelters or only for the provision of certain building materials. The latter are likely to be available within the country at a comparatively low cost.

On some occasions a nearby unafflicted community or an undeveloped part of the city may be able to shelter stricken people.

It is the duty of the assessment team to determine how much assistance is needed. It is the responsibility of relief and welfare authorities to provide any shelters which are necessary.

The canvas tent is the most convenient and most common type of emergency shelter. However, it does not stand up to cyclones.

Aluminium prefabricated shelters have been used in some countries for semi-permanent camps. Recreational camp sites near the place where disaster has struck frequently offer adequate conditions as they usually have sanitation installed.

The following points must be observed when evacuees/refugees are accommodated for more than a few days:

Tent camps

1. The site should be away from mosquito breeding-places and garbage dumps. It should have good access to roads.

2. The topography of the land should permit easy drainage; the sub-soil and found water conditions should also be studied. Land covered with grass will prevent dust, but bushes and excessive vegetation that can harbour insects, rodents, reptiles, etc., should be avoided or cleared.

3. Wherever possible, the area should be naturally protected from adverse weather conditions. Narrow valleys and ravines subject to floods are unsuitable.

4. Areas adjacent to commercial and industrial zones, exposed to noise, odours, air pollution, traffic jams, and other nuisances, should also be avoided.

5. There should be ample space for the people to be sheltered and for all the necessary public facilities. Roughly speaking, this means 3 to 4 hectares for every thousand people (30 to 40 m^2 per person).

6. The site should be within reasonable distance of a good and ample source of water.

7. The tents should be arranged in rows on either side of a road at least 10 metres wide to permit easy traffic. Between the edge of the road and the tent pegs there should be at least two metres.

8. Inside the tent there should be a minimum floor area of 3 m^2 per person.

9. There should be a minimum distance of eight metres between tents, so that people can pass freely without tripping over pegs and ropes. This spacing also provides a safety measure against the spread of fire.

10. Small tents for a few occupants are preferable to large tents for many people. This point should be taken into consideration when planning for emergencies.

11. The residual area of the camp should face the prevailing wind.

12. In cold weather kerosene stoves or other heating appliances should be provided, and people should be instructed in their use. Every precaution should be taken to prevent fires and explosions.

13. Natural ventilation is adequate for the tents.

14. Wind-proof kerosene or oil lamps should be provided. Lanterns with electric bulbs and dry batteries may also be provided.

15. Where there is no piped water, water tanks should be installed on both sides of the road. The tanks should have a capacity of 200 litres or more, depending on the frequency of refill, and should be so spaced that camp dwellers need not walk more than 100 metres to draw water. Several taps fixed to each tank eases distribution. It is advisable to put the water tanks on wooden stands of a convenient height.

16. Garbage collection cans (capacity 50 to 100 litres) with tightly fitting lids should be provided for every four to eight tents (25 to 50 persons).

Fig. 12.4 Using local materials for building temporary shelter (Bangladesh, 1972).

17. Privies or other types of excreta disposal installation should be located in blocks behind the tents.

18. One double-sided ablution bench (3 m long) should be provided for every fifty persons.

19. Drainage ditches should be dug round the tents and along the sides of the roads. Water supply points should also have adequate drainage to avoid mud and sludge.

20. When camp sites are in use for long periods, the surface of roads should be sprinkled with oil to keep dust down.

Fig. 12.5 Debris cleared away and a pharmacy set up within easy reach of everyone in the refugee camp.

21. Sanitation regulations should be laid down according to their feasibility in any particular situation and should be strictly observed.

22. The camp should be divided into two separate areas: a residential area and a community service area (mass feeding centre, field hospital, recreation).

23. For better management and control of communicable diseases, large camps should be avoided, or subdivided into independent units of not more than one thousand people.

24. The camp site should be cleaned regularly according to a pre-arranged schedule.

Buildings

If emergency shelter is provided within existing buildings, more attention should be given to ventilation and the removal of odours. The amount of fresh air needed is 30 m^3 per person per hour. It may be necessary to provide mechanical ventilation. A temperature of 20°C is desirable, but lower temperatures can be tolerated if warm clothing is available. The following points should be taken into consideration in relation to buildings used for shelter:

1. People sleeping on beds or mats should have a minimum floor area of 3.5 m^2, or 10 m^3 of air space. In rooms with high ceilings double bunks may be used.
2. A minimum distance of 0.75 m should separate beds or mats.
3. Emergency exits and fire escapes should be provided; the flues of stoves used for space heating should extend outside the building; overloading of electrical circuits should be avoided; lanterns and lamps should be so placed or suspended to eliminate danger; kerosene and gasoline should be stored outside buildings; clear instructions on fire hazards and safety practices should be displayed in conspicuous places; fire-fighting equipment should be properly maintained.
4. One wash basin should be provided for every 10 persons, or 4 to 5 m of wash bench for every hundred; there should be separate benches for men and women, and waste receptacles at each bench. One shower head is needed for every 50 persons in temperate climates and one for every 30 in hot climates. Floors must be disinfected daily.
5. For human waste disposal water-flushed toilets should be provided, if possible. Latrines should be located within 50 metres of the building but away from the kitchen and dining area.
6. One garbage can of 50 to 100 litres capacity, with tightly fitting lid, should be provided for every 12 to 25 persons.

Huts

These can be made in permanent, semi-permanent or temporary materials.

Permanent materials

Walls:	Burned brick Concrete blocks Stone	at least two metres high
Roofs:	Corrugated iron Aluminium Tiles Concrete slabs	

Floors:	Concrete	
	Brick	

Semi-permanent materials

Walls:	Sun-dried brick	at least 2 metres high
	Pisé de terre	
Roofs:	Corrugated iron	
	Aluminium	
Floors:	Concrete	
	Brick	
	Beaten mud	

Temporary materials

Walls:	Mud and wattle	at least 2 metres high
	Grass	
	Pieces of corrugated iron	
	Plastic material	
Roofs:	Grass	
	Palm leaves	
Floors:	Mud	

Beehive shaped huts (rondavels) should have a diameter of at least 12 feet (floor measurement) and the centre pole should be at least 8 feet high.

Cleaning of the camps

Each family should be responsible for the thorough cleaning of its unit/hut.

A rota should be drawn up of workers responsible for the cleanliness of kitchens, stores, wash-houses and latrines.

The units should be inspected at regular intervals to see that they are being kept clean and are not overcrowded.

Windows should be kept open when possible and ventilators kept clear of rubbish and packing.

Firewood should not be stored inside the rooms; a rough raised stand may be made for storing sticks outside the hut.

If cooking on charcoal is done inside the hut, the people must be told to keep the door open whilst the charcoal is hot: the fumes may have ill effects.

Simple temporary furniture and shelves can be made from old wooden boxes, crates, odd pieces of wood, petrol tins.

Rough stands should be made for cooking utensils to raise them off the ground.

Any temporary furniture made from branches or bamboo should be wiped over with a paraffin and water mixture to prevent bugs breeding.

A cheap cupboard for storing food can be made from wood and folded mosquito netting. Draped with damp material which has been soaked in a bowl of water, it will keep comparatively cool for a few hours.

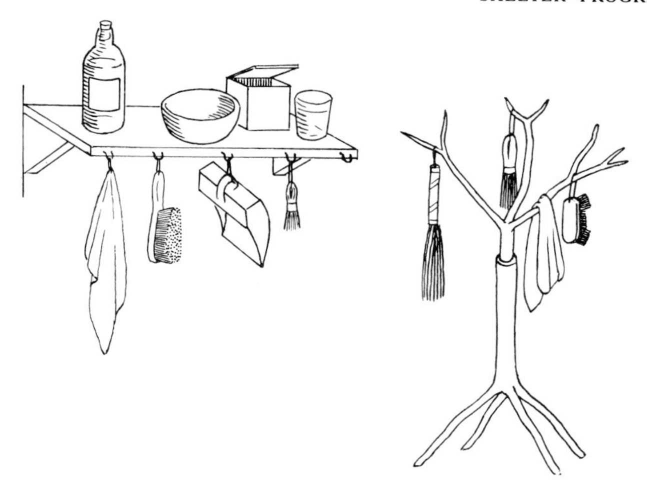

Fig. 12.6 Shelf with cleaning materials and apparatus hung from hooks; stand for cleaning equipment.

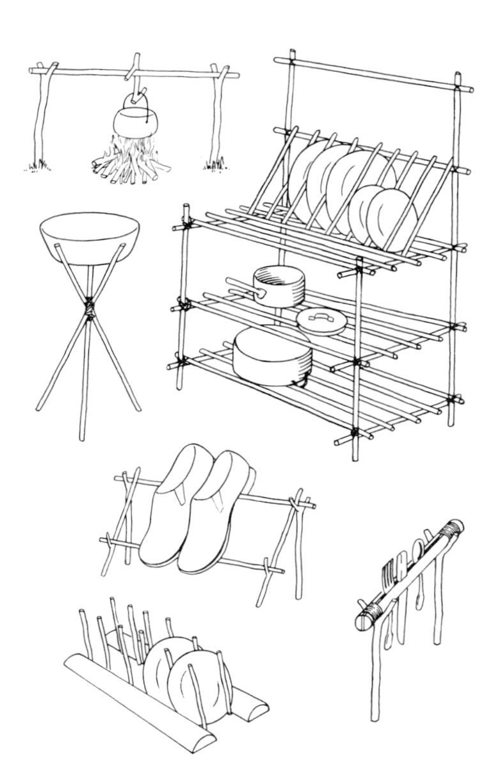

Fig. 12.7 Simple fittings which can easily be made from pieces of wood or bamboo. These include a pothook, kitchen dresser, wash-bowl stand, shoe rack, cutlery rack and plate rack.

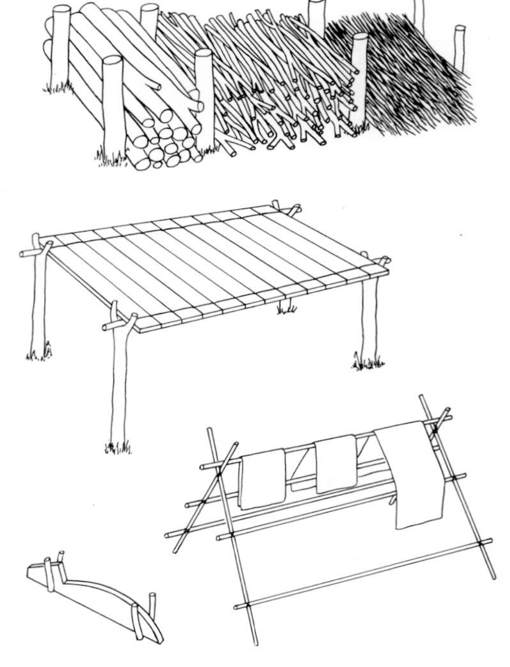

Fig. 12.8 A simple method of stacking firewood, a kitchen table, a mud scraper and a towel rail made from pieces of wood or bamboo.

Earthquake-resistant building techniques

A great deal of work has been carried out on earthquake-resistant design, but most of it is inapplicable to developing countries because the materials and structure recommended are far too expensive for general use.

Such designs are quite likely to be culturally alien and unacceptable to many communities and so each country must develop its building codes using local materials and traditional designs. Efforts have been made to devise simple, inexpensive methods of reducing earthquake risk to the types of construction common in seismic areas. However, it is still extremely difficult to enforce building codes in a poor country for various reasons:

1. Quality control of materials is virtually impossible when equipment is not available for standardising composition or testing strength.

2. Careful supervision of all stages of construction is necessary to ensure that the building code is enforced. This is very difficult and expensive to administer in a country where communications are poor and there are few suitably trained people for the work.

3. Usually the housing of the lower socio-economic groups manages to escape building codes, however rigorously these are enforced. A typical example of this was the squatting community at Quetta which sprang up just outside the city limits following the 1935 earthquake without any adherence to seismic building techniques.

4. Cultural resistance to modification of traditional building techniques is likely to be strong.

5. It is obviously not economically feasible for existing housing to be replaced by earthquake-resistant structures in developing countries, so the only time when building

codes can be introduced is immediately after a destructive earthquake when existing housing is destroyed and money for reconstruction is forthcoming. This is when earthquake risk is at its lowest. Another damaging tremor may not occur for a generation or more. It has been pointed out that grants or loans provided to the public for rebuilding purposes at times like this are likely to be spent on other things. In addition, plans for reconstruction of a town destroyed by an earthquake are usually slow to materialise and incompletely implemented, since money and enthusiasm rapidly run out. Meanwhile, haphazard rebuilding is likely to occur and there is often a migration of the young and mobile in the community to other areas which may have long-term deleterious repercussions. Measures for economic rehabilitation of the afflicted area should therefore be introduced.

Most of the problems outlined above could be solved by education of vulnerable populations and more research into appropriate building techniques. It might perhaps be worthwhile for research to be concentrated on low cost housing which would collapse sufficiently slowly in an earthquake for the occupants to get out safely. Towns should be sensibly planned with wide streets and provision for fire control and rapid repair of damaged water, power and sewage systems. Strict adherence to seismic codes is necessary in construction of roads, bridges and dams to reduce the risk of secondary disasters and to speed relief operations following an earthquake. This is well worth the expense since the economic costs of dam failure, for instance, are colossal.

Fig. 12.9 An igloo constructed of polyurethane foam. Equipment: a slowly revolving turntable, a hemispherical, inflatable plastic bag, polyurethane liquid and a spray gun. The inflated bag is fixed to the turntable and greased so that the foam does not stick. The foam, which sets hard within a few minutes, is sprayed onto the rotating plastic bag. The bag is then deflated, the igloo removed from the turntable and a door cut out. Painting will make it waterproof; it is extremely well insulated and nonflammable. A bag 10 feet in diameter will give 78 feet of floor area, living space for 6 or 7 people.

'Soft' and 'hard' technology

Some authorities believe that the problems of disaster relief should be tackled with the use of the most sophisticated equipment available ('hard' technology). However, there is considerable evidence that this is not the most cost-effective way of getting things done in a developing country. 'Hard' technology usually requires high capital expenditure, a reliable power supply and skilled operators and maintenance personnel. Sophisticated technology undoubtedly has an important use in relief work and research should be directed into efficient means of transport and communications for emergency conditions; medical and public health equipment which is simple to use and easy to transport; acceptable emergency shelters and improved methods of packaging, preservation and labelling of relief supplies. Information on types of equipment available for relief work is obtainable from the International Civil Defence Organisation in Geneva, and other relief agencies.

There is a growing body of opinion which considers that 'hard' technology may be unsuitable for both relief and development work, and that there is a need for development of 'soft' technology (also called 'intermediate' or 'appropriate' technology) which is relatively cheap and labour intensive, uses local resources and skills as much as possible, and which is operable within the existing infrastructure with minimal use of imported materials or expertise. Obviously, to be fully appropriate, this type of technology must be developed by the community itself. This is unlikely to be possible in a disaster situation and it should be remembered in all relief and rehabilitation operations that the services and the hardware imported into the disaster area are likely to have long-term effects on the community. It is thus of great importance that all the ramifications of any innovation be assessed, preferably by field trials, before being introduced into a new community.

Significant improvement in the health and nutrition of a community is likely to lead to rapid increase in population size which the land may not be able to support. It is therefore necessary to introduce family planning as an integral part of the health programme. Birth control is notoriously difficult to introduce in developing countries because of cultural resistance. Its successful application would be likely to have far-reaching effects on the social system.

13. Feeding programmes

Information on the nutritional status of a disaster-struck population is essential so that food may be directed to the most needy and wastage avoided. Various techniques for rapid assessment of protein energy malnutrition (PEM) have been developed. The term is applied to the conditions which result from protein or overall food shortage in children but, in times of famine, similar symptoms may be observed in adults.

The two chief manifestations of the conditions are kwashiorkor and marasmus.

The nutritional status of children, however, may not be representative of the population as a whole as cultural factors determine which sections of the community should have priority in times of food shortage. In most developing countries those who suffer first from malnutrition are young children, pregnant and lactating women, and the elderly. It has often been recommended that a scale of priority groups for food relief be set out and that aid be directed to young children and pregnant and lactating women in the disaster area.

Others recommend that a form of triage (i.e. sorting out) be practised in times of severe food shortage as more lives might be saved by directing relief to the healthy and moderately malnourished groups who need little food to survive, rather than to the severely malnourished whose chances of survival are small. It may also be advisable to supply food relief to manual workers and adults with dependants rather than to concentrate on malnourished children. This is emotionally unacceptable but should be considered, as the sickness or death of an adult often has serious effects on the dependants.

Once a scale of priorities has been decided upon and nutritional surveillance carried out to identify those most in need, the logistics of a supply operation and the problems due to culture, religion and customs have to be faced. It must be remembered that where group solidarity is high and united by bonds of religion or race, food taboos and social bonds may be retained until death.

The food must be acceptable. It must also be easy to prepare, store and transport. Packaging is important. If cooking utensils are not available it may be necessary to distribute cooked or reconstituted rations. Food given to young children should be eaten under supervision otherwise they may be starved by other members of the family.

Feeding centres must be conveniently situated and staffed by reliable local people. It is often difficult to ensure that those entitled to food relief get it. Ration cards are culturally 'alien' and it may well be that marking the recipent's finger is a better method. The feeding centre should be within easy access of the community. The food provided should be familiar, served in a familiar form and be palatable.

Food hygiene, especially at mass feeding centres, and the disposal of contaminated food and drink are vitally important. Advantage should be taken of every opportunity for education in food hygiene and nutrition.

The foods required to maintain an undernourished—but not malnourished—population are those with which the people are familiar. Where there is an acute shortage of food,

A NOMOGRAM FOR THE USE OF INTRAMUSCULAR IRON

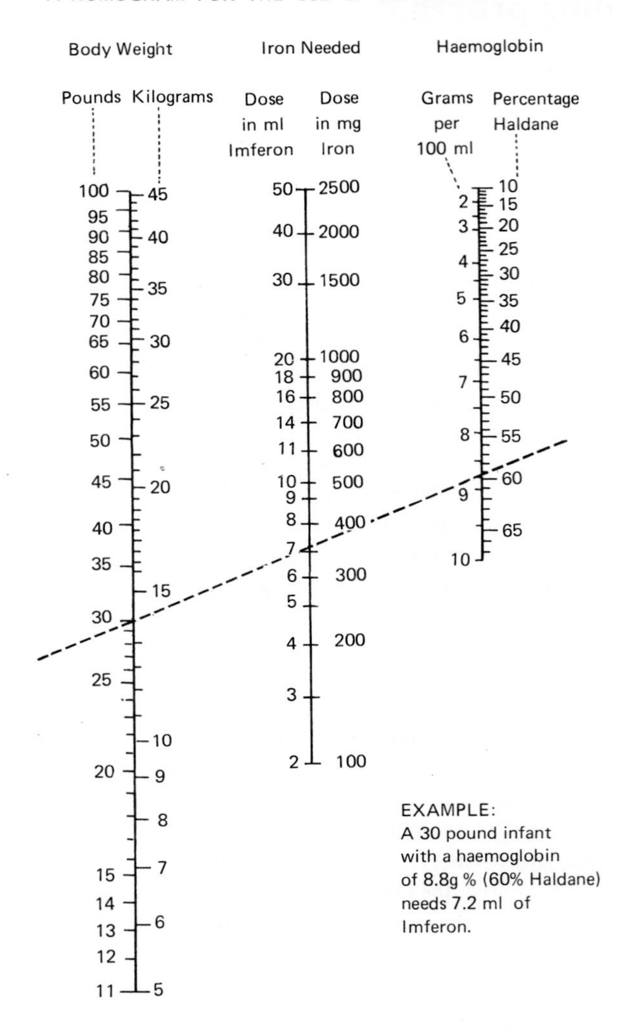

Weigh the child & measure his haemoglobin. Find these values on the scales & join them up with a ruler. The point where it cuts the central scale gives the dose of iron required. The dose in ml refers ONLY to those iron solutions containing 50 mg of iron in each ml, Imferon for example.

Fig. 13.1

nutritional value is not of first importance. It is far better to supply the staple diet without additives of alien protein or supplementary vitamins.

In times of chronic food shortage, endemic and specific vitamin deficiencies require long-acting vitamin therapy. Anaemia is often a widespread problem in countries where there is hookworm infestation and malaria. These conditions may be treated at the same time as other nutritional deficiencies.

It is usually more cost-effective to buy relief food locally than to import it from other countries, depending on the resources and transport available. Certainly, high protein food mixes are expensive and often the ingredients are available locally and may be made up in the field at a much lower cost.

Treatment of severe PEM requires a liquid diet and various formulae have been recommended. Dried skim milk is usually the chief constituent but it is important that adequate kilojoules be supplied to ensure that the protein is not catabolised. (Fat is an economical source of high energy but it is recommended that no more than 15 per cent of the kilojoules be supplied in this form.)

Frequent small feedings are necessary, and, in severe instances, these may be administered by naso-gastric tube. Hypoglycaemia and cardiac failure are the commonest causes of death from PEM.

The administration of rehydration fluids is of vital importance, especially in young children. The high mortality rate of children under 5 years of age is often a result of the combined effects of malnutrition, infection and parasite infestation.

Famine

Food shortages may come about as a result of political upheavals or from natural causes such as pests, drought or flood. Famine differs from other disasters in that it is usually predictable well in advance, and is often—at least theoretically—preventable.

In famine situations there is unequal distribution of resources between geographical areas and between socio-economic groups. The disaster could often, therefore, be avoided by equitable distribution of resources. In practice, because of cultural, political and economic factors, as well as a shortage of information and the presence of logistic difficulties, this is rarely possible.

However, disasters could be greatly alleviated by pre-planning on the part of the government of a country or by an agency. If resources were mapped out, relief agencies could purchase food supplies locally. If possible, appropriate food should be stockpiled. Price controls should be imposed at the first signs of food shortage.

BASICS OF NUTRITION

In the paragraphs which follow basic principles only are stated and are principally limited to those components of the diet which are commonly taken into account in the devising of a new or modified ration scale, or in assessing the adequacy of an existing dietary regime.

Details of physiology and information regarding other vitamins, mineral salts, trace elements, etc., should be sought in standard text books.

Nutrients

Food is any solid or liquid which, when swallowed, provides material for:

Production of heat and energy;

Growth, repair and reproduction;

Regulation of these.

The materials thus provided are called nutrients. They are:

a. Proteins, carbohydrates and fats (the proximate principles);

b. Minerals, including trace elements, vitamins and water.

A CHART FOR MILK DIETS IN PCM

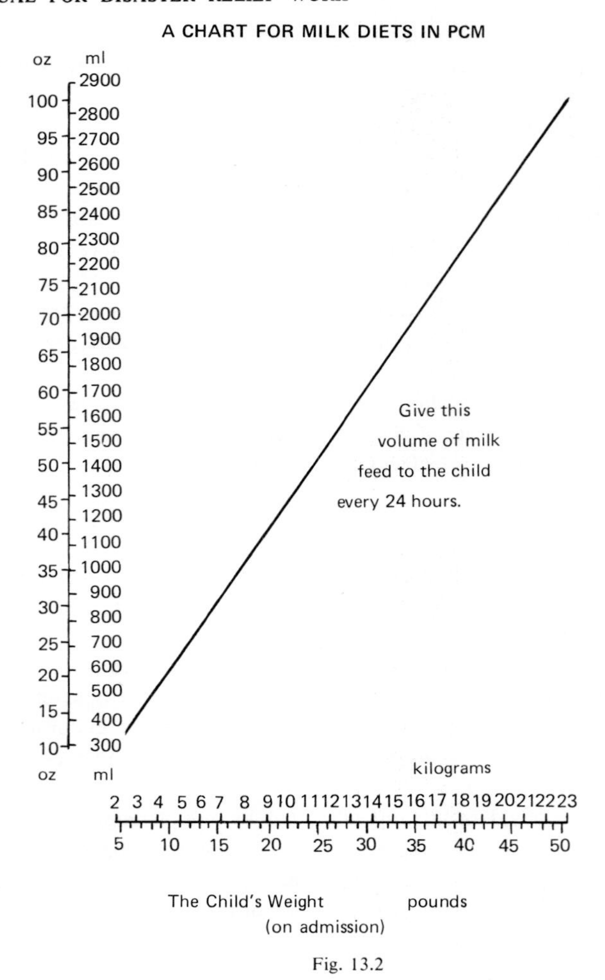

Fig. 13.2

Proteins

Sources: Animal and vegetable.

Function: Growth, repair and reproduction (provision of energy is 17 kJ (4 kcal/g)).

Composition: Chains of amino acid molecules containing carbon, hydrogen, oxygen and nitrogen, some also contain sulphur or phosphorus (note that proteins are the sole supply of nitrogen and sulphur).

Amino acids: Plants can synthetise from simple chemicals; animals, including man, cannot. Therefore man is dependent for supply of amino acids on plants or other animals. Man has powers of conversion of amino acids within the body from one type to another, but these are limited. This leads to the concept of *essential amino acids*, that is, amino acids which the body cannot, by conversion, make for itself and which therefore must be provided ready-made in the diet, e.g. lysine, tryptophane.

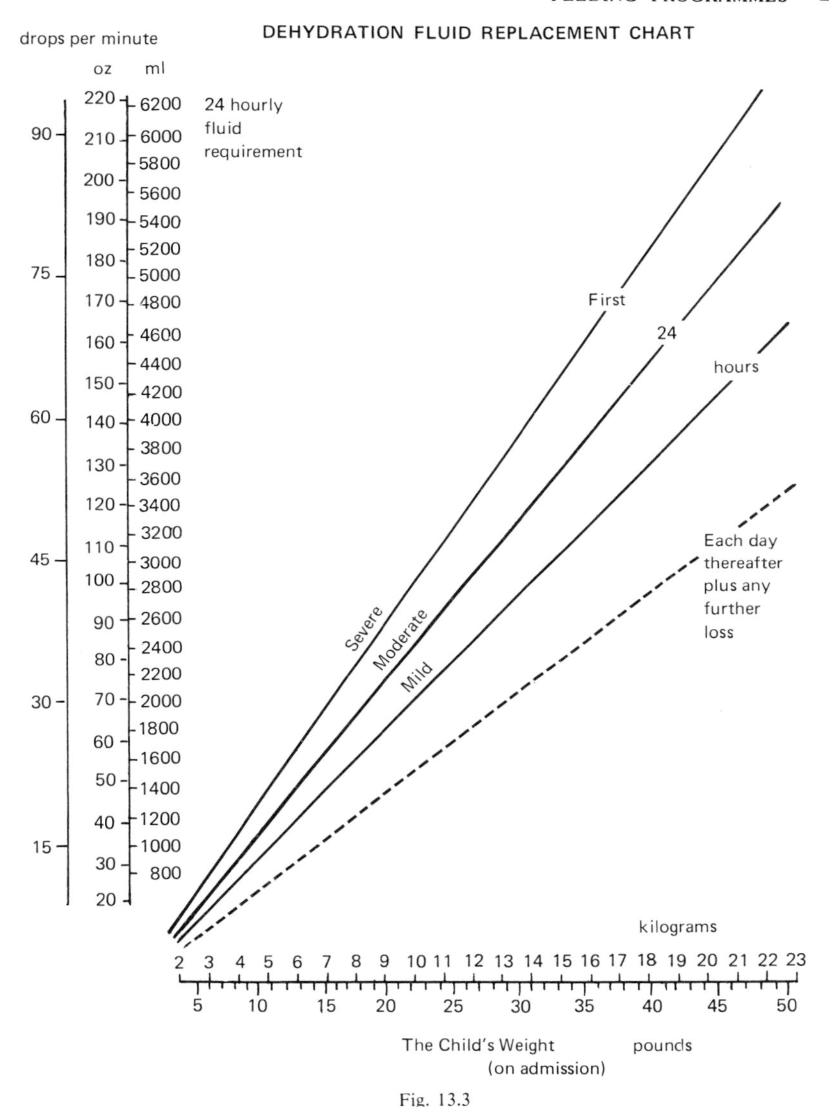

Fig. 13.3

Nutritional value: Depends largely on the relation of amino acids within the protein molecules to those required by the body, and in particular the essential amino acids.

Biological value: Egg albumin and milk contain all the essential amino acids in correct proportion and are of high biological value. Maize is deficient in both lysine and tryptophane and is of poor biological value. The degree of biological value is also related to the net utilisation of particular proteins.

Supplementary value of proteins. Animal protein is, in general, of higher biological value than vegetable protein, but it is important not to completely discard vegetables as poor sources. By a combination of two or more vegetable sources it is possible to provide the essential amino acids in the correct proportion. For maximum effect the mixture, e.g. pulses and cereals, should be taken at the same meal. Generally, this device has greater civilian than military application, but it may be of importance in making up LEP ration scales.

Requirements: Sufficient to provide 11 to 14 per cent of the total energy value of the diet. The higher values are for the special requirements of childhood, adolescence, pregnancy and lactation (the vulnerable groups).

Carbohydrates

Source: Principally vegetable, but some in milk.

Function: Energy production (17 kJ), surplus to immediate requirements stored as fat.

Protein-sparing action: Protein *can* produce energy, but this is wasteful both physiologically and economically. Therefore, a balanced diet should include enough carbohydrates to avoid waste of protein and to free it for its proper role of growth, repair and reproduction.

Composition: Mono-, di- and poly-saccharides, the latter mainly in the form of starch. Cellulose is not available as a source of energy, but valuable as roughage.

Requirements: Depends on energy expenditure on balanced diet, performing moderate work, say 400 g per day.

Fats

Sources: Animal or vegetable. Mineral oils cannot be utilised by the body.

Function: Energy production, energy reserve 37 kJ. Acid to palatability. Has satiety value. Is a source of fat-soluble vitamins.

Composition: Mixture of triglycerides.

Requirements: Largely linked with national food preference and practice. (In British diet, 30 to 40 per cent of total kilojoules is derived from fat.) High energy value useful when devising a low weight/high energy ration.

Minerals

(In addition to those appearing as an integral part of the proximate principles.)

Sodium

Sources: As sodium chloride, in the form of prepared salt as well as in animal and vegetable products.

Function: Concerned with growth, formation of bones and teeth, blood coagulation and muscle function. In association with Vitamin D deficiency concerned in aetiology of rickets, osteomalacia and dental disease.

Requirements: Related to building needs. Adults need 800 mg per day (increased in childhood, adolescence, pregnancy and lactation).

Iron

Sources: Skeletal muscle, liver, kidney, wholemeal cereals, vegetables.

Function: Haemoglobin synthesis and tissue iron.

Requirements: 12 mg per day; increased during pregnancy and lactation, because only about 10 per cent of ingested iron is absorbed from the intestines.

Fluorine

Sources: Drinking water.

Function: Prevention of dental caries at a strength of 1 to 1.5 ppm in drinking water when taken in childhood and adolescence. Anything over this level may cause fluoris with mottling and discolouration of the teeth. Also effective as a topical application.

Other minerals and trace elements
Potassium, phosphorus, iodine, magnesium, sulphur, copper, cobalt, zinc, manganese and selenium.

Vitamins

Vitamins are general organic compounds which are required for normal growth and maintenance of animal life and which are effective in small amounts.

Provision in diet: Ready-made as provitamins, i.e. substances occurring in food, not vitamins in themselves but capable of conversion into vitamins in the course of digestion and metabolism. Biosynthesis in the gut.

Main groups
Fat soluble—'A' 'D' 'E' and 'K'
Water soluble—'B' complex and 'C'

Stability: Considerable variation in resistance to heat, drying, etc.

Vitamin A

Sources: Carotene (a provision)—fruits and vegetables, especially of the red and yellow varieties. Preformed vitamin A—milk, butter, egg yolk, fish liver oil. Conversion of carotene to vitamin A is not complete. For convenience in scales of nutritive values, the total carotene in foods is converted to and expressed in International Units (IU).

Deficiency: Associated with night blindness, degeneration and keratinisation of epithelial cells, phrynoderma and xerophthalmia.

Requirements: –2500 IU daily.

Vitamin D

Artificial sources: Calciferol, manufactured by exposing ergosterol (found in ergot and other plants) to ultraviolet light.

Natural sources: Produced by the irradiation by sunlight of 7-dehydrocholesterol, found in animal fats under the skin.

Deficiency: Associated with ricketts and osteomalacia.

Requirements: Adults need no extra supply except possibly during pregnancy. Infants and young children, depending on diet and environmental conditions, need up to 400 IU daily.

Vitamin B complex

Includes vitamin B_1 (thiamine), riboflavin, nicotinic acid, B_{12} (cyanocobalamine), pyridoxin, pantothenic acid, biotin, folic acid, choline. Only the first three will be considered here.

Vitamin B_1 (thiamine)

Sources: Germ and outer coats of cereals, pulses, yeast. Lesser amounts in meat, milk and vegetables.

Deficiency: Associated with an accumulation of pyruvic acid in the blood and tissues—a feature of beriberi. Directly linked with energy expenditure and carbohydrate intake.

Stability: Roasting and stewing meat may reduce thiamine content by 20 to 30 per cent. Vegetables may lose 30 to 40 per cent in cooking. Apart from stability, serious losses of the vitamin occur (with other members of the 'B' complex and also protein) in the milling of cereals.

Requirements: 0.4 mg per 4.18 MJ (1000 kcal) daily.

Riboflavin

Sources: Yeast, fish roe, fruit, leafy vegetables, meat, liver, eggs, kidney.

Deficiency: Associated with the ariboflavinosis syndrome—stomatitis, redness of soft palate, and dermatitis of face and scrotum. Note that it is rare to see this syndrome by itself in the absence of evidence of other vitamin deficiency.

Stability: Cooking losses may be of the order of 30 to 40 per cent in vegetables and 13 per cent in fruit. Roasting or stewing of meat may result in a loss of about 30 per cent.

Requirements: 0.6 mg per 4.18 MJ daily.

Nicotinic acid (P P factor)

Sources: Meat, liver, milk, cheese, cereals and eggs.

Deficiency: Associated with pellagra—dermatitis, dementia and diarrhoea.

Stability: Up to 40 per cent lost in cooking.

Requirements: 4.0 mg per 4.18 MJ daily.

Vitamin C (ascorbic acid)

Sources: Fresh fruits (especially citrus), vegetables.

Deficiency: Causes scurvy.

Stability: It is the least stable of all vitamins; destruction is accelerated by a high temperature/time complex in cooking, alkalis and by prolonged storage of fruit and vegetables in bad conditions leading to wilting. In the worst conditions, losses may amount to 70 per cent.

Requirements: 20 mg per day.

General note on cooking losses of water soluble vitamin
Apart from losses due to heat, alkalis, etc., there may be considerable loss of vitamin in cooking waste if this is not consumed. Therefore, as little water as possible should be used, food should be cooked as quickly as possible and the cooking water used for soup.

DIET REQUIREMENTS

After taking into account losses in preparation and cooking it must provide in a balanced form:

Sufficient energy for:
- Basal metabolism
- Specific dynamic action
- Energy expenditure

Sufficient nutrients for:
- Growth (especially in the young)
- Repair (especially in illness or after injury)
- Metabolic regulation

Other factors. A diet must be:
- Digestible, varied, and capable of being attractively cooked and served

Economical
Locally available
Flexible, to allow for temporary non-availability
Acceptable on racial and religious grounds
Sufficiently bulky to satisfy the appetite

ENERGY REQUIREMENTS

Basal metabolism (BMR). The energy required to promote the activity of the vital organs and to maintain body temperature, in complete rest. Approximately equal to 167 kJ/m^2 of body surface per hour (290 kJ for an average sized man).

Specific dynamic action (SDA). When food is taken by a person at rest, there is a greater production of heat than would theoretically be expected from the amount of food taken. In the case of protein, the increase is around 30 per cent and with carbohydrate or fat, around 5 per cent. This phenomenon is said to contribute towards the maintenance of body temperature. When assessing the energy requirements of an individual or of a group, SDA is taken into account in regard to BMR.

Energy expenditure reflects the balance of total kilojoules required (in addition to BMR and SDA) to carry out everyday working and recreational activities.

Average energy requirements. The Food and Agriculture Organisation (FAO) of the United Nations (UN) have postulated a *Reference Man* and *Reference Woman* (Table 13.1).

Table 13.1 Average energy requirements (Food and Agriculture Organization of the United Nations)

Reference man *Weight:* 65 kg *Age*: 25 years	*Mean environmental temperature*: 10°c	
Activity	kJ/day	kcal/day
8 hours working (mainly standing)	5 040	1 200
8 hours non-occupational		
1 hour washing, dressing, etc.	750	180
$1\frac{1}{2}$ hours walking about	2 000	480
4 hours sitting	1 550	370
$1\frac{1}{2}$ hours recreation	1 970	470
8 hours rest in bed at BMR	2 100	500
	13 410	3 200
Reference woman 9 660 kJ/day (2 300 kcal/day)		

These are only reference figures, and certain variables must be taken into account to produce a range:

Man: 2400–4000 cal/day (9.9 MJ–16.6 MJ)
Woman: 1700–2900 cal/day (7 MJ–12 MJ)

The soldier on active service comes into the upper bracket of the male range.

Variables affecting calorie requirements

1. Physical activity.
2. Body size and weight.
3. Age.
4. Climate. Recent studies have shown that, contrary to old established belief, energy requirements are increased in hot as opposed to temperate climates, and only marginally increased, if at all, in cold climates and at high altitudes.

NUTRIENT REQUIREMENTS

The following approximation will serve as a working guide:

Protein	100 g = 1680 kJ (400kcal) (13 per cent of total energy requirement)
Fat	120 g = 4540 kJ (1080 kcal) (35 per cent of total energy requirements)
Carbohydrates	400 g = 6720 to 12 940 kJ (1600 to 3080 kcal) (52 per cent of total energy requirements)

Such a diet, with the appropriate proportion of vitamins and mineral salts, comes close to the requirements of the *Reference Man*—a moderately active worker.

Gross net nutritive values

Many foods which are purchased or supplied have a certain amount of inedible waste—bone in meat, vegetable peelings, etc. In addition, some waste occurs in preparation, cooking and serving of the edible portion. These losses are normally assessed at 10 per cent.

The loss of vitamins in processing, storage and preparation must be taken into account.

FOOD SANITATION

Food warehouses, wholesale and retail food shops, restaurants, etc. are frequently destroyed or damaged in a disaster, and much deterioration and spoilage of stored foodstuffs is to be expected. The interruption of electricity services may affect the operation of refrigeration plants, cold stores, and food processing plants, thus contributing to additional wastage of food. An acute shortage of food may result from such damage, and outside help may be needed for feeding the afflicted population until the normal food supply is re-established.

Under emergency conditions the efficient control of food quality becomes difficult: laboratory services may not be available, and food inspection will have to be based on the appearance, physical condition, taste and smell of food in relation to normal characteristics and keeping quality. Careful examination is required to determine whether food is unaffected and still fit for human consumption, impaired but still usable for certain purposes such as animal feeding, or completely spoilt and requiring immediate safe disposal. The condition of containers, particularly those made of perishable or breakable materials such as cardboard, paper, sacking or glass, offers a preliminary guide for this selection; a more thorough examination should follow. The sale of damaged food must be prevented, and the full co-operation of food retailers and distributors must be ensured.

Floods, in particular, are responsible for widespread spoilage and contamination of food. Flood water carries filth and pathogenic organisms from the ground surface, sewage systems, cesspools, and barnyards. To prevent typhoid fever and other gastro-intestinal infections, all foods that have been in contact with flood water and not contained in hermetically sealed tins must be destroyed. Even food in glass jars and bottles is suspect, as contamination may seep through crown caps and screw tops. Intact but soiled tins must be cleaned and disinfected before opening.

Food supplied from outside the disaster area by official agencies and voluntary relief societies must come from reliable sources, and should be inspected for deterioration during transit. The first supplies should consist of individual rations of pre-cooked assorted foods in sealed watertight wrappings or boxes, which can be distributed rapidly and used during the period when normal cooking and feeding services are impracticable. The composition of these emergency rations should be selected on the basis of concentration, nutritive value, palatability, and keeping properties.

Following in the wake of the disaster, cooked food will be distributed in individual packs or through mobile canteen units, but as soon as possible the feeding programme should develop along two main lines: (*a*) the provision of food for those who have facilities for preparing and cooking their meals under their own initiative and responsibility, and (*b*) the arrangement by the relief organisation of mass feeding services for those who lack such facilities.

Mass feeding services

Unless proper sanitary measures are applied to the storage, preparation, and distribution of food under emergency conditions, mass feeding will be a constant danger to health. Food is easily contaminated and has the ability to support the growth of pathogenic organisms. Moreover, other services connected with the protection of food—namely water supply, waste disposal and vector control—are carried out in an improvised manner during emergencies. Conditions, therefore, favour the outbreak of food-borne diseases, and the consequences of such an outbreak could be extremely grave because the medical and nursing services, which might be short-staffed and swamped with urgent cases, would not be able to cope with the situation. These considerations show clearly the necessity for the proper planning and operation of food sanitation programmes in emergencies.

The provision of food is not the responsibility of health authorities. However, the environmental health officials should know the quantities and types of food involved, the lines of supply, and the means of distribution so that they can devise and apply the proper sanitary safeguards. The first move, therefore, is to bring together all the health, supply, welfare, and other officials involved in the provision of food in order to develop a reasonable plan for the sanitary supervision of food supplies and installations.

The measures that can be applied in order to ensure good food sanitation include:

1. Quality control of incoming food in order to detect spoilage and contamination;
2. Quality control of water supplied to food-preparing centres;
3. Control of insects and rodents in stores, kitchens and feeding centres;
4. Provision for the proper storage and cooking of food;
5. Provision for the proper disposal of solid and liquid wastes;

6. Provision for the proper washing and sanitation of utensils;
7. Supervision of food preparation;
8. Supervision of food serving;
9. Supervision of the cleaning of premises where foods are handled;
10. Management of food-handling personnel, including
    a. Health checks
    b. Training
    c. Ensuring that numbers are adequate
    d. Provision of adequate sanitary facilities.

Fig. 13.4 Relief workers in Ethiopia have learned that big trees make good landmarks for helicopter pilots bringing supplies. They are also good rallying points for the local population. Note the roped-off area which will be needed when the food is distributed. L.R.C.S.

There are some areas that need special attention and supervision by sanitation personnel. They are:

1. Vehicles for food transport;
2. Food storage;
3. Mass feeding centres, including kitchens;
4. Emergency hospitals;
5. Milk distribution centres.

Some important points to be borne in mind in the organisation of mass feeding centres are:

1. The location and layout of field centres for mass feeding should be selected and arranged in consultation with responsible sanitation officers in order to ensure reasonable sanitary safeguards. Whenever possible, use should be made of existing buildings, such as restaurants, hotel dining rooms, schools, public assembly halls and churches, which offer suitable conditions for maintaining a satisfactory standard of cleanliness at all times and for preventing an invasion of rodents or insects.

Fig. 13.5 Distribution of food, using the forest as camouflage (Biafra, 1968).

Fig. 13.6 A relief worker teaches disaster victims in Niger how to mix and use cereals which are part of a supplementary feeding programme. It is important to allow time for questions to be asked.

2. Only potable water may be used in feeding premises. Where there is no piped supply, water must be transported, stored, and handled in a sanitary manner.

3. A sufficient number of basins, each with soap, nail brush and a clean towel, must be provided exclusively for the use of food handlers.

4. Separate basins must be provided for washing all sorts of eating and cooking utensils. Before washing, any grease or food scraps on the utensils should be scraped into a refuse bin, the utensils must be washed in a basin with hot water and detergent, laid on wire baskets or trays, and immersed in boiling water for disinfection for five-minutes. An alternative method of disinfecting utensils already washed is to immerse them in a sterilising solution, preferably hot, of either chlorine (100 mg/litre for 30 seconds) or quaternary ammonium compounds (200 ml/litre for two minutes). Wiping dry is unnecessary and undesirable, the baskets or trays being laid down for drying in a dust-free place.

5. Another basin should be provided for washing all fruits and vegetables before cooking. The serving of raw vegetables and soft-skinned fruits should be forbidden, unless this is unavoidable for dietary reasons. In such cases the vegetables and fruits must be thoroughly washed, immersed in a chlorine solution (100 mg/litre for three minutes) and rinsed until the smell of chlorine disappears.

6. Safe excreta disposal installations for the staff should be provided close to the mass feeding centre, it being assumed that people eating at the feeding centre can make use of the general facilities. Toilets and latrines must be kept in the best possible state of cleanliness at all times.

7. Liquid wastes from kitchens, if not discharged to public sewers, should be disposed of by other sanitary methods, such as soakage pit or covered cesspool. A grease trap or strainer must always be provided and properly maintained to prevent choking.

8. Solid wastes from kitchens must be deposited immediately in refuse bins. No filled bins may remain in preparation or cooking areas. They must be tightly covered and removed outside for collection and disposal.

9. A refuse removal service must be promptly started, as proper collection and disposal prevents many problems, particularly flies breeding, rodent invasion and fire risks. When this service is impracticable, an attempt must be made to separate refuse into:

a. *Inert refuse:* mainly bottles and tins. When intact they could be salvaged; disaster victims can find many uses for tins. If damaged, they should be crushed or flattened, and buried.

b. *Combustible refuse:* mainly wrappings, bags, boxes, etc. They could be burned in a kitchen incinerator.

c. *Putrescible refuse:* food wastes of all kinds. When there is sufficient combustible refuse this could be burned in the incinerator. Otherwise, it must be buried with inert refuse.

10. Basins, tables, chopping blocks, carving boards and all other furniture and equipment must be kept as clean as possible when in use and thoroughly cleaned after each meal.

11. Only food that is to be used the same day may be kept in the kitchen. Food not in the process of preparation or cooking must be kept in fly-proof cupboards and containers.

12. Where refrigeration facilities are non-existent or inadequate, perishable foods should be bought on a daily basis and cooked and served as soon as possible. The

Fig. 13.7 Sahraoui refugees in Algeria. Water holes are the points around which refugee camps are found. A child receives her precious ration of water.

slaughtering of animals for consumption the same day could be considered when a veterinarian or a qualified meat inspector is available.

13. Condensed or powdered milk must be reconstituted with potable water only, and under the best possible sanitary conditions. If natural milk is available for infants and hospital patients, it must be boiled before use.

14. An adequate supply of detergents, disinfectants, brushes, cloths, brooms, and other housekeeping necessities must be provided.

15. Disposable plates, cups, etc., may be used in mass feeding centres and especially when disaster victims are on the move. Communal drinking cups must not be tolerated.

The measures applied to maintain a sanitary environment in the feeding centres and to protect food from contact with contaminated matter will be useless if the cleanliness and health of the personnel of feeding centres are disregarded. Food handlers with dirty hands and clothing, unhygienic and careless habits, and active or latent communicable diseases are just as often responsible for food contamination as flies, soiled utensils, and other unsanitary conditions in kitchens and eating areas.

A disaster may result in a shortage of skilled personnel for feeding centres, and it may be necessary to rely upon voluntary help to supplement the staff. However, no one suffering from or carrying any communicable disease may be employed for this service. Persons with boils, sores, infected wounds, sore throats, or acute respiratory infections must be rejected. Medical examination of all food handlers should be established as early as possible.

The selection of voluntary helpers should be based on health, personal cleanliness and hygiene, and previous experience. To attain a satisfactory standard of personal and environmental hygiene, in-service training and close supervision are essential. Instruction in proper sanitary practices should be adapted to the improvised installations. Lifelong habits are difficult to change; the only way to ensure that the instruction is put into practice is through frequent inspection and constant vigilance.

If there are not enough trained sanitary workers for supervising feeding centres, suitable persons could, after an orientation course, assist the sanitation officers by inspecting the food premises and reporting any deficiency or fault.

The need for cleanliness at all times must be stressed. It is most important to teach all food handlers, including waiters, to wash their hands before starting work, after going to the toilet, and as often as may be necessary to remove soil and contamination; to refrain from touching unnecessarily any food or the food-contact surfaces of any utensils used for eating and drinking; to refrain from sneezing and coughing over, or close to, food; to wear outer garments that are for use exclusively while preparing or serving food, keeping these aprons and gowns as clean as possible, and changing them when they become soiled; to abstain from smoking in areas set aside for the preparation and cooking of mass feeding centres; to understand and apply the basic principles of food sanitation. Realistic and clear instructions, adapted to emergency conditions, should be posted at all strategic points to remind staff constantly of their obligations. Illustrated posters are most helpful, and are essential when some of the staff are illiterate.

PRINCIPLES OF FOOD PRESERVATION

Food spoilage occurs through chemical changes that take place in the constituents of the food. Thus, carbohydrates may ferment and produce acids and gases, fats may be hydrolysed to fatty acids, proteins may be degraded to simple amines—ammonia, hydrogen, sulphide, etc. Such changes may be brought about by the action of micro-organisms, but some, for example fat rancidity, may occur by direct chemical action. Anti-oxidants, chemical substances that reduce or stop the oxidation of fats by direct action between the fat and air, are permitted to be added to some fatty foods.

Spoilage by micro-organisms

Chemical changes in foodstuffs may be brought about by the action of micro-organisms, bacteria and moulds. Before understanding how such spoilage can be controlled, the factors that control the growth of micro-organisms must be understood:

1. They must have food.
2. They must have moisture.
3. They must be at a suitable temperature.
4. They must have a suitable chemical environment.

Food

Bacteria and moulds live on the same food materials (proteins, carbohydrates, fats) as human beings. It is of interest to know that if polluted water is stored for a long period, the number of bacteria decreases because the food supply gets used up. They can die of starvation, just like any other form of life.

Moisture

Bacteria need a relative humidity of almost 100 per cent for growth and multiplication to occur. Moulds and yeasts can exist at somewhat lower humidities. By removing moisture from foodstuffs, therefore, the action of micro-organisms can be slowed down or stopped. Well-known examples of foods preserved by dehydration are dried milk, eggs and vegetables. The stability of such foods as breakfast cereals, cocoa powder and sugar is due to the low moisture content. Bread often has insufficient moisture to support bacterial growth, but sufficient to support mould growth.

Food preserved by dehydration will often allow bacteria to be present in a state of suspended animation. They cannot multiply, but die off only very slowly. This has on some occasions led to food poisoning, e.g. Salmonella food poisoning from dried egg. Also, dehydrated foods may contain bacterial toxins if dangerous bacteria have multiplied in the foods prior to dehydration, e.g. food poisoning in dried milk due to Staphylococcal toxin being present.

The effect of a high water content can be altered by dissolving materials in the water. Thus, jams owe their stability to the high sugar content. Salt solutions also have a similar preserving action. Salted butter keeps better than fresh butter. Although the overall salt content of salted butter may not be large, it is the salt content of the aqueous portion that is important, and this can be quite high.

It should be understood that the sugar and salt are not acting as chemical poison in the usually accepted sense. They increase the osmotic pressure of the fluid in which the organisms can be present and this pressure is higher than the osmotic pressure of the cell contents, the cell walls acting as semi-permeable membranes. The cells thus tend to dehydrate and multiplication stops.

Temperature

For every organism there is a temperature at which its rate of growth or multiplication will be at a maximum. The further away from this temperature, down or up, the slower the rate of growth, thus bacteria that normally live in the mammalian gut grow best at about body heat ('mesophiles'), others grow best at much lower temperatures ('psychrophiles'), while some will only grow in the range of 45° to 60°C ('thermophiles'). However, most organisms that contaminate ordinary foodstuffs grow well in ordinary atmospheric temperatures. If food is chilled (most domestic refrigerators operate at about 3° to 5°C) it will keep fresh significantly longer. Most food poisoning bacteria will not grow at all under chill conditions so even when food spoils in a refrigerator it should be a harmless type of spoilage.

Bacterial multiplication virtually ceases when food is frozen but the organisms remain alive for very long periods and can start to multiply again if the temperature is raised sufficiently.

Chemical environment

Like the higher forms of life, bacteria and moulds can be poisoned by chemical substances. Acids are good poisons and products like pickles and mayonnaise keep well because of the vinegar (acetic acid) present. Fresh sausage contains the harmless (to humans) preservative, sulphur dioxide, which significantly prolongs the 'shelf life' of the product because of its action against bacteria. Some wrapping materials contain sorbates that prevent surface growth of moulds. Many foods are 'cured' and smoked. Curing salts used for bacon and hams, as well as containing sodium chloride also contain nitrite. This has a specific bactericidal effect. Smoke also contains volatile substances like acids, phenols and aldehydes which, as well as imparting a particular flavour to meats and fish, also help to preserve them. Hence the relative stability of bacon and kippers.

It will be seen that microbiological spoilage may be slowed down or stopped by producing conditions inimical for growth of micro-organisms. It is also possible to prolong the life of foodstuffs by killing organisms that may be present.

Canning

Canned foods are packed inside hermetically sealed cans which are then heated to high temperatures in retorts. The contents are rendered virtually sterile by the heating process and should remain so until the cans are opened. During the cooling of cans following the retorting process, strains are placed on the can seams and they may open temporarily.

Pasteurisation

Pasteurisation is a term indicating a process that greatly reduces the number of live bacteria present without necessarily sterilising the product. Thus, milk is treated at 63°C (145°F) for 20 minutes, or given an equivalent treatment at a higher temperature for a shorter time. This is sufficient to kill the organisms of tuberculosis and many more heat-resistant bacteria. Thus, pasteurised milk generally keeps better than raw milk, but it will eventually spoil. Many other foodstuffs receive heat pasteurisation processes.

Curing

Food can be 'cured' by the addition of common salt. Ions separate as water molecules collect about them by a process called ion hydration. The more salt added, the more the water in the food is withdrawn to hydrate ions. Eventually a point is reached at which no more water can be drawn away to dissolve the salt. At this point micro-organisms are no longer able to grow and multiply. Pig products such as bacon and ham are treated by curing.

Pickling

This is the process of soaking food in an acid solution, normally vinegar, where the pH is too low (i.e. the acidity is too high) to permit the growth of micro-organisms or the activity of enzymes. Many vegetables, for example onions, beetroot, cucumber, are preserved in this way.

Irradiation

One recent technological advance in methods of preserving involves neither heating, freezing, nor the addition of chemicals. This is irradiation whereby food is exposed to gamma, beta or X-rays from atomic sources or electron generators. The rays destroy micro-organisms, but unfortunately they set up chemical reactions about which little is understood at present. As a result, the food develops unpleasant flavours and changes towards a cooked texture, and many research workers believe that food preserved by irradiation is dangerous to health. In addition, the initial outlay on equipment is very high. For all these reasons, development in this field may be slow for several years to come.

The most satisfactory results so far have been produced when radiation is reduced to levels below those which spoil food flavour. The product is not sterile, but many of its surface micro-organisms are destroyed.

Losses in nutrients during preservation

It is vital in food preservation not only to destroy or inactivate the elements responsible for spoilage, but also to retain the original nutritional value as far as possible. Much research is being done to determine exactly the losses in nutrients sustained during the three major methods of processing—canning, quick freezing and dehydration—but the general indications of work carried out so far are as follows:

Proteins seem to be only slightly affected in nutritional value. A certain amount of desaturation takes place. In canning and dehydration this is due to heat treatment and, in freezing, to the increase in solute concentration as the water solidifies.

Fats suffer little. The chief danger is from rancidity, which can be induced by heat during the canning and dehydration processes. In quick-freezing, fats will go rancid if not stored at a sufficiently low temperature.

Carbohydrates suffer from oxidation reactions encouraged by heat. Prolonged heating at high temperatures also degrades sugars and starches very slightly. During storage after quick-freezing a gradual conversion of the disaccharide, sucrose, to the monosaccharides, dextrose and levulose, may take place. Since this conversion normally occurs during digestion it is of little significance.

Vitamins are more severely affected than any other nutrients by all methods of preservation. This is particularly true of the water-soluble vitamins, C and B groups. Losses of approximately 20 per cent of vitamin C content occur in all processes during the washing and blanching operation. In the vitamin B group, thiamine suffers most during canning and dehydration because it is extremely heat sensitive (about 25 per cent is lost). Riboflavin is lost to some extent because it is water-soluble, but stands up well to heat treatment. The fat-soluble vitamin A survives better than any other. Losses of vitamin D are incurred during dehydration.

Little is known of the effects of preservation methods on *minerals*, but it seems certain that some are lost in the drip from frozen meat and fish when it is thawed.

Prevention of infestations in stored food

All goods should be examined before being brought into a store and any having obvious infestation should be rejected.

Storage building

It is important that the building structure should be sound and the storage rooms dry, well-lit and ventilated. Dripping taps should be repaired, broken doors and window frames filled in and ill-fitting floor and skirting boards renewed. There should be no unnecessary panelling around pipes and cables, as this serves only to provide hiding places for insects and to make thorough inspection and control more difficult.

Careful and frequent cleaning of inaccessible corners, in cracks and behind stacks is important.

Methods of storage
Consignments of goods should be piled separately, away from the walls, allowing sufficient room for inspection and cleaning between and behind the stacks. Bags should not rest on the floor but on dunnage of some kind—ideally wooden duckboarding 150 mm high.

Rotation of stock
It is important to use stock in strict rotation. Goods should be clearly marked with date of storage and should never remain in store for longer than is necessary. Whenever a stack is removed, pallets, dunnage and the floor beneath should be cleaned before a new stack is built.

Types of infestation

There are two groups of insects which may infest a food store:

1. Insects which live in or near the structure of the building and emerge to feed on food debris and unprotected stores. Such scavengers include cockroaches, ants, crickets and silverfish.
2. Insects which live and breed in the stored food. These include certain beetles, moths and mites.

The presence of these pests can give rise to:

Food poisoning
It is possible for a cockroach to act as mechanical vector of disease germs and to contaminate food in the same way as the housefly. It is less likely to carry infection because it is not as mobile.

Loss and spoilage of stored food
The amount of food actually consumed by these insects is insignificant compared to the amount they render useless. In some cases, notably that of the cockroach, it can be tainted by excrement whilst in others, such as the grain weevils, the nutritional value of the food can be seriously impaired.

Damage to packaging
Paper and cardboard are easily penetrated by many insects. The resultant exposure of the contents may lead to rapid deterioration due to dampness, mould, etc.

1. Common 'visiting' pests

Cockroaches are one of the most commonly encountered store pests, especially in tropical regions. The adults vary in length from 60 to 100 mm according to the species. They often appear in vast numbers, though few may be seen during the day as they shun the light.

They are notoriously hard to eradicate because of:

a. Their powers of reproduction;
b. Their ability to adapt to different conditions;
c. Their resistance to common insecticides:
d. The inaccessibility of their breeding places; and
e. Their ability to survive on small quantities of almost any kind of food.

Warmth, darkness, moisture and a good food supply are the most favourable conditions. They are frequently found behind shelves, built-in furniture and drawers, notice boards and under loose floor and bench coverings. An old building may provide ideal harbourages around door and window frames, behind cracked wall tiles and loose skirting boards and within pipe runs and cable ducts that connect one room with another. Such places should be sealed with plaster or packed with steel or glass wool. Strips of gummed paper may also be used to seal narrow cracks. Scrupulous hygiene is necessary to ensure that no spilt or uncovered food is left around overnight. Cupboards and shelves must be swept out frequently.

The domestic species of cockroach is rarely encountered out-of-doors and is usually introduced into a store either through the drains or in wooden cases and packages.

Ants can also spoil unprotected food and some species, especially those in tropical countries, are able to penetrate paper and cardboard.

The common black ant (*Lasius niger*) is the most frequent intruder into food stores and kitchens. The nest building must be traced and destroyed.

Pharaoh's ant (*Monomorium pharaonis*) is sandy coloured and about half the size of the black ant. It favours warm humid conditions. Nests are often found in hollow spaces within walls, beneath floors and behind stoves and hot water pipes. It is a difficult pest to eradicate.

The lesser grain borer (*Rhizopertha dominica*) is a small brown beetle (under 5 mm) which is a serious pest of stored grain in India and other parts of the tropics.

The female lays 300 to 500 eggs either loose or attached to grains, at the rate of up to 25 per day. The larvae bore into the grains and feed on them from inside, until little is left but the husk. Pupation occurs inside the grain and the adults also feed on the cereal after emergence.

2. Pests in stored food

Use of insecticides

Fumigation means the use of poisonous gases, such as methyl bromide or hydrogen cyanide, which diffuse into a product and destroy all the insect life within. Because of the dangerous nature of these chemicals they should only be used by qualified personnel.

Residual insecticides

These may be applied to the surface of the building in the form of liquid sprays, dusting powders, smoke generators, lacquers or mixed with whiting powders or paints. Where sprayed surfaces are of an absorbent nature (e.g. untreated brick or wood) the use of a water dispersible powder preparation of BHC or malathion is recommended. When dry the active material remains on the surface. Emulsion concentrates are less satisfactory as much of the chemical may be absorbed into the fabric.

The use of compression sprayers will enable the operators to penetrate deep into cracks and crevices. Care should be taken not to contaminate any food while spraying.

The choice of insecticide depends upon the species of insect, the type of food in stock, and whether the insects are on the food or in the building structure.

Knock-down insecticides

Aerosols and space sprays have little value against the 'resident' pests but may be useful against ants and flies. Cockroaches are resistant to the pyrethrum used in these insecticides but they can be flushed out of their hiding places by its use.

In order to prevent insect damage in food stores, it is important to be alert for the first signs of a pest. Adults or larvae may be seen on shelves or on adjacent walls or windows. All holes in packets or bags should be investigated and small piles of dust and debris around the base of a stack may indicate mite infestation.

The first essential is to trace all the breeding sites and to segregate the infested products. Badly-infested materials should be removed and destroyed. Others may be salvaged. Dry foods, such as cereals, may be disinfested by heat treatment. They should be decanted into closed tins (such as biscuit tins) and exposed to a temperature of 100°C (212°F) for 1 to 1½ hours.

Permanent infestations are likely to develop only if standards of hygiene are poor.

The biscuit beetle (Stegobium paniceum) is reddish-brown in colour with a dense covering of short yellowish hairs. It is a common beetle pest of food and will attack cereal products, as well as drugs and beverage concentrates. It can do considerable damage to sacking, paper and cardboard. The grubs have been reported as being able to penetrate tin-foil.

The female lays about 100 eggs over a period of three-weeks, either in food or in crevices nearby. The tiny larva crawls around folds of packeted foods, penetrating into uninfected foodstuffs. It grows to about 5 mm, and the adult bites its way out. The females begin egg-laying after a few days. Adult biscuit beetles live for about six to eight weeks but take no food.

The Australian spider beetle (Ptinus tectus) is the most common of several species of spider beetles. They are small and round, look like small spiders but have only six legs instead of the spider's eight. They are pests of cereals, cereal products and spices but often exist as scavengers of miscellaneous debris. They are nocturnal insects and during the day most of them are concealed in cracks, dark corners and between bags or boxes. The larvae not only feed on almost any food substances but also bore holes into various inedible things such as cardboard boxes, books, sacks and even wood.

The female lays about 100 eggs or more eggs at intervals of a few days. They are sticky when laid and may adhere to various objects. The larvae eventually spin a cocoon and pupate inside it. If they are infesting food in sacks or cardboard boxes, they often bore through to the outside before pupating. After emerging, the adults rest for some time, often as long as three weeks in the pupal cell.

Flour beetles (Tribolium spp) are common and serious pests of cereal products, especially flour. They are rather flat, chestnut-brown beetles which may be found abundantly in grain which has already been attacked by weevils or moths or they may be a primary pest in softer products such as ground nuts and cocoa. The larva, which is a small, brownish, elongated meal worm, feeds amongst the grains on seeds and leaves producing much dust and excreta as it goes.

The female lays eggs singly, 2 to 10 per day, reaching a total of about 450. The larvae grow from about 1 to 5 mm, then pupate and darken before the emergence of the adult. The adults feed on the same substance as the larvae and certain species will fly in warm conditions. Males live up to about 600 days, females to about 450.

Weevils (Sitophilus spp) are easily recognisable by the snout-like projection of the head. Grain weevils attack all kinds of whole grain and some cereal products (e.g. macaroni) and are wingless. Other species show a preference for maize, wheat and rice. They are able to fly in very warm weather.

The female bores a small hole in the grain, deposits the egg in it and then seals the hole. The larva completes its development, and eventually pupates, inside the grain. Breeding does not occur below 13°C (55°F) and high humidity greatly increases the number of eggs laid. The adults normally feed on the grain and, to avoid the light, they often enter grains hollowed out by larvae.

The Mediterranean flour moth (Anagasta (or Ephestia) kuhniella) is a silvery moth 10 to 15 mm long which has a characteristic zig-zag flight when disturbed. It is the principal pest of flour mills but it may occur in a wide variety of stored foods, including ground cereal products, ground-nuts, seeds, spices, dried fruits, rolled oats and chocolate. It will flourish among neglected bags of flour and in accumulations of flour dust.

The female lays about 200 eggs. The larvae grow to a length of 15 to 19 mm. They cover food with the silk webbing they spin. For pupation, they leave food for a dark corner. The adults rest in shady corners in the daytime and fly at dusk or at night. There may be three or four generations in one year.

The warehouse moth (Ephestia elutella) is small and greyish in colour and may be seen during the summer months flying near the ceiling, resting inconspicuously or settling on food to lay eggs. The life cycle of this moth is adapted to storage conditions. For a large part of the year, the infestation remains hidden in the building structure and a complete turnover of stock during this period will have little or no effect on the numbers of larvae present. In this way, the infestation is maintained from one year to the next and new stock becomes infested as soon as the adult moths emerge (in early summer). The grubs attack a wide variety of food, including chocolate, cereals, cereal products, dried fruit, spices and nuts. They ruin the nutritive value of wheat by feeding on the germ of the grain.

The larvae are creamy white in colour and grow to nearly 25 mm in length. They eventually move away from the food to the building structure leaving sheets of silk webbing over the surface of the commodity. They crawl up nearby walls and enter small cracks and crevices where they spin cocoons and remain throughout the winter in a resting stage. They reach the pupal stage in the spring. New adults begin to emerge in May.

Mites are tiny arachnids having, like spiders, eight legs. They are only about 0.5 mm long, and are not readily seen individually, but a heavy infestation appears as a greyish or brownish dust around bags or boxes of food. Mites require a fairly high humidity and flourish in damp, ill-ventilated rooms and cellars, or in food which has a fairly high moisture content. In addition to reducing the food value, a heavy mite infestation causes tainting, which may result in unpalatable food.

Among the many species of mites which infest food, the most common are flour mites (*Acarus siro*), dried fruit mites (*Carpoglyphys lactis*) and house mites (*Elycyphagus domesticus*). Because of their small size, inconspicuous appearance and rapid rate of multiplication, a heavy mite infestation may develop before it is noticed. By that time, the mites may have spread a considerable distance away from their original source. When dealing with an infestation, it is wise to treat a far wider area than may at first seem necessary. They may also be spread by brushes and brooms and these should be treated with a suitable insecticide after coming into contact with mite infested dust.

SUPPLEMENTARY FEEDING

A typical warehousing network and operational programme is shown in Figure 13.8.

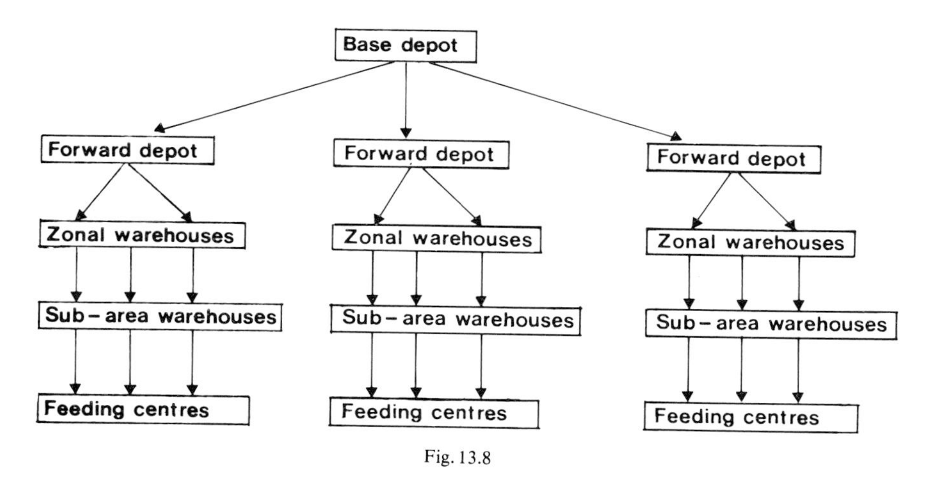

Fig. 13.8

Instructions for operating feeding centres

A. General instructions

1. The minimum of beneficiaries each feeding centre should aim to feed.
2. The category of beneficiaries (i.e. all children from 0 to 8 years of age and lactating/expectant women).
3. Whether beneficiaries must be registered before feeding is undertaken. If so, registration cards must be provided for each centre.

B. Instructions on feeding arrangements

The layout of the feeding centre should be as illustrated in Figure 13.9.

The feeding centre should be located within a fenced area, 15 m × 15 m. The fencing may be constructed of local materials (e.g. bamboo and roping). In one corner of the compound, a hospital size tent (9 m × 6 m) may be erected. The tent may be utilised for storage, distribution and registration. Next to the tent, a cooking shed should be built.

The prepared food should be placed on a bench or on a platform within the tent and handed out by the distributor from that point.

The recipient should enter the tent from one side, show his registration card, proceed to collect his milk (or other food), consume his food within the fenced area and leave via the exit.

The following equipment should be provided for each feeding centre:

Pans (aluminium with lids)
Buckets (plastic)
Stirrers
Measurers
Rope
Petrol stove
Plastic tarpaulin
Hospital tent (9 m × 6 m)
Registration cards
Posters
Milk recipes
Attendance sheet

Staff employed at each centre should be:

Supervisor
Cooks and distributors (a minimum number should be given)

C. Instructions on preparation of food

1. The type of food each feeding centre will be asked to distribute.
2. The daily fixed ration per child.
3. Any additive (e.g. sugar), where available.
4. Recipe for reconstitution of dried foods. (All water must be boiled before use.)

Main points relating to food supplies

1. Maximum use should be made of local resources. Information concerning the country's resources should be assembled as part of the national disaster plan.

2. Only essential supplies should be sent in from abroad.

3. Food must be acceptable to the recipient community and usable under local conditions. It must be suited to climate and distribution operable within the existing infrastructure.

4. Packaging, labelling (in a language which is understood) and standardisation are important considerations.

5. All necessary equipment should arrive at the same time. Uncooked food is useless if facilities for preparation and cooking are not available. Dependent items should be packed together.

6. Goods should be of a type which does not have a high black market value; price controls must be imposed.

7. Stocks must be stored in as ideal circumstances as possible and pest infestations eradicated at once.

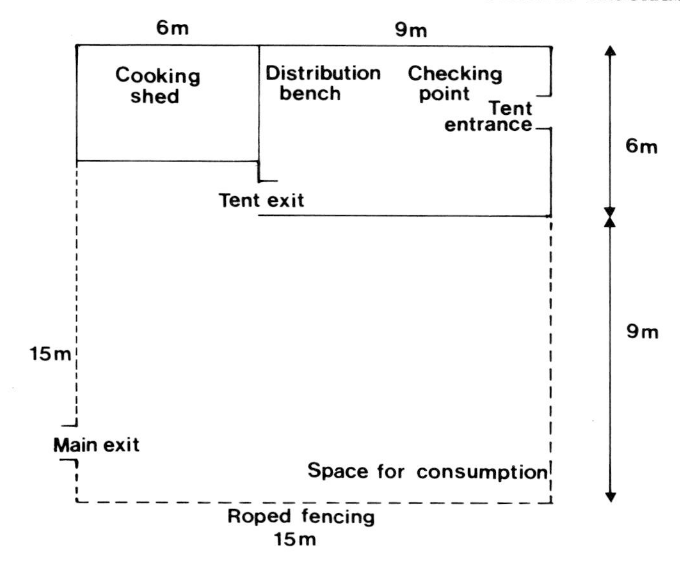

Fig. 13.9 Plan for a feeding centre.

8. A ration system should be started.

9. Supplementary vitamins are only necessary in certain situations of chronic food shortages.

It should be remembered that a population adapts to its food supply and, in most developing countries, the adults maintain their weight and also reproduce on a diet which would be inadequate for the population of many Western countries.

14. Supply systems—transport, use and storage of equipment and drugs

A disaster has been previously described as a situation in which the normal pattern of life within a community is suddenly disrupted and people are plunged into helplessness and suffering and urgently require the basic necessities of life such as medical care, food, shelter and clothing. These needs are often further aggravated by the disruption of local medical and welfare services and the destruction of stores and their sources of supply within the immediate vicinity of the disaster. This calls for a well organised section within all relief administrations capable of recruiting relief teams and procuring supplies and equipment in unaffected neighbouring areas, and arranging for such personnel and provisions to be speedily transported to the site of the calamity. In fact the effectiveness of the relief teams sent to the scene of the disaster will, to a large extent, be determined by the efficiency of this supporting machinery established to produce the exact quantities of medical and relief supplies when requested.

In normal circumstances the duties relating to supply and transportation will be delegated to government departments with the relevant experience and necessary equipment, such as the armed forces, ministry of supply and transportation department. Medical personnel will not usually be required to take on the responsibility of managing these departments but their advice will be sought in connection with the conditions required for the movement and storage of medical supplies and foodstuffs. An appreciation of the problems and techniques involved will facilitate better communications and co-operation with those charged with these responsibilities and equip a team with the knowledge to enable it to implement some of its own operating procedures. The features of the logistical administration pertaining to relief operations can be conveniently grouped under the following headings:

1. Transport systems

    a. Air
    b. Rail
    c. Road
    d. Sea

2. Purchasing
3. Warehousing
4. Packaging
5. Accounting

Transportation systems

Every national disaster relief plan should contain data relating to the availability and capacities of the internal transport systems and the facilities at ports and airports for the reception of foreign aid. Using this information an operational plan should be prepared which will enable personnel and goods to be moved with the minimum of delay to any part of the country should the need arise. The build up of bottle-necks at ports and airports should be prevented and the transfer of less urgent supplies in preference to priority needs avoided. Such an operation can be extremely difficult to organise in a developing country where 75 per cent of the population might be living in rural areas served by inadequate roads which are extremely susceptible to disasters and often unusable during the rainy season.

A great deal of time and effort can be saved if a local transit company is commissioned to supervise the unloading and clearing formalities associated with loads arriving by either sea or air. It may even be possible for such firms to arrange delivery of the goods to the warehouse or distribution centre.

Fig. 14.1 A Red Cross camel caravan carrying grain from Bali to the Hinterland (Ethiopia) where no roads exist.

In certain inaccessible locations consideration could be given to the possible use of camels or mules to transport relief materials. Details relating to the more common methods of moving supplies are given below:

Air transport

Although aircraft can take supplies and personnel to the stricken area quicker than any other form of transportation, they are very costly to operate and can only carry a limited amount of cargo. They are often used to transport relief supplies from abroad during the emergency phase when it may be possible for donors to obtain free space on the national airline under the International Air Transport Association (IATA) Resolution 200 which states that a member airline 'may issue a pass for transportation over its own lines or over the lines of another member if so authorised by the other member for . . . any person or supplies to provide relief in case of general epidemic, disaster, or other calamitous visitations but not transportation to or from the zones of military operation.' To obtain permissions for either free or reduced-cost transportation for personnel and supplies on a space-available basis an approach should be made to the director of the national airline (often controlled by the Government) of the afflicted country or, alternatively, to another IATA member airline serving the area.

Light aircraft and helicopters can be used for the internal movement of urgently required items such as drugs and medical equipment which are often of a high value but small in volume and therefore justify the expense of movement by air. It is also advisable to maintain contact with the armed forces and other commercial users of helicopters as in many recent earthquake situations in Central and South America they have provided the only means of getting rescue teams and supplies to the victims until the roads had been reopened. This is a task which can take several days in many isolated districts.

The details of goods sent by air are recorded on a document called an 'Airway Bill'. Airway bills, which are not negotiable, are usually prepared with three originals and nine copies by the carrying airline or handling agent. They contain a number which is quoted on the labels attached to every item covered by that particular airway bill.

Rail transport

Railways usually provide the most economical method of moving large quantities of supplies over long distances within a country or geographic region. They are often state-owned which should mean that relief supplies may be carried at reduced rates or even free of charge. Care should, however, be taken when evaluating the reliability of a railway network which may be suffering delays due to limited rolling stock, lack of spare parts, damage to track and bridges etc. The time required for the reception and loading of goods and the sorting out at the point of destination varies according to countries and local conditions to such an extent that in certain cases a delegate will be forced to use an alternative mode of transportation. Goods carried by rail are covered by a non-negotiable way-bill.

Road transport

A large number of lorries and personnel carriers will be required during the emergency phase of the relief operation. The type and quantity will be determined by the number of people to be assisted and the distances to be covered. Whenever possible use should be made of government vehicles or public carriers. Medium sized vehicles will be required to move goods from the airport and docks to the warehouse or forwarding centre. Large vehicles, possibly with trailers, will be used for moving consignments on long hauls across country and small four-wheel drive trucks or land-rovers used on the last leg of the journey.

Before using vehicles near the scene of a disaster, arrangements should be made to guarantee a supply of fuel, spare vehicle parts and facilities for emergency repairs and routine maintenance. When government vehicles are not available it is wise to pass these responsibilities on to a transport company with which a contract should be made based on either a daily or distance-carried rate. It is unwise to think in terms of purchasing trucks as they are expensive and very rarely obtainable in the affected area.

Whatever arrangement is made for the carrying of goods by road each vehicle used must be insured. The insurance should cover the vehicle, load, driver and passengers and be able to meet a claim from a third party. In the event of an accident, a report should be filed with the insurance company as soon as possible and the appropriate authorities informed.

All consignments sent by truck should be subject to a way-bill made out in three copies: one for the consigner, one for the consignee and the third for the transporter. The two latter copies should be signed by the consignee who should also note the condition of the load when received together with any shortfalls.

Four-wheel drive vehicles such as the Unimog or the Landrover make ideal personnel carriers but they are also expensive to buy and costly to run. Many cars in everyday use such as the Renault 4L or the Volkswagen combi-wagon work just as efficiently in hot humid climates and will serve a team well when used on metalled roads or dirt tracks in dry weather. It is important that personnel carriers are registered and insured if imported into a country during a disaster operation.

Sea/water transportation

Sending goods by sea is the most economical way of transporting supplies in bulk. It is, however, relatively slow and subject to delays caused by adverse weather conditions and handling problems at other ports of call. Most gifts from abroad not required in the rescue period are sent by sea. Consignments can either be dispatched on a vessel specially chartered for a particular voyage or on a regular shipping line. Shipping rates are fixed by Regional Shipping Conferences comprising the major operators within a given region and reduced rates for relief materials are usually available. Consignments sent by sea are accompanied by a document termed a bill of lading. The bill of lading is made out with several copies. Those retained by the captain and ship owner are non-transferable but the others held by the shipper and the consignee are normally negotiable. Great care has, therefore, to be taken when despatching the consignee's copy by post as anyone who presents a negotiable copy of the bill of lading at the port of arrival can take away or transfer the goods. The consignee's copy is mailed by the shipper after the vessel has left its port of origin or occasionally, on short trips, it may be carried by the purser.

On occasions when the affected area is served by a series of waterways, enquiries should be made with the shipping lines or local cargo carriers which may act as the carriers of relief supplies. Country boats in Bangladesh and Thailand have been successfully used in this way by relief agencies for many years and long shaft out-board motors are now held in reserve as they greatly improve the performance of such craft, especially against strong currents.

Purchasing

In order to save both time and money, and also to provide materials known to be acceptable to the victims, relief supplies should be purchased as close to the scene of the disaster as possible. As soon as the disaster assessment team has compiled a list of the type, quantity and quality of the supplies required, the purchasing officer should investigate the local markets. The disruptive effects of disasters often lead to the hoarding of foodstuffs, etc. and the proliferation of black-marketeers which may mean that certain commodities will be difficult to find and those offered for sale might be of a poor quality and probably at an extremely inflated price. Having, therefore, ascertained that placing a large order in the vicinity will not further add to such problems, tenders should be solicited from reliable merchants with a known capacity to produce the required items in the time permitted.

At the pre-arranged time the tenders with accompanying samples will be examined and a decision taken as to which merchant can provide the best value for money and deliver the goods in the shortest time. A firm order signed by an authorised delegate should then be submitted on either headed stationery or a specially prepared order form. The order must be written so that it can be easily understood by the supplier and contain:

Description and specifications of good required
Exact quantity
Packaging instructions
Date, method and place of delivery
Arrangements for payment.

The purchasing officer should retain a copy of this order for checking against the goods on completion and a further copy should be sent to the finance officer in order that the necessary budgeting allocations and payment can be carried out with the minimum delay.

Warehousing

Time and money are lost every time stores are moved or handled. Every effort should therefore be made to direct relief goods straight to the distribution centres or medical units in the disaster zone. This is not possible when supplies have to be used over a period of time or when large consignments have to be broken down into smaller allotments. In these circumstances a warehouse or forwarding centre will be established. It may not be necessary to hire such a building as governments or commercial companies are often prepared to offer such centres on a rent-free basis. Irrespective of the question of rent an agreement should always be prepared outlining the conditions of the occupancy. The warehouse should be sited near the airport, docks or railway yards and offer adequate protection from extremes of temperature, rain, damp and vermin. It must also offer adequate access to trucks and be secure. When the warehouse has been found an assessment of the likely amount of goods to be handled should be made in order that equipment such as fork-lift trucks, trolleys and conveyor belts can be obtained and porters, clerks and security guards employed.

Particular areas of the warehouse should be designated for the storage of certain commodities, e.g. blankets, food, drugs, clothing, and roads marked out between each area to permit access and free movement. Goods should be stacked on wooden pallets in such a manner as to allow adequate ventilation but not so high as to touch the walls or ceiling. Hooks should not be used to hang goods in paper and hessian sacks since these are apt to tear. A plentiful supply of empty bags or containers should be ordered so that damaged packaging can be replaced and to enable bulk consignments to be split into smaller quantities more suited for distribution in the field.

Drugs and medical equipment will, particularly in hot humid climates, need special attention as they must be kept in a controlled environment. Humidifiers, fans and air-conditioners will have to be used. A refrigerator will be required if such items as vaccine, antibiotics and blood derivatives are to be kept. Surgical instruments, needles, etc. will rust quickly if they are not stored in oil or petroleum jelly and placed in airtight containers.

Warehouses should be kept clean and tidy at all times and fire prevention rules adhered to. Supplies will be distributed on a first-in, first-out basis and notes of expiry dates should be taken. Outgoing consignments ought to be assembled in an area adjacent to the loading bay before the vehicle arrives in order to minimise the amount of time that it has to remain idle.

Accurate records must be maintained at all times which show the date of receipt and despatch and current stock levels of all goods held. Periodic inventories should also be made and copies sent to relief teams in order that they know the variety of supplies available.

Packaging

All relief materials should be packed in containers or bales which offer protection against loss and damage and are at the same time easily manageable, as the availability of mechanical loading machines in the disaster area cannot be counted upon. Each item should also be made waterproof by covering with a synthetic material or treated hessian.

Fig. 14.2 Loading of food; note the clear marking on the boxes (Cyprus, 1974).

Items to be used together, e.g. syringes and needles, tents and poles, should be packed together.

The League of Red Cross Societies has developed a colour band system of marking the labels on relief packages which, when used in conjunction with the agreed symbols for denoting the type of clothing contained in each carton as shown in Figure 14.3, greatly eases the problem of identifying and sorting consignments in the disaster area. This system

Fig. 14.3 Symbols denoting the type of clothing contained in each carton.

has now been adopted by most international relief agencies and the colours used are as follows:

Red:	Foodstuffs
Blue:	Clothing, shoes, cooking utensils, tents, blankets and bedding
Green:	Drugs and medical equipment

Packages or cartons should be clearly marked showing the names and addresses of both the consignee and consignor and the flight number of aeroplane or name of vessel used for transportation. The contents and number of each item should also be indicated and in the case of foods, cooking instructions in the appropriate language should be included. All shipping documents (airway bills, bills of lading, insurance certificates, customs declarations, etc.) and packing lists should be sent in advance to allow the necessary reception arrangements to be made.

Accounting

The administrative responsibility for a relief action and the financial control are interrelated. As soon as the scope of a relief operation has been decided a budget will be prepared and funds made available. All monies, equipment and relief supplies shall be utilised in accordance with local and internationally accepted principles and regulations. Budgetary limits will be fixed on all aspects of the operation and persons will be appointed to authorise expenditure up to agreed amounts. The field office will be responsible for maintaining financial records, local bank accounts, payment of locally approved accounts and the submission of regular statements to the sponsoring agency headquarters.

Each team will be issued with considerable amounts of cash to cover local purchases and operating costs for which it should make suitable security arrangements. The team administrator will keep a petty cash record listing all receipts, items of expenditure and the current balance in hand. Copies of this record together with supporting vouchers will be sent to the field office at fortnightly intervals.

Too much importance cannot be attributed to the keeping of accurate accounts and records at all levels during an emergency operation and the need to insure all vehicles, buildings and equipment as well as personnel.

15. Communication and co-operation

An attempt was made in Chapters 2 and 3 to outline the need for disaster preparedness and the establishment of a central body to coordinate the relief operation after the catastrophe has occurred. The existence of coordinating organs both within the afflicted country and in the office of the United Nations Disaster Relief Coordinator in Geneva are today fundamental requirements for a successful relief operation. This level of coordination is dependent on the gleaning of accurate information about the situation and the current requirements which must be transmitted through the proper channels to the coordinating machine in a clear and concise format. The proficiency of the coordinating body also relies on the ability of the various participants in the operation to co-operate with one another and to create honest and business-like working relationships.

Most information is relayed in the form of reports which, during a relief operation, are frequently made for the following:

The central relief coordinating body/the agency headquarters
The victims
The donors
The Press
Members of the relief organisation

Reports should have a clear title and contain a brief introduction, the relevant facts, a summary and a conclusion.

Reports to the coordinating body

Reports to the central coordinating body within the affected country and/or reports to the agency headquarters take the form of survey, progress and evaluation communiques. This is probably the most difficult report to compile as it will be prepared under great pressure and often in strange and uncomfortable surroundings. The report needs to contain an accurate assessment of the damage and a list of requirements upon which the relief operation can be mobilised. The gathering of the required statistical information can be somewhat of a problem in a rural developing community which might lack reliable records and census data.

It is not uncommon to find that local officials neglect to record the number of births and deaths, the prevalence of communicable diseases and the location of resources of food, equipment and skilled personnel. The assessor must in these circumstances check and cross-check information with as many local sources as possible, allowing for the fact that such verbal reports will more than likely be coloured with a certain amount of exaggeration. When completed, the report should be concluded with a proposed plan of action detailing requirements of cash, personnel, supplies and equipment.

Progress reports must be sent at regular intervals from the relief and medical teams to the field office which will then collate the information contained therein and produce situation reports on the extent of the operation for the coordinating bodies. These reports should pinpoint any particular problems and draw comparisons between the state of rehabilitation reached and that projected in the operational plan.

An evaluation report will be written at the end of the operation and will summarise the events and analyse the effectiveness of all aspects of the relief programmes. It should end with recommendations, based on lessons learned, for the next relief operation.

Reports to the victims

The victims of any disaster will express a strong desire to be kept informed about the developments of the relief operation and the condition of their homes and land from which they may have been evacuated. They will also wish to be told about the condition or whereabouts of friends and relatives from whom they have been separated. Reports of this nature should only be given when they are known to be accurate. They should whenever possible contain as much encouraging news as is appropriate without building up false hopes or expectations.

Reports to donors

Donors will wish to receive confirmation that their supplies have been safely received and put to good use. Any photographs or stories describing the area or people helped by the particular relief goods may result in further gifts.

Reports to the Press

Every effort should be made to hold Press conferences and give television and radio interviews especially during the early stages of the disaster operations when there will be a desperate need for facts. Persons being interviewed must consider that their performance will help formulate public opinion concerning the extent of the destruction, resultant needs and the effectiveness of the relief operation which might well influence the level of response to any public appeals for cash. People in other districts or countries with friends and relations in the stricken area will not wish to hear exaggerated or alarmist descriptions of the devastation and loss of human life. In general terms the best results will be achieved if the person interviewed simply describes the job he or she is doing in a positive manner.

Throughout the operation there will be need for Press releases describing the progress achieved, photographs depicting the victims receiving aid and human interest feature articles. Depending on the situation, Press reports can either be released in the field or by the headquarters of the relief agency.

Internal reports

In order to create a team spirit amongst the relief workers which tends to lead to greater efficiency, two-way communication between the field headquarters and relief teams should be established. Information concerning the progress of the operation and future plans should be disseminated by the head of operations at fortnightly or monthly staff meetings during which each team should be asked to make a presentation describing the situation and relief work undertaken in their area.

Co-operation

Co-operation with other relief bodies and U.N. agencies, described in Appendix 3, can best be achieved through the medium of information meetings at which matters of mutual interest are frankly discussed and plans formulated to make the best use of all available resources irrespective of source. These meetings should be chaired by the disaster relief coordinator appointed by the government. If co-operation and the free exchange of information exists between agencies working on the spot, then there is every hope that the trend will continue upwards resulting in less duplication of relief materials sent from abroad.

Foreign relief personnel should at all times appreciate that their presence in the disaster stricken country is at the invitation of the local government and that they are obliged to operate in accordance with its wishes. This might not always be in the best interest of the victims. Relief operations conducted during civil strife or international armed conflict are prone to such problems as the unfair distribution of relief supplies and much expropriation by armed groups. Agencies can in these situations either withdraw or compromise with the knowledge that a certain proportion of the supplies are getting to the people in real need. It is, however, more likely that the only threat to the working relationship between host government and relief agency will be brought about by the impatience of foreign staff unable to comprehend or tolerate the slow movement of the local bureaucracy. These problems are easily overcome if a more diplomatic approach is used.

Methods of communication

In order to maintain two-way communications for the transmission of urgent messages between the field office and the agency headquarters in one direction, and the field office and the field workers in the other, the following methods should be evaluated and the most efficient and economical adopted:

Telex/Teleprinter
Telegram
Telephone
Radio
Courier

Operations centre

Experience has shown that the setting up of an operations room or communications centre can greatly ease the flow of information and assist those responsible for the coordination of the relief operation. The operations centre will be responsible for collecting and collating all available information on the situation. This information will then be represented visually with the aid of maps, diagrams and charts. The operations room will also keep records of all messages received and transmitted and issue regular situation reports based on information received from field workers, the government, and other relief agencies. The facts monitored by this nerve centre and recorded in a daily log will provide all the material required for the final report evaluating the effectiveness of the operation.

16. Selection and training of personnel

Selection of personnel

As a general rule no one should be sent to the scene of a disaster in a foreign country unless his presence has been specifically requested by the government or other authoritative body within that particular country. When a request for certain experts such as doctors, nurses and administrators has been received, great diligence should be observed in order that the right candidate for the job is found. When chosen, relief workers should proceed immediately to the scene of the disaster where they should remain for a reasonable length of time or until the job has been completed.

There has in the past been a tendency to send large numbers of highly qualified specialist doctors and surgeons to developing countries where they have been unable to function due to the lack of equipment and supporting technicians. General physicians with experience of tropical medicine are more likely to be required after natural disasters in developing countries than surgeons. A typical medical team despatched to a disaster nowadays would be comprised of two doctors, four nurses and an 'administrator-cum-handyman'. Maximum use should always be made of local personnel who might be able to meet local needs. For example, many paramedicals in such areas will probably have received some training in simple diagnostic and treatment procedures.

When the need for a skilled delegate has been confirmed by the disaster assessment teams a selection panel consisting of medically qualified personnel with practical and management experience of disaster relief operations should be convened. The selection panel will judge the candidate's suitability with regard to:

Age. The candidate must be of legal age and reasonably mature.

Sex. Due to religious or social customs in the affected area preference may have to be given to male or female applicants.

Health. All team members should be medically examined and have chest X-rays taken. They should be able to work long hours under difficult conditions without sleep.

Qualifications. All personnel should produce certificates of qualification in their chosen fields of study.

Experience. At least two years' experience since qualification is desirable but the type of assignment will, in each case, determine the kind of experience to be given priority.

Personality. At least two satisfactory personal references should be acquired on completion of a successful interview. The following characteristics are essential:

Resourcefulness
Flexibility
Intelligence matched with common sense
Capacity to lead and direct personnel
Diplomacy

Family commitments. Responsibilities to any dependants must be considered.

Languages. The candidate should have a knowledge of foreign languages and the capacity to learn more.

Availability. Delegates should be prepared to leave with the maximum of a few days' notice.

The selection panel will also consider the candidate's psychological suitability to the conditions likely to be experienced in a developing country as the sudden immersion into an alien environment, with strange people, different cultures and social habits enveloped in a hot, humid atmosphere, can come as quite a shock. People harbouring racial or cultural prejudices or those with a family history of mental illness are unsuitable for this type of work.

In many isolated rural areas a team or delegate will be almost completely divorced from other expatriate contacts. It is therefore most important that members of a team are compatible and that they all share a willingness to mix socially with the local community. Generally speaking, those possessing a calm temperament are most successful in this type of assignment.

The candidate should be motivated by a strong desire to participate in a humanitarian relief operation but, at the same time, be able to appreciate that it is not possible to implement Western standards of health and medical care in areas lacking in financial resources. It should also be understood that the goals and objectives of a relief operation are limited to fulfilling relatively short-term needs created by the emergency and not those caused as a result of centuries of underdevelopment and poverty.

Training courses

Multi-disciplinary residential training courses should be held to prepare personnel to deal with disaster situations at home and abroad and, at the same time, to permit the closer evaluation of candidates wishing to work overseas. Most of the lectures will be of general interest and include a study of the types of incidents likely to affect that country together with a review of the effects of disasters and the methods used to relieve the resultant needs of the victims and the community in general. Emphasis will be given to practical exercises and students given the opportunity to set up emergency feeding centres, etc., and to handle the equipment issued to emergency relief teams.

The course will also include specialised lectures illustrated with slides and visual aids in order to familiarise medical personnel with the conditions likely to be found at the scene of a large accident or natural disaster.

The administrative and legislative aspects including an outline of the importance of the Geneva Conventions in situations of armed conflict will also be considered and problems from past experience presented for group study.

The training course should be followed some time later by a mock disaster exercise during which skills and management procedures can be put to the test and re-examined at the end of the day.

17. Briefing and information kit

The object of this chapter is to give the potential delegate an idea of the administrative arrangements which have to be completed by both the sponsoring agency and the team members prior to departure. It can therefore be used as a check list. Time and energy devoted to preparation and planning will increase the success of the mission and possibly eliminate a few of the frustrations experienced after arrival.

Contract

As soon as an offer of employment in an overseas relief operation has been accepted a contract should be prepared detailing the conditions and terms of employment, the salary and allowances to be paid. This should give the employer the right to terminate the agreement if the employee fails to abide by its rules. Similarly, the employee should have the right to resign. In the event of a resignation before the completion of the contract, consideration will have to be given to the payment or part payment of the return fare and equipment allowances.

The contract will usually contain the following provisions:

Salary. For contracts of up to 12 months' duration this is usually maintained at the rate received prior to taking up the assignment. Members of relief teams with similar qualifications and experience should receive the same financial remuneration.

Period of service. The dates upon which the employment commences and terminates should be clearly indicated. A note to the effect that a contract might be extended should also be included if appropriate.

Superannuation. If the employee is a member of a superannuation scheme the employer should continue the contribution during the period of contract.

National insurance. The employer should record the employee's national insurance payments and pay the employer's contribution.

Insurance. The employer should undertake to insure the employee against accident, sickness, loss of life and invalidism. A separate policy covering the loss and damage to the employee's possessions should also be taken out.

Clothing allowance. A kit or clothing allowance in the region of £75 to £100 should be made in advance to allow the delegate to purchase the necessary clothes and equipment. Alternatively, the employer might prefer to issue uniform and other suitable equipment.

Per diem. The rate of a per diem or local living allowance should be fixed according to the cost of living within the affected country. Such allowances are paid in local currency and in addition to the basic salary. The delegate should be able to live relatively comfortably but not luxuriously on this allowance.

Travel. The contract should confirm that the recruiting agency will meet all expenses incurred whilst travelling to and from the disaster.

Secondment from regular employment to work with relief agencies can often be arranged for periods of up to six months. During such times the relief agency will be responsible for reimbursing the employer who should continue to pay the delegate's salary and other benefits. Such arrangements ease the administration burdens on relief agencies which are usually dependent on public subscription.

Once the contract has been read and understood it should be signed by the employee and a representative of the relief agency.

Information kit

Approximately a week before departure the team should be called together for final briefing during which the administrative arrangements will be confirmed and the team addressed either by someone familiar with the area where it is to work or by a senior official who can adequately describe the situation and the conditions to be expected. Each member of the team should be issued with a comprehensive information pack containing the following information:

General information. History, size and make-up of population, type of government, political systems, business hours, economy, currency, communications, climate, time in relation to Greenwich Mean Time, principal religions, language, calendar, public holidays, educational standards, names and addresses of major hotels and prices charged, map.

The relief operation. The facts relating to the cause of the disaster and its known effects on the population. The total needs to be met and the overall scope of the operation. Special mention should be made of the town or area where the team will work and a job description supplied. The names and titles of the staff directing the operations should also be given.

The team. The names of the team members and their assigned duties. The team leader and administrator should be named.

Reporting procedures. Although the team may have been recruited by a national organisation they will probably be working under the direction of personnel from a large international agency. The chain of command and respective responsibilities should be provided in detail in order to avoid confusion at a later date. Instructions should also be given in respect of statements made to the Press.

Conduct. Delegates will be reminded of their status and the standard of professional and personal conduct required.

Health. A booklet describing the standards of hygiene required to remain healthy in a tropical climate should be included. Delegates should be reminded to have a dental check before departure.

Equipment. A list of all equipment supplied.

The information material should be placed in a strong folder which will enable the delegate to keep the papers intact for the duration of the mission.

Equipment

Relief teams should be entirely self-sufficient and should never rely on local resources of a disaster stricken country. It should take sufficient equipment for use during the assignment and an initial supply of general medicaments which will allow it to be operational as soon as it arrives. Further supplies of drugs and medical equipment can be flown in at a later date when the precise requirements are known. The following examples are offered in Appendix 4:

1. Suggested list of equipment (excluding provisions) for a six man medical team;
2. Suggested list of medical equipment;
3. Suggested list of medical supplies.

Personal medical kit

In addition to the general medical equipment each member of the team should be issued with a personal medical kit.

Clothing

Delegates should avoid taking new or expensive clothing as local laundry services can reduce the life of certain fabrics.

Travel documents

The relief agency financing the operation should ensure that every member of the team is in possession of a valid passport and, if required, a visa. It is a good idea to carry extra passport-size photographs as they might be required for driving licences, permits, etc. Each member should be responsible for his/her own ticket and the team leader should carry credit cards or miscellaneous-charges orders (purchased from airlines) to cover excess baggage charges, etc. A cash advance to cover local purchases and incidental costs incurred whilst travelling should also be issued in the appropriate local currencies to each member of the team before departure.

All foreign personnel entering the afflicted country should possess valid vaccination and inoculation certificates as required by the local health regulations.

Stationery

The team should carry a plentiful supply of stationery including airmail envelopes, adhesive tape, pens, pencils.

Relaxation

Every team member should take some reading material and it is also suggested that each team might consider purchasing a cassette tape recorder, with a varied selection of pre-recorded music cassettes, a pack of playing cards and a pocket chess set.

18. Evaluation, feedback and post action work

Foreign disaster relief

Basically the government of the country struck by national disaster is responsible for rescue, evacuation and survival of its people and for the timing and coordination of immediate emergency action. That government must determine the need of the disaster victims which the country itself cannot meet. It is important that governments establish effective working relations with representatives of other governments so that, in the event of a national disaster, negotiations for the procurement of urgently needed supplies and services can be expedited. Once such negotiations get under way these representatives should attempt to learn what other nations are doing, what help can be provided by national and international agencies and organisations and, specifically, what help can best be provided by their own country.

It is important to get the right equipment to the right place at the right time.

Avoiding waste and duplication

Experience has taught the need to avoid waste and duplication in the provision of supplies and services which are not needed, or which are not of value in meeting the needs of the specific current disaster situation. Such efforts are not only of no immediate help to the victims of the disaster but actually impede relief efforts by over-burdening transportation and storage facilities whose effectiveness is already compromised as a result of the disaster.

Representatives of the government, the national organisations, voluntary agencies and all those involved in disaster relief should be cautioned to control their eagerness. They should also avoid getting impatient when specific detailed information as to requirements, the number of disaster victims, the distribution capabilities and similar helpful information is not immediately available. When a disaster of major proportions occurs, such information is not easily obtainable even in modern societies having adequate communication facilities. On the other hand, assumptions not based on factual information may result in large quantities of unnecessary supplies and inappropriate medical personnel being rushed to the disaster site.

This type of response causes friction between governments, voluntary agencies and other relief groups and can endanger existing and future co-operation, relationships and programmes.

By responding to specific requests from governments in need of help, these various relief organisations can win acceptance for their work with the disaster victims and, at the same time, create goodwill for their programmes. No country wants its misfortunes publicised by others especially if it is done in a manner which makes it appear that the country is neglecting its own people. Care should be taken to acknowledge that the affected country is doing a great deal to help itself.

Relief action must start and continue in the disaster country. That is where the action is and it is imperative to avoid a situation where the donors are apparently in control. National sovereignty must be respected.

Decisions have to be taken of the scene of the disaster.

Assessing need

The only way one can have valid information about what has happened is to have adequate and comparable local assessment: 50 000 homeless means 'people' to some and 'families' to others. Representation in terms of a particular nation can also vary. In some nations the average family is three to five people whilst in others it is six to eight.

Assessors with the appropriate qualifications are essential. Engineers cannot assess the medical personnel and supplies required after a disaster. Doctors and nurses are not suitably qualified to report on the road and rail repairs necessary, and so on.

Use of local resources

The utmost use should always be made of local resources—not only of materials but also of personnel, the public health authorities (most countries have a Public Health Authority), WHO representatives, diplomatic missions, who are charged to know something about the country in which they are operating, and other officials of government.

If 'shopping-lists' are asked for, the request can be interpreted as meeting the medical requirements of the country for the next five years.

It is important, therefore, to learn to make an assessment of the situation and how to determine the kind of forces, assistance and categories of personnel and equipment which should be sent in, the duration, and the purpose. There must always be local outlets through which this assistance is channelled.

In addition to assessment, there is the question of transmission of requests. A list transmitted by radio can be picked up by 50 listeners—and supplied by just as many in one country alone.

The greatest waste arises from the misuse, mishandling, and misrepresentation of needs as well as from their wrongful assessment. There are warehouses in the world full of medical supplies, 50 per cent of which are outdated.

Local manpower resources must be used. Often teams of highly skilled experts go into a disaster area and proceed to do the job whilst the natives—homeless, jobless and moneyless—just sit and watch. The task is done for them by the experts who then go home—until the next disaster. The natives have learnt nothing.

It is of the utmost importance to work with the local inhabitants and to teach them how to cope. Leadership which entices, involves and incites is necessary, not a total task force.

Some Western standards must be lowered and use of routine dramatic drugs for the short period of disaster relief must be avoided at all costs. Often standards are set and treatments are initiated which cannot be continued when the teams pull out. A void of dissatisfaction and discontent results.

The population is accustomed to what existed before, that is, traditional treatment. Disaster relief teams must work with the headmen of the villages, the witch-doctors and the indigenous leaders. They should not build up a health service to a level which is impossible to sustain after the disaster emergency is over.

Co-operation and coordination

Daily assessments, assignments and allocations will facilitate the work load and divide it more fairly.

A few qualified people who know their job and who can work with the local population, showing them how to do the job and providing the material aid with which to do it, are worth more than a whole battalion sent in to do the task.

When a disaster occurs it is necessary to determine who is in charge, who gives the directions, who sets up the control centres, who coordinates the effects and help, and who takes the overall responsibility and accountability.

Helping others to help themselves

We have not assessed, to the extent that we should, the potential needs of disaster-prone countries. We could better use existing resources. For instance, we should develop, in appropriate countries, desalination equipment. Enormous quantities of water are flown in at vast expense in times of disaster. It would represent a great saving if teams worked in these disaster-prone countries helping to build systems of water purification and sanitation, and equipping people to face the droughts, floods and cyclones which will inevitably come as freaks of nature.

Monitoring relief aid

It is often difficult to determine how many people are affected by a disaster since census data for the area may not be available. Sometimes it is possible to estimate the population, using smallpox vaccination scars as markers.

This kind of data, coupled with surveillance, should permit the relief administrator to calculate type, quantity of relief goods, personnel and transport requirements.

1. Surveillance should be carried out frequently at field level and reports made directly to the administrative headquarters.

2. Data must be collected in a standardised way so that direct comparisons can be made.

3. The data should be available in useful form to all those involved in the relief effort to provide feedback at all levels.

4. Professionals should occupy key central positions, though volunteers may be useful at field level.

19. Dealing with the effects of bombs, explosives and gunshot wounds

1. Organisation

Urban guerilla warfare has become a part of life in the seventies.

Responsibilities for the organisation of relief work must be clearly defined and should be known by all emergency services as well as hospital staff. Terrorists' bombs may produce large numbers of casualties, placing a great strain on the resources of even a large hospital. The pattern of casualties varies greatly from one incident to another, so that considerable adjustment to a predesigned disaster plan may be required. It is an advantage to have a vacant space within each major hospital in which numerous casualties can be accommodated.

2. Alerting

By the emergency telephone network or direct reporting the ambulance and fire services are alerted and the information room of the national, regional or local police is informed. The first of the utility services involved will then alert the hospital nearest to the incident, using an up-to-date list known to and carried by the three main public service vehicles. The first alerted hospital will be informed that it is the designated pivotal hospital. It will automatically provide the senior medical officer to take charge of all medical and first aid resources at the site. It may also provide the first mobile team.

All other alerted hospitals will be termed supporting hospitals and, together with the designated hospital, must be given essential information indicating brief details of the time and location of the accident and, if possible, the type and estimated number of casualties. The name of the designated hospital must also be made known to all the supporting units alerted. It is important that the list of available units be kept up to date.

3. Medical officer in charge

This senior medical officer appointed to the site must contact as soon as possible the senior police and/or fire officers to get a first-hand appreciation of the situation. It is then his responsibility:

a. To establish a medical services report centre;

b. To coordinate the medical and first-aid resources, and

c. To formulate the casualty evacuation plan in consultation with the senior ambulance officer.

4. Decision regarding mobile team

In the early stages following a major accident the extent and type of medical aid needed at the site is difficult. The decision to despatch a mobile team may be made by the senior medical officer on duty at the designated hospital, if he is specifically requested to do so by the police, fire and/or ambulance service, any other authorised body or the senior medical officer on duty at the hospital if he considers, in the light of the information initially received, that a mobile medical team is necessary; or by the senior medical officer at the site after he has contacted the senior services officers and obtained a first-hand appreciation of the situation.

5. Deploying special squads and teams

Trapped casualties would be rescued by the fire service; the senior fire officer present would be responsible for initiating the rescue. The coordination of the rescue activities would be a joint function of all services. Amputation squads will be called forward by the senior medical officer to enable rescue squads to extricate seriously trapped live casualties and moribund victims from the wreckage.

The senior medical officer will also arrange, as necessary, for the provision of mobile surgical and resuscitation teams, and mobile teams from special centres—for example mobile plastic surgical teams. These squads or special teams must not be confused with the mobile medical team. Their functions are totally different and any change in application must only be determined by the senior site medical officer in consultation with the specialist team leaders.

6. Establishment of pivotal points

The site of a major disaster is always one of confusion and congestion and the establishment of clearly recognisable pivotal points is of vital importance to site control. The medical services report centre is one of these pivotal points and should be established directly adjacent to one of the other pivotal points by agreed pre-arrangement; ideally it is best located with the mobile ambulance control unit. This facilitates the determination and maintenance of the evacuation plan jointly with the chief ambulance officer. In some areas the police control is readily available and recognisable; alternatively the fire service, in its rescue capacity, may have an operational vehicle. All three site headquarters must be equipped with radio-telephones and have walkie-talkie sets for site use.

7. Coordination

As well as a focal point there must also be an 'incident officer' doing the coordination. Although his selection may vary, on balance the senior police officer would seem the most suitable choice. He must have a distinctly recognisable location, equipped with radio-telephone and walkie-talkie. Identification of the medical services report centre, the casualty post and the senior medical officer in charge of medical and first-aid services are of equal importance both by day and night. The senior medical officer in charge should wear a white coat with the words 'senior medical officer' across the back. Suitable armbands must be issued to doctors, nurses and first aiders offering their assistance.

A casualty post should be set up in the vicinity of the medical services report centre. This is normally established by the mobile medical team on arrival. Through this post all casualties should as far as possible be channelled. It is the filter that ensures that ambulance priority is given to the seriously injured, particularly to those requiring life-saving surgery. It is important to emphasise that:

a. When ambulance resources are limited and long journeys are involved, the slightly injured should be given treatment and held back, to ensure that ambulance priority is given to the seriously injured (unless there is delay in extracting the latter).

b. All casualties handled by the casualty post should be suitably labelled before being sent to hospital. Brief details of any treatment given at the site must be recorded on the label.

8. Disposal of casualties

One, if not the main, purpose of determining a definitive site organisation is the disposal of casualties. Before the senior medical officer arrives at the scene of a disaster, ambulance crews, from their daily contact with hospitals, will know which hospitals can deal with casualties and which are the nearest.

In formulating the casualty evacuation plan the senior medical officer will be guided by the characteristics of the disaster. If there are a large number of serious surgical cases he will direct them to as many hospitals as possible, depending on the availability of staff and theatre accommodation. If the senior officer in charge decides on arrival at the site and in consultation with the senior ambulance officer present that the originally alerted hospitals would be flooded by the number of casualties, and if he therefore includes in the casualty evacuation plan hospitals which have not already been alerted, he must ensure that the ambulance HQ control room, the police headquarters and the senior police officer at the site (incident officer) are all given the names of the additional hospitals to be involved. The routing of ambulances in and out of the disaster area, and also within it, will be part of the casualty evacuation plan.

9. Disaster inquiry bureau

With the up-to-date efficiency of communication services, telephones, radio and television, the news of a disaster is quickly known and widely spread. To avoid added disruption at the site, and disturbance at the receiving hospitals, a disaster inquiry bureau must be set up. One of the main responsibilities of the police at major accidents is to notify friends and relatives of the dead and injured, and the inquiry bureau should be established as early as possible and located away from the hospitals receiving casualties, preferably at a local police station.

Press

The media and the Press should be asked:

a. Specifically to include in their news items the telephone number and address of the inquiry bureau.

b. To stress that inquiries should be made to the bureau and *not* to the hospitals receiving casualties. The local exchange supervisor should be given the location of the inquiry bureau as soon as it is established and should be asked to arrange for telephone inquires to the hospitals to be diverted to the bureau.

Documentation

Police officers will be transported to all casualty-receiving hospitals for documentation duties, and they should be supplied by the hospital staff with the particulars of casualties arriving. The police officers will then transmit these particulars to the central casualty bureau. Those required will have been agreed when devising the casualty labels in advance.

10. Communications

The importance of site control has been stressed, but vital centres away from the actual disaster will also rely on communications; on these will largely depend the success of operations. Although the ambulance and fire services will have radio-telephone links with their bases as well, communications between the medical services report centre and the casualty-receiving hospitals should be provided by the police radio-telephone network. This is effected by automatically positioning police radio-telephone cars at the scene and at the hospitals alerted to receive casualties. The importance of this vital link between the site and the receiving hospitals cannot be sufficiently emphasised if over-concentration in the nearest hospital is to be avoided. The use of walkie-talkie sets must be strictly controlled as jamming can be a serious risk.

Fatal casualties

All the procedural arrangements are directed towards saving life and reducing pain and suffering to a minimum. This means, however, that the dead must also be considered, particularly at the site, from the point of view of ensuring that live casualties do not suffer because the dead are given ambulance priority. Emergency mortuary arrangements, including disposal of the dead, should be made by the police.

Using the public

One of the outstanding factors at the site of any disaster is the highly charged emotional atmosphere. One emotion which may affect many people is that of fear. People become incapable of speech and decision. Another common emotion is curiosity: the disaster acts as a magnet attracting crowds. If there is a delay in the arrival of excavators and shovels, the positive aspects of the crowd's response can be harnessed and they should be organised to lift masonry, to pass rubble from hand to hand and similar tasks.

Arrival at the hospital

On arrival at the hospital the patients are sorted so that space and facilities are used to the best advantage. Extensive cubicle space on the ground floor and a large number of trolleys are invaluable.

The X-ray department may become a bottleneck and requests should be screened by a senior doctor. Often some can be cancelled, others delayed for 24 hours and the remainder arranged in order of priority.

Documentation

The importance of documentation cannot be over-emphasised. Amongst other vital factors, safe transfusion depends upon it. The clinical record made on admission is likely to be the only pre-operations record. Because in some countries disaster situations can be vulnerable to public inquiries and litigation all facets require good records.

It has been found to be a good plan if, instead of sending patients and relatives to a receptionist, the patients are placed in suitable cubicles and receptionists walk from cubicle to cubicle issuing case papers as they find the patients in them.

If the routine case record is five sheets thick (as is often the case) the two top copies should be left with the patient and the lower copies collected at the central reception desk. From these a clerk can list the patients who have arrived in the hospital.

All clinical notes, X-ray requests and records of treatment are written on the two copies left with the patient.

If the patient goes to the theatre or ward or to another area one copy is handed in to the desk and the remaining copy travels with him. If the patient is discharged home both copies are collected at the desk. Efficient collection of papers is very important.

Listing of patients should be carried out soon after arrival. As they leave the accident and emergency department a copy of the record is handed in and information from it is added to the original basic information. For each patient a rough diagnosis and disposal (admission, transfer, discharge, etc.) should be entered. For patients who are being admitted it is noted whether their condition is critical, serious or fair. Lists with this information should be compiled as soon as possible and photocopied for the disaster inquiry bureau. In this way accurate information is quickly disseminated.

Staff dealing with the emotional reaction of survivors

Whilst it can be accepted that the provision of emergency medical treatment is of primary importance, the emotional reaction of survivors' relatives and friends and even of relief personnel themselves also requires attention. Most people show signs of emotional disturbance as an immediate reaction to a disaster, but most of these signs are transient and recover spontaneously or with the help of sympathetic management.

Different people react differently according to their constitutional predisposition and previous life experiences. The types of disaster and the type of community and its culture and folklore also contribute to the types of reaction seen. During the period of impact, which continues until the initial stresses of the disaster are no longer operating, about 12 to 25 per cent of the people are cool and collected. They retain their awareness, appraise the situation, formulate a plan of action, and see it through. About 75 per cent of the survivors are stunned and bewildered with restriction of their field of attention, blunting of emotional expression (although showing the physiological concomitants of fear) and automatic behaviour. The remaining 10 to 25 per cent show such responses as confusion, paralysing anxiety, crying and screaming.

During the period of recoil, which begins when the initial stresses have ceased or when the individual has escaped from them, there is a gradual return of awareness, recall, and emotional expression. Survivors show a childlike attitude of dependency, a need to be with others, and a desire to ventilate their feelings. The stresses of the post-traumatic period are social and, beginning after security from the initial stresses has been fully established, they are brought about by complete awareness of what the disaster has meant in terms of loss and bereavement.

Specific reactions

Anger may be seen in individuals or may be collective and organised. For instance, after the third plane crash in succession at Elizabeth, New Jersey, hundreds of people were going to destroy the airport if the authorities had not promptly closed it. Anger may be directed towards individuals or groups, such as minority ethnic groups, the financially successful, civic officials, or the Government.

Guilt has been described in the survivors of tornadoes and aeroplane crashes, among the passengers of a skyjacked aircraft, and after many other disasters. Some people felt guilty because they had survived while others had perished; others wondered if they could have done more in their rescue bids. In some instances guilt may be displaced from previously existing problems.

Defensive reactions may take the form of dissociation or conversion hysteria. Examples of hysterical conversion symptoms are blindness, a limp, paraplegia and inability to recognise immediately members of the family.

Panic. This has been described as an acute fear reaction, marked by loss of self-control, which is followed by nonsensical and irrational fright behaviour. Although comparatively uncommon in disasters, when it does occur it can be 'contagious' and lead to headlong mass fright.

Differential diagnosis

Different types of disasters may lead to a wide variety of cerebral traumata. These include the various types of head injury including blast concussion, cerebral anoxia due, for example, to carbon monoxide poisoning, toxic reactions to chemicals, and the effects of nuclear radiation.

In some disasters the superimposed effects of physical injuries will have to be considered, including blood loss and burns, hypothermia, as well as water, food, sleep and sensory deprivation. The clinical picture may also be altered by the effects of alcohol or drug intoxication, as might be found for instance in the survivors of bombed public houses. Occasionally one will encounter conditions brought about by the survivors' failure to take their regular medication because of the disaster, for example hypoglycaemic or diabetic complications in a patient whose regular eating and insulin habits have been disrupted.

Hysterical conversion symptoms will have to be distinguished from organic neurological deficits, especially in patients with head injuries. The effect of suggestion and contagion may lead to difficulties in distinguishing psychogenic from toxogenic complaints in a widespread incident of radiation sickness or chemical poisoning.

Reactions of children

Children's reactions to disaster include anxiety and fear, such as separation anxiety, restlessness, irritability, temper, dependent and demanding behaviour, disturbances of bodily functions including enuresis, difficulty in concentration, intellectual problems, school refusal, guilt, and rarely, visual hallucinations. Usually, however, children show a remarkable resilience. The worse effects of disasters occur when there is separation from their parents, when they reflect their parents' psychopathology, and when there are other anxiety-creating factors in their backgrounds.

Reactions of the elderly

Older people are more likely to react to their experiences of disasters with what has been called a high sense of deprivation. Two themes prevail—the loss of symbolic assets, particularly homes, and a feeling of destruction of time. It appears that, to the elderly, what has been destroyed is more than just an object but, in a sense, time itself.

Reactions of the mentally ill

Disasters may, of course, strike hospitals, where the risk of fire in particular has always worried administrators. It is therefore important to have preconceived ideas about how patients suffering from mental illness may react.

Meeting emotional needs

During the period of recoil, survivors need to be with others. For this reason and from our common knowledge that people in distress need human companionship, it should be ensured that injured and frightened people are not left alone and children in particular not separated from their parents. Only the occasional survivor who shows a severe psychiatric disturbance will need to be transferred to a psychiatric treatment centre, because of the demoralising effect that he may have and the risk of emotional contagion. People may also be demoralised by rumours that exaggerate the extent of the catastrophe. These should therefore be discouraged as soon as possible.

In the recoil period survivors also need to be given something, such as a hot drink (not of course if there is a possibility that surgery will be called for) or a blanket, or to be looked after; the importance of the 'giving' and 'nursing' appears to be related not so much to the kind of aid as to the psychological meaning of being cared for. At the same time they need to talk about their experiences. The aim therefore should be to encourage this as soon as possible, although no effort should be made to explore the background and disposition at this time.

After a short rest in which survivors become more fully aware of what has happened, they should be encouraged to return to purposive activity. To participate in simple and useful tasks is therapeutic in the sense that the survivor will more easily regain his shattered self-esteem. From the practical viewpoint this also means an extra pair of hands when there are mass casualties.

It is an important part of the doctors' and nurses' work:

a. To give reassurance during the period of heightened suggestibility;

b. To issue confident easy-to-follow instructions, thereby encouraging positive activity;

c. To convey accurate and responsible messages to survivors, their families and friends, and the media and to quash rumours as they emerge.

d. To transfer disturbed and disturbing patients to a special treatment centre;

e. To use psychotropic drugs conservatively and only when definitely indicated;

f. To transfer patients sharing emotional sequelae for psychiatric assessment and or treatment.

CIVILIAN BOMB INJURIES

Types of injury

Those closest to a large explosion may be blown to pieces by the force of the blast and do not need the services of the hospital. In those coming to hospital it has been found that the wounds are characterised by their multiplicity and by the associated gross soiling which may occur. The common basic injury is a combination of bruises, abrasions and lacerations. Wounds have varied in size from minute punctures, due to glass or metal fragments, to large lacerations, often impregnated with foreign bodies.

The terrorist's bomb differs from that of conventional warfare as it is nearly always delivered by hand or in a motor vehicle. In these catastrophes quite a small charge, up to about 30 lb (14 kg) can be carried in a suitcase or parcel; damage is caused by the blast itself, by flying debris and occasionally by falling masonry.

The car bomb may contain a 500 lb (230 kg), or even larger, charge of explosive, placed within the vehicle. When such a bomb explodes without warning, people nearby may suffer serious injury, but the majority of casualties receive relatively minor injuries from flying debris.

The majority of such wounds have been found to be peripheral, the legs accounting for over a third of all injuries. The head has been the site of injury in a large number of victims, the majority of wounds, whilst being of a superficial nature, requiring the skills of a maxillofacial team.

Isolated eye injuries may occur with other facial injuries and range from simple corneal abrasions to serious penetrating wounds for which enucleation is the only possible treatment. Penetrating skull injuries and brain damage are uncommon after explosions. Shockwaves spreading concentrically from the blast centre cause damage to the middle and inner ear. Burns are uncommon but may be of two types, the flash burn due to radiant heat, affecting only persons close to the centre of the explosion (clothing is a protection and thus the hands and face are the areas usually burned), and the flame burn, arising chiefly from burning clothing and affecting all areas of the body.

Blast injuries of the lung take the form cf alveolar haemorrhage, which in severe cases gives rise to obstruction of the respiratory passages with blood and froth.

The main difference between the management of injuries produced by high-speed motor accidents and those produced by a bomb explosion is the gross tissue damage and wound contamination which makes gas gangrene a major hazard, particularly with wounds of the thighs or buttocks. It is essential therefore that debridement should be thorough. If muscle has been involved no primary suturing should be attempted. After debridement the wounds should be dressed and, where appropriate, splinted with plaster of Paris. These should be left until the fifth or sixth day unless there is pain, pyrexia, odour or soaking of the dressing. Delayed primary suturing or grafting may be carried out after the fifth day if the wound appears clean. Often this has to be delayed further. Tetanus toxoid and a broad spectrum antibiotic should be given to all casualties.

Traumatic amputations should be treated by skin flap trimming and primary closure, only attempted when all divided muscle is seen to be absolutely healthy and uncontaminated. It is safer to leave the flaps approximated with a few loose sutures and perform delayed primary suture later.

Apparent superficial wounds of the trunk should be carefully assessed as the underlying wound may be serious. All penetrating wounds of the chest and abdomen should be explored.

Resuscitation and early treatment

The close proximity of the intensive care unit to the accident and emergency centre enables a consultant anaesthetist in charge to deal with difficult airway problems and to advise on the care of unconscious patients, especially those with head injuries. Often intravenous infusions can be established by routes more familiar to the anaesthetist than to his surgical colleagues when conventional sites are not available.

Airway problems

Injuries to the face, jaw, or neck due to either bullets or shrapnel from bombs may rapidly produce upper airway obstruction. This usually arises from oedema of the soft tissues or from direct damage to the larynx or trachea. The insertion of a cuffed tracheal tube at the earliest opportunity is of paramount importance both to ensure a clear airway and to prevent regurgitation of stomach contents and aspiration into the lungs, with subsequent pneumonitis. The latter is a very real danger, as many of the patients have been injured in bars and clubs.

Deeply unconscious patients may usually be intubated without any great difficulty. On the other hand many are restless, irritable, uncooperative and hypoxic. Intubation in these circumstances cannot be performed without some form of sedation. The administration of diazepam (5 to 10 mg) intravenously will enable rapid intubation to be performed without a struggle and without compromising the patient's already hazardous condition. In our experience emergency tracheostomy has fortunately been very seldom required. It has been the practice in many instances to perform an elective tracheostomy after exploration of the wounds and surgical repair. This facilitates management in the postoperative period, and many respiratory problems can be prevented. An additional advantage of tracheostomy in these circumstances is that the difficulties of giving further anaesthetics are overcome. Frequently these patients require many visits to the operating theatre for further surgery and wound dressings.

Fluid replacement

Much has been written on the type of fluid which should be given initially to the injured patient in haemorrhagic shock. The emphasis varies from centre to centre and from one country to another, but certain principles are common to all. Hartmann's solution (Ringer's lactate) is readily available, and since it is stable at room temperature it can be given without the problems associated with blood stored at 4° C. One to two litres can be given rapidly while cross-matched blood is being prepared. Group O Rh negative blood is kept in a refrigerator in the resuscitation room, but is used only if the patient's condition fails to respond or deteriorates on the above regimen. Dextran solutions (MW 70 000) are used in addition to Hartmann's solution, but the volume is restricted to 10 ml/kg body weight in order to avoid acute tubular necrosis of the kidney.

The volumes of intravenous fluids given must be closely monitored to avoid over- or under-correction of fluid loss. Measurement of urinary output and central venous pressure is started at the earliest possible moment and will usually provide a helpful guide to fluid replacement.

Blood transfusion

Blood provided by blood banks is seldom fresh; the older the blood the greater the amount of clot and debris present. If massive transfusion is required a considerable amount will enter the circulation and may give rise to microemboli. The filters on standard blood transfusion sets will prevent the passage only of particles greater than 170 μm. The recent introduction of microfilters which remove all particles greater than 10 μm has helped to prevent pulmonary emboli and post-traumatic pulmonary insufficiency. These filters do not significantly restrict the rate of transfusion but should not be used when fresh blood and platelets are being given.

Head injuries

The initial management of head injuries resulting from bomb blasts and gunshot wounds is of considerable importance. It is well known that hypoxia, hypercarbia, acidosis, and electrolyte disturbances will increase cerebral oedema. Pioneer work by Lundberg, Lassen, Gordon and Rossanda has shown the value of hyperventilation therapy in head injuries. Within a few minutes of admission a tracheal tube is introduced and hyperventilation therapy started with the aim of reducing the partial pressure of carbon dioxide in the arterial blood to approximately 25 torr (3 kPa). This allows the undamaged blood vessels of the brain to contract and reduces intracranial blood volume, with a fall of intracranial pressure.

Minor variations in intracranial volume such as those caused by coughing, vomiting, restlessness, shivering, and convulsions can increase intracranial pressure with dramatic and sometimes irreversible cerebral damage. This complication can be prevented or alleviated by this form of therapy. During the period of hyperventilation it is desirable to monitor intracranial pressure, cerebrospinal fluid lactate content, and cerebral blood flow to detect the presence of an expanding intracranial haematoma and as a guide to prognosis and the effectiveness of treatment. Close observation of the pupils still remains an important feature of management.

A most satisfying response is sometimes found in patients who suddenly develop a high intracranial pressure associated with dilated unreactive pupils, for the introduction of hyperventilation produces a dramatic fall in intracranial pressure, with a return of normal pupillary reflexes. We have found hyperventilation of value both before and during surgery, and it can also be continued for several days into the postoperative period with beneficial results.

Artificial ventilation

Indications for artificial ventilation in patients injured in bomb blasts and from bullets can be considered in three main groups:

Prophylactic

This group includes not only patients who are electively ventilated, such as those with severe head injuries, but also those who have undergone prolonged and extensive surgery. Artificial ventilation enables adequate analgesia to be provided without fear of respiratory depression and nursing procedures to be carried out without discomfort to the patient, and it postpones the patient's distress at realising the extent of his injuries until a more favourable time.

Direct lung damage

It is easy to understand how a crushing injury of the chest can result in respiratory insufficiency, but the mechanism is less obvious after high velocity bullets and bomb blasts. The bullets travel faster than the speed of sound, and the great energy dissipated in the tissues results in shock waves. In the case of the lung this produces tissue damage some distance away from the bullet track. As the lung is elastic, permanent damage seldom results, but initially fulminant pulmonary oedema often threatens life. Though the bullet may have penetrated only one lung, the other lung may be as severely damaged and its function impaired.

Blast injuries of the lungs occur when people are close to an explosion, especially when it occurs in a confined space such as a bar or restaurant. The clinical picture is remarkably consistent in that for a period of 24 to 48 hours the patient remains free from respiratory distress and the arterial blood gases are essentially normal; then gradually increasing dyspnoea associated with a dry cough becomes apparent. Moist sounds are then audible throughout both lungs, and the chest X-ray film shows a diffuse interstitial pulmonary oedema. The blood gas analysis now shows increasing hypoxaemia and carbon dioxide retention.

Treatment of this condition consists in artificial ventilation with a positive end-expiratory pressure (P.E.E.P.), giving high inspiratory concentrations of oxygen, and administering diuretics and steroids. Though the management of these cases is often complicated by the development of pneumothorax and artificial ventilation may be required for several weeks, (in one known patient for 60 days), the prognosis is surprisingly good.

Lung damage is due to the shock waves of the explosion travelling at high velocity and being transmitted through the chest wall to the liquid phase of the lung before an equalising pressure can be transmitted through the tracheobronchial tree. These pressure differentials give rise to alveolar damage and haemorrhage. The lungs also become compressed between the inward moving chest wall and the rising diaphragm, because the pressure wave also compresses the abdominal wall.

Post-traumatic insufficiency

There are many possible explanations for this syndrome, especially in patients with multiple injuries who have received massive blood transfusion and have undergone extensive surgery. It is clear that, whatever the mechanism of its production, the end result is an increase in both pulmonary vascular resistance and in pulmonary capillary permeability. This produces pulmonary oedema, which may either resolve completely or progress into fatal consolidation of both lungs. The clinical course is unpredictable, and once consolidation occurs it is almost totally refractory to treatment.

GUNSHOT WOUNDS

Gunshot wounds of the limbs

In gunshot wounds the injuries vary from minor soft-tissue damage to gross disruption of tissues of all types. The degree of severity depends on several factors. The type of gun used is important: the faster the muzzle velocity the greater the damage caused. The damage will also be greater if the bullet strikes a hard object such as metal on clothing or equipment before entering the body or strikes a bone on entering.

There may be multiple wounds caused by a machine pistol or shot gun. High-velocity rifles such as self-loading and Armalite rifles produce very severe injuries from cavitation caused by an initial positive pressure wave followed by an equally strong negative pressure wave. These pressure waves can be severe enough to cause permanent damage to structures such as the spinal cord even though the bullet does not directly injure the cord.

Diagnosis

Careful inspection of all wounds is essential to determine the type of missile used and if possible its direction of travel through the tissues. Detailed examination must be carried out for damage to major vessels, nerves, bones and joints.

A history from the patient, if possible, and others involved in the incident may be helpful. From this one may learn the type of weapon used and also acquire some idea of the volume of blood loss.

Early management

The wounds should be dressed with a large pad and bandaged. If there is considerable bleeding a pressure dressing should be applied, and this usually controls most bleeding. If there is a fracture a temporary splint should be used.

This general management at this stage usually includes treatment for shock and blood loss. Intravenous infusions must be started and the patient given adequate fluid and blood.

All wounds must be carefully examined. Small superficial wounds should have the skin edges trimmed and a dressing applied. Superficial through-and-through wounds should also have the skin edges excised and the so called 'pull-through technique' may be used. This means that forceps are passed through the wound, and a swab soaked in a mild antiseptic such as cetrimide and chlorhexidine (Savlon) is pulled through the wound. This refers to low-velocity injuries with minimal damage to tissues.

Deep wounds

These must be thoroughly explored, if necessary by enlarging the wound or in some cases joining the entrance and exit wounds. All dead tissues must be removed, and the dissection may be extensive. The skin edges should be carefully excised. The wound is then left open and packed lightly with tulle. To avoid infection the skin should never be sutured at the initial treatment. Even with the most careful surgery some dead tissue may remain, and there will probably be some haematoma formation. Suturing of wounds at this stage is positively dangerous, and may lead to infection and even gas gangrene. The wound is normally sutured five to seven days later. This delayed primary suture will produce an excellent result.

Wounds of bone or joint

Careful debridement is carried out. Small isolated pieces of bone may be removed, but those with soft tissue attachments must be left. The wound is then treated as already described and a splint applied.

Internal fixation is used only if there has been a concomitant vascular injury requiring vascular repair. It is necessary to fix the fracture to make the limb steady, and allow the vascular repair to heal. If internal fixation is not possible, traction should be used with great caution when a vascular repair has been performed. An injudicious pull on a repaired vessel will narrow its lumen and lead to thrombosis.

Joints

Joint injuries must be carefully explored and all foreign material and loose fragments of bone removed. It may be necessary to wash out the joint with saline to ensure removal of all fragments.

Wounds involving nerves

Fortunately most nerve injuries are not permanent. If nerve tissue is lost, there is usually a considerable gap, and this means that primary repair is rarely possible. However, the nerve ends may be marked with a black silk suture to aid identification if delayed repair is carried out.

Wounds of major vessels

When major blood vessels are damaged it is usual to approach them directly, pressure and packing being applied to control the blood loss until definitive control has been achieved. This can be done in most cases without using Spencer Wells type forceps; DeBakey or bulldog arterial clamps are used together with tapes for intermittent control. Because of the nature of the injuries the incisions are seldom conventional arterial exposures. Deep veins are as important as arteries and they should be dealt with in a similar manner. The urgency to control the haemorrhage means that proper debridement and exploration of the wound is delayed until the haemorrhage is controlled.

The next step with the vessel involves some proximal and distal dissection and possibly the passage of tapes or soft catheters round them. The damaged ends are then trimmed back until healthy tissue is exposed. This may preserve a section of a vessel in continuity as a ribbon, or a gap of varying length may exist.

The content of the vessels distal to the injury should now be considered. In cases which reach the operating theatre within an hour, and an obvious back flow of blood occurs from the distal artery 20–40 ml of heparin saline solution is injected distally. In cases arriving any later than this a Fogarty balloon catheter size 3 or 4 is passed before heparin saline is injected. Veins are dealt with similarly. The use of systemic heparin is not advised in such cases.

Fig. 19.1 illustrates the usual methods available for repairing damaged blood vessels. Simple end-to-end anastomosis is often possible with the limb joints flexed, but this attractive and easy procedure can lead to failure when the joints are extended, and it has been used very rarely. Some failures after this procedure have been retrieved by inserting a graft. The graft should be autogenous vein, since any foreign material is likely to become infected. The source of vein graft can present a problem, particularly as many of these injuries are in the popliteal area and the patient may well be prone. Rarely should the graft be taken from the injured limb, because the last intact venous channel may be sacrificed. Occasionally a proximal length of saphenous vein is taken from the sound limb at the outset, or the arm veins may be used. Flexing the knee allows the distal saphenous vein to be obtained when arm veins are being used for resuscitation of the prone patients.

Fig. 19.2 shows a proved method of obtaining a graft made from two strips of this rather muscular vein; it functions well in the popliteal and lower femoral arteries. Damaged deep veins should be repaired, and when every vessel has been torn one good deep venous channel should be obtained if possible.

Silk has been the usual suture material, 5/0 atraumatic for arteries and 5/0 or 6/0 for

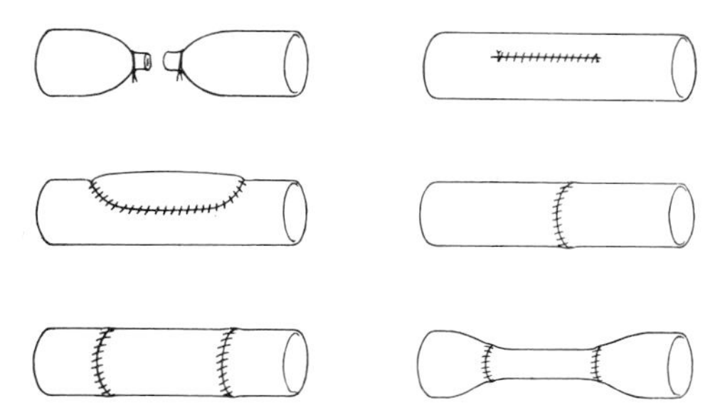

Fig. 19.1 Top left: ligation to be avoided. Top right: simple suture seldom possible in arteries but sometimes in veins. Middle left: vein patch. Middle right: end-to-end anastomosis. Bottom left: ideal graft inset difficult to achieve. Bottom right: unusual situation with vein graft, and if seriously narrowed can lead to failure.

veins. This material is a little more manageable than the smoother synthetic materials in these emergency cases.

Grafted vessels are best covered with neighbouring tissues, and this happens naturally in the majority of cases. Occasionally a catgut suture is necessary to hold a muscle or a fascial layer against a vessel, but otherwise the wound is dealt with in the previously described manner.

Fasciotomy has not been practised often enough, and severe postoperative oedema has been encountered in muscle compartments, leading to infarction. All cases seen after a delay of several hours should have the anterior tibial compartment decompressed by fasciotomy.

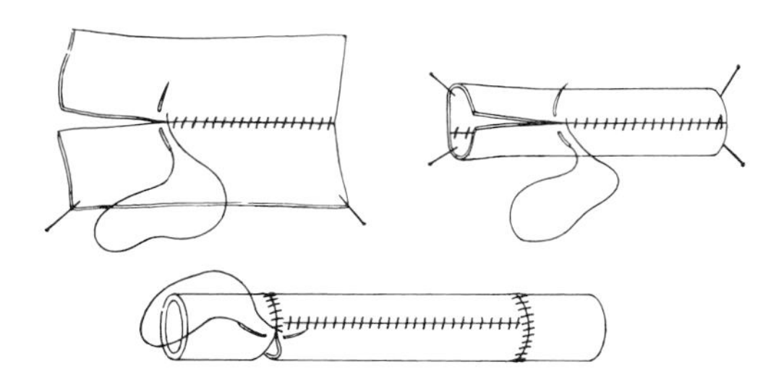

Fig. 19.2 Method of fabricating a sizable vein graft from two strips of vein. Pin the vein, intima side down, on a sterile board and suture longitudinally. Then turn intima inwards and repeat procedure. Finally insert the graft and remember to trim the arteries to fit the graft, because cutting the graft would undo the suture knots and lead to disruption of the graft.

Later management

Delayed primary suture. This technique is imperative in dealing with gunshot wounds. Five to seven days after initial injury the wounds are inspected, and if there is no gross infection they are sutured. Indeed, it may be necessary to make release incisions to allow closure of the original wound. Skin grafting is necessary in many cases and may require several operations.

Severe, extensive injuries, with destruction of the major vessels, nerves, bones, and gross muscle damage, may necessitate primary amputation. Consultation with a colleague before deciding on amputation is advisable.

Inspection. With careful surgical techniques infection is not a serious problem. All patients are given antibiotics as a routine. A combination of ampicillin and flucloxacillin is given in full doses until delayed primary suture is performed. In cases with fractures or joint injuries antibiotic treatment may be continued for two to three weeks.

Gunshot wounds of the trunk

In the management of wounds of the chest and abdomen the basic principles outlined for reception and resuscitation of the patient are of paramount importance. Blood loss and shock must be treated with urgency.

Thoracic wounds

A chest drain is inserted into one or both pleural cavities when obvious penetration by a bullet has occurred or when there is any clinical evidence of blood or air in the pleural cavity. An estimate is made of the probable track of the missile or missiles, and careful clinical examination, especially of the abdomen, is carried out. Low-velocity missiles are often retained, and X-ray films of chest and abdomen should accompany the patient to the operating theatre.

Type of missile

Gun-fired missiles are commonly divided into low- and high-velocity groups. The former are fired from revolvers and pistols and a variety of short-barrelled automatic weapons and the latter from rifles. Within these two groups the bullets differ in size, weight, and muzzle velocity and also in actual construction. The kinetic energy of the missile is a product of its mass times the square of the velocity; the gyroscopic or spin energy, as well as the type of bullet, also determines its effect on the target.

The low-velocity bullet, while certainly lethal on many occasions, is often deflected by soft-tissue planes. For example, in a young man shot from a height, the bullet, passing through the tip of his chin, behind his right clavicle and neatly down the side of the superior vena cava under the mediastinal pleura, finally passed out through the lung. Another patient had a single bullet wound in his left anterior axillary fold. His first chest X-ray showed a left haemothorax but no bullet. Luckily a further view was taken, which showed it lying over his right acromion process. In view of the projected track of this missile through the superior mediastinum it was decided to explore his chest through a median sternotomy. This was, however, a mistaken decision, since the track was well posterior and the missile had penetrated the mediastinum between the oesophagus and the vertebral column—almost inaccessible from the anterior approach.

Injury by a high-velocity missile is a much more lethal event, and far fewer of these patients have come to surgery. Where a rifle bullet has passed cleanly through the chest the characteristic effect of high energy dissipation may not be observed, but, if the sternum, ribs, or particularly the vertebral column is struck, widespread pulmonary effects can follow, such as disruption and rapid development of a bilateral wet lung syndrome. Associated damage to the spinal cord is common in this type of injury.

Indications for surgery

Absolute indications for surgery in penetrating chest injuries are: (1) significant or continued haemorrhage; (2) a dangerous predicted track; (3) associated intra-abdominal injury.

The management of the through-and-through wound, with minimal drainage of blood and air, when the patient's condition remains satisfactory, is debatable. In a series reported by Heaton and others from Vietnam, 65 per cent were treated by intercostal tube drainage, 15 per cent by aspiration, and 20 per cent by thoracotomy, with a mortality of 7.9 per cent. In our different circumstances, however, where the number of such casualties at any one time has been smaller, and where full surgical facilities are readily available, thoracotomy has usually been considered desirable except when the injury is obviously trivial or is confined to the chest wall.

The wisdom of this policy was illustrated by the case of a young man who was admitted with an entry wound in his third left intercostal space anteriorly and an exit wound in his eighth left intercostal space in the posterior axillary line. He responded well to minimal resuscitation, and only a little blood drained from his left pleural cavity. There was some guarding, however, in the left subcostal region. On left thoracotomy there were two small holes, one above the other, in the pericardium, two holes side by side in the diaphragm, and a track through the lingula. Further exploration showed that the bullet, presumably of very low velocity, had grooved the left ventricle, traversed the diaphragm, and bounced back off the spleen, which was superficially lacerated.

Surgical approach

This is obviously dictated by circumstances. A posterio-lateral thoracotomy gives much better access to the hemithorax than does an anterior approach and is preferable, even with bilateral injuries, provided priority can be given to opening one side first. When there appears to be serious bleeding into both pleural cavities a bilateral trans-sternal approach has been used. The low thoraco-abdominal incision has been useful when the abdomen has also been penetrated; it allows good access to the liver or spleen, liver injuries having been particularly troublesome.

One type of injury in which the selection of surgical approach may be difficult is a gunshot wound in the supraclavicular region accompanied by serious bleeding both externally and into the chest cavity. Immediate temporary control of haemorrhage from the subclavian artery and vein at the point of injury is required, but full control to allow repair of the vessels necessitates a much wider access. The first part of the subclavian artery, especially on the left side, lies well posteriorly, and one would be tempted to use a thoracoplasty type of incision for this reason. This is impracticable, however, in the usual circumstances of injury, and we always employ a median sternotomy with extension up into the neck, excising part of the clavicle if necessary, and a further extension into the third intercostal space anteriorly, giving a wide, trap-door, type of opening.

Procedure

Chest wall wounds are usually small and may be excised and sutured. Where damage is more extensive the necessary excision should be carried out, the chest cavity closed, and the superficial layers closed by delayed primary suture.

Postoperative course

Some degree of lung contusion may be present, but development of pulmonary insufficiency and the wet lung syndrome are dependent on the velocity of the missile, the extent of the chest wall injury, and the severity of other injuries.

When this syndrome is expected to develop, a decision to institute special intensive care, including controlled ventilation, should usually be taken at the end of operation.

Abdominal wall

Many wounds are limited to the anterior abdominal wall, and these can be excised and treated by primary suture. Others should be treated by delayed primary suture or allowed to heal by second intention.

Stomach, duodenum, and pancreas

Damage to the stomach is relatively infrequent, and is often a simple through-and-through wound, which can be treated by simple suture.

Injuries to the pancreas and duodenum are often associated with spinal and liver damage. Perforation of the posterior wall of the duodenum can easily be missed, and if a severe retroperitoneal haematoma has formed a duodenal injury must be carefully looked for. Complete transection of the pancreas is infrequent and may be treated by resection of the distal portion.

Liver

Injuries of the liver, which were often associated with injuries of the gastrointestinal tract or lung, range from small surface lacerations to complete avulsion of part of the liver. Any degree of liver injury may result in severe haemorrhage, and massive blood transfusion is often necessary. Control of bleeding may be very difficult. Removal of damaged fragments, followed by deep catgut sutures, may be sufficient. Formal hepatic lobectomy is seldom practicable because of the extra degree of shock in these patients and multiple coexistent injuries.

Small bowel

Injuries of the small bowel are usually multiple; colonic injuries are often found in association. The most frequent injuries are small puncture wounds, which may be treated by simple two-layer suture. In a number of cases segments of small bowel are so lacerated or devascularised by damage to the mesentery that resection will be necessary. Patients with small-bowel injury usually make an excellent postoperative recovery, though the rate for postoperative wound sepsis may be high.

Colon

The colon is the most frequently damaged part of the gastrointestinal tract, the right colon being more frequently damaged than the left. Injuries vary from single perforation to severe contusion and laceration of the bowel wall; multiple lesions are frequent. Division of the mesocolon or severe vascular damage sometimes results in devascularisation of the bowel wall. These colonic injuries may be treated in a variety of ways. Single perforations, with no associated injury to the mesocolon, can be safely oversewn in two layers by means of non-absorbable suture material for the seromuscular layer. With severe contusion of the bowel wall or damage to the mesocolon interfering with the blood supply, primary resection with end-to-end anastomosis in two layers is usually the treatment of choice, particularly in lesions of the caecum and ascending colon.

In all cases, drainage of the peritoneal cavity should be carried out and postoperative antibiotics given routinely. After primary closure, or resection and anastomosis without proximal decompression, the intraperitoneal sepsis rate is likely to be extremely high. The sepsis rate can be reduced by proximal decompression.

Renal tract

Nephrectomy may be required for severe laceration of the kidney. An attempt should be made to define the extent of renal damage, as profuse perirenal bleeding need not necessarily represent irreparable damage.

Damage to the ureter is often associated with large-bowel injury and sometimes missed at the initial inspection. When later diagnosed, local sepsis is almost inevitable, and secondary repair usually impossible. In this situation the kidney should be drained by nephrostomy or ureterostomy with a view to later replacement or, better still, implantation of the proximal ureter into the opposite side.

Appendix 1. Hazards to man of nuclear and allied radiations

Sources of radiation

The natural radiation to which mankind has been exposed comes from certain radioactive elements which have always existed in the earth and atmosphere, although their presence has been recognised only for a few decades. These, and cosmic radiation, are usually referred to as 'background radiation'.

Man himself has added to these sources and the extra radiations are derived from:

1. The use of various forms of radiation in medicine and industry, e.g. X-radiography and luminising.
2. The isotopes and elements produced in nuclear reactors and by the explosion of nuclear weapons.

Types of radiation

Radioactivity is the word used to describe the spontaneous disintegration of certain atoms into other forms, with the emission of radiations. Basically there are four types:

1. Alpha radiation, consisting of particles of high energy, but with a power of penetration of less than one-tenth of a millimetre in human tissues. Because of their poor powers of penetration these particles are not considered a serious external health hazard but, if ingested, they become a serious danger to health. An alpha particle is positively charged, and is similar to the nucleus of the helium atom, i.e. two protons, two neutrons.

2. Beta radiation, consisting of electrons (the orbital particles in the atomic structure) which carry a negative charge of electricity. Powers of penetration are poor, and the range of a few feet in the air. Again, the main health hazard is internal. If, however, the skin is bombarded for a sufficiently long period, burns will result.

3. Gamma rays and X-rays, electro-magnetic radiations of ranging energy, with high powers of penetration and capable of irradiating the whole human body uniformly.

4. Neutrons, consisting of uncharged particles (a component of the nucleus in the atomic structure), with very high powers of penetration; able to irradiate the whole body. A characteristic of neutrons released during a nuclear explosion is that they are capable of inducing radioactivity and can, of course, present immense problems in decontamination after the detonation.

'External' and 'internal' radiation

Radiation from natural or artificial sources may be regarded as 'external' or 'internal' according to whether the source is outside or inside the body. External radiation refers to those radiations that strike the body from such sources as radioactive fall-out from a nuclear explosion or the radiation released at the time of detonation of a nuclear weapon. At the other end of the scale this also includes cosmic radiation.

'Internal' radiation arises from the ingestion or inhalation of radioactive materials into the body, an example being strontium 90 incorporated into the bones after ingestion/inhalation.

Effects of radiations in living tissues

Millions of cells in the tissues of the human body die and are replaced every day. The effect upon cells exposed to radiations varies considerably (Table 1):

1. With massive, whole-body doses of radiation there is gross tissue destruction and the damage done is too great to enable effective repairs to be carried out. If this occurs, death is almost certain.
2. With smaller doses of whole-body radiation the effect would be probable recovery of the individual but with certain malfunctions occurring either later in life or, perhaps, even in later generations caused by surviving irradiated cells eventually dividing, e.g. cancerous growths in later years and increases in the mutation rate.

Table 1 The effects of differing amounts of whole-body penetrating radiation

Dose (in up to 1 week) rads	Effect
Up to 150	No acute effects. Serious long-term hazard, e.g. shortening of life-span; changes affecting the mutation rates.
150–250	Nausea and vomiting within 24 hours. Minimal incapacity after two days.
250–350	Nausea and vomiting in under four hours. Symptom-free period for 48 hours. Some deaths will occur in two to four weeks.
350–600	Nausea and vomiting in under two hours. Many deaths in two to four weeks. Incapacity prolonged.
600+	Nausea and vomiting almost immediately. Death within about a week.

Recovery from radiation exposure does occur but it must be understood that doses received are cumulative. However, the eventual outcome will depend upon:

1. The amounts received and the rate at which they are received;
2. The time between doses;
3. The type of radiation and the area or part of the body exposed.

For example, an exposure of 5 rads per year for workers handling radioactive substances is permitted. The total amount which they are allowed to receive during a working life of 40 years is 200 rads. This is the maximum and, although a dose of 200 rads is received, the time taken to receive it is so long that no ill effects would be felt. If the worker was to receive, for example, two exposures of 100 rads within a relatively short time, clinical effects might become apparent. Some ill effects would almost definitely be felt by the individual at the time of the exposure. Symptoms would then appear either days or weeks later, similar to those shown in Table 2.

Table 2 Natural history of exposure of human beings to 400 rads as an immediate dose of whole-body penetrating radiation

History	Symptoms	Duration
Exposure	None	
Interval	None	Lasting three hours
Initial symptoms	Nausea and vomiting	Lasting 12 to 24 hours
Interval	Period of indefinite symptoms	Lasting about a week
Radiation sickness	Loss of hair, loss of appetite, fever, inflammation of throat, haemorrhage, death of about 30 per cent commencing two weeks after exposure, those recovering will have prolonged incapacity	Beginning about 10 days after exposure

Although radiations cannot be detected by any human sense, it is possible that exposure to large doses of highly penetrating radiation may be felt by the individual at the time of exposure. On the other hand, exposure over a longer period may or may not be felt.

Appendix 2. Rights and duties of nurses under the Geneva Conventions 12 August 1949

When the Geneva Conventions are ratified by a State, their application in time of war becomes obligatory for all members of medical personnel of the armed forces and for personnel of civilian hospitals. Anyone acting consciously, or through ignorance, against these provisions would be contravening his national laws either as a civilian or as a member of the armed forces and would have to answer for his actions before the relevant authorities.

It seems especially important that nurses, designated 'Medical personnel', with rights and obligations derived from, and defined in, the Geneva Conventions of 1949, should make themselves familiar with the provisions thereof which concern them.

Red Cross principles

1. Humanity
The Red Cross, born of a desire to bring assistance without discrimination to the wounded on the battlefield, endeavours—in its international and national capacity—to prevent and alleviate human suffering wherever it may be found. Its purpose is to protect life and health and to ensure respect for the human being. It promotes mutual understanding, friendship, co-operation and lasting peace amongst all peoples.

2. Impartiality
The Red Cross makes no distinction between peoples of different nationality, race, religious beliefs, class or political opinions. It endeavours only to relieve suffering, giving priority to the most urgent cases of distress.

3. Neutrality
In order to continue to enjoy the confidence of all, the Red Cross may not take sides in hostilities or engage at any time in controversies of a political, racial, religious or ideological nature.

4. Independence
The Red Cross is independent. The National Societies, while auxiliaries in the humanitarian services of their governments, and subject to the laws of their respective countries, must always maintain their autonomy so that they may be able at all times to act in accordance with Red Cross principles.

5. Voluntary service
The Red Cross is a voluntary relief organisation not prompted in any manner by desire for gain.

6. Unity
There can be only one Red Cross Society in any one country. It must be open to all. It must carry on its humanitarian work throughout its territory.

7. Universality
The Red Cross is a world-wide institution in which all Societies have equal status and share equal responsibilities and duties in helping each other.

THE GENEVA CONVENTIONS

(12 August 1949)

What they are

1. For the Amelioration of the Condition of the Wounded and Sick in Armed Forces in the Field;

2. For the Amelioration of the Condition of Wounded, Sick and Shipwrecked Members of the Armed Forces at Sea;

3. Relative to the treatment of Prisoners of War;

4. Relative to the Protection of Civilian Persons in Time of War.

With the ratification of these four Conventions by 140 sovereign States, one can regard them as being universally recognised.

The Geneva Conventions are diplomatic agreements between sovereign States.

The plenipotentiary representatives of States, invited by the Swiss Federal Council to attend a diplomatic conference, examine the texts prepared by the International Committee of the Red Cross with a view to drawing up a new Convention or to improving or completing a Convention already in existence and relative to the protection of the victims of war. These representatives are empowered to sign, on behalf of their governments, the terms of a Convention adopted by the Diplomatic Conference.

The government, once it has been so authorised by its Parliament, confirms its representative's signature. By such act, known as ratification, the State undertakes to fulfil its obligations as regards these Conventions. It must then put them into application, adapts its legislation accordingly and have them made known to the armed forces and the population.

A State not represented at a diplomatic conference which has codified or revised a Convention can accede to it at a later date. It undertakes by this act to apply the said Convention.

The official records are deposited with the Swiss Federal Council which informs States parties to the Geneva Conventions and the International Committee of the Red Cross of each new accession.

Their object

Each Convention protects well-specified categories of persons not, or no longer, taking part in hostilities, in order to ensure that they receive humane treatment in all circumstances.

Provided they fulfil the conditions laid down and are only used for the service of the victims specified in the Conventions, personnel, establishments, equipment, zones and the emblem will benefit, not as such, but by reason of their services, from the same protection as the victims themselves.

The circumstances in which a Convention is applicable are themselves also clearly defined.

It is only this restriction which can guarantee that the Conventions will be effectively applied and will enable supervision to be carried out.

In order to encourage nursing personnel to study the Conventions as a whole, extracts of the more important articles which are of special concern to them, based on the original French text, are quoted later in this Chapter.

FIRST GENEVA CONVENTION

General provisions

Apart from the agreements expressly provided for in certain articles the Contracting Parties may conclude special agreements for all matters concerning which they may deem it suitable to make separate provision. No special agreement shall adversely affect the situation of the wounded and sick, of members of the medical personnel, or of chaplains, as defined by the present Convention, nor restrict the rights which it confers upon them.

Wounded and sick, as well as members of the medical personnel and chaplains, may in no circumstances renounce in part or in entirety the rights secured to them by the present Convention and the special agreements referred to in the foregoing Article, if such there be.

Wounded and sick

Members of the armed forces and other persons mentioned in the following Article, who are wounded or sick, shall be respected and protected in all circumstances.

They shall be treated humanely and cared for by the Party to the conflict in whose power they may be, without any adverse distinction founded on sex, race, nationality, religion, political opinions, or any other similar criteria. Any attempts upon their lives, or violence to their persons, shall be strictly prohibited; in particular, they shall not be murdered or exterminated, subjected to torture or to biological experiments; they shall not wilfully be left without medical assistance and care, nor shall conditions exposing them to contagion or infection be created.

Only urgent medical reasons will authorise priority in the order of treatment to be administered.

Women shall be treated with all consideration due to their sex.

The Party to the conflict which is compelled to abandon wounded or sick to the enemy shall, as far as military considerations permit, leave with them a part of its medical personnel and material to assist in their care.

Medical units and establishments

Fixed establishments and mobile medical units of the Medical Service may in no circumstances be attacked, but shall at all times be respected and protected by the Parties to the conflict. Should they fall into the hands of the adverse Party, their personnel shall be free to pursue their duties, as long as the capturing Power has not itself ensured the necessary care of the wounded and sick found in such establishments and units.

The responsible authorities shall ensure that the said medical establishments and units are, as far as possible, situated in such a manner that attacks against military objectives cannot imperil their safety.

Medical personnel

Medical personnel exclusively engaged in the search for, or the collection, transport or treatment of, the wounded or sick, or in the prevention of disease, staff exclusively engaged in the administration of medical units and establishments, as well as chaplains attached to the armed forces, shall be respected and protected in all circumstances.

The staff of National Red Cross Societies and that of other Voluntary Aid Societies, duly recognised and authorised by their Governments, who may be employed on the same duties as the personnel named in Article 24, are placed on the same footing as the personnel named in the article just quoted, provided that the staff of such societies are subject to military laws and regulations.

Personnel designated in Articles 24 and 26 who fall into the hands of the adverse Party, shall be retained only in so far as the state of health, the spiritual needs and the number of prisoners of war require.

Buildings and material

The material of mobile medical units of the armed forces which falls into the hands of the enemy shall be reserved for the care of wounded and sick.

The buildings, material and stores of fixed medical establishments of the armed forces shall remain subject to the laws of war, but may not be diverted from that purpose as long as they are required for the care of wounded and sick. Nevertheless, the commanders of forces in the field may make use of them, in case of urgent military necessity, provided that they make previous arrangements for the welfare of the wounded and sick who are nursed in them.

The material and stores defined in the present Article shall not be intentionally destroyed.

Medical transports

Transports of wounded and sick or of medical equipment shall be respected and protected in the same way as mobile medical units.

Should such transports or vehicles fall into the hands of the adverse Party, they shall be subject to the laws of war, on condition that the Party to the conflict who captures them shall in all cases ensure the care of the wounded and sick they contain.

The civilian personnel and all means of transport obtained by requisition shall be subject to the general rules of international law.

Medical aircraft, that is to say, aircraft exclusively employed for the removal of wounded and sick and for the transport of medical personnel and equipment, shall not be attacked, but shall be respected by the belligerents, while flying at heights, times and on routes specifically agreed upon between the belligerents concerned.

SECOND GENEVA CONVENTION

Wounded, sick and shipwrecked

Members of the armed forces and other persons mentioned in the following Article, who are at sea and who are wounded, sick or shipwrecked, shall be respected and protected in all circumstances, it being understood that the term 'shipwreck' means shipwreck from any cause and includes forced landings at sea by or from aircraft.

Hospital ships

Military hospital ships, that is to say, ships built or equipped by the Powers specially and solely with a view to assisting the wounded, sick and shipwrecked, to treating them and to transporting them, may in no circumstances be attacked or captured, but shall at all times be respected and protected, on condition that their names and descriptions have been notified to the Parties to the conflict ten days before those ships are employed.

The characteristics which must appear in the notification shall include registered gross tonnage, the length from stem to stern and the number of masts and funnels.

Medical personnel

The religious, medical and hospital personnel of hospital ships and their crews shall be respected and protected; they may not be captured during the time they are in the service of the hospital ship, whether or not there are wounded and sick on board.

THIRD GENEVA CONVENTION

Prisoners of war must at all times be humanely treated. Any unlawful act or omission by the Detaining Power causing death or seriously endangering the health of a prisoner of war in its custody is prohibited and will be regarded as a serious breach of the present Convention. In particular, no prisoner of war may be subjected to physical mutilation or to medical or scientific experiments of any kind which are not justified by the medical, dental or hospital treatment of the prisoner concerned and carried out in his interest.

Likewise, prisoners of war must at all times be protected particularly against acts of violence or intimidation and against insults and public curiosity.

Measures of reprisal against prisoners of war are prohibited.

The Power detaining prisoners of war shall be bound to provide free of charge for their maintenance and for the medical attention required by their state of health.

Medical personnel and chaplains retained to assist prisoners of war

Members of the medical personnel and chaplains, while retained by the Detaining Power with a view to assisting prisoners of war, shall not be considered as prisoners of war. They shall, however, receive as a minimum the benefits and protection of the present Convention, and shall also be granted all facilities necessary to provide for the medical care of, and religious ministration to, prisoners of war.

They shall continue to exercise their medical and spiritual functions for the benefit of prisoners of war, preferably those belonging to the armed forces upon which they depend, within the scope of the military laws and regulations of the Detaining Power and under the control of its competent services, in accordance with their professional etiquette. They shall also benefit by the following facilities in the exercise of their medical or spiritual functions:

a. They shall be authorised to visit periodically prisoners of war in working detachments or in hospitals outside the camp. For this purpose, the Detaining Power shall place at their disposal the necessary means of transport.

b. The senior medical officer in each camp shall be responsible to the camp military authorities for everything connected with the activities of retained medical personnel. For this purpose, Parties to the conflict shall agree at the outbreak of hostilities on the subject of the corresponding ranks of the medical personnel including that of societies mentioned in Article 26 of the Geneva Convention for the Amelioration of the Condition of the Wounded and Sick in Armed Forces in the Field of 12 August 1949. Thus senior medical officers, as well as chaplains, shall have the right to deal with the competent authorities of the camp on all questions relating to their duties. Such authorities shall afford them all necessary facilities for correspondence relating to these questions.

c. Although they shall be subject to the internal discipline of the camp in which they are retained, SUCH PERSONNEL MAY NOT BE COMPELLED TO CARRY OUT ANY WORK OTHER THAN THAT CONCERNED WITH THEIR MEDICAL OR RELIGIOUS DUTIES.

During hostilities, the Parties to the conflict shall agree concerning the possible relief of retained personnel and shall settle the procedure to be followed.

None of the preceding provisions shall relieve the Detaining Power of its obligations with regard to prisoners of war from the medical or spiritual point of view.

FOURTH GENEVA CONVENTION

General protection of populations against some effects of war

The wounded and sick, as well as the infirm, and expectant mothers, shall be the object of particular protection and respect.

As far as military considerations allow, each Party to the conflict shall facilitate the steps taken to search for the killed and wounded, to assist the shipwrecked and other persons exposed to grave danger, and to protect them against pillage and ill-treatment.

The Parties to the conflict shall endeavour to conclude local agreements for the removal from besieged or encircled areas, of wounded, sick, infirm, and aged persons, children and maternity cases, and for the passage of ministers of all religions, medical personnel and medical equipment on their way to such areas.

Civilian hospitals organised to give care to the wounded and sick, the infirm and maternity cases, may in no circumstances be the object of attack but shall at all times be respected and protected by the Parties to the conflict.

States which are Parties to a conflict shall provide all civilian hospitals with certificates showing that they are civilian hospitals and that the buildings which they occupy are not used for any purpose which would deprive these hospitals of protection in accordance with Article 19.

Civilian hospitals shall be marked by means of the emblem provided for in Article 38 of the Geneva Convention for the Amelioration of the Condition of the Wounded and Sick in Armed Forces in the Field of 12 August 1949, but only if so authorised by the State.

The Parties to the conflict shall, in so far as military considerations permit, take the necessary steps to make the distinctive emblems indicating civilian hospitals clearly visible to the enemy land, air and naval forces in order to obviate the possibility of any hostile action.

In view of the dangers to which hospitals may be exposed by being close to military objectives, it is recommended that such hospitals be situated as far as possible from such objectives.

Persons regularly and solely engaged in the operation and administration of civilian hospitals, including the personnel engaged in the search for, removal and transporting of and caring for wounded and sick civilians, the infirm and maternity cases, shall be respected and protected.

In occupied territory and in zones of military operations, the above personnel shall be recognisable by means of an identity card certifying their status, bearing the photograph of the holder and embossed with the stamp of the responsible authority, and also by means of a stamped, water-resistant armlet which they shall wear on the left arm while carrying out their duties. This armlet shall be issued by the State and shall bear the emblem provided for in Article 38 of the Geneva Convention for the Amelioration of the Condition of the Wounded and Sick in Armed Forces in the Field of 12 August 1949.

Other personnel who are engaged in the operation and administration of civilian hospitals shall be entitled to respect and protection and to wear the armlet, as provided in and under the conditions prescribed in the Article, while they are employed on such duties. The identity card shall state the duties on which they are employed.

The management of each hospital shall at all times hold at the disposal of the competent national or occupying authorities an up-to-date list of such personnel.

Convoys of vehicles or hospital trains on land or specially provided vessels on sea, conveying wounded and sick civilians, the infirm and maternity cases, shall be respected and protected in the same manner as the hospitals provided for in Article 18, and shall be marked, with the consent of the State, by the display of the distinctive emblem provided for in Article 38 of the Geneva Convention for the Amelioration of the Condition of the Wounded and Sick in Armed Forces in the Field of 12 August 1949.

Protected persons

The internment or placing in assigned residence of protected persons may be ordered only if the security of the Detaining Power makes it absolutely necessary.

In no circumstances shall a protected person be transferred to a country where he or she may have reason to fear persecution for his or her political opinions or religious beliefs.

Occupied territory

Individual or mass forcible transfers, as well as deportations of protected persons from occupied territory to the territory of the Occupying Power or to that of any other country, occupied or not, are prohibited, regardless of their motive.

To the fullest extent of the means available to it, the Occupying Power has the duty of ensuring the food and medical supplies of the population; it should, in particular, bring the necessary foodstuffs, medical stores and other articles, if the resources of the occupied territory are inadequate.

The Occupying Power may not requisition foodstuffs, articles or medical supplies available in the occupied territory, except for use by the occupation forces and administration personnel, and then only if the requirements of the civilian population have been taken into account. Subject to the provisions of other international Conventions, the Occupying Power shall make arrangements to ensure that fair value is paid for any requisitioned goods.

The Protecting Power shall, at any time, be at liberty to verify the state of the food and medical supplies in occupied territories, except where temporary restrictions are made necessary by imperative military requirements.

To the fullest extent of the means available to it, the Occupying Power has the duty of ensuring and maintaining with the co-operation of national and local authorities, the medical and hospital establishments and services, public health and hygiene in the occupied territory, with particular reference to the adoption and application of the prophylactic and preventive measures necessary to combat the spread of contagious diseases and epidemics. Medical personnel of all categories shall be allowed to carry out their duties.

The Occupying Power may requisition civilian hospitals only temporarily and only in cases of urgent necessity for the care of military wounded and sick, and then on condition that suitable arrangements are made in due time for the care and treatment of the patients and for the needs of the civilian population for hospital accommodation.

The material and stores of civilian hospitals cannot be requisitioned so long as they are necessary for the needs of the civilian population.

Internal disorders, civil wars, armed rebellions

In such cases, Article 3, which is common to all four Conventions, is applicable.

In case of armed conflict not of an international character occurring in the territory of one of the High Contracting Parties, each Party to the conflict shall be bound to apply, as a minimum, the following provisions:

1. Persons taking no active part in the hostilities, including members of armed forces who have laid down their arms and those placed *hors de combat* by sickness, wounds, detention, or any other cause, shall in all circumstances be treated humanely, without any adverse distinction founded on race, colour, religion or faith, sex, birth or wealth, or any other similar criteria.

To this end, the following acts are and shall remain prohibited at any time and in any place whatsoever with respect to the above-mentioned persons:

a. Violence to life and person, in particular murder of all kinds, mutilation, cruel treatment and torture;

b. Taking of hostages;

c. Outrages upon personal dignity, in particular humiliating and degrading treatment;

d. The passing of sentences and the carrying out of executions without previous judgement pronounced by a regularly constituted court affording all the judicial guarantees which are recognised as indispensable by civilised peoples.

2. The wounded and sick shall be collected and cared for.

An impartial humanitarian body, such as the International Committee of the Red Cross, may offer its services to the Parties to the conflict.

The Parties to the conflict should further endeavour to bring into force, by means of special agreements, all or part of the other provisions of the present Conventions.

Appendix 3. Summary of resources available through the UN system

United Nations Disaster Relief Office (UNDRO)

The UNDRO has been vested with the responsibility for developing the coordinating assistance from the United Nation's system and ensuring co-operation with governments, the League of Red Cross Societies and other voluntary agencies, at the time of natural disasters.

The UN may give up to US $15 000 for *emergency aid only* to a country in respect of any one disaster. A request for this, and other UN related assistance, must be made by the government concerned through the Resident Representative of the United Nations Development Programme (UNDP).

Before forwarding the request, the Resident Representative must ascertain whether the required assistance is available from any other source and he is expected to discuss the request with a representative of the Red Cross *before* reporting the situation and request to the UN headquarters.

The following are summaries of United Nations programmes which may provide assistance in disaster situations:

1. United Nations Development Programme (UNDP)

The Resident Representative serves as the contact for governments requesting assistance from UN organisations and also serves in the country as the representative of the World Food Programme, which can give assistance on an emergency basis.

The Programme itself can only provide assistance in economic and social development. Emergency assistance is outside its scope but rehabilitation and reconstruction may be considered. Some exceptions may, however, be made to meet unforeseen needs.

2. United Nations Children's Fund (UNICEF)

UNICEF provides assistance primarily to long-range programmes for children in developing countries. However, aid in emergency situations is given in cases where help from other sources is not available. Supplies usually provided are: children's foods, drugs, vaccines and vitamin capsules, and sometimes rice or other food grains. Blankets, clothes, motor vehicles, well-drilling equipment, etc., have been supplied at times. Long-term measures to meet children's needs have priority. The bulk of UNICEF assistance is given in materials and sometimes there are supplies available which may be diverted for emergency relief.

3. Office of the United Nations High Commissioner for Refugees (UNHCR)

When a disaster occurs in a country where the inhabitants include refugees, the Office may assist, when requested by the government, by making available an allocation to meet the initial needs.

4. Food and Agriculture Organisation of the UN (FAO)

A sum of US $7 000 000 in commodities is earmarked for use by the World Food Programme in emergencies. The amount of food aid given is determined by the need, taken from other sources. Once a decision is made by the Director General of the FAO on the amount of food aid to be given, responsibility for the location of stocks, external transportation, etc., is taken by the World Food Programme. Normally, food aid can be provided in approximately three months, unless supplies happen to be in the affected area. In some instances, biological products for the control of animal disease, portable sawmills and similar relief items in the food and agricultural sector, which are not available from local resources, can be provided.

5. World Food Programme (WFP)

This is a joint UN/Food and Agriculture Organisation (FAO) project. *Emergency* assistance is confined exclusively to food which is available at the specific request of a government. Requests are transmitted through the UNDP Resident Representative, who is the official representative of the WFP in the country to which he is assigned. However, direct requests from a government to the Executive Director of the WFP, or to the Director General of the FAO, are not precluded. The recipient government is responsible for internal transport, storage, distribution and proper use of supplies.

The World Food Programme normally has to 'shop around' with donor countries regarding the availability of commodities from pledged stocks for shipment to a disaster area. The only occasion on which prompt emergency action can be taken is when there is WFP food for development projects within the stricken country, in a neighbouring country, aboard a ship near the disaster area, or when there are local stocks from which it is possible to borrow. In such cases, if the request is approved by the Director General of the Food and Agriculture Organisation the food can be borrowed for the emergency and be replaced later. Otherwise, it normally takes several months for WFP food to arrive.

The Programme's emergency aid is allocated to natural disasters, man-made emergencies (such as the flight of millions of East Pakistan refugees to India), and food shortages due to drought, crop failures, pests and diseases. The WFP now possesses the largest resources for disaster relief in the UN system. Its efforts are coordinated with other UN and non-governmental organisations and in a disaster situation it is in constant contact with the office of the UN Disaster Relief Coordinator in Geneva.

WFP also has a role in preventing or forestalling emergencies which includes projects for flood control, soil conservation, land reclamation, canal lining, access roads and building up of national food reserves.

In co-operation with other UN agencies it has been possible to formulate ready-made work projects in advance which can be implemented on the basis of food-for-work when the need arises. For example, when a drought condition was confirmed in the Sahelian countries of western Africa, projects prepared in advance were quickly approved and made operational on a food-for-work basis.

6. International Labour Organisation (ILO)

The ILO is not in a position to provide emergency relief, but can assist in the early reconstruction and rehabilitation phase with the training of construction workers.

7. United Nations Educational, Scientific and Cultural Organisation (UNESCO)

The work of UNESCO is directed mainly to the study and prevention of natural disasters which occur most frequently and which are most destructive to human life and property, i.e. earthquakes, tsunamis, cyclonic storms, floods and volcanic eruptions.

8. World Health Organisation (WHO)

WHO acts upon the receipt of a request from the competent health authorities.

WHO assumes basic responsibility for overall coordination of WHO emergency measures relating to health with those of other UN organisations, voluntary agencies and national and non-governmental assistance from the outside. WHO assistance is limited to provision of technical personnel and urgently-needed supplies and equipment until other outside assistance arrives.

WHO can generally command technical facilities for rapid on-the-spot assessment of the needs of the situation and can arrange immediate movement of vaccines and drugs. WHO can purchase supplies and equipment with funds provided in advance by the requesting government and also can extend immediate credit, if needed.

Regional Directors of WHO are responsible for the transmission of information regarding the emergency and the needs resulting therefrom. Staff and WHO transport may be made available in emergency situations.

9. International Bank for Reconstruction and Development (IBRD) and International Finance Corporation (IFC)

The institutions of the World Bank Group are not authorised by their charters to provide direct

Structure of the United Nations

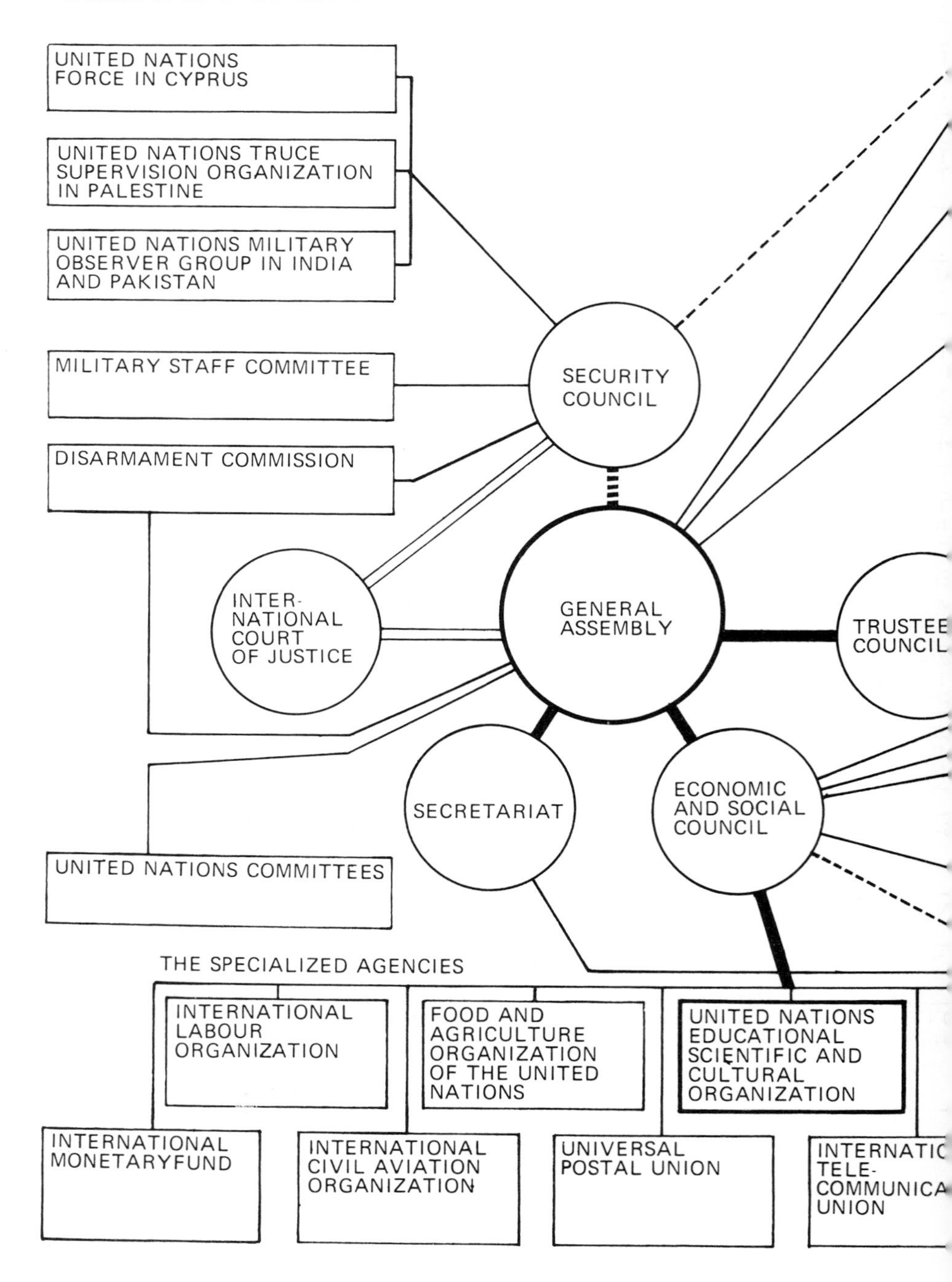

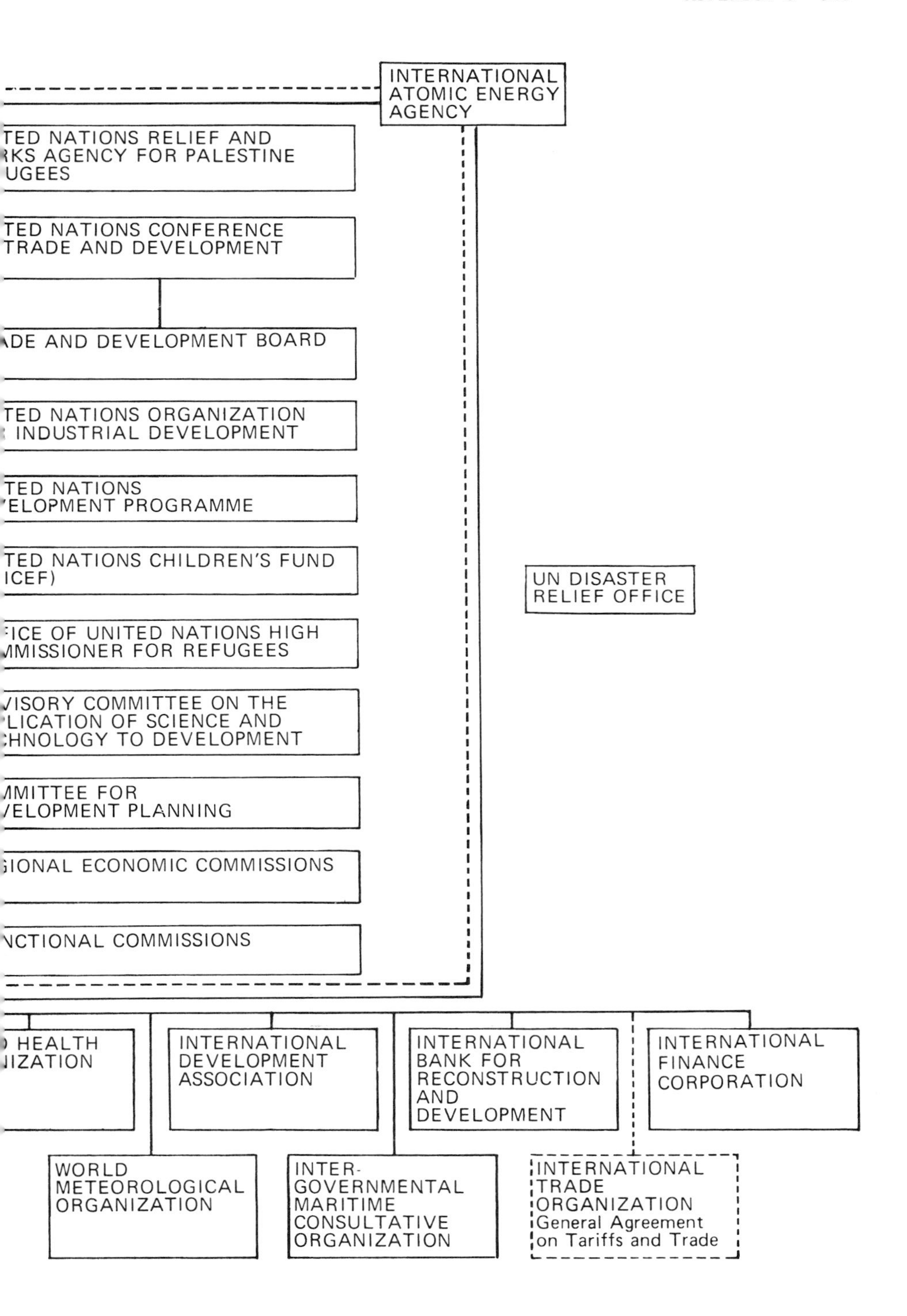

INTERNATIONAL ATOMIC ENERGY AGENCY
TED NATIONS RELIEF AND
KS AGENCY FOR PALESTINE
UGEES
TED NATIONS CONFERENCE
TRADE AND DEVELOPMENT
DE AND DEVELOPMENT BOARD
TED NATIONS ORGANIZATION
INDUSTRIAL DEVELOPMENT
TED NATIONS
ELOPMENT PROGRAMME
TED NATIONS CHILDREN'S FUND
ICEF)
ICE OF UNITED NATIONS HIGH
MISSIONER FOR REFUGEES
VISORY COMMITTEE ON THE
LICATION OF SCIENCE AND
HNOLOGY TO DEVELOPMENT
MITTEE FOR
VELOPMENT PLANNING
IONAL ECONOMIC COMMISSIONS
NCTIONAL COMMISSIONS
UN DISASTER RELIEF OFFICE
HEALTH
IZATION
INTERNATIONAL DEVELOPMENT ASSOCIATION
INTERNATIONAL BANK FOR RECONSTRUCTION AND DEVELOPMENT
INTERNATIONAL FINANCE CORPORATION
WORLD METEOROLOGICAL ORGANIZATION
INTER-GOVERNMENTAL MARITIME CONSULTATIVE ORGANIZATION
INTERNATIONAL TRADE ORGANIZATION
General Agreement on Tariffs and Trade

assistance in cases of natural disaster. However, the World Bank Group has been ready to give serious consideration to requests for assistance from the governments of countries affected by natural disasters having regard to their programmes for reconstruction and development.

10. International Monetary Fund
Assistance to a member would be handled expeditiously in accordance with Articles of Agreement. A basic concern of the Fund is the maintenance of exchange stability.

11. International Civil Aviation Organisation (ICAO)
Staff may be provided to supervise and operate aeronautical ground services. In certain situations and areas the ICAO can provide equipment, but not without some delay.

12. Inter-Governmental Maritime Consultative Organisation (IMCO)
IMCO would be a resource in emergency situations involving mass evacuation of persons by ship, loading and unloading and carriage of goods to and from the area, search and rescue operations, etc., requiring the immediate services of experts.

IMPORTANT

Requests to all these agencies must be made by the governments of the countries affected by the disasters.

Appendix 4. Standard list of medicaments and equipment for medical field teams

Introduction

This list does not aim to be comprehensive; personal choice and medicament availability may dictate variations. The aim is to provide some guidance as to medicaments most commonly required for use by teams in the initial phase of disaster relief situations where no adequate medical facilities exist. In the interests of logistics and economy, the list has been kept to a minimum. No attempt has been made to provide for therapy for diseases requiring long-term treatment nor for systematic eradication programmes, such as tuberculosis, as this is considered outside the scope of disaster relief teams.

General points

Categorisation
An attempt has been made to divide the medicaments into those required for different areas.

Code A: Medicaments required throughout the world.

Code B: Medicaments which may not be required in every disaster situation. These refer predominantly to medicaments for the treatment of tropical diseases.

Generic names
All medicaments have been identified by the appropriate generic name. In some instances a pharmaceutical trade name has been given, but these are intended only as examples rather than recommendations for any particular manufacturer's product. Trade names will obviously vary in different parts of the world.

Packaging
Items should be packed in containers which are easily transportable, which allow easy access and which afford protection to the contents. Each container should be clearly marked to indicate its contents.

Non-breakable polyethylene containers are a suitable alternative to glass for the transport of medicaments.

List of medicaments

	Quantity	*Code*
Anaesthetics		
Local anaesthetic, e.g. Lignocaine 2% (50 ml)	6 bottles	A
Short acting anaesthetic or analgesic agent, (i) short acting barbiturate e.g. Thiopentone Inj. 2.5%, (ii) Neurolept analgesic, e.g. Ketamine Inj.	6 bottles	A
Analgesics and antipyretics		
Strong analgesic for injection (in case of narcotics, provision should comply with international regulations in force)	50 ampoules	A
Profadol hydrochloride for injection 50 mg or equivalent	200 ampoules	A
Acetylsalicylic acid 500 mg	5000 tablets	A
Anthelmintics		
Levamisole 30 or 40 mg	300 tablets	B
Niclosamide 500 mg	150 tablets	B

	Quantity	*Code*
Antiallergics and antihistaminics		
Promethazine tablets 25 mg	300 tablets	A
Promethazine injection 50 mg	500 ampoules	A
Antianaemics		
Ferrous sulphate tablets 200 mg film coated	3000 tablets	A
Antiasthmatics and antitussives/expectorant		
Aminophylline injection 250 mg	30 ampoules	A
Anti-asthmatic oral combined tablets containing at least two of the following ingredients: Theophylline, Phenobarbital, Ephedrine, Belladonna	500 tablets	A
Anti-cough mixture	1 litre	A
Antibiotics		
Chloramphenicol capsules 250 mg	500 capsules	A
Chloramphenicol for injection 1 gm I.M. (succinate)	100 vials together with solvent	A
Penicillin G. (Benzylpenicillin) 5 to 10 million units inj.	50 vials	A
Penicillin G. 300 000 units; Penicillin procain 300 000 units; Benzathine penicillin 600 000 units } per vial (depot inj.)	200 vials	A
Penicillin procain 1 to 3 million units; Sodium penicillin G. 300 000 to 1 million units } per vial	1000 vials together with solvent	A
Phenoxymethylpenicillin tablets 1 million units each	1000 tablets	A
Tetracycline capsules 250 mg	1000 tablets	A
Tetracycline for injection I.M. 250 mg	100 vials together with solvent	A
Ampicillin caps 100 mg (for children)	500	A
Antiprotozoals		
Metronidazole 250 mg	1000 tablets	A
Chloroquine tablets 150 mg (base) or Amodiaquine 150 mg (base)	2000 tablets	B
Chloroquine injection 300 mg (base)	100 ampoules	B
Chloroquine syrup 75 mg base per 5 ml	200 bottles × 60 ml	B
Corticosteroids		
Prednisolone tablets 5 mg	200 tablets	A
Prednisolone injection 25 mg	50 ampoules	A
Cardiovascular medicaments		
Epinephrine injection 1 : 1000 (Adrenaline)	10 ampoules 1 ml each	A
Lanatoside C injectable 0.4 mg	20 ampoules of 2 ml each	A
Cathartics		
Senna tablets for adults	150 tablets	A
Dermatological preparations		
Methylrosanilinium chloride (Gentian violet) powder, medicinal, 25 mg bottle	2 bottles	A
Antiseptic preparation, e.g. Cetrimonium bromide concentrate	5 litres	A
Surgical skin preparation, e.g. Merchurochrome	1 litre	A
Zinc oxide ointment, jars of 1 lb	2 jars	A
Saponated benzyl benzoate concentrate (1 litre)	5 bottles	A
Diuretics		
Furosemide for injection 20 mg	20 ampoules	A
Ear and throat preparations		
Analgesic and anti-inflammatory drops	50 bottles	A
Paraformaldehyde combined lozenges for mouth disinfection	1000 lozenges	A

	Quantity	*Code*
Eye preparations		
Oxybuprocaine drops 0.4%	10 bottles	A
Zinc sulphate drops	25 bottles	A
Tetracycline ophthalmic ointments 1%	50 tubes	A
*Gastrointestinal trace medicaments**		
Antacid tablets	500 tablets	A
Clioquinol 250 mg	1000 tablets	A
Phthalylsulphathiazole 500 mg	2000 tablets	A
Kaolin pectine food type preparations for children's diarrhoea, such as Arabon 150 mg packs	20 packs	A
Kaolin pectine preparations for adults Kaolin 20% Pectine 1%	100 treatments	A
Insecticide		
D.D.T. powder 10% (for team use)	5 small containers	A
Pharmaceutical basic solvent		
Agua bi-distilled for injection 20 ml	50 units	A
Sedatives and anticonvulsant		
Phenobarbital tabl. 100 mg	500 tablets	A
Diazepam Inj. 10 mg	50 ampoules	A
Spasmolytics		
Atropine sulfate injection 0.5 mg	30 ampoules	A
Hyoscine butyl bromide injection 20 mg	50 ampoules of 1 ml	A
Sulphonamides		
Triple sulphonamide tablets 500 mg each tablet contains: Sulphadiazine 167 mg Sulphamerazine 167 mg Sulphadimidine 167 mg	1000 tablets	A
Sulphamethoxypyridazine 300 mg—to be reserved for the treatment of Cerebrospinal Meningitis only or Sulphadoxine 500 mg—to be reserved for the treatment of Cerebrospinal Meningitis only		B
Urinary tract chemotherapeutic		
Nitrofurantoin tablets 100 mg	500 tablets	A
Uterine contractility drugs		
Ergometrine maleate or tartrate for injection 0.2 mg	20 ampoules	A
Oxytocin injection 2 I.U. in 2 cc	20 ampoules	A
Vaccines and sera		
Human antitetanus immunoglobulin inj. 2 cc	20 vials	
Tetanus vaccine (absorbed)	100 doses	
Diphtheria serum 20 000 I.U.	10 vials	
Rabies vaccine		
The above items should be taken with the teams only if it is known in advance that storage facilities exist at destination; otherwise, they should be called forward only after the teams have confirmed this.		
Vigamins		
Vitamin A capsules high potency 200 000 I.U. for xeropthalmia Important: Dosage 1 capsule per child not to be repeated before 4 months.	50 capsules	B
Vitamin B complex injection	50 vials	A

	Quantity	*Code*
Volume replacement preparations		
Gelatin blood plasma substitute for intravenous infusion, 500 ml	50× 500 ml	A
WHO new formula electrolytes powder package for preparation of oral rehydration fluid, pack for the preparation of one litre	1000 packs	A
Formula: NaCl 3.5 g		
$NaHco_3$ 2.5 g		
KC_1 1.5 g		
Dextrose 20.0 g		
20% concentrated albumin solution 100 ml ampoule	50 ampoules	A
Diarrhoea treatment solution, in plastic bag with giving and needle, 500 ml	100 bags × 500 ml	A
Formula: NaCl 4.0 g		
Na Lactate 5.4 g		
KC_1 1.0 g		
Dextrose 8.0 g		
Water for 1000 ml injection		
Glucose 5% isotonic solution, in plastic bag of 500 ml, together with giving set and needle	25 bags × 500 ml	A
Water purification tablets		
Halazone tablets 4 mg	1000 tablets	
This item is required for the needs of the members of the Red Cross team only. This recommendation was made on the assumption that adequate supplies of this product for the needs of the victims of the disaster will already be available in the country of destination or provided by other sources.		

* Diarrhoea: Several non-specific drugs have been included for the symptomatic relief of diarrhoea. It should be remembered that in such patients, especially children, these measures should in no way discourage adequate rehydration and the use of specific antibiotic therapy where indicated.

List of equipment

	Quantity
Minor surgical instruments and syringes	
Scissors: Straight	2
Curved	2
Scalpel handle	2
Blades, assorted disposable	100
Forceps: Anatomical	4
Surgical	2
Haemostatic	4
Bone cutting (Luer)	1
Dental	1
Retractor: Automatic	1
Sharp 2 prongs	2
Needle-holder	1
Atraumatic needles with silk 0,00	30
Surgical needles—assorted	1 box
Myrtle leaf probe	1
Splinter forceps	1
Catgut, single packed threads	15 pieces
Sterile disposable syringes, Luer 2.4 ml	100
10 ml	100
Disposable needles G 21 × 1½	100
G 20 × 1½	100
Interchangeable glass syringes, Luer 2.5 ml	5
10 ml	5
With assorted needles	
Sterile disposable intravenous cannulae	25

	Quantity
Lumbar puncture needle (2 sizes)	2
Trocar	1
Luer cannulae trackael, silver: Small	1
Large	1
Sterile rubber drain	1
Small operating headlamp	1

Medical equipment

Thermometers (Centigrade)	5
Sphygmomanometer	1
Stethoscope	2
Scissors, bandage Lister	1 pair
Basin, kidney—350 ml stainless steel	3
Diagnostic set in case comprising: Otoscope with 3 speculae, Nasal speculum, Lamp holder, Ophthalmoscope, 2 spare bulbs	1
Metal syringe for ear washing 90 ml	1
Gloves, disposable, small, medium and large	10 of each
Alcohol 70%	4 × ½ litre
5 cc balloon catheter: F G No. 16	1
F G No. 18	1
Lubricant jelly	3 tubes
Red rubber tube and plastic funnel	1
Feeding set intragastric	1
First aid resuscitation kit	1
Steriliser, pressure type, fuel heated (with container for dressings)	1
Laboratory set (on request) (field type microscope and centrifuge, stains, urine testing strips, blood grouping serum)	1

Dressing

Gauze swabs, B.P.C.*, 5 × 5 cm, 8 ply in packets of 100 swabs	12 packs
Gauze swabs, B.P.C., 10 × 10 cm, 8 ply in packets of 100 swabs	12 packs
Triangular bandages, unbleached calico B.P.C., 90 × 127 cm., in packets of 12	12 packs
Sterilized eye pads, B.P.C.	12 packs
Paraffin gauze dressings B.P.C., size 3¾″ × 3¾″ tins of 36 pieces	36
White absorbent cotton wool, B.P.C. quality, rolls of 500 grams	2 rolls
Paragon zinc oxide plaster, 1″ × 5 yards	12 rolls
Sterile wound and ward dressings (Elastoplast Airstrip) Size 2½″ × 3½″ and 7½ × 3½″	
Safety pins, assorted	1 lb
Plaster of Paris bandages (Gypsona) B. P.C. 3″ × 3 yards Tins of one dozen	2 tins
Netelast type bandage (assorted sizes)	
Gauze bandages, assorted	100
Pneumatic splint sets	2

Auxiliary equipment

Medical soap	1 kg
Detergent (in plastic bottles)	2 litres

	Quantity
Collapsable stretchers	2
Bucket	2
Sweeping brush	1
Nail brush	1
Jerrycans (plastic)	4
Disposable containers	
Plastic pouches	100
Envelopes for drugs (small, white)	500
Hammer	1
Saw	1
Pliers	1 pair
Nails (different sizes)	1 assortment
Flashlights	5
Spare bulbs	5
Batteries	10
Storm lamps	3
Portable burner for heating	1
Water filter	2
Candles	50
Matches (waterproof packages)	100 boxes
Loud speaker (Bull Horn)	1
Stationery	
Magic Markers (different colours)	2 sets
Scotch tape	5
Towels	12
Basins	6
Cleaning rags	12
Sponges	3
Portable cooler	2
Can openers	2
String (different widths)	6 rolls
Gummed labels	100
Typewriter	1
Disposable bed sheets	50
Paper rolls	6
Treatment tags or cards	500
Knives	5
Tape measures	3
Blankets	10

* B.P.C.—British Pharmaceutical Codex or equivalent.

Appendix 5. Some new products and equipment

A new rescue line, that can be thrown to reach its full length of 132 feet by a special device has been developed in Great Britain. The B.E.L.L. (Balcan Emergency Life Line), together with the Flikstik throwing stick, consists of a compact, bottleshaped plastic capsule 9 ½ inches long, coloured bright orange and containing a specially-wound floating line. One end of the line is threaded through the capsule mouth and tied to the capsule, and a plastic cap seals the contents within the capsule. In use the cap is removed and the hand-grip is retained in the non-throwing hand. When the capsule is thrown the line is paid out as the capsule travels through the air. To achieve maximum throwing range the line capsule has a hollow core that can be fitted over the plastic throwing stick, which is 2 inches long. This device would be particularly useful in rescuing persons trapped by fire in the upper floors of high-rise buildings.

An electronic speech circuit-telephone set, with a linear electromagnetic microphone capsule, has been introduced in Sweden. The new instrument is called Diatronic, and is a new development of the company's light-weight Dialog instrument. In the new telephone the conventional carbon microphone has been replaced by a linear electromagnetic microphone capsule and amplifier which reportedly results in improved transmission qualities and lower maintenance costs. The speech circuit of the Diatronic consists of an integrated microcircuit located within the cover of the microphone capsule in the headset. The compact design, it is claimed, facilitates screening of the microphone and the speech circuit against electromagnetic radiation and the standard rotary dial can be replaced by a push-button unit with electronic impulsing.

An electronic fire alarm system, which transmits an alarm direct to the fire department while simultaneously sounding an alert at key points on the premises, has been developed in Sweden. The alarm system, which is of modular construction, incorporates four main types of detector, each of which is adjustable within certain limits to different types of environment. The smoke detector sounds an alarm the moment the threat of fire arises and before carbon monoxide levels become dangerously high. The heat detector goes off when temperature rises to a certain level, and the differential detector is triggered off by abnormally rapid rises in temperatures. The new system's flame detector gives an alarm when it receives the variable pattern of infrared rays that are emitted by actual flames. This unit is said to be particularly suited to premises on which highly flammable liquids are stored.

A small air cushion vehicle, called the 'Neovo', has been developed in Australia. The 13 foot long vehicle, which is being marketed in do-it-yourself kit form, has been designed with both functional and recreational use in mind. This multi-terrain air cushion vehicle can glide across water, snow, ice, mud, swamp, sand and land. It can climb a gradient of one-in-eight from a standing start. On water the vehicle floats like a boat, when its motor is not in operation. The vehicle is lifted 8 inches off the surface across which it is travelling by air trapped beneath it by a rubber synthetic 'skirt', which hangs down from the vehicle's perimeter to the surface. Two jets of air at its rear propel the vehicle and control its direction.

A small radio telephone, that can be fitted into an automobile glove compartment or equivalent space is being manufactured in Great Britain. The solid state 'Safari' radio telephone will operate from a standard 12 volt car battery and is designed for a long range operation. The company says that its high performance is achieved by the use of integrated circuits and solid state design, thus insuring a high level of reliability with low power consumption. A choice of 6 channels is offered in the band 2–16 MHz, and all the channels controlled to a frequency accuracy of better than 25 Hz in a continuously controlled thermostatic oven.

(The Equipment Service of the International Civil Defence Organisation 10–12 chemin de Surville CH-1213 Petit-Lancy, Geneva, Switzerland, will provide information on the above material.)

The miniature microscope for disaster relief

In disasters, as elsewhere, a microscope is an invaluable item of laboratory equipment. However, conventional microscopes are bulky and delicate and require solid installation and illumination. In order to overcome the problems associated with conventional equipment, Dr. John McArthur of Cambridge, England, has developed a portable, rugged and easily used microscope suitable for disaster work.

The McArthur microscope is approximately the size and weight of a miniature camera (actual dimensions $4 \times 2 \times 2\frac{1}{2}$in., weight 18 ozs.) yet is capable of magnifications of up to 1200× with a resolution equal to that of a standard bench microscope. A simple prismatic system provides the equivalent of a standard tube length and gives a sharp picture. A further, unique advantage of the prismatic system is that it provides an erect image. Focussing is automatic, both for dry and oil immersion lenses. A battery operated lamp may be fitted to give powerful illumination.

The microscope is rugged, waterproof and capable of working in extremes of temperature. It has been widely used both in tropical and arctic climates, and has successfully survived under the most adverse circumstances.

A wide range of accessories are available: these include slides which may be used to examine sedementing particles and organisms in suspension; eyepiece counteres and direct reading scales, a dissection stage for use in field biology, binocular attachment and tripod.

Further details can be obtained from: Dr. J. McArthur, Landbeach, Cambridge CB4 4ED, U.K.

British Hovercraft Corporation containers

British Hovercraft Corporation manufacture a range of light weight portable containers which are commonly used for temporary storage and transport of industrial and agrochemical liquids. These containers are made in two shapes: pillow shaped, which have capacities up to 11,000 gallons and can be transported on the back of a flat-bed lorry; and box shaped, which are made with capacities up to 5000 gallons and are used for storage. When empty, both travel as a compact package.

In disaster situations these flexible containers can bring fresh water supplies to areas where the water has been contaminated. In 1974 these containers were used following the Honduras earthquake. They can also provide storage facilities in remote areas where existing capacity might be inadequate. Recently, 45 box shaped units were supplied to Ethiopia for transport of water and are available for emergency drought relief. In addition they have been employed as fire-fighting reservoirs, and in the collection of tanker spillage.

The possible advantages of these containers for disasters in developing countries would seem to be many. In particular, in cases of earthquakes and tropical cyclones which have brought about a disruption to the potable water supply, these containers can be used on ordinary flat bed lorries thus obviating the need for an emergency pool of more expensive specialised tankers. In other circumstances where rapid access is needed to remote and inaccessible places, as has been the case in some famine stricken countries, the container can be used as emergency fuel stores to help extend the range of both air and road transport.

The containers are made of polymer coated reinforced nylon fabric and are coated according to the function they are expected to perform. They are fabricated by bonding under heat and pressure and should give several years of service. Cleaning is done simply by swilling with fresh water and detergent. These containers comply with international regulations for food contact application.

Appendix 6. Food composition tables for international use

	Cal. per 100 gm	Protein %	Calcium mg	Iron mg	Vit. A I.U.	Vit. B mg	Vit. C mg
Milk							
cow, whole fluid							
3.5% fat	65	3.5	119	.1	140	.04	1
cow, skim fluid	39	3.6	122	.1	20	.04	1
cow, whole dried	492	26	897	.7	1080	.35	4
cow, skim dried	360	36	1235	.9	40	.35	6
Eggs							
hen, in shell	144	11	44	2.2	890	.09	0
Cereals							
Wheat flour, medium	350	11.7	24	2.4	0	.32	0
rice, parboiled	359	7.1	14	1.0	0	.22	0
rye flour, medium	341	9	26	2.5	0	.28	0
maize meal, coarse	360	9.3	6	1.8	400	.35	0
macaroni	367	11	16	1.0	0	.13	0
Starches							
potatoes	70	1.7	7	.6	0	.08	0
cassava meal, flour	338	1.5	12	1.0	0	0	0
yam	90	2.1	19	.7	0	.08	0
Seeds							
soya beans, dry	335	38	208	6.5	140	1.03	0
lentils	346	24.2	56	6.1	100	.50	3
peas	346	22.5	64	4.8	100	.72	4
Fresh vegetables							
tomatoes	19	1.1	11	.6	680	.06	23
beets, red	32	1.3	22	.7	15	.01	7
onions	37	1.3	30	.5	50	.03	8
asparagus	14	1.4	14	.6	670	.11	22
beans lima	43	2.9	25	.9	110	.08	12
broccoli	26	2.5	75	.8	2030	.06	68
cabbage	17	1.1	35	.3	70	.04	35
carrots	37	1	31	.7	1840	.06	6
cassava leaves	53	5.8	175	1.7	100	.14	225
chicory, endives	12	1.1	49	1.1	1870	.04	7
spinach	17	1.8	66	2.4	7630	.09	48
cauliflower	13	1.3	12	.6	50	.06	37
Fruits							
bananas	67	.9	6	.4	140	.03	8
grapefruit	25	.4	15	.3	10	.03	28
oranges	32	.6	24	.3	120	.06	36
breadfruit	65	1.0	28	.4	10	.07	17
figs	64	1.2	52	.6	80	.06	2
dried, all unspecified	267	2.8	65	2.6	490	.09	5

	Cal. per 100 gm	Protein %	Calcium mg	Iron mg	Vit. A I.U.	Vit. B mg	Vit. C mg
Fish							
all unspecified, round	62	8.8	15	.5	20	.03	0
medium cure, fat-rich	178	27	54	1.6	70	.07	0
dried, fat-rich	446	60	2400	3.6	210	.15	0
medium cure, fat-poor	125	25	38	1.0	0	.05	0
fully dried, fat-poor	365	75	112	3.0	0	.15	0
canned in oil, all kinds	314	22	44	1.3	110	.06	0
canned, fat-rich not in oil	188	20	40	1.2	110	.03	0
Syrup							
cane	259	0	60	3.6	0	.03	0

The daily need for calories depends normally on individual physical condition, weight, age, sex and normal activities, as well as on the climatic conditions and average outside temperature. Any scale of rations or menu for under-nourished or sick persons should be prepared by nutrition specialists. The table below is only meant to give an indication of the average number of calories needed per person per day when the group consists of people of different ages.

Average outside temperature	Number of calories per person per day
25°C	1,860
10°C	2,260
5°C	2,390

Appendix 7. Nutritive value of wheat-soy blend (WSB), April, 1969

	Per pound	Per 100 g	1968 RDA for 6 to 8 year old	Percent RDA for 6 to 8 year old per 100 g	Per 50 g	1968 RDA for 1 to 2 year old	Percent RDA for 1 to 2 year old per 50 g
Food energy (cal)	1635	360	2000	18	180	1100	16
Protein (g)	89	20	35	57	10	25	39
Fat (g)	28	6	—	—	3	—	—
Carbohydrate (g)	272	60	—	—	30	—	—
Vitamin A value (I.U.)	7536	1658	3500	47	829	2000	41
Vitamin D (U.S.P. units)	900	200	400	50	100	400	25
Vitamin E (tocopherol) (I.U.)	43.5	9.6	15	64	4.8	10	48
Thiamin (mg)	6.73	1.49	1.0	149	0.74	0.6	123
Riboflavin (mg)	2.66	0.59	1.1	54	0.30	0.6	50
Niacin (mg)	41.4	9.1	13	70	4.6	8	58
Vitamin B_6 (mg)	2.35	0.52	1.0	52	0.26	0.5	52
Vitamin B_{12} (mg)	0.018	0.004	0.004	100	0.002	0.002	100
Pantothenic acid (mg)	16.74	3.70	—	—	1.85	—	—
Folacin (mg)	1.47	0.33	0.2	165	0.16	0.1	160
Ascorbic acid (mg)	182	40	40	100	20	40	50
Calcium (mg)	3105	685	900	76	342	700	49
Iron (mg)	94.6	20.8	10	208	10.4	15	69
Phosphorus (mg)	2549	562	900	62	281	700	40
Magnesium (mg)	919	202	250	81	101	100	100
Sodium (mg)	1343	296	—	—	148	—	—
Potassium (mg)	2833	624	—	—	312	—	—
Iodine (mg)	0.24	0.05	0.1	50	0.025	0.055	45
Zinc (mg)	20.8	4.6	—	—	2.3	—	—

Appendix 8. Amounts of 12 nutrients provided by 100 grams of CSM and other foods

	CSM*	Liquid nonfat milk	Ground beef	Egg	Cheddar cheese	White enriched rice	All-purpose enriched flour	Corn meal**
Calories	373	35.4	372	143	404	363	364	364
Protein (g)	20	3.5	22.35	11.30	25.35	6.7	10.5	7.9
Fat (g)	6	0.80	30.58	10.18	32.50	0.04	1.0	1.2
Carbohydrate (g)	60	5.08	—	0.55	2.14	80	76.1	78.4
Calcium (mg)	513	123	9	48	736	24	16	6
Phosphorus (mg)	381	97.15	157.64	187.03	500	94	87	99
Iron (mg)	18.5	0.08	2.82	2.40	1.07	4.6	2.9	1.1
Vitamin A (I.U.)	1940	4.06	—	1018	1429	—	—	440
Vitamin B_1 or thiamin (mg)	0.65	0.03	0.08	0.07	0.35	0.44	—	0.14
Vitamin B_2 or riboflavin (mg)	0.59	0.17	0.18	0.24	0.43	0.03	0.26	0.05
niacin (mg)	10	0.12	4.82	—	—	3.5	3.5	1.0
Vitamin C or ascorbic acid (mg)	40	1.21	—	—	—	—	—	—

* Typical analysis
** Degermed, not enriched
Source: US Department of Agriculture Handbook No. 8, and Journal of the American Dietetic Association, Dec. 1970.

Appendix 9. Measurements

1. Temperature conversion tables

Fahrenheit	*Centigrade*
−9.4	−23
0.4	−18
5.0	−15
10.4	−12
15.8	− 9
21.2	− 6
25.0	− 4
32.0	0
35.6	+ 2
41.0	+ 5
50.0	+10
60.8	+16
71.6	+22
75.2	+24
80.6	+27
91.4	+33
95.0	+35
100.4	+38
109.4	+43
120.2	+49
131	+55
140	+60

How to convert

Centigrade to Fahrenheit: Multiply by 1.8 and add 32
Fahrenheit to Centigrade: Subtract 32 and multiply by 0.555

2. Linear measure

1 league (l)	3 miles	4.827 km
1 statute mile (mi or m)	8 furlongs	1.609 km
1 furlong (fur)	40 rods	0.201 km
1 rod (rd)	5½ yards	5.029 m
1 yard (yd)	3 feet	0.914 m
1 foot (ft)	12 inches	30.480 cm
1 inch (in)	2.540 cm	
1 kilometre (km)	0.6214 miles	
1 metre (m)	3.2808 feet	1.0936 yards
1 centimetre (cm)	0.3937 inches	
1 nautical mile	(US) 6,076.10 feet	1.852 km
	(UK) 6,080 feet	1.853 km

3. Square measure

1 square mile (sq. mi or m^2)	640 acres	2.590 km^2
1 acre	160 sq. rods	4047 m^2
1 square rod (sq. rd. or rd^2)	30¼ sq. yd	25.293 m^2
1 square yard (sq. yd or yd^2)	9 sq. feet	0.836 m^2
1 square foot (sq. ft or ft^2)	144 sq. inches	929 cm^2
1 square inch (sq. in or in^2)	6.451 cm^2	
1 square kilometre (sq. km or km^2)	0.3861 sq. miles	
1 hectare (ha)	2.4710 acres	
1 acre (a)	119.60 sq. yards	
1 square metre (m^2)	10.764 sq feet	

4. Cubic measure

1 cubic yard (cu. yd)	27 cubic feet	0.764 m^3	
1 cubic foot (cu. ft)	1.728 cubic inches	0.028 m^3	
1 cubic inch (cu. in)	16.39 cm^3		
1 stere (s)	1 cubic metre (m^3)	1.308 cubic yards	35.315 cubic feet

5. Dry measure

1 bushel (bu)	4 pecks	(US) 35.23 l	(UK) 36.37 l
1 peck (pk)	8 quarts	(US 8.809 l	(UK) 9.092 l
1 quart	2 pints	(US) 1.101 l	(UK) 1.136 l
1 pint (US) 0.550 l	(UK) 0.568 l		

6. Liquid measure

1 gallon (gal)	4 quarts	(US) 3.785 l	(UK) 4.545 l
1 quart (qt)	2 pints	(US) 0.946 l	(UK) 1.136 l
1 pint (pt)	4 gills	(US) 0.473 l	(UK) 0.568 l
1 US gallon	0.832 UK gallon		
1 UK gallon	1.2 US gallon		
1 quart	4 cups	946 ml (US)	
1 pint	2 cups	473 ml	
1 cup	16 tablespoons	236.56 ml	
1 tablespoon	3 teaspoons	15 ml	
1 teaspoon	5 ml		
1 litre	(US) 2.114 pints	0.264 gallons	
	(UK) 1.760 pints	0.220 gallons	

7. Weight—avoidupois

1 long ton (UK)	20 hundredweights	2,240 pounds	0.907 tons
1 short ton (US)	20 hundredweights	2,000 pounds	1.016 tons
1 metric ton	0.984 long tons	1.102 short tons	
1 hundredweight (cwt)	short cwt	100 pounds	45.359 kg
	long cwt	112 pounds	50.802 kg
1 pound (lb)	16 ounces	453.5 g	
1 ounce (oz)	16 drams	28.35 g	
1 dram (dr)	1.771 g		
1 kilogram (kg)	2.2046 pounds		
1 gram (g)	0.035 ounces		

Appendix 10. WSB uses and recipes

Food habits and tastes differ from country to country and within countries. Availability of utensils, equipment, and of ingredients varies widely. Following is a summary of the uses of WSB and various recipes which may be enjoyed in different areas. People everywhere will find some uses for WSB that please their palates while also providing dietary requirements.

What is WSB?

WSB is a Wheat Soya Blend.
WSB is a very rich food which can be used instead of meat, egg or cheese in making nourishing meals.

Cooking WSB

WSB is cooked before it comes to you. So, just 'warm it up'. DON'T BOIL WSB.

WSB Beverages

Practically any beverage, such as milk and fruit juices, can be enriched by adding WSB to the desired consistency.

WSB and water

Use 1 part WSB to 10 parts water. As a baby food for children of two years and under, heat mixture to a boil while stirring to a smooth consistency. (Omission of flavouring is recommended.) Feed either by bottle or spoon. For adult consumption use with hot or cold water, adding flavouring. Nutrients in WSB are equivalent to those found in human milk.

WSB chocolate drink

1 cup WSB
6 cups water
1 chocolate bar
pinch of salt
sugar, to taste
cinnamon, or lemon peel

Mix all ingredients, preventing them from forming into small chunks. Cook for 10 minutes and strain. Serve hot or cold.

WSB bakery products

WSB can be substituted in whole or part for ordinary flour to fortify the whole range of bakery products, including breads, rolls, biscuits, pasta, crackers, cakes and cookies. Equal parts of WSB and white flour (10 per cent protein) produce a bakery product of 15 to 17 per cent protein, solid basis, plus added vitamins and minerals.

A mix of 20 per cent WSB is recommended in bread and rolls when using high speed mixing equipment as is available in the United States. With low speed mixers (or hand mixing) up to 50 per cent WSB may be used with good results depending upon the type of product. Up to one hundred per cent WSB can be used in flat breads, chapattis, and pancakes.

WSB cookies

Sift together:
$\frac{1}{2}$ cup WSB
$\frac{1}{2}$ tsp salt
$\frac{1}{2}$ tsp baking soda
$\frac{1}{2}$ cup plus 2 tbsp flour

Cream together:
$\frac{1}{2}$ cup softened shortening
6 tbsp each granulated and brown sugar
$\frac{1}{2}$ tsp vanilla
1 egg
$\frac{1}{4}$ tsp water

Combine and add 1 cup raisins and $\frac{1}{2}$ cup nuts, if desired. Drop by tsp on greased cookie sheet. Bake at 375°F. 10 to 12 min.

Makes 50 two inch cookies.

WSB fried cakes

$1\frac{1}{2}$ cups WSB
1 tbsp butter oil
1 egg (beaten)
$1\frac{3}{4}$ cups water or milk
1 tsp soda or baking powder
salt, to taste

Mix all ingredients to smooth paste. Make thin, small cakes and fry in oil (not too hot). For sweeter cakes, add sugar instead of salt.

WSB yeast bread

(Makes two $1\frac{1}{2}$-pound loaves, or 2 dozen rolls)

4 cups enriched flour
1 cup WSB
2 packages dry yeast
$\frac{1}{4}$ cup sugar
1 tbsp salt
2 cups warm water (115°)
2 tbsp vegetable oil

Mix together 1 cup flour (spoon flour into dry measuring cup; level; do not scoop), WSB, yeast, sugar and salt. Add water and 2 tablespoons oil to flour mixture and beat until smooth, about 2 minutes on medium speed of electric mixer or 300 stokes by hand. Add 1 cup flour and beat 1 minute on medium speed or 150 strokes by hand. Stir in more flour to make a moderately stiff dough. Place on lightly floured surface and knead until smooth, about 8 to 10 minutes. Shape into ball and place in lightly greased bowl, turning to grease all sides. Cover; let rise in warm place about 45 minutes (80 to 85°) to twice the original size. Knead down Divide dough in half; shape into balls. Cover; let sit for 10 minutes. Brush with oil. Let rise again in warm place until doubled in size, about 45 minutes for loaves, 15 to 20 minutes for rolls. Bake in preheated 400° oven 30 to 35 minutes for loaves, 15 to 20 minutes for rolls. Remove from pans immediately. Brush with oil.

To shape loaves, roll dough into rectangle 9 inches wide. Starting at one end, roll up in jelly roll fashion. Seal seam. With side of hand, press ends to seal. Fold ends under loaf. Place in pan, seam side down.

Cinnamon bread

Divide dough in half; roll each half into 9 inch wide rectangle. Sprinkle with mixture of 2 tablespoons sugar and 1 teaspoon ground cinnamon, and roll up (as above). Place in greased $4\frac{1}{2} \times 8\frac{1}{2}$-inch pan; brush with oil; let rise and bake as directed.

Orange pinwheel bread

Divide dough in half; roll each half into 9-inch wide rectangle. Sprinkle with mixture of 3 tablespoons sugar, 2 teaspoons orange juice, 1 teaspoon grated orange rind and 2 tablespoons chopped nuts, and roll up (as above). Place in greased $4\frac{1}{2} \times 8\frac{1}{2}$-inch pan; brush with oil; let rise and bake as directed.

Cloverleaf rolls

Shape dough into balls one inch in diameter. Place 3 balls in greased muffin cup. Brush with oil; let rise and bake as directed.

WSB pancakes

(Makes 16 to 18 pancakes)

$\frac{3}{4}$ cup enriched flour
$\frac{3}{4}$ cup WSB
1 tbsp sugar
1 tbsp baking powder
$\frac{1}{2}$ tsp salt
1 egg (beaten)
$1\frac{1}{2}$ cups water
2 tbsp oil

Mix together dry ingredients. (Spoon flour into dry measuring cup; level. Do not scoop.) Combine egg, water and oil. Add liquid all at once to flour mixture, stirring only until dry ingredients are moistened. Bake on pre-heated greased medium hot griddle 2 to 3 minutes on each side, or until done.
Note: 2 to 3 tablespoons water may be added if batter thickens upon standing.

WSB dumplings

2 cups WSB
$\frac{1}{2}$ cup corn starch
$\frac{1}{2}$ teaspoon salt
$\frac{1}{2}$ teaspoon baking powder

Mix dry ingredients; add enough water to make dough, form into dumplings. Boil or fry. (Makes 12 small dumplings.)

Indian pacora

1 part WSB
1 part water
curry to taste

Mix and mould into desired shape. Fry in deep fat.

Sweet fritter

2 parts WSB
1 part sugar
1½ parts water
vanilla or other flavour

Mix and mould into desired shape. Fry in deep fat.

Arabic flat bread

10 parts white flour
5 parts WSB
11 parts water
0.3 parts fresh yeast
0.15 parts salt

Mix and treat exactly as regular Arabic bread.

WSB tortillas

(Makes about 12 tortillas)

1 cup WSB
1 cup enriched flour
½ tsp salt
1 to 1¼ cups water

Mix together WSB, flour, and salt. (Spoon flour into dry measuring cup; level. Do not scoop.) Stir in 1 cup water. Add more water if necessary to form firm dough. Shape into ball. On lightly floured surface, knead dough 1 to 2 minutes. Shape into balls 1½ inches in diameter; roll into 6 inch circles. Bake on preheated greased medium hot griddle 2 minutes on each side, or until done.

WSB uppama

1 cup WSB
salt, to taste
2 tbsp cooking oil
½ tsp mustard seeds
1 tsp black gram dal
2 tbsp groundnuts
1 tbsp Bengal gram dal
2 medium onions (chopped)
1 tsp lime juice
a few curry leaves
a few coriander leaves

Mix WSB, salt and boiling water to a soft dough. Make small marble-sized balls, and steam for 10 minutes. Fry mustard seeds, onions, black gram dal, ground nuts and Bengal gram dal in oil until golden brown. Add the marbles and stir well. Sprinkle with lime juice in serving dish. Garnish with curry leaves and coriander leaves.

Greens Paratha

1 cup WSB
1 cup chopped greens
salt, to taste
1 medium onion (chopped)
2 green chillies (chopped)
2 tbsp cooking oil

Mix WSB, salt, and sufficient water to make stiff dough. Knead well. Let stand for $\frac{1}{2}$ hour and knead again. Wash, dry, and chop fresh greens finely. Add onions and chillies. Roll a paratha to 6 inches in diameter. Place 2 tablespoons of greens mixture in the centre. Fold edges together. Roll gently into flat paratha. Fry in frying pan with a few drops of cooking oil. Serve hot.

Puri cutlet

1 cup WSB
1 cup atta
4 small potatoes
4 small carrots
10 green beans
1 small head cabbage
2 large onions (chopped)
10 green chillies (chopped, fried)
salt, to taste
1 tsp masala powder
1 tbsp cooking oil

Cook the potatoes, carrots, beans and cabbage. Peel potatoes and slice all vegetables into thin pieces. Add masala powder and salt. Stir until well blended. Add WSB and atta to this mixture. Knead it into a thick dough. Shape into inch sized balls. Roll each ball into a puri. Fry in deep fat or on a tawa.

Rawa kela thalli

$\frac{3}{4}$ cup WSB
$\frac{3}{4}$ cup semolina
$\frac{3}{4}$ cup jaggery (brown sugar)
$1\frac{1}{2}$ cups coconut milk
3 medium bananas
pinch of salt
4 drops vanilla
2 tbsp cooking oil

Make fine paste of jaggery and bananas. Fry WSB and semolina. Add coconut milk and vanilla. Spread the mixture on a greased plate. Steam for 15 minutes. Cut into cubes and serve hot.

Pansiet egg roll

$\frac{3}{4}$ kg WSB
1 or 2 eggs
water
salt

Ingredients for filling:
$\frac{3}{4}$ kg pork
200 kg shrimp
8 small white onions
koetjai
celery
onion greens
pepper and salt, to taste

Chop or grind pork and shrimp together and mix well. Chop separately the white onions, koetjai, celery and onion greens, and fry in oil with some vetsin added. In separate fry pan, brown chopped pork and shrimp in oil and vetsin. Mix all ingredients and fry together.

Prepare dough with WSB and water; add eggs and salt. Mix well. Roll dough as thin as possible, using some flour to keep from sticking. Cut dough into squares and spoon on two teaspoons of filling to each square. Fold dough over and seal; deep fry.

Boeboer soem soem (Porridge)

1 cup WSB or bulgur, or
mixture of both
2 to 3 cups coconut milk (santan)
1 pandan leaf
salt

Cook ingredients together until thickened. Serve warm or cold with brown sugar or Javanese sugar.

WSB mashed potatoes

2 parts mashed potatoes
1 part WSB
water, to make desired consistency
salt, to taste

WSB gruel or soup

1 part WSB
4 to 8 parts water or milk
salt, sugar, spices or
curry powder, to taste

Stir WSB into boiled water or into milk. Add flavouring as desired. (Curry powder and WSB go especally well together.) Serve hot or cold.

WSB pumpkin soup

1 lb salt beef
1 lb yam
2 lbs pumpkin
1 gallon water
$\frac{1}{2}$ cup WSB
seasoning

1. Cook salt beef, yam and pumpkin until tender.
2. Mash pumpkin into soup.
3. Mix WSB into 1 cup cold water; stir into hot soup. Cook until soup thickens.

WSB can be added to any soup (e.g. red peas, pepper pot, gungo peas).

WSB dessert

½ cup WSB
1 cup water
3 tablespoons dark sugar

Mix WSB with cold water; heat over low flame until thick; sweeten and cool. (Makes 1 cup.)

WSB pudding

1 part WSB
3 to 4 parts water
1 part sugar, vanilla, or spices

Combine ingredients and cook until smooth. Serve hot or cold.

WSB candy and cream fillings

¼ cup water
¾ cup brown sugar
½ cup WSB
½ cup powdered milk
1 tsp vanilla extract (or vanilla sticks)
½ cup cooked bulgur

Bring water to boil, adding WSB and powdered milk and brown sugar. Cook for about 15 minutes. Simmer for additional 15 minutes, or until mixture thickens. Add vanilla extract and cooked bulgur. Mix well. To make candy, allow mixture to cool. When hardened, cut into squares, and dip in melted chocolate (optional). Shredded coconut can be added while mixture is still in liquid form. For cake and cupcake fillings, prepare as above, but cook just long enough to obtain the desired consistency.

Appendix 11. CSM (blended food product, formula No. 2)

What it is

CSM is a mixture of 70 per cent processed (precooked) cornmeal, 25 per cent toasted defatted soy flour, 5 per cent nonfat dry milk, with added vitamins and minerals. It is a highly nutritious supplementary food, particularly for infants and children in a low protein status.

The calorie value of CSM is about 1650 calories per pound. It contains 20 per cent protein and the Protein Efficiency Ratio (PER) s 2.48, compared with 2.50 for casein.

CSM is almost completely precooked. It is bran-free, bland in flavour, and smooth in texture.

What it does

CSM may be used to prepare simple soups and gruels or porridges.

CSM may be baked, fried or steamed.

When mixed with water, CS forms a smooth dough, from which unleavened bread may easily be prepared, such as the 'tortilla' of Mexico or the 'chapati' of Asia.

CSM can be prepared as a delicious custard dessert.

CSM forms a highly nutritious, appetizing beverage.

General instructions

Always mix CSM with *cold water*.

It is best to first place the water (with salt to taste) in a bowl, and then slowly add the CSM while stirring.

Cooking time for soups and gruels will be from 2 to 8 minutes at sea level, depending upon the size of the cooking utensil and the heat of the fire. *Always continue stirring while CSM is boiling.* Cook until smooth.

Consistency may be varied by increasing or decreasing amount of water used.

Recipes

The basic recipes in this appendix are intended to show how easily simple foods can be made from CSM. But you will discover many more ways in which you can readily make locally popular foods from nutritious CSM (blended food product, formula No. 2)

Soup

1 cup CSM
6 cups cold water
salt to taste
seasonings, vegetables, meat,
stock, as available

Place water in a bowl. Slowly add the CSM, stirring. Heat mixture to a boil, stirring constantly. Add other ingredients as available, to taste. Cook until smooth, from 2 to 8 minutes. *If soup is too thick, add more water.*

Beverage

Follow instructions given for soup but use 8 or 9 cups of cold water, depending on consistency desired. Add sugar and flavouring to taste. Serve hot or cold.

Gruel or porridge

1 cup CSM
4 cups cold water
salt, sugar to taste

Place water in a bowl. Slowly add the CSM, *stirring constantly*. Add other ingredients, heat to a boil, stirring constantly. If gruel is too thick, add more water. When mixture is smooth, remove from fire, and serve.

Pudding (dessert)

1 cup CSM
4 cups cold water
1 cup sugar
few drops of vanilla,
or spices, as available

Place water in a bowl. Add CSM slowly, stirring constantly. Place on fire. When mixture starts to boil, add sugar. *Continue stirring until boiling starts again*, cook until smooth, then remove from fire. Add vanilla or other flavouring. Serve hot or cold.

Basic dough (for unleavened breads)

1 cup CSM
$\frac{3}{4}$ cup cold water
salt to taste

Place water in a bowl. Slowly add CSM, mixing with a spoon or by hand. If dough is too stiff, add a little more water. If too sticky, add more CSM. Let stand for 5 minutes or more. Then knead, shape as desired into tortilla, chapatti or other popular unleavened bread, and bake, fry or steam, in accordance with local preference.

Basic dough for bread or rolls (for leavened breads)

$1\frac{1}{3}$ cups CSM
$\frac{2}{3}$ cup wheat flour
$\frac{1}{2}$ cup luke warm water
$\frac{1}{2}$ ounce yeast + 1 teaspoon sugar + $\frac{1}{4}$ cup lukewarm water

No-knead rolls (or bread)

1 ounce compressed yeast
$\frac{1}{4}$ cup lukewarm water
$\frac{1}{4}$ cup sugar
$\frac{1}{3}$ cup shortening
1 teaspoon salt
$1\frac{1}{4}$ cups lukewarm water
1 egg
2 cups CSM
$1\frac{1}{2}$ cups wheat flour

Soften yeast in $\frac{1}{4}$ cup lukewarm water. In bowl, combine the sugar and shortening along with the salt and egg. Beat until fluffy. Blend in the water and the yeast. Beat in the CSM and wheat flour.

Cover bowl with a piece of plastic and let rise in a warm place (80°F) until double in bulk, about 1 hour. Stir dough. Spoon into well-buttered muffin tins, filling half full. Let rise in a warm place for about 45 minutes until batter has risen to top of muffin cup. Bake in pre-heated oven at 375°F for 20 minutes.

Glossary

Carrier. An infected person who harbours a specific infectious agent in the absence of discernible clinical disease and who serves as a potential source of infection to other persons. The carrier state may occur with infections not apparent throughout their course (commonly known as healthy carriers), and also as a feature of an incubation period, convalescence, and post-convalescence of a clinically recognisable disease (commonly known as incubatory and convalescent carriers). Under either circumstance the carrier state may be short or long (temporary or chronic carriers). The same applies to other vertebrate animals.

Chemoprophylaxis. The administration of a chemical, including antibiotics, to prevent the development of an infection, or progression of an infection to active manifest infectious disease. Not to be confused with chemothepary which refers to use of a chemical to cure a clinically recognisable infectious disease, or to limit its further progress.

Cleaning. The removal from surfaces by scrubbing and washing with hot water, soap or suitable detergent, of infectious agents and of organic matter on, and in, which infectious agents may find favourable conditions for prolonging life and virulence.

Communicable disease. An illness due to a specific infectious agent or its toxic products, which arises through transmission of that agent or its products from a reservoir to a susceptible host, either directly as from an infected person or animal, or indirectly through an intermediate plant or animal host, a vector, or the environment.

Communicable period. The time or times during which the infectious agent may be transferred directly or indirectly from an infected person to another person, from an infected animal to man, or from an infected man to animal, including arthropods.

In diseases such as diphtheria and scarlet fever, in which mucous membranes are involved from the first entry of the pathogen, the period of communicability is from the date of first exposure to a source of infection, until the infecting micro-organism is no longer disseminated from the involved mucous membranes; i.e. from before the prodromata until the termination of a carrier state, if such develops.

In diseases such as tuberculosis, syphilis and gonorrhoea, the communicable state may be at any time during a long and sometimes intermittent period when unhealed lesions of the disease permit the discharge of infectious agents from the surface of the skin or through any of the body orifices. In certain diseases communicability does not occur during the early incubation period or after full recovery, e.g. measles and chickenpox.

In diseases transmitted by arthropods, such as malaria and yellow fever, the periods of communicability are those during which the infectious agent occurs in the blood or other tissues of the infected person in infective form and in sufficient numbers for vector infection. A period of communicability is also to be distinguished for the arthropod vector, namely, that time during which the agent is present in the tissues of the arthropod in such form (infective state) as to be capable of transmitting infection.

Contact. A person or animal who has been in association with an infected person or animal or with a contaminated environment and has had the opportunity to acquire an infection. Exposure may be direct and involve physical touching, e.g. kissing, shaking hands, or sexual intercourse. Persons thus exposed are variously characterised as direct, immediate or intimate contacts. Exposure may be indirect, with no established physical touching, through living in the same household, being in the same room, or through remote or close association at school, work or play. Exposure may be long or short, single, continued or repetitive, casual or close. Such indirectly exposed persons are often denoted, in expression of varying degrees of risk of a developing infection, as either familial, school or work contacts, or as close, casual or remote contacts.

Contamination. The presence of an infectious agent on a body surface; also on clothes, bedding, toys, surgical instruments or dressings, or other inanimate articles or substances including water, milk and food. Contamination is distinct from pollution, which implies the presence of offensive but non-infectious matter in the environment.

Disinfection. Killing of infectious agents outside the body by chemical or physical means, directly applied.

Concurrent disinfection is the application of disinfection as soon as possible after the discharge of infectious matter from the body of an infected person, or after the soiling of articles with such infectious discharges, all personal contact with such discharges or articles being prevented prior to such disinfection.

Terminal disinfection is no longer practised after the patient has been removed by death or to a hospital, has ceased to be a source of infection, or after isolation practices have been discontinued. Terminal cleaning suffices along with airing and sunning of rooms, furniture and bedding. Necessary only for diseases spread by indirect contact. Steam sterilisation of bedding is desirable after smallpox.

Disinfestation. Any physical or chemical process serving to destroy undesired small animal forms, particularly arthropods or rodents, present upon the person, the clothing, or in the environment of an individual, or on domestic animals. This includes de-lousing as applied to infestation with *Pediculus humanus,* the body louse.

Endemic. The habitual presence of a disease within a given geographical area. May also refer to the usual prevalence of a given disease within such an area. Hyperendemic expresses a persistent activity in excess of expected prevalence.

Epidemic. An epidemic, or outbreak, is the occurrence in a community or region of a group of illnesses of similar nature, clearly in excess of normal expectancy, and derived from a common or propagated source. The number of cases indicating presence of an epidemic will vary according to the infectious agent, size and type of population exposed, previous experience of, or lack of exposure to, the disease, and time and place of occurrence. Epidemicity is thus relative to usual frequency of the disease in the same area, among the specified population, at the same season of the year. A single case of a communicable disease long absent from a population (as smallpox in Boston) or first invasion by a disease not previously recognised in that area (as American trypanosomiasis in Arizona), is to be considered as a potential epidemic meeting the requirements in respect of the reporting of epidemics.

Fatality. An expression of the severity of disease as judged by the frequency of deaths among the patients or sick persons in which those deaths occur. It may express the general characteristic in relation to an area, a disease, or a class of diseases. It is commonly employed quantitatively as a ratio of the number of fatal cases to total cases in a specific clinical or epidemiological experience where all cases have been followed to completion (acute disease) or for a stated period of time (chronic disease). Common usage of the ratio is disease-specific; thus, the case fatality of diphtheria is 4 per cent.

Fumigation. Any process by which the killing of animal forms, especially arthropods and rodents, is accomplished by the employment of gaseous agents.

Health education. The process by which individuals and groups of people learn to promote, maintain, or restore health. To be effective, the methods and procedures used to achieve this aim must take account of the ways in which people develop various forms of behaviour, of the factors that lead them to maintain or alter their acquired behaviour, and of the ways in which people acquire and use knowledge. Therefore, education for health begins with people as they are, with whatever interest they may have in improving their living conditions, and aims at developing in them a sense of responsibility for health conditions, as individuals and as members of families and communities. In communicable disease control, health education commonly includes an appraisal of what is known of a disease by a population; as assessment of habits and attitudes of the people as they relate to spread and frequency of the disease; and the presentation of specific means of remedy observed deficiencies.

Host. A man, or other living animal, including birds and arthropods, affording, under natural conditions, subsistence or lodgements to an infectious agent. Some protozoa and helminths pass successive stages in alternate hosts of different species. Hosts in which the parasite attains maturity, or passes its sexual stage, are primary or definitive hosts; those in which the parasite is in a larval or a sexual state are secondary or intermediate hosts.

Immune person. An immune person is one who possesses specific protective antibodies or cellular immunity as a result of previous infection or immunisation, or is so conditioned by such previous specific experience as to respond adequately with production of antibodies sufficient in either instance to protect from illness following exposure to the specific infectious agent of the disease. This applies also to animals. Immunity is relative; an ordinarily effective protection may be overwhelmed by an excessive dose of the infectious agent or an unusual portal of entry.

Inapparent infection. The presence of infection in a host without occurrence of recognisable clinical signs or symptoms. Some inapparent infections are specifically identifiable by laboratory means.

Incidence. A general term used to characterise the frequency of occurrence of a disease, an infection, or other event over a period of time and in relation to the population in which it occurs. Incidence is expressed more specifically as a rate, commonly the number of new cases during a prescribed time in the unit of population in which they occur. Thus, cases of tuberculosis per 100 000 population per year.

Incubation period. The time interval between the infection of a susceptible person or animal and the appearance of the first sign or symptom of the disease in question.

Infected person. Includes both individuals with manifest disease and those with inapparent infection.

Infection. The entry and development or multiplication of an infectious agent in the body of man or animal. Infection is not synonymous with infectious disease; the result may be inapparent or manifest. The presence of living infectious agents on exterior surfaces of the body or upon articles of apparel or soiled articles is not infection but contamination of such surfaces and articles. The term 'infection' should not be used to describe conditions of inanimate matter such as soil, water, sewage, milk, or food—the term 'contamination' applies here.

Infectious agent. An organism, mainly micro-organisms (bacterium, protozoan, spirochaete, fungus, virus, rickettsia, bedsonia, or other), but including helminths, capable of producing infection or infectious disease.

Infectious disease. A disease of man or animal resulting from an infection.

Infestation. The lodgement, development, and reproduction of arthropods on the surface of the body or in clothing. Infested articles or premises are those which harbour or give shelter to animal forms, especially arthropods and rodents.

Insecticide. Any chemical substance used for the destruction of arthropods, whether applied as powder, liquid, atomised liquid, aerosol, or as a paint spray. Residual action is usual. The word larvicide is generally used to designate insecticides applied specifically for destruction of immature stages of arthropods; imagocide or adulticide to designate those applied to destroy mature or adult forms.

Isolation. The process of isolating, as, for example, the separation of an individual with an infectious disease to prevent his transmitting it to others.

Morbidity. A general and variously-used term expressing the number of sick persons or cases of disease in relation to the population in which they occur. A quantitative expression of morbidity is best attained by incidence rates, occasionally by prevalence ratios. Disease-specific incidence rates are common usage in expressing morbidity, sometimes further qualified for age, sex or other attribute, and usually representing cases per 100 000 population per year. Attack rate is an incidence rate often used for particular populations, observed for limited periods and under special circumstances, as in an epidemic. The secondary attack rate in communicable disease practice expresses the number of cases among familial or institutional contacts occurring within the accepted incubation period directly following exposure to a primary case, in relation to the total of such contacts. It may be restricted to susceptible contacts when determinable. Case rate expresses the incidence of clinically-recognised cases; infection rate the sum of infection and infectious disease. Admission rate (USA) is the usual term for morbidity in military populations, an incidence rate that includes both patients admitted to hospital and those confined to quarters.

Mortality. A general term characterising the frequency of deaths over a period of time in the total population (the sick and the well) in which those deaths occur. Commonly expressed quantatively as a mortality rate (death rate), the number of deaths in a unit of population occurring within a prescribed time. Crude mortality rates, deaths from all causes, are usually stated as the number of deaths per 1000 population per year. Disease-specific mortality rates are usually expressed as the number of deaths per 100 000 population per year.

Molluscicide. A chemical substance used for the destruction of snails, generally through ingestion.

Pathogenicity. The capacity of an infectious agent to cause disease in a susceptible host.

Patient or sick person. A person who is ill; here limited to a person suffering from a recognisable attack of a communicable disease.

Personal hygiene. Those protective measures primarily within the responsibility of the individual, which promote health and limit the spread of infectious diseases, mainly those transmitted by direct contact. They include (*a*) keeping the body clean by frequent soap and water baths; (*b*) washing hands in soap and water immediately after voiding bowels or bladder, and always before eating; (*c*) keeping hands and unclean articles, or articles that have been used for toilet purposes by others, away from the mouth, nose, eyes, ears, genitalia, and wounds; (*d*) avoiding the use of common or unclean eating, drinking, or toilet articles of any kind, such as cutlery and crockery, drinking cups, towels, handkerchiefs, combs, hairbrushes, and pipes; (*e*) avoiding exposure of other persons to spray from the nose and mouth as in coughing, sneezing, laughing or talking; (*f*) washing hands thoroughly after handling a patient or his belongings, and wearing a protective overall or apron while in a sickroom.

Prevalence. A general term used to characterise the frequency of a disease or other event at a particular time and in relation to the population from which it is drawn. Prevalence is expressed more specifically as a ratio. Prevalence ratio is the number of cases of a disease present in a specified population unit at a particular time. Thus, the prevalence ratio of tuberculosis is the number of active cases (all forms—old and new) existing at a designated time per 100 000 persons.

Quarantine. (*a*) Complete quarantine is the limitation of freedom of movement of such well persons or domestic animals as have been exposed to a communicable disease, for a period of time equal to the longest usual incubation period of the disease, and in such a manner as to prevent effective contact with those not so exposed. (*b*) Modified quarantine is a selective, partial limitation of freedom of movement of persons or domestic animals, commonly on the basis of known or presumed differences in susceptibility, but sometimes because of danger of disease transmission. It may be designed to meet particular situations, e.g. exclusion of children from school or exemption of immune persons from provisions required of susceptible persons, such as contacts acting as food handlers, or restriction of military population to the post or to quarters. (*c*) Personal surveillance in the practice of close medical or other supervision of contacts in order to promote prompt recognition of infection or illness but without restricting their movements. (*d*) Segregation is the separation for special consideration, control, or observation of some members of a group of persons, or of some domestic animals from others, to facilitate the control of a communicable disease. Other examples are the removal of susceptible children to homes of immune persons, or the establishment of a sanitary boundary to protect uninfected from infected portions of a population.

Repellent. A chemical applied to the skin or clothing to discourage arthropods from lighting on and attacking an individual; and other agents such as worm larvae from penetrating the skin.

Report of a disease. Official report is notification to appropriate authority of the occurrence of specified communicable or other disease in man or animals. Diseases in man are reported to the local health authority; those in animals to the livestock, sanitary or agriculture authority. A few diseases in animals, which are also transmissible to man, are reportable to both authorities. Each health jurisdiction declares a list of reportable diseases appropriate to its particular needs. Report should include suspect cases of diseases of particular public health importance, ordinarily those requiring epidemiologic investigation or initiation of special control measures.

When a person is infected in one health jurisdiction and the case is reported from another, the authority receiving the report should notify the other jurisdiction, especially if the disease is such as to require examination of contacts for infection, or food and water as vehicles.

In addition to routine report of cases of specified diseases, special notification of all epidemics or outbreaks of disease is required, including diseases not in the list declared reportable.

Reservoir of infectious agents. Reservoirs are man, animals, plants, soil or inanimate organic matter, in which an infectious agent lives and multiplies and upon which it depends for survival, reproducing itself in such manner that it can be transmitted to a susceptible host. Man himself is the most frequent reservoir of infectious agents pathogenic for man.

Resistance. The sum total of body mechanisms which interpose barriers to the progress of invasion or multiplication of infectious agents, or to damage by their toxic products. (*a*) *Immunity.* Immunity is that resistance usually associated with possession of antibodies having a specific action on the micro-organism concerned with a particular infectious disease or its toxin. Passive immunity is attained either naturally by maternal transfer, or artificially by inoculation of specific protective antibodies (convalescent or immune serum or immune gamma globulin) and is of brief duration. Active immunity is attained either naturally by infection, with or without clinical manifestations, or artificially by inoculation of fractions or products of the infectious agent, or of the agent itself in killed, modified or variant form. (*b*) *Inherent resistance.* An ability to resist disease independently of antibodies or specifically developed tissue response. It commonly rests in anatomic or physiologic characteristics of the host and may be genetic or acquired, permanent or temporary.

Rodenticide. A chemical substance used for the destruction of rodents, generally through ingestion.

Source of infection. The thing, person, object or substance from which an infectious agent passes immediately to a host. Transfer is often direct from reservoir to host in which case the reservoir is also the source of infection (measles). The source may be at any point in the chain of transmission, as a vehicle, vector, intermediate animal host, or contaminated article, e.g. contaminated water (typhoid fever), an infective mosquito (malaria), beef (tapeworm disease), or a toy (diphtheria). In each instance cited, the reservoir is an infected person. Source of infection should be clearly distinguished from source of contamination, such as overflow of a septic tank contaminating a water supply, or an infected cook contaminating a salad.

Surveillance of disease. Disease surveillance, as distinct from surveillance of persons, is the continuing scrutiny of all aspects of occurrence and spread of a disease which are pertinent to effective control. Included are the systematic collection and evaluation of (*a*) morbidity and mortality reports; (*b*) special reports of field investigations, epidemics and individual cases; (*c*) isolations and identifications of infectious agents in laboratories; (*d*) data concerning the availability and use of vaccines, immune globulin, insecticides and other substances used in control; (*e*) information regarding immunity levels in segments of the population, and (*f*) other relevant epidemiologic data. The procedure applies to all jurisdictional levels of public health, from local to international.

Susceptible. A person or animal presumed not to possess resistance against a particular pathogenic agent and for that reason liable to contract a disease if, or when, exposed to such agent.

Suspect. A person whose medical history and symptoms suggest that he may have, or may be, developing some communicable disease.

Transmission of infectious agents. Methods of transmission of infection are the mechanisms by which an infectious agent is transported from reservoir to susceptible human host. They are: (*a*) *Contact.* (i) Direct contact. Actual touching of the infected person or animal or other reservoir of infection, as in kissing, sexual intercourse, or other contiguous personal association. In the systemic mycoses, by skin contact with soil, compost or decaying vegetable matter where the agent leads a saprophytic existence. (ii) Indirect contact. Touching of contaminated objects such as toys, handkerchiefs, soiled clothing, bedding, surgical instruments and dressings, with subsequent hand to mouth transfer of infective material. Less commonly, transfer to abraded or intact skin or mucous membrane. (iii) Droplet spread. The projection on to the conjunctivae and the face or into the nose or mouth, of the spray emanating from the infected person during sneezing, coughing, singing or talking. Such droplets usually travel no more than a metre from the source. Transmission by droplet infection is considered a form of contact infection, since it involves reasonably close association between two or more persons. (*b*) *Vehicle.* Water, food, milk, biological products to include serum and plasma, or any substance serving as an intermediate means by which an infectious agent is transported from a reservoir and introduced into a susceptible host through ingestion, inoculation, or by desposit on skin or mucous membrane. (*c*) *Vector.* Arthropods or other invertebrates which transmit infection by inoculation into or through the skin or mucous membrane by biting, or by deposit of infective materials on the skin or on food or other objects. The vector may be infected itself (in some instances becoming infective only after appropriate extrinsic incubation) or act as a mechanical carrier of the agent. (*d*) *Air-borne.* The dissemination and inhalation of microbial aerosols, or their deposition on skin, mucous surfaces or wounds. Microbial aerosols are suspensions in air of particles, ordinarily with diameters from 100 microns to 1 micron or less, consisting partially or wholly of micro-organisms. Particles in the lower sizes may remain suspended in air for long periods of time. Microbial aerosols arise from: (i) Droplet nuclei. The small residues which result from evaporation of droplets. Droplet nuclei also may be created purposely by a variety of atomising devices, or accidentally in abattoirs, rendering plants, autopsy rooms, or by many laboratory procedures. (ii) Dust. The particles of widely varying size which may arise from contaminated floors, clothes, bedding or other articles; from soil, especially mycotic spores or cells leading a saprophytic existence there; or from contaminated animal hair, cotton or similar products. The larger particles remain suspended in the air for relatively short periods of time; the finer particles may be indistinguishable from droplet nuclei.

Zoonosis. An infection, or an infectious disease, transmissable under natural conditions between vertebrate animals and man.

Bibliography

Aki, K. (1955) Some problems on flood control in Japan. In *Proceedings of the UNESCO Symposium on Typhoons (November 1954)* Japanese National Commission for UNESCO.

Alter, A. J. (1970) Environmental health experience in disaster. *American Journal of Public Health,* **60,** 475.

Anderson Burley, L. (1973) Disaster relief administration in the Third World. *International Development Review,* XV, no. 1, 8–12.

Arnhold, R. (1969) The 'Quac' stick. A field measure used by the Quaker Service Team in Nigeria. *Journal of Tropical Pediatrics* 15, monograph no. 8, 243–247.

Assar, M. (1971) Guide to sanitation in natural disaster. World Health Organisation. Geneva.

Barton, A. H. (1963) Social organisation under stress: A sociological review of disaster studies. Disaster Study No. 17, National Academy of Sciences/National Research Council: Washington, DC.

Beelman, F. C. (1967) Disaster planning. Report of tornado casualties in Topeka. *Journal of Kansas Medical Society,* **68,** 153–161

Bengoa, J. M. (1971) Nutritional rehabilitation under emergency conditions. In *Symposium of the Swedish Nutrition Foundation,* ed. Blix, G. *et al.* **IX,** 84–91.

Bennett, G. (1970) Bristol floods, 1968. Controlled survey of effects on health of local community disaster. *British Medical Journal,* iii, 454–458.

Bennett, G. (1972) Human reaction to disaster. Paper presented at a meeting of the Disaster Aid Working Party (DAWP) of the London Technical Group.

Berg, A. (1971) Famine contained. Notes and lessons from the Bihar experience. In *Symposium of the Swedish Nutrition Foundation,* ed. Blix, G. *et al,* **IX,** 84–91.

Bohn, G. A. & Ritchie, C. G. (November 1970) Learning by simulation. The validation of disaster simulation: Medical scheme planning. *Journal of Kansas Medical Society,* **1,** 418–425.

Boughey, W. N. F. (1968) Accidents, emergencies and ambulances in Portsmouth. *British Medical Journal,* i, 369–372.

Bouzarth, W. F. & Mariano, J. P. (1969) Philadelphia regional emergency medical disaster operations plan (PREMDOP). *Archives of Environmental Health,* **18,** 203–210.

Brown, R. E. (1972) Some nutritional considerations in times of major catastrophe. *Clinical Paediatrics,* **11,** no. 6, 334–342.

Brown, R. K. (1966) Disaster medicine: What is it? Can it be taught? *Journal of the American Medical Association,* **197,** 1081–1084.

Bywaters, E. G. L. (1971) The treatment of the 'crush syndrome' as occurring in earthquake disasters, etc. Unpublished paper, presented at the London Technical Group seminar on Disaster Technology.

Carruthers, W. B. & Zavela, D. (1965) A narrative report of the tornado disaster in the Anchor Bay area, May 8, 1964. *Michigan Medical News,* **64,** 843.

Casberg, M. A. (1954) Medical organisation in national catastrophe. *Journal of the American Medical Association,* **154,** 501.

Chen, L. C. & Rohde, J. E. (1971) Famine and civil war in East Pakistan. *Lancet,* ii, 557–560.

Cochrane, A. (September 1972) A selected, annotated bibliography on natural hazards. *Natural Hazards Research Working Paper* no. 22, University of Toronto.

Collins, J. (1966) Organisation and function of an accident flying squad. *British Medical Journal,* ii, 578–580.

Collis, W.R. F. (1945) Belsen Camp: A preliminary survey. *British Medical Journal,* i, 814–816.

Crawford, J. N. (1957) Primary treatment services. *Canadian Medical Association Journal,* **76,** 359–361.

Daldy, A. F. (1972) Small buildings in earthquake areas. H.M.S.O., London.

De Candole, C.A. (1967) Blast injury. *Canadian Medical Association Journal,* **96,** 207.

Derby, A. C. (1957) Early medical management of mass trauma. *Canadian Medical Association Journal,* **76,** 371–376.

Diamant, B. Z. (1972) A portable unit for the supply of drinking water in emergencies. (Community water supply research and development programme). World Health Organisation report, 5 pages.

Drabek, T. E. (1970) Methodology of studying disasters: Past patterns and future possibilities. *American Behavioural Scientist,* **13,** no. 3, 331–343.

Dynes, R. R. (1970 Organisational involvement and changes in community structure in disaster. *American Behavioural Scientist,* **13,** no. 3, 430–439.

Editorial (1967) Medical appraisal team visits South Vietnam. *Journal of the American Medical Association,* **202,** 220–222.

Editorial (1969) Human behaviour in disasters. *Canadian Medical Association Journal,* **101,** 632–633.

Elson, R. A. & Eastwood, F. (1969) Documentation for a major incident. *British Medical Journal,* ii, 38–39.

Evans, F. W. (1973) Earthquake engineering for the smaller dwelling. Paper presented at the Fifth World Conference on Earthquake Engineering, Rome.

Fairley, J. (1969) Mass disaster schemes. *British Medical Journal,* iv, 551–553.

Fogelman, M. J. (1958) The Dallas tornado disaster. *American Journal of Surgery,* **95,** 501–506.

Fogg, J. K. & Wang, G. (1955) The effects of typhoons at Taipei and Tainan, Formosa. In *Proceedings of the UNESCO Symposium on Typhoons (November 1954).* Japanese National Commission for UNESCO.

Follis, R. H. (1963) The ecology of hunger. *Military Medicine,* **128,** 384.

Fournier D'Albe, E. M. (1970) Natural disasters, their study and prevention. *UNESCO Chronicle,* **16,** 195–208.

Fraser, R. M. (1971) the cost of commotion. An analysis of psychiatric sequelae of the 1969 Belfast Riots. *British Journal of Psychiatry,* **118,** 257–264.

Gans, B. (1969) A Biafran relief mission. *Lancet,* i, 660–665.

Gardiner, P., Rohde, J. E. & Majumdar, M. B. (International Rescue Committee) (1972) Health priorities among Bangladesh refugees. *Lancet,* i, 834–836.

Glass, R. (19 September 1970) Aid fiasco in Peru. *The New Republic,* 14.

Gleason, E. H. (1959) The sanitarian in disaster situations. *Military Medicine,* **124,** 354–362.

Gopalan, C. (1963) Long term and emergency solutions for protein-calorie deficiencies. *Journal of Tropical Paediatrics,* **9,** 67–73.

Greentree, L. B. (1971) The medical realities of Civil Defence. *New English Journal of Medicine,* **284,** 1011.

Haas, J. E. & Ayre, R. S. (1969) The Western Sicily earthquake of 1968. National Academy of Sciences/National Academy of Engineering: Washington DC.

Hart, D. (March 1972) Feeding and shelter on a large scale at minimal cost. Unpublished paper.

Henderson, D. A. (Smallpox Eradication Unit, WHO, Geneva) (1972) Epidemiology in the global eradication of smallpox. *International Journal of Epidemiology,* **1,** 25–30.

Heywood, G. S. P. (1955) The pressure of typhoon winds on structures. In *Proceedings of the UNESCO Symposium on Typhoons (November 1954)* Japanese National Commission for UNESCO.

Hickman, R. (Field Co-ordinator for the Save the Children Fund) (1970) The relief operation in former Biafra. *Lancet,* ii, 815–816.

Hickman, R. (Former Senior Medical Officer, Save the Children Fund, West Bengal) (1971) Deteriorating health of refugee children in India. *Lancet,* ii, 917–918

Hight, D., Blodgett, J. T., Croce, E. J., Horne, E. O., McKoan, J. W. & Whelan, C. S. (1956) Medical aspects of the Worcester tornado disaster. *New English Journal of Medicine,* **254,** 267.

Hughes, S. P. F. (Medical Officer, Save the Children Fund) (1969) Malnutrition in the field, Nigerian civil war. *British Medical Journal,* ii, 436–438.

International Civil Defence Organization (September 1971) Don'ts and do's when handling a casualty. *Bulletin of the International Civil Defence Organization,* No. 195, 9.

International Civil Defence Organization (October 1971) Storing foodstuffs and their keeping properties. *Bulletin of the International Civil Defence Organization,* No. 196, 3–5.

International Civil Defence Organization (June 1972) Sanitation in natural disasters. *Bulletin of the International Civil Defence Organization,* No. 204, 1–6.

Jelliffe, D. B. (1966) The assessment of the nutritional status of the community. Monograph Series World Health Organisation, 53, Geneva.

Kazmi, A. H. (July 1968) Earthquake problems and programmes in Pakistan. Paper presented at the Central Treaty Organisation Conference on Earthquake Hazard Minimisation, Ankara, Turkey.

Keep, V. R. (1966) Planning for major civil disasters. *Medical Journal of Australia,* **2,** 618.

Kennedy, J. A. (October 1968) Violence in Chicago. *American Journal of Nursing,* **68,** 2168–2169.

Kerpel-Fronius, E. (1947) Infantile mortality in Budapest in the year 1945. *Journal of Paediatrics,* **30,** 244–249.

Key, D. E., Tomblin, J. & Imbert, I. D. C. (1968). Preliminary report on the design of earthquake resistant structures. Seismic Committee, The Association of Professional Engineers of Trinidad and Tobago.

Keys, A. (1948) Caloric undernutrition and starvation with notes on protein deficiency. *Journal of the American Medical Association,* **138,** 500–511.

Kirkley, H. L. (Director of Oxfam) (1971) Marshalling of international response to disasters. ICVA General Conference, Document 21.

League of Red Cross Societies (1970) Red Cross disaster relief handbook. Geneva, League of Red Cross Societies.

Lechat, M. (Professor of Epidemiology, Ecole de Sante Publique, Universite Catholique de Louvain, Belgium). (1972) Bibliographie sommaire sur les catastrophes naturelles. Unpublished bibliography.

Lechat, M. *et al.* (Ecole de Sante Publique, Universite Catholique de Louvain, Belgium) (7–10 December 1971) The ecology of natural disasters. Summary of recommendation of a seminar in Brussels.

Lorraine, N. S. R. (1954) Canvey Island flood disaster, February 1953. *Medical Officer,* **91,** 59–62.

Loupekine, I. S. (July 1966) Uganda: The Toro earthquake of March 1966. Earthquake Reconnaissance Mission, United Nations Educational, Scientific and Cultural Organisation, Paris. (UNESCO)

Lycett, A. (4 March 1973) Relief work in Bangladesh, how effective? *The Illustrated Weekly of India.*

Malone, R.H. and O'Connor, R., Jr. (16 February 1968) Handling a large influx of patients in a disaster situation. *Hospitals,* **42,** 67–70.

Masefield, G. B. (1971) Calculations of the amounts of different foods to be imported into the famine area: emergency subsistence level; temporary maintenance level. In *Symposium of the Swedish Nutrition Foundation,* ed. Blix, G. *et al.* **IX,** 170–177.

McClure, R. S. (1971) United States Aid emergency programs and the role of voluntary agencies. ICVA General Conference, Document 14.

Miller, J. P. (1970) Medical relief in the Nigerian civil war. *Lancet,* i, 1330–1334.

Morley, D. (1972) Contingency planning for children in a tropical disaster area. Unpublished transcript of Millbank Lecture.

Murlis, J., Rvers, J. & Zitron, I. (London Technical Group) (1971) Disasters, development and international aid. Unpublished paper presented at London Technical Group Seminar on Disaster Technology.

Nalin, D. R., Cash, R. A., Islam, R., Molla, M. & Phillips, R. A. (P-SCRL) (1968) Oral management therapy for cholera in adults. *Lancet,* ii, 370–373.

National Voluntary Civil Aid Services (1970) The Turkish earthquake, 1970. Unpublished report.

Nigerian Red Cross Society (NRC) (1970) Nigerian Relief Action (1966–1970): Report. League of Red Cross Societies: Geneva.

North, A. (June 1972) Shelter provision in disaster situations. Paper presented at Disaster Aid Working Party meeting.

Odling-Smee, G. W. (1970) Ibo civilian casualties in the Nigerian civil war. *Military Medicine,* **124,** 505.

O'Halloran, R. D. *et al.* (1969) A plan for broadening the base of disaster planning. *Hospitals,* **43,** 45–48.

Orth, G. L. (1959) Disaster and disposal of the dead. *Military Medicine,* **124,** 505.

Oxfam (July 1972) Standing operational procedures for disasters. Second issue.

Pan American Sanitary Bureau (1971) Assistance for the medical rehabilitation of the area affected by the earthquake of 31 May 1970. XVIII Pan American Sanitary Conference; XVII Meeting Regional Committee of the World Health Organisation for the Americas, Washington DC, 28 September–8 October 1970. Pan American Health Organisation World Health Organisation Official Document No. 108, Washington DC, 164, 165, 189, 453–459.

Passmore, R. (1951) Historical survey of famine in India. *Lancet,* i, 303–307.

Peavy, J. E. (1970) Hurricane of Beulah. *American Journal of Public Health,* **60,** 481.

Piercey, W. D. & Fryer, G. E. (1947) Hospital preparedness. *Canadian Medical Association Journal,* **76,** 361–364.

Popovic, M. & Petrovic, D. (1964) After the earthquake. *Lancet,* ii, 1169.

Pyke, M. (1970) Man and food. World University Library: Weidenfeld and Nicholson.

Raker, J. W. & Friedsham, H. J. (1960) Disaster-scale medical care problems: A study of medical management of casualties resulting from a tornado in Dallas, Texas. *Journal of the American Medical Association,* **173,** 143.

Raker, J. W., Wallace, A. F. C. & Rayner, J. C. (1956) Emergency medical care in disaster: A summary of recorded experience. Disaster Study No. 6, Washington DC National Academy of Sciences/National Research Council.

Rennie, D. (October 1970) After the earthquake. *Lancet,* ii, 704–707

Richwagen, W. C. (16 August 1967) The 'predictive' approach to disaster planning: How it failed. *Hospitals,* **41,** 48–51.

Roeschlaub, E. L. (May 1968) Essentials in emergency care: police, fire department's views. *Hospital Topics,* **43,** 61–64.

Roeschlaub, E. L. (May 1968) Hospitals in riot-torm cities meet patients head on. *Hospital Topics,* **46,** 57–61.

Saidi, F. (1963) The 1962 Earthquake in Iran: Some medical and social aspects. *New English Journal of Medicine,* **268,** 929.

Savage, P. E. A. (1972) Disaster planning: the use of action cards. *British Medical Journal,* iii, 42.

Savage, P. E. A. (1972) Disaster planning: A major accident exercise. *British Medical Journal,* iv, 168–171.

Schmitt, N., Catlin, H. B., Bowmern, E. J. & Larsen, A. A. (1970) Flash flood at Trail, British Columbia, 1969. *Canadian Journal of Public Health,* **61,** 104–111.

Scrimshaw, N. S. (1966) Ecological factors in nutritional disease. *American Journal of Clinical Nutrition,* **14,** 112.

Seaman, J. A. (1972) Relief work in a refugee camp for Bangladesh refugees in India. *Lancet,* ii, 866–870.

Secours Catholique (1968) Emergency aid and preparatory action in case of disaster. ICVA General Conference. Document 12.

Selwyn, P. (Institute of Development Studies, University of Sussex, U.K.) (September 1971) Disaster relief and development policies. Unpublished paper, presented at London Technical Group seminar on Disaster Technology.

Skinner, H. S. (1970) Specialised training in communicable diseases: The army. *Proceedings of the Royal Society of Medicine,* **63,** 523–525.

Smith, C. A. (1947) Effects of maternal undernutrition upon the newborn infant in Holland (1944–1945). *Journal of Paediatrics,* **30,** 229–243.

Sommer, A. & Mosley, W. H. (Pakistan SEATO Cholera Research Laboratory) (1972) East Bengal cyclone of November, 1970: Epidemiological approach to disaster assessment. *Lancet,* i, 1029–1036.

Storey, P. B. & Roth, R. B. (1971) Emergency medical care in the Soviet Union: A study of the Skoraya. *Journal of American Medical Association,* **217,** 588–592.

Taylor, A. (1972) A survey and analysis of administrative, organisational and technical experiences accruing to Oxfam and to other voluntary agencies arising out of the Bangladesh refugee operations, April 1971 to February 1972. Unpublished report, Oxfam.

Tripp, S. R. (1968) The United States' role in co-ordination of international emergency assistance. ICVA General Conference, Document 30.

Tyhurst, J. S. (1957) Psychological and social aspects of civilian disaster. *Canadian Medical Association Journal,* **76,** 385–393.

Wharton, B. A., Howells, G. R. & McCance, R. A. (1967) Cardiac failure in kwashiorkor, *Lancet,* ii, 384.

Whitaker, B. (July 1972) The Biharis in Bangladesh. *Minority Rights Group Report* No. 11.

Wills, V. G. & Waterlow, J. C. (1958) The death rate in the age group 1–4 years as an index of malnutrition. *Journal of Tropical Paediatrics,* **3,** 167.

Witkow, A. (1956) 'And the waters prevailed'. Public health aspects of the 1955 New England flood. *New English Journal of Medicine,* **254,** 843–846.

Witkow, A. & Smith, J. F. (1953) Public health aspects of the Worcester tornado. *American Journal of Public Health,* **43,** 1572–1573.

Woodham-Smith, C. (1964) *The Great Hunger: Ireland 1845–9.* Reader's Union. London: Hamish Hamilton.

Woolhouse, F. M. (1957) The definitive treatment of burns in mass casualties. *Canadian Medical Association Journal,* **76,** 376–380.

Yarom, R. & McFie, J. (1963) Kwashiorkor in the Congo. *Journal of Tropical Paediatrics,***9,** 56–63.

Yudkin, J. (Professor of Nutrition, Queen Elizabeth College, London) (September 1971) Nutritional problems in a disaster; presented at London Technical Group seminar on Disaster technology.

Yudkin, J., Miller, D., & Payne, P. (1972) Food for disaster. Paper presented at Disaster Aid Working Party (DAWP) meeting.

Zingg, W. (1967) The management of accidental hypothermia. *Canadian Medical Association Journal,* **96,** 214.

Zipperman, H. H. (1956) Sorting; the key to management of victims of disaster. *Journal of American Medical Association,* **162,** 1438–1441.

Index